APPLICATIONS INDEX

A further source of applied problems is *Linear Algebra Problems for Computer Solution* (for use with MAX software) by Charles Jepsen and Eugene Herman, available from Brooks/Cole Publishing Company.

Linear Algebra with Applications Third Edition

Jeanne L. Agnew
Oklahoma State University

Robert C. Knapp
University of Wisconsin, Whitewater

Brooks/Cole Publishing Company
Pacific Grove, California

Consulting Editor: *Robert J. Wisner*

Brooks/Cole Publishing Company
A Division of Wadsworth, Inc.

Printed in the United States of America
10 9 8 7 6 5 4 3 2

Library of Congress Cataloging-in-Publication Data
Agnew, Jeanne, [date]
Linear algebra with applications / Jeanne L. Agnew, Robert C. Knapp.—3rd ed.
p. cm.
Bibliography: p.
Includes indexes.
ISBN 0-534-09456-2
1. Algebra, Linear. I. Knapp, Robert C., [date]. II. Title
QA184.A36 1988
512.5—dc19 88-15432
CIP

Sponsoring Editor: *Jeremy Hayhurst*
Editorial Assistant: *Virge Kelmser*
Production Editor: *Ellen Brownstein*
Manuscript Editor: *Linda Thompson*
Permissions Editor: *Carline Haga*
Interior & Cover Design: *Lisa Thompson*
Cover Photo: *Charlotte Kahler*
Cover Artwork: *David Aguero*
Art Coordinator: *Lisa Torri*
Interior Illustration: *Lori Heckelman*
Typesetting: *The Alden Press, London, England*
Cover Printing: *The Lehigh Press Company, Pennsauken, NJ*
Printing and Binding: *R.R. Donnelley & Sons, Harrisonburg, PA*

Preface

Philosophy

In this book we address the diverse needs of those who study linear algebra. Such students may attend 2-year colleges, 4-year colleges, or universities. Ordinarily they are sophomores. They may have been introduced to matrices and their uses in high school. Their major interests include not only mathematics but also business and economics, computer science, certain branches of engineering, the physical sciences, or the social sciences.

Our purpose is to present the traditional material of elementary linear algebra in such a way that it is accessible and meaningful, whatever the student's major interest may be. With this in mind, we include in each chapter a section describing applications that involve the material discussed. Applications illustrate how material can be put to use in many varied fields. They help satisfy the natural desire to ask, "Is what I am studying good for something?" They encourage the student to "think applications"—a point of view that helps one appreciate the underlying mathematical ideas. We do not claim to include all possible applications. Often the most important applications require too much preparatory discussion for an introductory text.

Along with applications we emphasize the use of the computer as a computational tool. In our earlier editions we included programs so that students could work realistic problems. At that time the personal computer was just appearing on the scene. Even scarcer than the hardware systems, however, were carefully designed software packages devoted to linear algebra. Today, however, both small computer systems and user-friendly software are readily available. In this edition we take the view that students will have access to these systems. Some examples show how a student might interact with a matrix algebra program in solving a problem. In a few cases we have included especially useful programs in the appendix. We sincerely encourage the use of the computer throughout this book. Students find it not only entertaining but also helpful in understanding the principles underlying the computations. A particularly useful matrix algebra calculation package by Eugene A. Herman and Charles H. Jepsen, named MAX, is available through Brooks/Cole.

Structure

In the first three chapters the student progresses through the basic operations of linear algebra. In mastering this material the student should acquire both technical skill and an appreciation for the purpose of the manipulations involved. In Chapter 1 we introduce the matrix and the n-tuple, define and discuss algebraic operations with these, and encourage the student to think of sets of data as single entities. In order to help the student relate the material to previous knowledge, geometric vectors are introduced.

Chapter 2 deals with systems of linear equations. We use row operations on the augmented matrix to look for sets of n-tuples that satisfy such a system and to establish conditions under which solutions exist. We also introduce briefly the important ideas of linear independence, basis, and dimension in preparation for a more rigorous development in Chapter 4.

The discussion in Chapter 3 centers on square matrices. We define inverses and determinants and relate them to systems of equations. At this point we introduce eigenvalues and eigenvectors of a square matrix. The introduction of eigenvalues at this stage is, in our opinion, one of the main strengths of the arrangement of the topics in this book. We are trying to overcome the frustration felt by both students and instructors when, after a semester of working toward this topic, they find too little time left to do it justice.

Chapters 4, 5, and 6 emphasize the basic structural setting for the study of linear algebra. In Chapter 4 we define a vector space and treat linear dependence, basis, coordinates, and dimension in more general finite-dimensional vector spaces. The vector spaces emphasized are the polynomial spaces P_n, the space of $m \times n$ matrices $M_{m \times n}$, and R^n. One section is devoted to the vector spaces associated with a matrix.

Chapter 5 contains a brief introduction to linear transformations, emphasizing the matrix of a transformation. This sets the stage for a more thorough treatment of diagonalization in Chapter 6.

The return to eigenvalues in Chapter 6 reinforces what the students have learned in Chapter 3 and makes the ideas of Chapter 4 more meaningful. The special case of diagonalization of symmetric matrices is included at this point as is a brief treatment of quadratic forms.

Writing Style

The style of this book is informal. The emphasis is on student understanding of the material presented. Examples are plentiful. Important results are stated as theorems. In general, theorems are motivated by examples that precede them. Some theorems are proved in detail. Others are justified in special settings. Some proofs are given in outline form in the exercises. As an aid to organization and review, there is a short summary at the end of each section.

Each section has an extensive exercise set. Some of these are computational and some theoretical; some are quite straightforward and some demand thought. We cannot emphasize enough the importance of exercises. But, like aerobic exercises, mathematical exercises are of value only to those who do them.

Some Suggestions for Use

Chapters 1 and 2 contain material to which students may have been introduced in algebra, trigonometry, or calculus. Sections 1.4 and 1.5 could be omitted, if desired, or passed over lightly. The definition of the length of a vector and the concept of orthogonality are important. In Chapter 2 the idea of expressing solutions as sets of vectors may be new. The ideas of linear independence, basis, and dimension can be treated as intuitive extensions of ideas in geometry. Chapter 3 will reinforce the ideas in Chapters 1 and 2 as well as introduce the student to new material. After these chapters are covered, topics can be selected from Chapters 4, 5, and 6. Students interested in computer science or engineering should include as much of Chapter 6 as possible.

An instructor who wants to emphasize the more theoretical aspects of the subject can omit the section on applications from each chapter without disturbing the continuity of the text. Even if this is done, these topics are an important part of the book. All students should be encouraged at least to read the types of applications discussed. A course emphasizing applications and the computational aspects of the subject can be constructed from Chapters 1, 2, 3, and parts of Chapters 4, 5, and 6.

New in the Third Edition

The topics from the previous edition have been reorganized. Computer programs have been removed from the body of the text and either deleted, included in the exercises, or placed in the appendix. The chapter on linear programming has been deleted. Chapter 6 has been enlarged to include a discussion of symmetric matrices previously included in Chapter 7.

The exercise sets have been redone to include new problems. Some topics not in the main stream of the development have been included in the exercises as supplemental topics—for example, geometric proofs, partitioned matrices, the Cauchy-Schwarz Inequality, and the LU factorization.

A number of new applications have been added: searching for oil, computer graphics, balancing a chemical reaction, Markov Chains, homogeneous coordinates, orientation in space, and robotics.

This book has been written to and for the student. However, in the opinion of the authors, no text can do for the student what can be done by an inspired teacher. We hope that the point of view taken in this presentation will add to the enjoyment of both student and teacher as they work together in the fascinating study of linear algebra and its applications.

Acknowledgments

The authors wish to thank Betty Barr, University of Houston; Frank Cheek, University of Wisconsin at Platteville; Norman F. Lindquist, Western Washington University; Hal G. Moore, Brigham Young University; K. Thanigasalam, Pennsylvania State-Beaver Campus; and John Woods, Oklahoma Baptist University at Shawnee for their thoughtful reviews of the manuscript. We also want to give special thanks to Joanne Trimble, Marist College, Poughkeepsie, for the time and energy she gave to her thorough and perceptive reviews. Without her suggestions and encouragement this revision might never have been accomplished.

Finally we express our enormous appreciation to Judy Magnuson Knapp, who has been absolutely indispensable in this writing. She has critiqued the presentation, worked all the problems, and checked all the references. She has prepared the answer sections and assisted in clarifying several key arguments. The authors, however, claim entire credit for any errors that may remain.

Jeanne L. Agnew
Robert C. Knapp

Contents

4 *Vector Spaces* *173*

5 *Functions from One Vector Space to Another* *238*

6 *Diagonalization* *284*

1 The Matrix

1.1 The Matrix, the n-tuple, and Addition

It has been said that linear algebra is the oxygen of the engineer. Certainly it plays an increasingly important role in analyzing the complex problems that arise in many areas today. On the one hand, the symbolism and structure of linear algebra reveal the fact that the same mathematical model can be used to represent a variety of seemingly different problems. On the other hand, the logical, concise and consistent structure of linear algebra is in itself beautiful and satisfying. As you read and study the following pages, we hope that you will both understand the utility and feel the beauty of this area of mathematics.

You are probably already familiar with much of the material in this chapter. However it will be wise to read through it and familiarize yourself with the notation and terminology used. Throughout this book, the numbers that appear will be real numbers unless otherwise stated, and we will assume the ordinary rules of real numbers.

We begin by introducing the matrix and the algebraic rules for operating with it. To handle data as if it were a single entity, arrange the data in a rectangular array. Such an array is called a **matrix**.

Example 1 The Ace Computer Shop specializes in personal computer systems. Prices for its PC clones depend on the kind of equipment ordered (monochrome or color monitor; two floppy drives or one floppy and one 40-megabyte hard drive). The shop wants to sell three major bundled systems: an *entry-level* system (consisting of 640K memory, monitor, and keyboard); a *scientific-level* system (consisting of 2048K memory, monitor, keyboard, numeric coprocessor chip, and laser printer); and a *business-level* system (consisting of 1024K memory, monitor, keyboard, laser printer, and business applications software). Prices for these systems in dollars are given in the following table.

	Mono Double Floppies	*Mono Hard Drive*	*Color Double Floppies*	*Color Hard Drive*
Entry Level	2000	2400	2500	2900
Scientific	4000	4400	4600	5000
Business	5000	5500	5600	6100

The table has three rows, each referring to a particular type of system and each listing the prices for that type.

The rectangular array of numbers in this table is the matrix

$$\mathbf{C} = \begin{bmatrix} 2000 & 2400 & 2500 & 2900 \\ 4000 & 4400 & 4600 & 5000 \\ 5000 & 5500 & 5600 & 6100 \end{bmatrix}$$

This matrix has three horizontal rows and four columns. ■

Our purpose is to set up definitions for adding and multiplying matrices and to study the laws that govern addition and multiplication. To do this we must have vocabulary.

Matrix
Element
Row
Column
Size
Square Matrix
Scalar

Definition 1

A **matrix** is a rectangular array of real numbers, which are called the **elements** of the matrix. The plural of matrix is **matrices**. Each horizontal array of elements in a matrix is called a **row**. Each vertical array of elements in a matrix is called a **column**. The number of rows and columns determines the **size** of a matrix. If there are m rows and n columns, then the matrix is of size m by n, written $m \times n$. If $m = n$, the matrix is said to be **square**. A single real number is called a **scalar**.

Because we want to think of the entire array at one time, we use single letters to designate arrays. In this book we use boldface type for the letters that represent arrays, and ordinary type for the letters that represent numbers. The subscripts on the elements tell us the location of the element.

The $m \times n$ matrix is written in several ways:

$$\mathbf{A} = \begin{bmatrix} a_{11} & a_{12} & \cdots & a_{1n} \\ a_{21} & a_{22} & \cdots & a_{2n} \\ \vdots & \vdots & & \vdots \\ a_{m1} & a_{m2} & \cdots & a_{mn} \end{bmatrix} = [a_{ij}] = [a_{ij}]_{m \times n}$$

The element in row i and column j is a_{ij}.

Two matrices are equal only if they are identical—that is, if the information contained in them is exactly the same and presented in the same location.

Equality $\mathbf{A} = \mathbf{B}$

Definition 2

The matrices $\mathbf{A} = [a_{ij}]$ and $\mathbf{B} = [b_{ij}]$ are **equal** if and only if they are the same size and $a_{ij} = b_{ij}$ for each i and j.

Example 2

Let $\mathbf{A} = \begin{bmatrix} -1 & 0 \\ 1 & 2 \end{bmatrix}$ and $\mathbf{B} = \begin{bmatrix} b_{11} & b_{12} \\ 1 & 2 \end{bmatrix}$. If $\mathbf{A} = \mathbf{B}$, then $b_{11} = -1$ and $b_{12} = 0$. The matrix $\mathbf{C} = \begin{bmatrix} -1 & 0 & 2 \\ 1 & 2 & c_{23} \end{bmatrix}$ cannot equal $\mathbf{A}$ for any choice of c_{23} since $\mathbf{C}$ is not the same size as $\mathbf{A}$. ■

Example 3

The table in Example 1 can also be written as follows:

	Entry Level	*Scientific*	*Business*
Mono, Double Floppies	2000	4000	5000
Mono, Hard Drive	2400	4400	5500
Color, Double Floppies	2500	4600	5600
Color, Hard Drive	2900	5000	6100

This leads to the matrix

$$\mathbf{B} = \begin{bmatrix} 2000 & 4000 & 5000 \\ 2400 & 4400 & 5500 \\ 2500 & 4600 & 5600 \\ 2900 & 5000 & 6100 \end{bmatrix}$$

The matrix $\mathbf{B}$ contains the same information as the matrix $\mathbf{C}$ in Example 1, but the rows of $\mathbf{B}$ are the columns of the earlier matrix. The two arrays are not equal according to Definition 2. The matrix $\mathbf{B}$ is called the **transpose** of $\mathbf{C}$. ■

Transpose $\mathbf{A}^T$

Definition 3

If $\mathbf{A}$ is an $m \times n$ array, the **transpose** of $\mathbf{A}$, written $\mathbf{A}^T$, is the $n \times m$ array formed as follows: the n rows of $\mathbf{A}^T$ are the n columns of $\mathbf{A}$ and the m columns of $\mathbf{A}^T$ are the m rows of $\mathbf{A}$. Thus, $\mathbf{A}^T$ is formed from $\mathbf{A}$ by interchanging rows with columns.

The idea of ordered sets of numbers is familiar in analytic geometry. Here an ordered pair of real numbers (x, y) represents the location of a point in the plane with respect to coordinate axes. An ordered triple (x, y, z) represents a point in three-space. The idea can be extended to an ordered set of n numbers, where n is any positive integer. Such a set is called an *n-tuple* and is written $\mathbf{u} = (a_1, a_2, \ldots, a_n)$.

Two n-tuples are equal if and only if they are identical. The n numbers must be the same and in the same order. The set of all n-tuples of real numbers is designated by the symbol R^n. In particular, the set of ordered pairs of real numbers is called R^2, and the set of ordered triples of real numbers is designated by R^3.

Notice that the ith row of an $m \times n$ matrix is an n-tuple of real numbers, $\mathbf{u}_i = (a_{i1}, a_{i2}, \ldots, a_{in})$. The jth column of an $m \times n$ matrix is an m-tuple of real numbers, $\mathbf{v}_j = (a_{1j}, a_{2j}, \ldots, a_{mj})$.

An n-tuple $\mathbf{u} = (a_1, a_2, \ldots, a_n)$ can be identified with the $n \times 1$ matrix, which has one column, the elements of which are the real numbers $a_1, a_2, \ldots, a_n$. Call this matrix $\mathbf{U}$. We can also identify the n-tuple $\mathbf{u}$ with the $1 \times n$ matrix that has one row, the elements of which are the real numbers $a_1, a_2, \ldots, a_n$. This matrix is $\mathbf{U}^T$.

n-tuple
Equality: $\mathbf{u} = \mathbf{v}$
Notation: $\mathbf{u}, \mathbf{U}, \mathbf{U}^T$

Definition 4

An ***n*-tuple** is an ordered set of n real numbers $\mathbf{u} = (a_1, a_2, \ldots, a_n)$. The n-tuples $\mathbf{u} = (a_1, a_2, \ldots, a_n)$ and $\mathbf{v} = (b_1, b_2, \ldots, b_n)$ are **equal** if and only if $a_i = b_i$, $i = 1, 2, \ldots, n$. An n-tuple can be written as an $n \times 1$ matrix or as a $1 \times n$ matrix. The following **notation** is used:

$$\mathbf{u} = (a_1, \ a_2, \ldots, a_n), \qquad \mathbf{U} = \begin{bmatrix} a_1 \\ a_2 \\ \vdots \\ a_n \end{bmatrix},$$

$$\mathbf{U}^T = [a_1 \quad a_2 \quad \ldots \quad a_n]$$

Example 4

State University has two sections of linear algebra. Section 1 has 31 students and Section 2 has 25. The students are sophomores and juniors who are enrolled in Arts and Sciences, Engineering, and Business. The following table shows the makeup of the sections:

	Section 1			*Section 2*		
	Arts and Sciences	*Engineering*	*Business*	*Arts and Sciences*	*Engineering*	*Business*
Sophomore	10	5	2	7	4	4
Junior	5	8	1	3	4	3

Section 1 is described by the matrix $\mathbf{A} = \begin{bmatrix} 10 & 5 & 2 \\ 5 & 8 & 1 \end{bmatrix}$ and Section 2 by the matrix $\mathbf{B} = \begin{bmatrix} 7 & 4 & 4 \\ 3 & 4 & 3 \end{bmatrix}$. The matrix that displays the total enrollment is the 2×3 matrix obtained by adding the corresponding entries in **A** and **B**. It is reasonable to think of the matrix as $\mathbf{A} + \mathbf{B}$ and write

$$\mathbf{A} + \mathbf{B} = \begin{bmatrix} 17 & 9 & 6 \\ 8 & 12 & 4 \end{bmatrix}$$

Each student in linear algebra receives three credit hours for the course. The total number of credit hours earned in linear algebra at each level in the different colleges is displayed in the 2×3 array $\begin{bmatrix} 51 & 27 & 18 \\ 24 & 36 & 12 \end{bmatrix}$, which is obtained by multiplying each element of $\mathbf{A} + \mathbf{B}$ by 3. A reasonable way to define $3(\mathbf{A} + \mathbf{B})$ is

$$3(\mathbf{A} + \mathbf{B}) = \begin{bmatrix} 51 & 27 & 18 \\ 24 & 36 & 12 \end{bmatrix}$$

By the same definition,

$$3\mathbf{A} = \begin{bmatrix} 30 & 15 & 6 \\ 15 & 24 & 3 \end{bmatrix} \quad \text{and} \quad 3\mathbf{B} = \begin{bmatrix} 21 & 12 & 12 \\ 9 & 12 & 9 \end{bmatrix}$$

Notice that $3(\mathbf{A} + \mathbf{B}) = 3\mathbf{A} + 3\mathbf{B}$. ■

Sum: A + B
u + v
Scalar Multiple:
***k*A**
***k*u**

Definition 5

Let $\mathbf{A} = [a_{ij}]$ and $\mathbf{B} = [b_{ij}]$ be matrices of the same size, and let k be any scalar. The **sum** of the matrices **A** and **B** is $\mathbf{A} + \mathbf{B} = [a_{ij} + b_{ij}]$—that is, the matrix formed by adding the elements in corresponding positions. The **product of a matrix and a scalar** is formed by multiplying each element of the matrix by the scalar: $k\mathbf{A} = \mathbf{A}k = [ka_{ij}]$. This product is usually written $k\mathbf{A}$.

Let $\mathbf{u} = (a_1, a_2, \ldots, a_n)$ and $\mathbf{v} = (b_1, b_2, \ldots, b_n)$; then

$$\begin{aligned} \mathbf{u} + \mathbf{v} &= (a_1 + b_1, a_2 + b_2, \ldots, a_n + b_n) \\ k\mathbf{u} &= (ka_1, ka_2, \ldots, ka_n) \end{aligned}$$

Example 5

Let $\mathbf{A} = \begin{bmatrix} 1 & 2 & 1 \\ 1 & 0 & -4 \end{bmatrix}$, $\mathbf{B} = \begin{bmatrix} 0 & 1 & 0 \\ -1 & 1 & 2 \end{bmatrix}$, and $\mathbf{C} = \begin{bmatrix} 1 & 1 \\ 1 & 3 \end{bmatrix}$. Then

$$\mathbf{A} + \mathbf{B} = \begin{bmatrix} 1+0 & 2+1 & 1+0 \\ 1-1 & 0+1 & -4+2 \end{bmatrix} = \begin{bmatrix} 1 & 3 & 1 \\ 0 & 1 & -2 \end{bmatrix}$$

The matrices **A** and **C** cannot be added because they are not of the same size. The sum $\mathbf{B} + \mathbf{C}$ is not defined for the same reason. ■

Example 6 Let $\mathbf{u} = (1, 1, -3)$ and $\mathbf{v} = (0, 1, -1)$. Calculate $\mathbf{u} + \mathbf{v}$, $2\mathbf{u}$, $3\mathbf{v}$, and $2\mathbf{u} + 3\mathbf{v}$.

Solution

$$\mathbf{u} + \mathbf{v} = (1, 1, -3) + (0, 1, -1) = (1 + 0, 1 + 1, -3 - 1) = (1, 2, -4)$$
$$2\mathbf{u} = 2(1, 1, -3) = (2, 2, -6)$$
$$3\mathbf{v} = 3(0, 1, -1) = (0, 3, -3)$$
$$2\mathbf{u} + 3\mathbf{v} = (2, 2, -6) + (0, 3, -3) = (2, 5, -9)$$ ■

Definition 6 makes it possible to combine arrays of the same size in a very meaningful way.

Definition 6

Let $\mathbf{A}_1, \mathbf{A}_2, \ldots, \mathbf{A}_k$ be k arrays of the same size and $c_1, c_2, \ldots, c_k$ be scalars. An expression of the form

$$c_1\mathbf{A}_1 + c_2\mathbf{A}_2 + \cdots + c_k\mathbf{A}_k$$

Linear Combination

is called a **linear combination** of the arrays $\mathbf{A}_1, \mathbf{A}_2, \ldots, \mathbf{A}_k$.

Example 7 gives a very simple use of a linear combination of 1×3 arrays, that is, triples.

Example 7 State University has soft-drink dispensers in each of its eight dormitories, its six classroom buildings, and its three administration buildings. Each dorm uses 2250 cans of regular cola, 300 cans of diet cola, and 100 cans of other soft drinks each week. This can be described by the triple $\mathbf{d} = (2250, 300, 100)$.

The weekly purchases in each classroom building can be described by $\mathbf{c} = (2300, 450, 125)$. The number of soft drinks used in each administration building is $\mathbf{a} = (125, 125, 40)$. To determine how much of each type of soft drink is required to keep the dispensers in operation each week, form the linear combination

$$\begin{aligned} 8\mathbf{d} + 6\mathbf{c} + 3\mathbf{a} &= 8(2250, 300, 100) + 6(2300, 450, 125) + 3(125, 125, 40) \\ &= (32175, 5475, 1670). \end{aligned}$$

This tells us that 32175 cans of regular cola, 5475 cans of diet cola, and 1670 cans of other drinks are consumed each week. ■

Recall the basic properties of addition and multiplication of real numbers. Here a, b, c represent arbitrary real numbers.

1. Addition is *commutative*: $a + b = b + a$.
   Multiplication is *commutative*: $ab = ba$.
2. Addition is *associative*: $(a + b) + c = a + (b + c)$.
   Multiplication is *associative*: $(ab)c = a(bc)$.

3. Multiplication is *distributive over addition*: $a(b + c) = ab + ac$.
4. The real number 0 is the *additive identity*: $a + 0 = a$.
   The real number 1 is the *multiplicative identity*: $a(1) = a$.
5. For every real number a there is an *additive inverse* b such that $a + b = 0$. We write $b = -a$.
   For every real number $a \neq 0$ there is a *multiplicative inverse* b such that $ab = 1$. We write $b = 1/a$ or $b = a^{-1}$.

The properties of addition and multiplication of real numbers lead to similar properties for addition of matrices and for multiplication of a matrix by a scalar.

Example 8 Let $\mathbf{A} = \begin{bmatrix} 1 & 3 & 1 \\ 2 & 5 & 0 \end{bmatrix}$, $\mathbf{B} = \begin{bmatrix} -2 & 1 & -2 \\ 0 & 4 & 3 \end{bmatrix}$, and $\mathbf{C} = \begin{bmatrix} 2 & 2 & 1 \\ 1 & 0 & -1 \end{bmatrix}$.

$$\mathbf{B} + \mathbf{A} = \begin{bmatrix} -2+1 & 1+3 & -2+1 \\ 0+2 & 4+5 & 3+0 \end{bmatrix} = \begin{bmatrix} -1 & 4 & -1 \\ 2 & 9 & 3 \end{bmatrix}$$

$$\mathbf{A} + \mathbf{B} = \begin{bmatrix} 1-2 & 3+1 & 1-2 \\ 2+0 & 5+4 & 0+3 \end{bmatrix} = \begin{bmatrix} -1 & 4 & -1 \\ 2 & 9 & 3 \end{bmatrix}$$

Thus $\mathbf{A} + \mathbf{B} = \mathbf{B} + \mathbf{A}$ in this numerical example. Also,

$$(\mathbf{A} + \mathbf{B}) + \mathbf{C} = \begin{bmatrix} -1 & 4 & -1 \\ 2 & 9 & 3 \end{bmatrix} + \begin{bmatrix} 2 & 2 & 1 \\ 1 & 0 & -1 \end{bmatrix} = \begin{bmatrix} 1 & 6 & 0 \\ 3 & 9 & 2 \end{bmatrix}$$

$$\mathbf{A} + (\mathbf{B} + \mathbf{C}) = \begin{bmatrix} 1 & 3 & 1 \\ 2 & 5 & 0 \end{bmatrix} + \begin{bmatrix} 0 & 3 & -1 \\ 1 & 4 & 2 \end{bmatrix} = \begin{bmatrix} 1 & 6 & 0 \\ 3 & 9 & 2 \end{bmatrix}$$

This illustrates the associative law for addition. ■

Theorem 1 Let **A**, **B**, and **C** be matrices of the same size, and let k and m be scalars.

1. Addition is commutative: $\mathbf{A} + \mathbf{B} = \mathbf{B} + \mathbf{A}$.
2. Addition is associative: $(\mathbf{A} + \mathbf{B}) + \mathbf{C} = \mathbf{A} + (\mathbf{B} + \mathbf{C})$.
3. Multiplication by a scalar is associative: $k(m\mathbf{A}) = (km)\mathbf{A}$.
4. Multiplication by a scalar is distributive over addition: $k(\mathbf{A} + \mathbf{B}) = k\mathbf{A} + k\mathbf{B}$.

Proof Theorem 1 is a direct consequence of the properties of real numbers and the fact that the operations of addition and multiplication by a scalar are carried out elementwise. A formal proof follows for part 4. The other parts are proved in a similar way.

Let $\mathbf{A} = [a_{ij}]_{m \times n}$ and $\mathbf{B} = [b_{ij}]_{m \times n}$. Then:

$k(\mathbf{A} + \mathbf{B})$	$= k[a_{ij} + b_{ij}]$	Definition of addition of matrices
	$= [k(a_{ij} + b_{ij})]$	Definition of multiplication by a scalar
	$= [ka_{ij} + kb_{ij}]$	Multiplication of real numbers is distributive over addition
	$= [ka_{ij}] + [kb_{ij}]$	Definition of matrix addition
	$= k\mathbf{A} + k\mathbf{B}$	Definition of multiplication by a scalar □

Since addition has been defined for matrices, it is natural to look for a matrix that is an additive identity.

Example 9 Let $\mathbf{A} = [a_{ij}]_{3\times4}$ represent a 3×4 matrix. If $\mathbf{B}$ is an additive identity, then $\mathbf{A} + \mathbf{B} = \mathbf{A}$. First, $\mathbf{B}$ must be a 3×4 matrix for $\mathbf{A} + \mathbf{B}$ to be defined, so let $\mathbf{B} = [b_{ij}]_{3\times4}$. The statement $\mathbf{A} + \mathbf{B} = \mathbf{A}$ requires that $a_{ij} + b_{ij} = a_{ij}$ for $i = 1, 2, 3$ and $j = 1, 2, 3, 4$. These twelve equations imply $b_{ij} = 0$ for all i, j. Thus,

$$\mathbf{B} = \begin{bmatrix} 0 & 0 & 0 & 0 \\ 0 & 0 & 0 & 0 \\ 0 & 0 & 0 & 0 \end{bmatrix}$$

This 3×4 matrix acts as an additive identity for the set of all 3×4 matrices.

Let $\mathbf{A} = \begin{bmatrix} 1 & -2 & 3 & 4 \\ 5 & 6 & 0 & 8 \\ 1 & 2 & 1 & 2 \end{bmatrix}$. The matrix $\mathbf{C}$ is an additive inverse of $\mathbf{A}$ if

$$\mathbf{A} + \mathbf{C} = \begin{bmatrix} 0 & 0 & 0 & 0 \\ 0 & 0 & 0 & 0 \\ 0 & 0 & 0 & 0 \end{bmatrix}$$

The only matrix that satisfies this equation is

$$\mathbf{C} = \begin{bmatrix} -1 & 2 & -3 & -4 \\ -5 & -6 & 0 & -8 \\ -1 & -2 & -1 & -2 \end{bmatrix} = (-1)\mathbf{A}$$

Thus, the additive inverse of $\mathbf{A}$ is the matrix $(-1)\mathbf{A}$, which we write $-\mathbf{A}$. ■

Definition 7

Zero Matrix A matrix in which each element is the real number 0 is called a **zero matrix**. It is usually designated $\mathbf{0}$. For clarity, the size of a zero matrix is sometimes indicated by subscripts:

$$\mathbf{0}_{2\times2} = \begin{bmatrix} 0 & 0 \\ 0 & 0 \end{bmatrix}, \qquad \mathbf{0}_{3\times4} = \begin{bmatrix} 0 & 0 & 0 & 0 \\ 0 & 0 & 0 & 0 \\ 0 & 0 & 0 & 0 \end{bmatrix}$$

Additive Inverse $-\mathbf{A}$, the **additive inverse** of $\mathbf{A}$, is the matrix $(-1)\mathbf{A}$.

The following theorem follows directly from Definitions 5 and 7.

Theorem 2 For the set of $m \times n$ matrices, the matrix $\mathbf{0}_{m\times n}$ is the additive identity; that is, for any $m \times n$ matrix $\mathbf{A}$, $\mathbf{A}_{m\times n} + \mathbf{0}_{m\times n} = \mathbf{A}_{m\times n}$. The additive inverse of an $m \times n$ matrix is the matrix $-\mathbf{A} = (-1)\mathbf{A}$; that is, $\mathbf{A}_{m\times n} + (-1)\mathbf{A}_{m\times n} = \mathbf{0}_{m\times n}$. □

In Problems 10 and 11 you are asked to show that the zero n-tuple $(0, 0, \ldots, 0)$ is the additive identity in the set of n-tuples and that the additive inverse of the n-tuple $\mathbf{u}$ is $(-1)\mathbf{u}$.

SUMMARY A matrix is a rectangular array of elements called scalars. In this book scalars are real numbers. An n-tuple is an ordered set of real numbers. Matrices and n-tuples are used extensively in elementary linear algebra. Arrays of the same size can be added. Arrays can be multiplied by a scalar. These operations are defined elementwise. Addition is commutative and associative; scalar multiplication is distributive over addition. An expression of the form $c_1\mathbf{A}_1 + c_2\mathbf{A}_2 + \cdots + c_k\mathbf{A}_k$, which combines both these operations, is called a linear combination of the arrays $\mathbf{A}_1, \mathbf{A}_2, \ldots, \mathbf{A}_k$.

EXERCISES 1.1

1. Let $\mathbf{u}_1 = (1, 0, -3)$, $\mathbf{u}_2 = (2, 0, 4)$, and $\mathbf{u}_3 = (4, 0, 1)$.
a. Calculate $3\mathbf{u}_1 - 4\mathbf{u}_2 + 3\mathbf{u}_3$.
b. Calculate $c_1\mathbf{u}_1 + c_2\mathbf{u}_2 + c_3\mathbf{u}_3$.
c. What property is common to every linear combination of the triples $\mathbf{u}_1$, $\mathbf{u}_2$, and $\mathbf{u}_3$?

2. Let $\mathbf{u} = (3, 1, 5)$ and $\mathbf{v} = (1, -1, 1)$.
a. Calculate $3\mathbf{u} + 4\mathbf{v}$. **b.** Calculate $\mathbf{u} - 3\mathbf{v}$.
c. Find $\mathbf{w}$ such that $2\mathbf{u} + \mathbf{w} = \mathbf{v}$.

3. Let

$$\mathbf{A}_1 = \begin{bmatrix} 1 & -1 & 2 \\ 3 & 1 & 4 \end{bmatrix}, \quad \mathbf{A}_2 = \begin{bmatrix} 2 & 1 & 1 \\ 0 & 3 & 3 \end{bmatrix},$$

and

$$\mathbf{A}_3 = \begin{bmatrix} 1 & 0 & 1 \\ -1 & 1 & 2 \end{bmatrix}$$

a. Calculate $2\mathbf{A}_1 - 3\mathbf{A}_2 + 4\mathbf{A}_3$.
b. Write $c_1\mathbf{A}_1 + c_2\mathbf{A}_2 + c_3\mathbf{A}_3$ as a single matrix.

4. Let

$$\mathbf{A}_1 = \begin{bmatrix} 2 & 1 \\ 0 & 3 \\ 4 & -1 \end{bmatrix}, \quad \mathbf{A}_2 = \begin{bmatrix} 1 & 2 \\ 1 & -1 \\ 1 & 0 \end{bmatrix},$$

and

$$\mathbf{A}_3 = \begin{bmatrix} 3 & 3 \\ 1 & 2 \\ 5 & -1 \end{bmatrix}$$

a. Write $c_1\mathbf{A}_1 + c_2\mathbf{A}_2 + c_3\mathbf{A}_3$ as a single matrix.
b. Show that $\mathbf{A}_1 + \mathbf{A}_2 = \mathbf{A}_3$.
c. For what choice of c_1, c_2, c_3 is $c_1\mathbf{A}_1 + c_2\mathbf{A}_2 + c_3\mathbf{A}_3 = \mathbf{0}$, where $\mathbf{0}$ is the 3×2 zero matrix?

5. Let $\mathbf{u}_1 = (1, 1, 1)$, $\mathbf{u}_2 = (-1, 1, 1)$, $\mathbf{u}_3 = (1, -1, 1)$, and $\mathbf{u}_4 = (1, 1, -1)$.
a. Find a linear combination of $\mathbf{u}_1$, $\mathbf{u}_2$, $\mathbf{u}_3$, $\mathbf{u}_4$ with coefficients not all zero that is equal to the zero triple.
b. Write $\mathbf{u}_1$ as a linear combination of $\mathbf{u}_2$, $\mathbf{u}_3$, and $\mathbf{u}_4$.

6. a. Let $\mathbf{u} = (5, 1, 2)$, $\mathbf{v} = (3, -1, 4)$, $\mathbf{w} = (1, 0, 1)$. Illustrate the associative law in this case: $(\mathbf{u} + \mathbf{v}) + \mathbf{w} = \mathbf{u} + (\mathbf{v} + \mathbf{w})$.
b. Let $\mathbf{u}$, $\mathbf{v}$, $\mathbf{w}$ be n-tuples. Prove that addition of n-tuples obeys the associative law.

7. a. Let $\mathbf{u} = (1, -1, 3)$, and $\mathbf{v} = (0, 1, 2)$. Show that $4(\mathbf{u} + \mathbf{v}) = 4\mathbf{u} + 4\mathbf{v}$.
b. Prove that for any n-tuples $\mathbf{u}$, $\mathbf{v}$ and any scalar k, $k(\mathbf{u} + \mathbf{v}) = k\mathbf{u} + k\mathbf{v}$.

8. Let

$$\mathbf{A} = \begin{bmatrix} 1 & 2 & 1 \\ 2 & 1 & 3 \\ 0 & 0 & 1 \end{bmatrix}, \quad \mathbf{B} = \begin{bmatrix} -1 & 1 & 0 \\ 0 & 1 & 1 \\ 1 & -1 & -1 \end{bmatrix},$$

$$\mathbf{C} = \begin{bmatrix} 1 & 1 \\ 2 & 1 \\ 0 & 4 \end{bmatrix}, \quad \mathbf{D} = \begin{bmatrix} 2 & 1 \\ 1 & 3 \end{bmatrix}, \quad \mathbf{E} = \begin{bmatrix} 1 & 1 \\ 3 & 5 \end{bmatrix}$$

a. Which pairs of matrices can be added?
b. Calculate $3\mathbf{A} + 4\mathbf{B}$.
c. Write a matrix $\mathbf{F}$ such that $\mathbf{D} + \mathbf{F} = \mathbf{D}$.

d. Write a matrix $\mathbf{G}$ such that $\mathbf{D} + \mathbf{G} = \mathbf{0}_{2\times 2}$.
e. Find a matrix $\mathbf{H}$ such that $\mathbf{D} + \mathbf{H} = \mathbf{E}$.

9. Let $\mathbf{A} = \begin{bmatrix} 1 & 3 & 1 \\ 3 & 1 & 2 \end{bmatrix}$ and $\mathbf{B} = \begin{bmatrix} -1 & 1 & 0 \\ 1 & 4 & 3 \end{bmatrix}$.
a. Calculate $2\mathbf{A} + 3\mathbf{B}$.
b. Calculate $\mathbf{A} - \mathbf{B}$.
c. Find $\mathbf{C}$ so that $\mathbf{A} - \mathbf{B} + \mathbf{C} = \mathbf{0}$.
d. What is the size of the matrix $\mathbf{0}$ in part c?

10. **a.** Let $\mathbf{u} = (1, 2, 3)$ and $\mathbf{v} = (a, b, c)$. For what values of a, b, c is $\mathbf{u} + \mathbf{v} = \mathbf{u}$?
b. Show that the n-tuple $\mathbf{0} = (0, 0, \dots, 0)$ is an additive identity in the set of all n-tuples; that is, $\mathbf{u} + \mathbf{0} = \mathbf{u}$ for all n-tuples $\mathbf{u}$.

11. **a.** Let $\mathbf{u} = (-1, 2, 4, -3)$ and $\mathbf{v} = (a, b, c, d)$. For what values a, b, c, d is $\mathbf{u} + \mathbf{v} = (0, 0, 0, 0)$?
b. Show that the additive inverse of the n-tuple $\mathbf{u}$ is the n-tuple $(-1)\mathbf{u}$.

12. Let $\mathbf{u} = (15, 3, 12, t)$, and $\mathbf{v} = (5, 1, s, 2)$. For what values of s and t and k is $\mathbf{u} = k\mathbf{v}$?

13. Show that if $\mathbf{A}$ is an $m \times n$ matrix, $c_1\mathbf{A} + c_2\mathbf{A} = (c_1 + c_2)\mathbf{A}$.

14. Let $\mathbf{A}$, $\mathbf{B}$ be $m \times n$ matrices. Prove that addition is commutative—that is, $\mathbf{A} + \mathbf{B} = \mathbf{B} + \mathbf{A}$.

15. Let $\mathbf{A}$, $\mathbf{B}$, $\mathbf{C}$ be $m \times n$ matrices. Prove that addition is associative—that is, $(\mathbf{A} + \mathbf{B}) + \mathbf{C} = \mathbf{A} + (\mathbf{B} + \mathbf{C})$.

16. Let $\mathbf{A} = \begin{bmatrix} 1 & -4 \\ 2 & 5 \\ 3 & 7 \end{bmatrix}$ and $\mathbf{B} = \begin{bmatrix} 0 & 1 \\ 1 & 5 \\ 2 & -1 \end{bmatrix}$.
a. Calculate $\mathbf{A} + \mathbf{B}$.
b. Write $\mathbf{A}^T$ and $\mathbf{B}^T$.
c. Calculate $\mathbf{A}^T + \mathbf{B}^T$.
d. Write $(\mathbf{A} + \mathbf{B})^T$.
e. Compare $(\mathbf{A} + \mathbf{B})^T$ and $\mathbf{A}^T + \mathbf{B}^T$.

17. Let $\mathbf{A} = \begin{bmatrix} -1 & 4 \\ 2 & -1 \end{bmatrix}$ and $\mathbf{B} = \begin{bmatrix} 3 & 2 \\ 1 & 0 \end{bmatrix}$.
Verify that $(\mathbf{A} + \mathbf{B})^T = \mathbf{A}^T + \mathbf{B}^T$.

18. Prove that if $\mathbf{A}$ and $\mathbf{B}$ are $m \times n$ matrices, $(\mathbf{A} + \mathbf{B})^T = \mathbf{A}^T + \mathbf{B}^T$.

19. Show that $(k\mathbf{A})^T = k\mathbf{A}^T$, for any scalar k.

20. Show that the transpose of a linear combination of $m \times n$ matrices is the same linear combination of their transposes—that is,

$$\left(\sum_{i=1}^{k} c_i \mathbf{A}_i\right)^T = \sum_{i=1}^{k} c_i \mathbf{A}_i^T$$

21. A gasoline company has 100 service stations in different parts of the country. Each sells some supplies as well as gasoline. The first row of the table refers to supplies (fan belts, tires, windshield wipers) and the second row refers to gasoline (regular, unleaded, premium unleaded). The following table shows the average sales in a month in each type of station.

	City Stations			*Country Stations*		
Supplies	15	40	10	20	70	15
Gasoline	1000	5000	3000	1200	1000	500

There are 40 city stations and 60 country stations. Write a linear combination of two matrices from which the total monthly sales in each category can be found. Which entry represents the total number of windshield wipers sold?

22. A short-order breakfast bar offers four choices: #1 (toast and juice); #2 (2 eggs and toast); #3 (1 egg, 2 slices of bacon and toast); #4 (4 slices of bacon, toast, and juice). Each day they serve 100 orders of #1, 30 each of #2 and #3, and 40 of #4. How much of each item is required? Write the linear combination of n-tuples that is involved in this calculation.

1.2 Products

It is natural and meaningful to add matrices elementwise. Addition of matrices has the same properties as addition of real numbers. We now need a meaningful definition of multiplication of arrays.

Example 10 State University is considering three different types of computer laboratories; each lab will contain ten computer systems. The makeup of each kind of lab can be described in the following table.

	Lab 1	*Lab 2*	*Lab 3*
Mono, Double Floppies	0	4	0
Mono, Hard Drive	8	2	0
Color, Double Floppies	0	4	2
Color, Hard Drive	2	0	8

To find the cost of filling Lab 1 completely with entry-level systems from the Ace Computer Shop, we multiply the cost of each system type by the number of that type required and add the results:

$$(0)(2000) + (8)(2400) + (0)(2500) + (2)(2900) = \$25{,}000$$

In this calculation, the 4-tuple describing the cost of entry-level systems is combined with the 4-tuple describing the equipment to be placed in Lab 1, resulting in a scalar, the total cost of the laboratory equipment. ■

In Example 10, two 4-tuples are combined to generate a scalar by multiplying corresponding elements and adding the results. The product of two n-tuples defined in this way is called the *scalar product* because the result of the operation is a scalar. It is sometimes called the *dot product* because the notation used to represent such a product is $\mathbf{u} \cdot \mathbf{v}$.

In the notation of Definition 4, we can write $\mathbf{u} \cdot \mathbf{v}$ in the form $\mathbf{U}^T\mathbf{V}$, the product of a $1 \times n$ matrix and an $n \times 1$ matrix.

Scalar Product
$\mathbf{u} \cdot \mathbf{v}$
$\mathbf{U}^T\mathbf{V}$

Definition 8

Let $\mathbf{u} = (a_1, a_2, \ldots, a_n)$ and $\mathbf{v} = (b_1, b_2, \ldots, b_n)$. The **scalar product**, written $\mathbf{u} \cdot \mathbf{v}$, is defined by $\mathbf{u} \cdot \mathbf{v} = a_1b_1 + a_2b_2 + \cdots + a_nb_n$. The product $\mathbf{U}^T\mathbf{V} = \mathbf{u} \cdot \mathbf{v}$.

Example 11 Let $\mathbf{u} = (1, 3, -1)$, $\mathbf{v} = (-1, 4, 2)$, and $\mathbf{w} = (3, 2, 1)$. Then
$\mathbf{u} \cdot \mathbf{v} = (1)(-1) + (3)(4) + (-1)(2) = -1 + 12 - 2 = 9$ and
$\mathbf{v} \cdot \mathbf{u} = (-1)(1) + (4)(3) + (2)(-1) = -1 + 12 - 2 = 9$.
Note that $\mathbf{u} \cdot \mathbf{v} = \mathbf{v} \cdot \mathbf{u}$. Also $(2\mathbf{u} \cdot \mathbf{v}) = (2, 6, -2) \cdot (-1, 4, 2) = 18$ and $2(\mathbf{u} \cdot \mathbf{v}) = 2(9) = 18$, so that $(2\mathbf{u} \cdot \mathbf{v}) = 2(\mathbf{u} \cdot \mathbf{v})$.

Similarly, $\mathbf{u} \cdot \mathbf{w} = 3 + 6 - 1 = 8$, $\mathbf{u} \cdot (\mathbf{v} + \mathbf{w}) = (1, 3, -1) \cdot (2, 6, 3) = 2 + 18 - 3 = 17$,
and $\mathbf{u} \cdot \mathbf{v} + \mathbf{u} \cdot \mathbf{w} = 9 + 8 = 17$, so that $\mathbf{u} \cdot (\mathbf{v} + \mathbf{w}) = \mathbf{u} \cdot \mathbf{v} + \mathbf{u} \cdot \mathbf{w}$. ■

In Example 11 some properties of the scalar product are illustrated. These and others follow from the definition. They are listed in Theorem 3.

Theorem 3 Let **u**, **v**, and **w** be n-tuples, and let k be a scalar. Then:

1. $\mathbf{u} \cdot \mathbf{v} = \mathbf{v} \cdot \mathbf{u}$
2. $(k\mathbf{u}) \cdot \mathbf{v} = k(\mathbf{u} \cdot \mathbf{v}) = \mathbf{u} \cdot (k\mathbf{v})$
3. $\mathbf{u} \cdot (\mathbf{v} + \mathbf{w}) = \mathbf{u} \cdot \mathbf{v} + \mathbf{u} \cdot \mathbf{w}$ □

The scalar product just defined was used in Example 10 to multiply the row $[2000 \quad 2400 \quad 2500 \quad 2900]$ by the column $\begin{bmatrix} 0 \\ 8 \\ 0 \\ 2 \end{bmatrix}$. In Example 12 we extend this idea to multiple arrays with several rows and columns.

Example 12 The matrix **C** of Example 1 gives the cost information for computer systems:

	Mono 2 fl.	Mono Hard	Color 2 fl.	Color Hard	
C =	2000	2400	2500	2900	Entry level
	4000	4400	4600	5000	Scientific system
	5000	5500	5600	6100	Business system

In Example 10 we found the cost of outfitting Lab 1 with entry-level systems by taking the dot product of the first row of **C** with the 4-tuple (0, 8, 0, 2). Similar calculations can be done for row 2 of **C** to find the cost of scientific systems and for row 3 to find the cost of business systems. This collection of information is the product:

$$\begin{bmatrix} 2000 & 2400 & 2500 & 2900 \\ 4000 & 4400 & 4600 & 5000 \\ 5000 & 5500 & 5600 & 6100 \end{bmatrix} \begin{bmatrix} 0 \\ 8 \\ 0 \\ 2 \end{bmatrix} = \begin{bmatrix} 25000 \\ 45200 \\ 56200 \end{bmatrix}$$

Notice that for this calculation to be made, the rows of the left-hand matrix must have the same number of elements as the column matrix. In this case, both are 4-tuples.

Cost information for Lab 2 can be obtained in the same way using **C** and the 4-tuple (4, 2, 4, 0), which describes the equipment needed for Lab 2. The cost information for all three types of labs is the product of two matrices:

$$\underset{\text{(unit price)}}{\begin{bmatrix} 2000 & 2400 & 2500 & 2900 \\ 4000 & 4400 & 4600 & 5000 \\ 5000 & 5500 & 5600 & 6100 \end{bmatrix}} \times \underset{\text{(quantity)}}{\begin{bmatrix} 0 & 4 & 0 \\ 8 & 2 & 0 \\ 0 & 4 & 2 \\ 2 & 0 & 8 \end{bmatrix}} = \underset{\text{(cost)}}{\begin{bmatrix} 25000 & 22800 & 28200 \\ 45200 & 43200 & 49200 \\ 56200 & 53400 & 60000 \end{bmatrix}}$$

■

Definition 9

Product AB

Let **A** be a matrix of size $m \times n$ and let **B** be a matrix of size $n \times r$. The **product AB** is the matrix **C** with m rows and r columns, in which each element c_{ij} is the scalar product of the ith row of **A** and the jth column of **B**. The product **AB** is defined if and only if the number of columns of **A** is the same as the number of rows of **B**.

Example 13

Let $\mathbf{A} = \begin{bmatrix} 2 & 1 & 0 \\ 1 & 1 & 1 \\ -1 & 4 & 3 \end{bmatrix}$ and $\mathbf{B} = \begin{bmatrix} 1 & 1 \\ 0 & 1 \\ -1 & 3 \end{bmatrix}$. Calculate $\mathbf{C} = \mathbf{AB}$. The calculations involved in finding the product **AB** are:

$$c_{11} = [2 \quad 1 \quad 0]\begin{bmatrix} 1 \\ 0 \\ -1 \end{bmatrix} = 2, \qquad c_{12} = [2 \quad 1 \quad 0]\begin{bmatrix} 1 \\ 1 \\ 3 \end{bmatrix} = 3$$

$$c_{21} = [1 \quad 1 \quad 1]\begin{bmatrix} 1 \\ 0 \\ -1 \end{bmatrix} = 0, \qquad c_{22} = [1 \quad 1 \quad 1]\begin{bmatrix} 1 \\ 1 \\ 3 \end{bmatrix} = 5$$

$$c_{31} = [-1 \quad 4 \quad 3]\begin{bmatrix} 1 \\ 0 \\ -1 \end{bmatrix} = -4, \qquad c_{32} = [-1 \quad 4 \quad 3]\begin{bmatrix} 1 \\ 1 \\ 3 \end{bmatrix} = 12$$

Thus, **AB** is the 3×2 matrix $\begin{bmatrix} 2 & 3 \\ 0 & 5 \\ -4 & 12 \end{bmatrix}$. The matrix **BA** cannot be calculated, since **B** has only two columns and **A** has three rows. Let $\mathbf{D} = \begin{bmatrix} 1 & 1 \\ -1 & 2 \end{bmatrix}$ and $\mathbf{E} = \begin{bmatrix} 1 & 2 \\ 3 & 4 \end{bmatrix}$. Then $\mathbf{DE} = \begin{bmatrix} 4 & 6 \\ 5 & 6 \end{bmatrix}$ and $\mathbf{ED} = \begin{bmatrix} -1 & 5 \\ -1 & 11 \end{bmatrix}$. Although both **DE** and **ED** are defined, they are not equal. ■

Example 13 shows that *multiplication of matrices is not commutative.* The associative law, however, does hold. That is, when the product **A(BC)** is defined, **(AB)C** is also defined and **A(BC)** = **(AB)C**. Example 14 illustrates this fact.

Example 14

Let $\mathbf{A} = \begin{bmatrix} 4 & 3 & 1 \\ 2 & -1 & 5 \end{bmatrix}$, $\mathbf{B} = \begin{bmatrix} 1 & 0 \\ 2 & 3 \\ 1 & 4 \end{bmatrix}$, and $\mathbf{C} = \begin{bmatrix} 2 & 1 \\ -1 & 4 \end{bmatrix}$. $\mathbf{AB} = \begin{bmatrix} 11 & 13 \\ 5 & 17 \end{bmatrix}$

and $(\mathbf{AB})\mathbf{C} = \begin{bmatrix} 11 & 13 \\ 5 & 17 \end{bmatrix} \begin{bmatrix} 2 & 1 \\ -1 & 4 \end{bmatrix} = \begin{bmatrix} 9 & 63 \\ -7 & 73 \end{bmatrix}$. On the other hand,

$$\mathbf{BC} = \begin{bmatrix} 2 & 1 \\ 1 & 14 \\ -2 & 17 \end{bmatrix}$$

and

$$\mathbf{A}(\mathbf{BC}) = \begin{bmatrix} 4 & 3 & 1 \\ 2 & -1 & 5 \end{bmatrix} \begin{bmatrix} 2 & 1 \\ 1 & 14 \\ -2 & 17 \end{bmatrix} = \begin{bmatrix} 9 & 63 \\ -7 & 73 \end{bmatrix}$$

In this numerical case, $\mathbf{A}(\mathbf{BC}) = (\mathbf{AB})\mathbf{C}$. The general case is proved in Theorem 4. ■

The distributive law states that multiplication is distributive over addition. Example 15 shows how this law can be verified for general 2×2 and 3×2 matrices.

Example 15 Let $\mathbf{A}$ be 3×2 and $\mathbf{B}$ and $\mathbf{C}$ be 2×2 matrices. Then $\mathbf{A}(\mathbf{B} + \mathbf{C}) = \mathbf{AB} + \mathbf{AC}$. We verify this for general matrices $\mathbf{A}$, $\mathbf{B}$, and $\mathbf{C}$ of the sizes given.

$$\mathbf{A} = \begin{bmatrix} a_{11} & a_{12} \\ a_{21} & a_{22} \\ a_{31} & a_{32} \end{bmatrix}, \qquad \mathbf{B} = \begin{bmatrix} b_{11} & b_{12} \\ b_{21} & b_{22} \end{bmatrix}, \qquad \mathbf{C} = \begin{bmatrix} c_{11} & c_{12} \\ c_{21} & c_{22} \end{bmatrix}$$

Notice that $\mathbf{B}$ and $\mathbf{C}$ must be of the same size. Since $\mathbf{B} + \mathbf{C} = [b_{ij} + c_{ij}]$,

$$\mathbf{A}(\mathbf{B} + \mathbf{C}) = \begin{bmatrix} a_{11}(b_{11} + c_{11}) + a_{12}(b_{21} + c_{21}) & a_{11}(b_{12} + c_{12}) + a_{12}(b_{22} + c_{22}) \\ a_{21}(b_{11} + c_{11}) + a_{22}(b_{21} + c_{21}) & a_{21}(b_{12} + c_{12}) + a_{22}(b_{22} + c_{22}) \\ a_{31}(b_{11} + c_{11}) + a_{32}(b_{21} + c_{21}) & a_{31}(b_{12} + c_{12}) + a_{32}(b_{22} + c_{22}) \end{bmatrix}$$

On the other hand, however,

$$\mathbf{AB} = \begin{bmatrix} a_{11}b_{11} + a_{12}b_{21} & a_{11}b_{12} + a_{12}b_{22} \\ a_{21}b_{11} + a_{22}b_{21} & a_{21}b_{12} + a_{22}b_{22} \\ a_{31}b_{11} + a_{32}b_{21} & a_{31}b_{12} + a_{32}b_{22} \end{bmatrix}$$

and

$$\mathbf{AC} = \begin{bmatrix} a_{11}c_{11} + a_{12}c_{21} & a_{11}c_{12} + a_{12}c_{22} \\ a_{21}c_{11} + a_{22}c_{21} & a_{21}c_{12} + a_{22}c_{22} \\ a_{31}c_{11} + a_{32}c_{21} & a_{31}c_{12} + a_{32}c_{22} \end{bmatrix}$$

It is now clear that the elements of $\mathbf{AB} + \mathbf{AC}$ are equal to the corresponding elements of $\mathbf{A}(\mathbf{B} + \mathbf{C})$. ■

The properties of matrix multiplication are listed in Theorem 4.

Theorem 4 Let **A**, **B**, and **C** be matrices.

1. If **AB** is defined, then **BA** may or may not be defined; if both **AB** and **BA** are defined, they are not necessarily equal; that is, matrix multiplication is not commutative.
2. If **A(BC)** is defined, then **(AB)C** is defined and **A(BC)** = **(AB)C**; that is, matrix multiplication is associative.
3. For k, a scalar, if **AB** is defined, $k(\mathbf{AB}) = (k\mathbf{A})\mathbf{B} = \mathbf{A}(k\mathbf{B})$.
4. If **A** is $m \times n$ and **B** and **C** are $n \times q$, then $\mathbf{A}(\mathbf{B} + \mathbf{C}) = \mathbf{AB} + \mathbf{AC}$; that is, matrix multiplication is distributive over addition. Since multiplication is not commutative, a second distributive law must be stated: if **A** and **B** are $m \times n$ and **C** is $n \times q$, then $(\mathbf{A} + \mathbf{B})\mathbf{C} = \mathbf{AC} + \mathbf{BC}$.

Proof Part 1 of this theorem has already been established in Example 13. Parts 2, 3, and 4 can be proved by a straightforward application of the definitions. Example 15 illustrates part 4 when **A** is 3×2 and **B** and **C** are 2×2. The argument in the general case is somewhat cumbersome. It is outlined for parts 2 and 3.

Part 2: Let $\mathbf{A}_{m\times n} = [a_{ij}]$, $\mathbf{B}_{n\times q} = [b_{jk}]$, and $\mathbf{C}_{q\times r} = [c_{ks}]$. The product **BC** is defined and has size $n \times r$, and the product **A(BC)** is defined and has size $m \times r$. Also **AB** is defined and has size $m \times q$, and **(AB)C** is defined and has size $m \times r$. Thus, **(AB)C** is defined when **A(BC)** is defined, and the matrices have the same size. To show that they are equal, we must get an expression for the elements in the products. We use sigma notation to represent the elements.

$$\mathbf{BC} = \left[\sum_{k=1}^{q} b_{jk}c_{ks}\right] \quad \text{and} \quad \mathbf{A}(\mathbf{BC}) = \left[\sum_{j=1}^{n} a_{ij} \sum_{k=1}^{q} b_{jk}c_{ks}\right] = \left[\sum_{j=1}^{n}\sum_{k=1}^{q} a_{ij}b_{jk}c_{ks}\right]$$

$$\mathbf{AB} = \left[\sum_{j=1}^{n} a_{ij}b_{jk}\right] \quad \text{and} \quad (\mathbf{AB})\mathbf{C} = \left[\sum_{k=1}^{q}\left(\sum_{j=1}^{n} a_{ij}b_{jk}\right)c_{ks}\right] = \left[\sum_{k=1}^{q}\sum_{j=1}^{n} a_{ij}b_{jk}c_{ks}\right]$$

Part 3: Suppose **A** is $m \times n$ and **B** is $n \times r$. Then $k\mathbf{A}$ is also $m \times n$ so that $(k\mathbf{A})\mathbf{B}$ is an $m \times r$ matrix. The matrix **AB** is $m \times r$ and so is $k(\mathbf{AB})$. Thus $(k\mathbf{A})\mathbf{B}$ and $k(\mathbf{AB})$ have the same size. We must show that they also have the same elements. The ith row of $k\mathbf{A}$ is $(ka_{i1}, ka_{i2}, \ldots, ka_{in})$ and the jth column of **B** is $(b_{1j}, b_{2j}, \ldots, b_{nj})$ so that the ijth element of $(k\mathbf{A})\mathbf{B}$ is $ka_{i1}b_{1j} + ka_{i2}b_{2j} + \cdots + ka_{in}b_{nj}$. On the other hand, the ijth element of **AB** is $a_{i1}b_{1j} + a_{i2}b_{2j} + \cdots + a_{in}b_{nj}$ so that the ijth element of $k(\mathbf{AB})$ is $k(a_{i1}b_{1j} + a_{i2}b_{2j} + \cdots + a_{in}b_{nj})$, the same as the ijth element of $(k\mathbf{A})\mathbf{B}$. A similar argument shows that $k(\mathbf{AB}) = \mathbf{A}(k\mathbf{B})$. □

In Section 1.1, the matrix $\mathbf{A}^T$ is defined (Definition 3). The property $(\mathbf{A} + \mathbf{B})^T = \mathbf{A}^T + \mathbf{B}^T$ follows directly from this definition. The effect of transposing a matrix product is not quite so obvious.

Example 16

Let $\mathbf{A} = \begin{bmatrix} 1 & 2 & 1 \\ 1 & 0 & 1 \end{bmatrix}$ and $\mathbf{B} = \begin{bmatrix} -1 & 0 & 1 \\ 1 & -2 & -1 \\ 3 & 3 & 1 \end{bmatrix}$, so that $\mathbf{AB} = \begin{bmatrix} 4 & -1 & 0 \\ 2 & 3 & 2 \end{bmatrix}$,

$\mathbf{A}^T = \begin{bmatrix} 1 & 1 \\ 2 & 0 \\ 1 & 1 \end{bmatrix}$, and $\mathbf{B}^T = \begin{bmatrix} -1 & 1 & 3 \\ 0 & -2 & 3 \\ 1 & -1 & 1 \end{bmatrix}$. Since $\mathbf{A}^T$ is 3×2 and $\mathbf{B}^T$ is 3×3, $\mathbf{A}^T\mathbf{B}^T$ cannot be calculated. However, if we reverse the order and calculate $\mathbf{B}^T\mathbf{A}^T$, we get

$$\begin{bmatrix} -1 & 1 & 3 \\ 0 & -2 & 3 \\ 1 & -1 & 1 \end{bmatrix} \begin{bmatrix} 1 & 1 \\ 2 & 0 \\ 1 & 1 \end{bmatrix} = \begin{bmatrix} 4 & 2 \\ -1 & 3 \\ 0 & 2 \end{bmatrix}$$

which is the matrix $(\mathbf{AB})^T$. ■

The following theorem describes the transpose of scalar multiples, sums, and products of matrices.

Theorem 5 Let **A** and **B** be matrices and k a scalar.

1. $(k\mathbf{A})^T = k\mathbf{A}^T$
2. $(\mathbf{A}^T)^T = \mathbf{A}$
3. If $\mathbf{A} + \mathbf{B}$ is defined, $\mathbf{A}^T + \mathbf{B}^T$ is defined and $(\mathbf{A} + \mathbf{B})^T = \mathbf{A}^T + \mathbf{B}^T$.
4. If **AB** is defined, $\mathbf{B}^T\mathbf{A}^T$ is defined and $(\mathbf{AB})^T = \mathbf{B}^T\mathbf{A}^T$.

Proof Parts 1, 2, and 3 follow directly from the definitions. The proof of part 4 is outlined here. Suppose **A** is $m \times n$ and **B** is $n \times r$ so that **AB** is $m \times r$. Since $\mathbf{A}^T$ is $n \times m$ and $\mathbf{B}^T$ is $r \times n$, $\mathbf{B}^T\mathbf{A}^T$ is defined. Also the size of $\mathbf{B}^T\mathbf{A}^T$ is $r \times m$ —that is, the same as the size of $(\mathbf{AB})^T$. We must now compare the elements in these matrices. The ijth element of $(\mathbf{AB})^T$ is the jith element of **AB**—that is, the dot product of row j of **A** and column i of **B**:

$$a_{j1}b_{1i} + a_{j2}b_{2i} + \cdots + a_{jn}b_{ni}$$

The ijth element of $\mathbf{B}^T\mathbf{A}^T$ is the dot product of row i of $\mathbf{B}^T$ and column j of $\mathbf{A}^T$. But row i of $\mathbf{B}^T$ is column i of **B**, and column j of $\mathbf{A}^T$ is row j of **A**. Thus the ijth element of $\mathbf{B}^T\mathbf{A}^T =$

$$(b_{1i}, b_{2i}, \ldots, b_{ni}) \cdot (a_{j1}, a_{j2}, \ldots, a_{jn}) = a_{j1}b_{1i} + a_{j2}b_{2i} + \cdots + a_{jn}b_{ni}$$

This proves that $(\mathbf{AB})^T = \mathbf{B}^T\mathbf{A}^T$. □

Definition 10

Symmetric Matrix

A matrix **A** is **symmetric** if $\mathbf{A}^T = \mathbf{A}$; that is, $a_{ij} = a_{ji}$ for $i = 1, 2, \ldots, n$ and $j = 1, 2, \ldots, n$.

Skew-Symmetric Matrix

A matrix **A** is **skew-symmetric** if $\mathbf{A}^T = -\mathbf{A}$.

Symmetric and skew-symmetric matrices must be square.

Example 17 Let

$$\mathbf{A} = \begin{bmatrix} 1 & 3 \\ 3 & 5 \end{bmatrix}, \qquad \mathbf{B} = \begin{bmatrix} 1 & 3 & -5 \\ 3 & 5 & -1 \\ -5 & -1 & 4 \end{bmatrix},$$

$$\mathbf{C} = \begin{bmatrix} 1 & 0 & 2 \\ 0 & -1 & 5 \\ 5 & 2 & 3 \end{bmatrix}, \quad \mathbf{D} = \begin{bmatrix} 0 & 1 & 5 \\ -1 & 0 & -3 \\ -5 & 3 & 0 \end{bmatrix}$$

Matrices **A** and **B** are symmetric. Matrix **C** is not symmetric, since $a_{31} = 5$ and $a_{13} = 2$. Matrix **D** is skew-symmetric. ∎

Theorem 6 lists some simple properties of symmetric and skew-symmetric matrices that follow from the definition and Theorem 5. Other properties are included in Exercises 1.2.

Theorem 6

1. The sum of two symmetric matrices of the same size is symmetric.
2. The transpose of a symmetric matrix is symmetric.
3. For any matrix **A**, the product $\mathbf{A}^T\mathbf{A}$ is a symmetric matrix.
4. The sum of two skew-symmetric matrices of the same size is skew-symmetric.
5. The transpose of a skew-symmetric matrix is skew-symmetric.

Proof

1. Let **A** and **B** be symmetric; $(\mathbf{A} + \mathbf{B})^T = \mathbf{A}^T + \mathbf{B}^T = \mathbf{A} + \mathbf{B}$ so $\mathbf{A} + \mathbf{B}$ is symmetric.
2. $(\mathbf{A}^T)^T = \mathbf{A} = \mathbf{A}^T$, so $\mathbf{A}^T$ is symmetric by definition.
3. $(\mathbf{A}^T\mathbf{A})^T = \mathbf{A}^T(\mathbf{A}^T)^T = \mathbf{A}^T\mathbf{A}$, as required for symmetry.
4. Let **A** and **B** be skew-symmetric matrices. $(\mathbf{A} + \mathbf{B})^T = \mathbf{A}^T + \mathbf{B}^T = -\mathbf{A} - \mathbf{B} = -(\mathbf{A} + \mathbf{B})$, so $\mathbf{A} + \mathbf{B}$ is skew-symmetric.
5. $(\mathbf{A}^T)^T = \mathbf{A} = (-1)(-\mathbf{A}) = (-1)\mathbf{A}^T = -\mathbf{A}^T$, so $\mathbf{A}^T$ is skew-symmetric. □

Many algebraic expressions can be written conveniently in matrix form. Such expressions are illustrated in Problems 18, 19, and 23–27.

To illustrate how matrix products can simplify calculations, we consider a geometric problem: the change of coordinates by rotation of axes in the plane.

Figure 1.1 illustrates a rotation in the plane through an angle θ from coordinate axes Ox, Oy to axes Ox', Oy'. If OP makes an angle Φ with Ox', it makes an angle $\Phi + \theta$ with Ox. Let r represent the length of OP. Then the coordinates of P are

$$x' = r\cos\Phi, \qquad y' = r\sin\Phi$$

or

$$x = r\cos(\Phi + \theta), \qquad y = r\sin(\Phi + \theta)$$

The trigonometric formulas for sine and cosine of the sum of two angles give

$$x = r\cos\Phi\cos\theta - r\sin\Phi\sin\theta$$
$$y = r\sin\Phi\cos\theta + r\cos\Phi\sin\theta$$

Since $x' = r\cos\Phi$ and $y' = r\sin\Phi$, we have

$$x = x'\cos\theta - y'\sin\theta$$
$$y = y'\cos\theta + x'\sin\theta$$

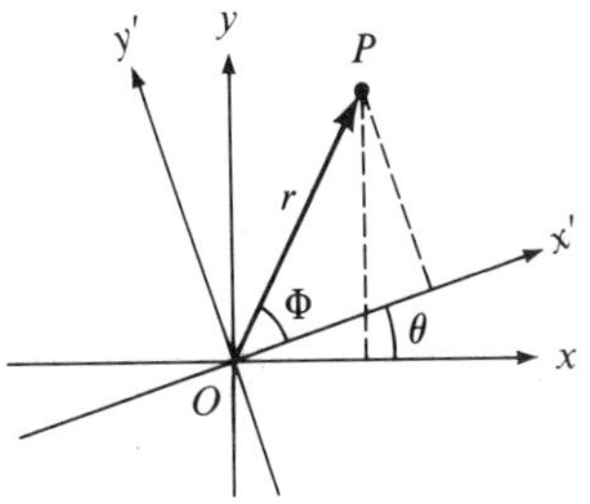

FIGURE 1.1

We can write these equations as a matrix product in two ways:

$$\begin{bmatrix} x \\ y \end{bmatrix} = \begin{bmatrix} \cos\theta & -\sin\theta \\ \sin\theta & \cos\theta \end{bmatrix} \begin{bmatrix} x' \\ y' \end{bmatrix}$$

or

$$[x \quad y] = [x' \quad y'] \begin{bmatrix} \cos\theta & \sin\theta \\ -\sin\theta & \cos\theta \end{bmatrix}$$

Notice that the second form comes from taking the transpose of each side of the first equation.

Example 18 The equation $17x^2 - 12xy + 8y^2 = 80$ represents a conic in the plane. It is difficult to identify this conic because of the presence of the term $12xy$. Geometry tells us that if an equation has the form $Ax^2 + Bxy + Cy^2 = F$, we can eliminate the xy-term by rotating the axes through an angle θ for which $\cot 2\theta = \dfrac{A - C}{B}$. In this case $\cot 2\theta = -\frac{3}{4}$. This implies $\cos\theta = 1/\sqrt{5}$ and $\sin\theta = 2/\sqrt{5}$, so that

$$\begin{bmatrix} x \\ y \end{bmatrix} = \begin{bmatrix} \frac{1}{\sqrt{5}} & -\frac{2}{\sqrt{5}} \\ \frac{2}{\sqrt{5}} & \frac{1}{\sqrt{5}} \end{bmatrix} \begin{bmatrix} x' \\ y' \end{bmatrix} \quad \text{and} \quad [x \quad y] = [x' \quad y'] \begin{bmatrix} \frac{1}{\sqrt{5}} & \frac{2}{\sqrt{5}} \\ -\frac{2}{\sqrt{5}} & \frac{1}{\sqrt{5}} \end{bmatrix}$$

To perform the rotation we first write $17x^2 - 12xy + 8y^2$ as a matrix product:

$$17x^2 - 12xy + 8y^2 = [x \quad y] \begin{bmatrix} 17 & -6 \\ -6 & 8 \end{bmatrix} \begin{bmatrix} x \\ y \end{bmatrix}$$

Now substitute for $\begin{bmatrix} x \\ y \end{bmatrix}$ and $[x \quad y]$. We obtain

$$[x' \quad y']\begin{bmatrix} \frac{1}{\sqrt{5}} & \frac{2}{\sqrt{5}} \\ -\frac{2}{\sqrt{5}} & \frac{1}{\sqrt{5}} \end{bmatrix}\begin{bmatrix} 17 & -6 \\ -6 & 8 \end{bmatrix}\begin{bmatrix} \frac{1}{\sqrt{5}} & -\frac{2}{\sqrt{5}} \\ \frac{2}{\sqrt{5}} & \frac{1}{\sqrt{5}} \end{bmatrix}\begin{bmatrix} x' \\ y' \end{bmatrix}$$

Multiplication of the three 2×2 matrices gives $\begin{bmatrix} 5 & 0 \\ 0 & 20 \end{bmatrix}$, so the product becomes

$$[x' \quad y']\begin{bmatrix} 5 & 0 \\ 0 & 20 \end{bmatrix}\begin{bmatrix} x' \\ y' \end{bmatrix} = 5x'^2 + 20y'^2$$

In the x', y' coordinate system the equation of the conic is then

$$5x'^2 + 20y'^2 = 80$$

which is readily identified as an ellipse. ■

In Chapter 6, we will see how linear algebra also determines an appropriate choice of Ox', Oy'.

SUMMARY The scalar product (or dot product) of two n-tuples $\mathbf{u} = (a_1, a_2, \dots, a_n)$ and $\mathbf{v} = (b_1, b_2, \dots, b_n)$ is defined by $\mathbf{u} \cdot \mathbf{v} = a_1b_1 + a_2b_2 + \cdots + a_nb_n$. The matrix product **AB** is defined only if the number of columns of **A** is equal to the number of rows of **B**. The ijth element of **AB** is the scalar product of row i of **A** and column j of **B**. Multiplication of matrices is associative and distributive over addition. Matrix multiplication is not commutative: in general, $\mathbf{AB} \neq \mathbf{BA}$ even if both are defined.

EXERCISES 1.2

1. In each case verify that $\mathbf{u} \cdot \mathbf{v} = \mathbf{v} \cdot \mathbf{u}$ and that $\mathbf{u} \cdot (\mathbf{v} + \mathbf{w}) = \mathbf{u} \cdot \mathbf{v} + \mathbf{u} \cdot \mathbf{w}$.

a. $\mathbf{u} = (1, 2, 1)$, $\mathbf{v} = (1, -1, 3)$, $\mathbf{w} = (2, 0, 5)$

b. $\mathbf{u} = (-1, -1, 4, 3)$, $\mathbf{v} = (0, 1, 2, -4)$, $\mathbf{w} = (2, -3, 3, -2)$

2. Let $\mathbf{u}_1 = (1, 0, 1)$, $\mathbf{u}_2 = (-1, 1, 2)$, $\mathbf{v}_1 = (1, -1, 1)$, and $\mathbf{v}_2 = (2, 0, 1)$. Calculate $\mathbf{u}_1 \cdot \mathbf{v}_1$, $\mathbf{u}_1 \cdot \mathbf{v}_2$, $\mathbf{u}_2 \cdot \mathbf{v}_1$, and $\mathbf{u}_2 \cdot \mathbf{v}_2$. Use these calculations to write the matrix product **AB**, where

$$\mathbf{A} = \begin{bmatrix} 1 & 0 & 1 \\ -1 & 1 & 2 \end{bmatrix} \quad \text{and} \quad \mathbf{B} = \begin{bmatrix} 1 & 2 \\ -1 & 0 \\ 1 & 1 \end{bmatrix}$$

3. Fill in the blank spaces in the product

$$\begin{bmatrix} 1 & 2 & -1 & 3 \\ 1 & 4 & 1 & 5 \end{bmatrix}\begin{bmatrix} \square & 3 \\ 1 & 1 \\ 0 & 2 \\ 1 & 2 \end{bmatrix} = \begin{bmatrix} 9 & \square \\ \square & 19 \end{bmatrix}$$

4. Calculate each of the following when it is defined, given that

$$\mathbf{A} = \begin{bmatrix} 1 & 2 & 1 \\ 2 & 1 & 3 \\ 0 & 0 & 1 \end{bmatrix}, \quad \mathbf{B} = \begin{bmatrix} -1 & 1 & 0 \\ 0 & 1 & 1 \\ 1 & -1 & -1 \end{bmatrix},$$

$$\mathbf{C} = \begin{bmatrix} 1 & 1 \\ 2 & 1 \\ 0 & 4 \end{bmatrix}, \quad \mathbf{D} = \begin{bmatrix} 2 & 1 \\ 1 & 3 \end{bmatrix}$$

a. **AB** b. **AC** c. **CD** d. **BC**
e. **DC** f. **BC** + **CD** g. (**A** + **B**)**C**
h. **AC** + **BC**

5. Let $\mathbf{U} = [a_1\ a_2\ a_3\ a_4]$ and $\mathbf{V} = [b_1\ b_2\ b_3\ b_4]$. Verify that $\mathbf{UV}^T = \mathbf{u} \cdot \mathbf{v}$ where $\mathbf{u} = (a_1, a_2, a_3, a_4)$ and $\mathbf{v} = (b_1, b_2, b_3, b_4)$.

6. Let

$$\mathbf{A} = \begin{bmatrix} 1 & 2 & 1 \\ 3 & 1 & 5 \end{bmatrix}, \quad \mathbf{V}_1 = \begin{bmatrix} 1 \\ 2 \\ 0 \end{bmatrix},$$

$$\mathbf{V}_2 = \begin{bmatrix} 1 \\ -1 \\ 1 \end{bmatrix}, \quad \mathbf{V}_3 = \begin{bmatrix} 0 \\ 1 \\ 0 \end{bmatrix},$$

$$\mathbf{B} = \begin{bmatrix} 1 & 1 & 0 \\ 2 & -1 & 1 \\ 0 & 1 & 0 \end{bmatrix}$$

Calculate $\mathbf{AV}_1$, $\mathbf{AV}_2$, $\mathbf{AV}_3$, and **AB**. Verify that the columns of **AB** are $\mathbf{AV}_1$, $\mathbf{AV}_2$, and $\mathbf{AV}_3$.

7. Let **A** and **B** be defined as in Problem 6, and let $\mathbf{U}_1 = [1\ 2\ 1]$ and $\mathbf{U}_2 = [3\ 1\ 5]$. Calculate $\mathbf{U}_1\mathbf{B}$ and $\mathbf{U}_2\mathbf{B}$, and verify that the rows of **AB** are $\mathbf{U}_1\mathbf{B}$ and $\mathbf{U}_2\mathbf{B}$.

8. Let

$$\mathbf{A} = \begin{bmatrix} 1 & 3 & 2 \\ 1 & 0 & 1 \end{bmatrix} \quad \text{and} \quad \mathbf{B} = \begin{bmatrix} 1 & -1 & 2 \\ 1 & 0 & 3 \\ 1 & 1 & 0 \end{bmatrix}$$

Calculate **AB** and $\mathbf{B}^T\mathbf{A}^T$. How are these matrices related? Can you calculate $\mathbf{A}^T\mathbf{B}^T$?

9. Write the transpose of each of the following matrices:

a. $\mathbf{A}^T$ b. $\mathbf{AA}^T$ c. $\mathbf{A}(\mathbf{B} + \mathbf{C})$
d. **ABC** e. $\mathbf{A}^T\mathbf{BA}$ f. $\mathbf{A}^T\mathbf{B} + \mathbf{B}^T\mathbf{A}$

10. a. Construct examples of 2×2 matrices and 3×3 matrices that are symmetric.
b. Construct examples of 2×2 matrices and 3×3 matrices that are skew-symmetric. What special property do the diagonal elements have if the matrix is skew-symmetric?

11. Show that a linear combination of $n \times n$ symmetric matrices is symmetric.

12. Show that a linear combination of $n \times n$ skew-symmetric matrices is skew-symmetric.

13. Given $n \times n$ matrices **A** and **B**, show that $\mathbf{A}^T\mathbf{B} + \mathbf{B}^T\mathbf{A}$ is symmetric and that $\mathbf{A}^T\mathbf{B} - \mathbf{B}^T\mathbf{A}$ is skew-symmetric.

14. Write the proof of Theorem 4 part 2 for the case in which **A**, **B**, **C** are all 2×2 matrices.

15. Prove that if **AB** is defined and k and k' are scalars, $(k\mathbf{A})(k'\mathbf{B}) = (kk')(\mathbf{AB})$.

16. In Example 7 it was found that the soft drink consumption at State University is represented by the triple (32175, 5475, 1670). The profit on cola drinks is 4¢ per can for regular and 3¢ per can for diet drinks, while the profit on other drinks is 1¢ per can. Calculate the weekly profit from the soft drink dispensers. What dot product did you calculate?

17. a. Calculate the product $\begin{bmatrix} 3 & 5 \\ -1 & 4 \end{bmatrix} \begin{bmatrix} x \\ y \end{bmatrix}$.
b. Write as a product of two matrices the 2×1 array $\begin{bmatrix} 3x + 4y \\ 2x - y \end{bmatrix}$.

18. The system of equations

$$\begin{aligned} 3x + 4y &= 5 \\ 2x - y &= 1 \end{aligned}$$

can be written in the form

$$\mathbf{A} \begin{bmatrix} x \\ y \end{bmatrix} = \begin{bmatrix} 5 \\ 1 \end{bmatrix}$$

Write out the matrix **A** for this system.

19. Write the system of equations

$$\begin{aligned} x + 3y - 2z &= 7 \\ 2x - 5y + z &= -1 \\ x + y - 3z &= 0 \end{aligned}$$

in the form

$$\mathbf{A} \begin{bmatrix} x \\ y \\ z \end{bmatrix} = \begin{bmatrix} 7 \\ -1 \\ 0 \end{bmatrix}$$

20. Let

$$\mathbf{X} = \begin{bmatrix} x_1 \\ x_2 \\ x_3 \end{bmatrix} \quad \text{and} \quad \mathbf{A} = \begin{bmatrix} a_{11} & a_{12} & a_{13} \\ a_{21} & a_{22} & a_{23} \\ a_{31} & a_{32} & a_{33} \end{bmatrix}$$

a. Show that **AX** is a linear combination of the columns of **A**.
b. Show that $\mathbf{X}^T\mathbf{A}$ is a linear combination of the rows of **A**.

21. Show that, given a set of k m-tuples $\{\mathbf{u}_1, \mathbf{u}_2, \ldots, \mathbf{u}_k\}$, any linear combination of these m-tuples has the form $\mathbf{AC}$, where $\mathbf{C}$ is a $k \times 1$ matrix and $\mathbf{A}$ is an $m \times k$ matrix with columns the k m-tuples $\mathbf{u}_1, \mathbf{u}_2, \ldots, \mathbf{u}_k$.

22. Show that for any $m \times n$ matrix $\mathbf{A}$, $\mathbf{AA}^T$ and $\mathbf{A}^T\mathbf{A}$ are defined and are square matrices.

23. Calculate the product

$$[x_1 \quad x_2]\begin{bmatrix} 2 & 3 & 1 \\ 1 & 0 & 5 \end{bmatrix}\begin{bmatrix} y_1 \\ y_2 \\ y_3 \end{bmatrix}$$

24. Write as a matrix product the expression

$$3x_1y_1 + 2x_1y_2 + 5x_1y_3 - 3x_2y_1 + x_2y_2 - 2x_2y_3 - 4x_3y_1 + 3x_3y_2 - x_3y_3$$

25. Write as a quadratic expression the product

$$[x_1 \quad x_2]\begin{bmatrix} 3 & 1 \\ 1 & 2 \end{bmatrix}\begin{bmatrix} x_1 \\ x_2 \end{bmatrix}$$

26. Write as a quadratic expression the product $\mathbf{X}^T\mathbf{AX}$, where

$$\mathbf{X} = \begin{bmatrix} x_1 \\ x_2 \\ x_3 \end{bmatrix} \quad \text{and} \quad \mathbf{A} = \begin{bmatrix} 1 & -1 & 3 \\ -1 & 2 & 1 \\ 3 & 1 & 4 \end{bmatrix}$$

27. Write the quadratic expression $x_1^2 + 6x_1x_2 + 4x_2^2$ as $\mathbf{X}^T\mathbf{AX}$. Can the matrix $\mathbf{A}$ be chosen in more than one way? Find a way of writing this in which the matrix is symmetric.

28. Show that

$$\begin{bmatrix} \cos\theta & \sin\theta \\ -\sin\theta & \cos\theta \end{bmatrix}\begin{bmatrix} \cos\theta & -\sin\theta \\ \sin\theta & \cos\theta \end{bmatrix} = \begin{bmatrix} 1 & 0 \\ 0 & 1 \end{bmatrix}$$

Interpret this result geometrically.

29. Remove the xy term from $5x^2 + 6xy + 5y^2 = 9$ by rotating the axes through an angle of 45°.

30. Remove the xy term from $3x^2 + 4xy = 4$ by rotating the axes through an angle θ with $\cot 2\theta = \frac{3}{4}$.

31. State University is considering equipment for six computer laboratories. (See Examples 1, 10, and 12.) They are considering three plans:

	Entry Level	*Scientific*	*Business*
Plan 1	2	2	2
Plan 2	4	1	1
Plan 3	0	3	3

Let $\mathbf{P}$, the plan matrix, be

$$\mathbf{P} = \begin{bmatrix} 2 & 2 & 2 \\ 4 & 1 & 1 \\ 0 & 3 & 3 \end{bmatrix}$$

As before, the unit cost matrix is

$$\mathbf{C} = \begin{bmatrix} 2000 & 2400 & 2500 & 2900 \\ 4000 & 4400 & 4600 & 5000 \\ 5000 & 5500 & 5600 & 6100 \end{bmatrix}$$

Let the quantity matrix be

$$\mathbf{T} = \begin{bmatrix} 0 & 4 & 0 \\ 8 & 2 & 0 \\ 0 & 4 & 2 \\ 2 & 0 & 8 \end{bmatrix}$$

a. Verify the associative law $\mathbf{P(CT)} = \mathbf{(PC)T}$.
b. Describe the meaning of the entries in the matrix $\mathbf{CT}$.
c. Describe the meaning of the entries in the matrix $\mathbf{PC}$.
d. Why does it make sense to have $\mathbf{P(CT)} = \mathbf{(PC)T}$?
e. The cost of the least expensive option is \$187,800. What configuration of labs will this amount purchase?

1.3 Some Matrices with Special Properties

The numbers 1 and 0 play special roles in the set of real numbers. The number 1 is the multiplicative identity: $1 \cdot a = a \cdot 1 = a$ for every real number a. Zero is the additive identity: $0 + a = a + 0 = a$ for every real number a.

A zero matrix (Definition 7) acts as an additive identity in the set of matrices of the same size. What matrix is a multiplicative identity?

If the matrix **I** is a multiplicative identity, **IB** = **B**. If **B** is $m \times n$, then **I** must have m columns for multiplication to be defined, and **I** must have m rows for the product **IB** to have m rows. Thus the condition **IB** = **B** forces **I** to be a square matrix.

Example 19

Let **B** be a 2×3 matrix, and $\mathbf{I}_2 = \begin{bmatrix} 1 & 0 \\ 0 & 1 \end{bmatrix}$. Then

$$\begin{bmatrix} 1 & 0 \\ 0 & 1 \end{bmatrix} \begin{bmatrix} b_{11} & b_{12} & b_{13} \\ b_{21} & b_{22} & b_{23} \end{bmatrix} = \begin{bmatrix} b_{11} & b_{12} & b_{13} \\ b_{21} & b_{22} & b_{23} \end{bmatrix}$$

so that $\mathbf{I}_2\mathbf{B} = \mathbf{B}$ for every 2×3 matrix **B**. The product $\mathbf{BI}_2$ is not defined since **B** has three columns. However,

$$\begin{bmatrix} b_{11} & b_{12} & b_{13} \\ b_{21} & b_{22} & b_{23} \end{bmatrix} \begin{bmatrix} 1 & 0 & 0 \\ 0 & 1 & 0 \\ 0 & 0 & 1 \end{bmatrix} = \begin{bmatrix} b_{11} & b_{12} & b_{13} \\ b_{21} & b_{22} & b_{23} \end{bmatrix}.$$

■

Identity Matrix

> **Definition 11**
>
> An $n \times n$ matrix with the property that $a_{ii} = 1$ and $a_{ij} = 0$ for $i \neq j$ is called an **identity matrix**, $\mathbf{I}_n$. When the context makes the size of **I** clear, the subscript is omitted.

A zero matrix, like the number 0, also has special properties related to multiplication. For example, if defined, a product in which one factor is a zero matrix always produces a zero matrix.

Example 20

$$\begin{bmatrix} 0 & 0 & 0 \\ 0 & 0 & 0 \end{bmatrix} \begin{bmatrix} a_{11} & a_{12} \\ a_{21} & a_{22} \\ a_{31} & a_{32} \end{bmatrix} = \begin{bmatrix} 0 & 0 \\ 0 & 0 \end{bmatrix}$$

In this case $\mathbf{0}_{2\times 3}\mathbf{A}_{3\times 2} = \mathbf{0}_{2\times 2}$. The matrix $\mathbf{A}_{3\times 2}\mathbf{0}_{2\times 3}$ can also be calculated and the result is the zero matrix, $\mathbf{0}_{3\times 3}$. ■

One property of the real number 0 does not carry over into the matrix setting. If the product of two real numbers is 0, we can conclude that at least one of the factors is 0; that is, $ab = 0$ implies either $a = 0$ or $b = 0$. There is no such property in matrix multiplication.

Example 21

Let $\mathbf{A} = \begin{bmatrix} 1 & -1 \\ 2 & -2 \end{bmatrix}$ and $\mathbf{B} = \begin{bmatrix} 1 & 3 \\ 1 & 3 \end{bmatrix}$. Neither **A** nor **B** is a zero matrix, yet $\mathbf{AB} = \begin{bmatrix} 0 & 0 \\ 0 & 0 \end{bmatrix}$. ■

The special properties of a zero matrix and of an identity matrix come from the fact that the n-tuples that make up the rows and columns of these matrices are especially simple. The rows of $\mathbf{0}_{m \times n}$ are n-tuples of the form $\mathbf{0} = (0, 0, 0, \ldots, 0)$. Clearly the scalar product $\mathbf{0} \cdot \mathbf{u} = 0$ for every n-tuple $\mathbf{u}$. The rows of the identity matrix $\mathbf{I}_n$ are almost as simple in form. Each row has exactly one nonzero element, and this is 1.

Let

$$\begin{aligned} \mathbf{e}_1 &= (1, 0, 0, \ldots, 0) \\ \mathbf{e}_2 &= (0, 1, 0, \ldots, 0) \\ &\vdots \end{aligned}$$

and, in general,

$$\mathbf{e}_i = (0, 0, \ldots, 1, \ldots, 0)$$

in which the ith element is 1 and all other elements are 0. The n-tuples $\mathbf{e}_1, \mathbf{e}_2, \ldots, \mathbf{e}_n$ are called the **standard *n*-tuples**. The following example illustrates some special properties of such n-tuples.

Example 22

Suppose $n = 4$. Then $\mathbf{e}_1 = (1, 0, 0, 0)$, $\mathbf{e}_2 = (0, 1, 0, 0)$, $\mathbf{e}_3 = (0, 0, 1, 0)$, and $\mathbf{e}_4 = (0, 0, 0, 1)$.

If $\mathbf{u} = (2, 4, 1, 3)$, then $\mathbf{e}_2 \cdot \mathbf{u} = (0)(2) + (1)(4) + (0)(1) + (0)(3) = 4$. In general, if $\mathbf{u} = (a_1, a_2, a_3, a_4)$, then $\mathbf{e}_1 \cdot \mathbf{u} = a_1$, $\mathbf{e}_2 \cdot \mathbf{u} = a_2$, $\mathbf{e}_3 \cdot \mathbf{u} = a_3$, and $\mathbf{e}_4 \cdot \mathbf{u} = a_4$. Particularly simple results follow in taking dot products of these 4-tuples with each other:

$$\begin{aligned} \mathbf{e}_i \cdot \mathbf{e}_i &= 1 \quad i = 1, 2, 3, 4 \\ \mathbf{e}_i \cdot \mathbf{e}_j &= 0, \quad i \neq j, i = 1, 2, 3, 4, j = 1, 2, 3, 4 \end{aligned}$$

Notice also that any 4-tuple $\mathbf{u}$ can be written as a linear combination of the standard 4-tuples $\mathbf{e}_1, \mathbf{e}_2, \mathbf{e}_3, \mathbf{e}_4$.

If $\mathbf{u} = (a_1, a_2, a_3, a_4)$, then $\mathbf{u} = a_1\mathbf{e}_1 + a_2\mathbf{e}_2 + a_3\mathbf{e}_3 + a_4\mathbf{e}_4$. ■

If **A** is a square matrix, the elements a_{ii} ($i = 1, 2, \ldots, n$) are called the **main diagonal elements**. In the identity matrix $\mathbf{I}_n$, the main diagonal elements are all 1, and every other element is 0. Other matrices may have the property that they contain "well-placed" zeros.

Example 23

Let $\mathbf{A} = \begin{bmatrix} 1 & 0 & 0 \\ 2 & 3 & 0 \\ 4 & 0 & 6 \end{bmatrix}$ and $\mathbf{B} = \begin{bmatrix} 1 & 0 & 0 \\ -1 & 1 & 0 \\ 2 & -2 & 3 \end{bmatrix}$. These matrices are called **lower**

triangular matrices because nonzero elements can appear only on or below the main diagonal. Similarly, the matrix $\mathbf{C} = \begin{bmatrix} 2 & 3 & 5 \\ 0 & -5 & 1 \\ 0 & 0 & 9 \end{bmatrix}$ is upper triangular.

The matrix $\begin{bmatrix} 4 & 0 & 0 \\ 0 & 0 & 0 \\ 0 & 0 & 1 \end{bmatrix}$ is a diagonal matrix because nonzero elements appear only on the main diagonal.

The matrix $\begin{bmatrix} 4 & 0 & 0 \\ 0 & 4 & 0 \\ 0 & 0 & 4 \end{bmatrix} = 4\mathbf{I}$ is a special kind of diagonal matrix called a **scalar matrix**, since the elements on the main diagonal are all the same scalar. The matrix $\begin{bmatrix} 0 & 0 & 0 \\ 0 & 0 & 0 \\ 0 & 0 & 0 \end{bmatrix} = 0\mathbf{I}$ is a scalar matrix, but the zero matrix $\begin{bmatrix} 0 & 0 & 0 \\ 0 & 0 & 0 \end{bmatrix}$ is *not* a scalar matrix, since a scalar matrix must be square.   ∎

Triangular Matrices

Definition 12

Let $\mathbf{A}$ be a square matrix. If all the elements above the main diagonal are 0, the matrix is called a **lower triangular matrix**.

If all the elements below the main diagonal are 0, the matrix is called an **upper triangular matrix**.

Diagonal Matrix

Scalar Matrix

If the only nonzero elements appear on the main diagonal ($a_{ij} = 0$ for $i \neq j$), the matrix is a **diagonal matrix**. A diagonal matrix is both upper and lower triangular.

A diagonal matrix is a **scalar matrix** in the special case that $a_{ii} = k$ for all i. In this case $\mathbf{A} = k\mathbf{I}$.

$$\begin{bmatrix} d_{11} & & & \text{all} \\ d_{21} & d_{22} & & \text{zeros} \\ \vdots & \vdots & & \\ d_{n1} & d_{n2} & \cdots & d_{nn} \end{bmatrix} \qquad \begin{bmatrix} d_{11} & d_{12} & \cdots & d_{1n} \\ & d_{22} & \cdots & d_{2n} \\ & \text{all} & & \vdots \\ & \text{zeros} & & d_{nn} \end{bmatrix}$$

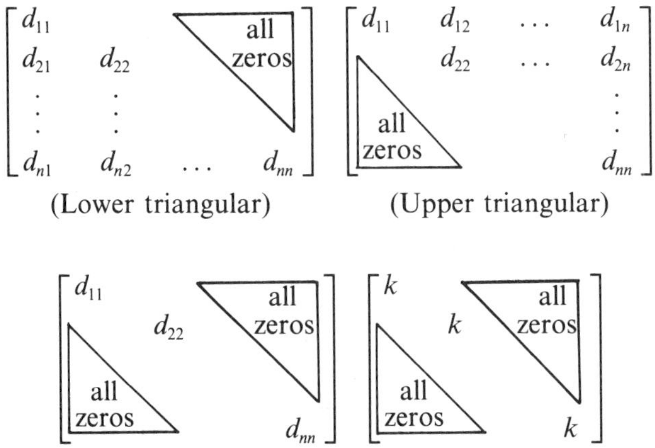

(Lower triangular)   (Upper triangular)

$$\begin{bmatrix} d_{11} & & \text{all} \\ & d_{22} & \text{zeros} \\ \text{all} & & \\ \text{zeros} & & d_{nn} \end{bmatrix} \qquad \begin{bmatrix} k & & \text{all} \\ & k & \text{zeros} \\ \text{all} & & \\ \text{zeros} & & k \end{bmatrix}$$

(Diagonal)   (Scalar)

The special properties of the n-tuples $\mathbf{0}$ and the n-tuples $\mathbf{e}_i$ can sometimes be used to help shorten calculations in a matrix product **AB**. Recall (Definition 9) that in the product **AB** the element c_{ij} is the scalar product of the ith row of **A** and the jth column of **B**. The calculation of the element c_{ij} is very simple if either the ith row of **A** or the jth row of **B** is $\mathbf{0}$ or $\mathbf{e}_i$.

Example 24

a. Because the third column of $\begin{bmatrix} 1 & 2 & 0 \\ 0 & 0 & 0 \\ 3 & 1 & 0 \end{bmatrix}$ is all zeros, the third column of the product $\begin{bmatrix} 1 & 2 & 3 \\ 4 & 1 & 5 \\ 6 & 2 & 2 \end{bmatrix}\begin{bmatrix} 1 & 2 & 0 \\ 0 & 0 & 0 \\ 3 & 1 & 0 \end{bmatrix}$ is also all zeros.

b. Since the second row of $\begin{bmatrix} 1 & 2 & 0 \\ 0 & 0 & 0 \\ 3 & 1 & 0 \end{bmatrix}$ is all zeros, the second row of the product $\begin{bmatrix} 1 & 2 & 0 \\ 0 & 0 & 0 \\ 3 & 1 & 0 \end{bmatrix}\begin{bmatrix} 1 & 2 & 3 \\ 4 & 1 & 5 \\ 6 & 2 & 2 \end{bmatrix}$ is also all zeros.

c. Consider $\begin{bmatrix} 3 & 5 & 1 \\ 1 & 1 & 2 \\ 2 & 7 & 6 \end{bmatrix}\begin{bmatrix} 1 & 2 \\ 0 & 1 \\ 0 & 1 \end{bmatrix} = \begin{bmatrix} 3 & 12 \\ 1 & 5 \\ 2 & 17 \end{bmatrix}$. The first column of the product can be written by inspection, since its elements are $(3, 5, 1) \cdot (1, 0, 0) = 3$, $(1, 1, 2) \cdot (1, 0, 0) = 1$, and $(2, 7, 6) \cdot (1, 0, 0) = 2$.

d. In the following product, notice that the second row and the first and third columns can be written by inspection:

$$\begin{bmatrix} 2 & 5 & 1 & 7 & 9 \\ 0 & 0 & 0 & 1 & 0 \\ 1 & 2 & -1 & 6 & 3 \\ -4 & 1 & 8 & 1 & 9 \end{bmatrix}\begin{bmatrix} 0 & 2 & 1 \\ 0 & 2 & 0 \\ 1 & 4 & 0 \\ 0 & 8 & 0 \\ 0 & -7 & 0 \end{bmatrix} = \begin{bmatrix} 1 & * & 2 \\ 0 & 8 & 0 \\ -1 & * & 1 \\ 8 & * & -4 \end{bmatrix}$$

The elements represented by $*$ require calculation. ■

If the matrix is square, multiplication of the matrix by itself is defined. Thus for an $n \times n$ matrix, it is possible to calculate **AA**, **AAA**, **AAAA**, and so on. This means that positive integral powers of a square matrix are defined. The usual exponential notation is used: $\mathbf{A} = \mathbf{A}^1$, $\mathbf{AA} = \mathbf{A}^2$, $\mathbf{AAA} = \mathbf{A}^3$, $\mathbf{AAAA} = \mathbf{A}^4$, and so on.

The algebraic rules for exponents hold for matrix powers: $\mathbf{A}^p\mathbf{A}^q = \mathbf{A}^{p+q}$ and $(\mathbf{A}^p)^k = \mathbf{A}^{pk}$ for p, q, and k positive integers. The justification of these rules is similar to that for algebraic quantities. In Chapter 3, negative integer powers will be defined for some special square matrices **A**.

Example 25

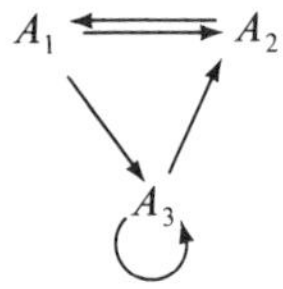

An ice-cream vendor travels through a suburban area with three intersections: A_1, A_2, and A_3. Traffic goes two ways between A_1 and A_2, one way from A_1 to A_3, and one way from A_3 to A_2. A cul de sac exists at A_3. In how many ways can the vendor cover this area?

A path joining A_i and A_j has length 1 if it goes directly from A_i to A_j. In the matrix **P**, the ith row tells the number of paths from A_i directly to A_1, A_2, A_3. The jth column counts the number of paths of length 1 beginning at A_1, A_2, A_3 and ending at a particular A_j.

$$\mathbf{P} = \begin{bmatrix} 0 & 1 & 1 \\ 1 & 0 & 0 \\ 0 & 1 & 1 \end{bmatrix}$$

The entry $p_{13} = 1$ says there is one direct path from A_1 to A_3.

A path from A_i to A_j has length 2 if it passes through an intermediate point. For example, A_1 to A_3 to A_2 is a path of length 2 from A_1 to A_2. Consider the elements of the product $\mathbf{P}^2$. To be specific, consider c_{32}, the element in row 3 column 2 of $\mathbf{P}^2$. This is the scalar product of row 3 and column 2. Row 3 is (0, 1, 1) and column 2, (1, 0, 1). A path of length 2 from A_3 to A_2 must consist of a path of length 1 from A_3 to one of A_1, A_2, or A_3 followed by a path of length 1 from A_1, A_2 or A_3 to A_2. The number of such paths is given by c_{32}. To see this, analyze the dot product

$$(0, 1, 1) \cdot (1, 0, 1) = (0)(1) + (1)(0) + (1)(1) = 1$$

(0)(1) means there is no direct path from A_3 to A_1 so no path of length 2 can exist passing through A_1;

(1)(0) means there is a direct path from A_3 to A_2, but none from A_2 to A_2, so no path of length 2 from A_3 to A_2 can pass through A_2;

(1)(1) means there is a path of length 1 from A_3 to A_3 and a path of length 1 from A_3 to A_2, hence one path of length 2 from A_3 to A_2 passing through A_3.

Altogether, there is one path of length 2 from A_3 to A_2. A similar analysis should convince you that the matrix $\mathbf{P}^2 = \begin{bmatrix} 1 & 1 & 1 \\ 0 & 1 & 1 \\ 1 & 1 & 1 \end{bmatrix}$ indicates the number of paths of length 2 from A_i to A_j for each i and j. Incidentally, this shows that our ice-cream truck has nothing to worry about, because every point can be reached directly from every other point through at most one intermediary. ■

Example 26

A path is of length 3 if it passes through two intermediate points. Let us calculate $\mathbf{P}^3 = \begin{bmatrix} 1 & 2 & 2 \\ 1 & 1 & 1 \\ 1 & 2 & 2 \end{bmatrix}$. This matrix gives the number of paths of length 3 from A_i to A_j. For example, the two paths of length 3 from A_1 to A_3 are: A_1A_2, A_2A_1, A_1A_3 and A_1A_3, A_3A_3, A_3A_3. ■

SUMMARY Several classes of matrices have special properties: zero matrix, identity matrix, scalar matrix, and triangular matrix. Note that there exist **nonzero** matrices **A** and **B** such that $\mathbf{AB} = \mathbf{0}$. Positive integral powers of square matrices are defined and the usual exponential notation is used to represent them. The standard n-tuples are $\mathbf{e}_i = (0, 0, \ldots, 0, 1, 0, \ldots, 0)$, $i = 1, 2, \ldots, n$, where the ith element in $\mathbf{e}_i$ is 1 and all other elements are 0.

EXERCISES 1.3

1. Find the product $\begin{bmatrix} 1 & 4 \\ 2 & 8 \\ 3 & 9 \end{bmatrix}\begin{bmatrix} 0 & 0 & 0 & 0 \\ 0 & 0 & 0 & 0 \end{bmatrix}$.

Find the product $\begin{bmatrix} 0 & 0 & 0 \\ 0 & 0 & 0 \end{bmatrix}\begin{bmatrix} 3 & 6 \\ 1 & 5 \\ 4 & 8 \end{bmatrix}$.

Complete the following: $\mathbf{A}_{m\times n}\mathbf{0}_{n\times r} =$ _____

$\mathbf{0}_{m\times n}\mathbf{A}_{n\times r} =$ _____

2. Calculate each of the following:

$$\begin{bmatrix} 1 & 2 \\ 1 & 2 \end{bmatrix}\begin{bmatrix} 2 & -4 & 6 \\ -1 & 2 & -3 \end{bmatrix},$$

$$\begin{bmatrix} 1 & 0 & 2 \\ -1 & 2 & 0 \\ 0 & -1 & -1 \end{bmatrix}\begin{bmatrix} 2 & -2 \\ 1 & -1 \\ -1 & 1 \end{bmatrix}$$

If a and b are real numbers, then $ab = 0$ implies that $a = 0$ or $b = 0$. Is it true that if **A** and **B** are matrices, then $\mathbf{AB} = \mathbf{0}$ implies $\mathbf{A} = \mathbf{0}$ or $\mathbf{B} = \mathbf{0}$? Justify your answer.

3. Let

$$\mathbf{A} = \begin{bmatrix} 2 & 1 & 1 \\ 1 & 0 & 1 \\ 0 & 1 & -1 \end{bmatrix}, \quad \mathbf{B} = \begin{bmatrix} 2 & 1 & 3 & 7 \\ 1 & 0 & 8 & 2 \\ 1 & 4 & 3 & 6 \end{bmatrix},$$

$$\mathbf{C} = \begin{bmatrix} 3 & -1 & 8 & 4 \\ 0 & 2 & 3 & 5 \\ 0 & 6 & -2 & 9 \end{bmatrix}$$

Calculate **AB** and **AC**. If **A**, **B**, and **C** are matrices such that $\mathbf{AB} = \mathbf{AC}$, is it necessarily true that $\mathbf{B} = \mathbf{C}$? Justify your answer.

4. Let

$$\mathbf{D} = \begin{bmatrix} 2 & 0 & 0 \\ 0 & 4 & 0 \\ 0 & 0 & -1 \end{bmatrix} \quad \text{and} \quad \mathbf{E} = \begin{bmatrix} 3 & 0 & 0 \\ 0 & -1 & 0 \\ 0 & 0 & 2 \end{bmatrix}$$

a. Calculate $\mathbf{D} + \mathbf{E}$.
b. Calculate $a\mathbf{D} + b\mathbf{E}$, where a and b are scalars.
c. Find a matrix **B** such that $\mathbf{D} + \mathbf{B} = \mathbf{0}_{3\times 3}$. What kind of matrix is **B**?

5. Show that every linear combination of $n \times n$ diagonal matrices is a diagonal matrix.

6. Let

$$\mathbf{D} = \begin{bmatrix} 2 & 0 & 0 \\ 0 & 4 & 0 \\ 0 & 0 & -1 \end{bmatrix} \quad \text{and} \quad \mathbf{A} = \begin{bmatrix} 1 & 2 & 1 \\ 0 & 3 & 4 \\ 2 & 1 & 1 \end{bmatrix}$$

a. Calculate **DA**.
b. Calculate **AD**.

7. Let

$$\mathbf{D} = \begin{bmatrix} d_{11} & 0 & 0 \\ 0 & d_{22} & 0 \\ 0 & 0 & d_{33} \end{bmatrix} \quad \text{and} \quad \begin{bmatrix} a_{11} & a_{12} & a_{13} \\ a_{21} & a_{22} & a_{23} \\ a_{31} & a_{32} & a_{33} \end{bmatrix}$$

Using these forms verify the following statements:

a. The second row of **DA** is d_{22} times the ~~third~~ second row of **A**.
b. The third column of **AD** is d_{33} times the third column of **A**.
c. Describe the general form of **AD** and of **DA**.

8. Compute $\begin{bmatrix} 2 & 5 & 7 \\ 0 & 2 & 3 \\ 0 & 0 & 4 \end{bmatrix} + \begin{bmatrix} -3 & 2 & 1 \\ 0 & -2 & 4 \\ 0 & 0 & 2 \end{bmatrix}$.

Show that every linear combination of $n \times n$ upper triangular matrices is an upper triangular matrix.

9. Compute $\begin{bmatrix} 3 & 0 & 0 & 0 \\ -2 & -1 & 0 & 0 \\ 3 & 4 & 3 & 0 \\ 4 & -3 & 2 & -1 \end{bmatrix} + 3\begin{bmatrix} -1 & 0 & 0 & 0 \\ 2 & 1 & 0 & 0 \\ 3 & 2 & -1 & 0 \\ 1 & 1 & 1 & -1 \end{bmatrix}$. Show that every linear combination of $n \times n$ lower triangular matrices is a lower triangular matrix.

10. Compute $\begin{bmatrix} 1 & 0 & 0 \\ -1 & 3 & 0 \\ 3 & 2 & -1 \end{bmatrix}\begin{bmatrix} 4 & 0 & 0 \\ 3 & 1 & 0 \\ 1 & 2 & 1 \end{bmatrix}$.

11. If **A** and **B** are 3×3 lower triangular matrices, prove that **AB** is also a 3×3 lower triangular matrix.

12. Is the difference of an upper triangular matrix and a lower triangular matrix always a diagonal matrix? Is it ever a diagonal matrix? Is the product of an upper triangular matrix and a lower triangular matrix always a diagonal matrix? Is it ever a diagonal matrix?

13. Derive the following special properties of the standard n-tuples:

a. $\mathbf{e}_i \cdot \mathbf{e}_i = 1$

b. $\mathbf{e}_i \cdot \mathbf{e}_j = 0$ if $i \neq j$

14. Let $\mathbf{u}_1 = (\frac{1}{3}, \frac{2}{3}, \frac{2}{3})$, $\mathbf{u}_2 = (\frac{2}{3}, \frac{1}{3}, -\frac{2}{3})$, and $\mathbf{u}_3 = (-\frac{2}{3}, \frac{2}{3}, -\frac{1}{3})$. Show that $\mathbf{u}_i \cdot \mathbf{u}_i = 1$ for $i = 1, 2, 3$ and $\mathbf{u}_i \cdot \mathbf{u}_j = 0$ if $i \neq j$.

15. a. Calculate $5\mathbf{e}_1 - 4\mathbf{e}_2 + 3\mathbf{e}_3$, where $\mathbf{e}_1, \mathbf{e}_2, \mathbf{e}_3$ are the standard triples.

b. Calculate $a_1\mathbf{e}_1 + a_2\mathbf{e}_2 + a_3\mathbf{e}_3$.

c. Write $(3, -2, -1)$ as a linear combination of the standard triples.

16. Let $\mathbf{e}_1$, $\mathbf{e}_2$, and $\mathbf{e}_3$ be the standard triples. Prove that $a_1\mathbf{e}_1 + a_2\mathbf{e}_2 + a_3\mathbf{e}_3 = (0, 0, 0)$ if and only if $a_1 = 0$, $a_2 = 0$, and $a_3 = 0$.

17. Making use of any special properties, calculate the following products:

a. $\begin{bmatrix} 1 & 0 & 0 \\ 0 & 0 & 0 \\ 0 & 0 & 2 \end{bmatrix}\begin{bmatrix} 1 & 2 \\ 4 & 1 \\ 5 & 3 \end{bmatrix}$ **b.** $\begin{bmatrix} 2 & 1 & 4 \\ 1 & 3 & 7 \\ 1 & 8 & 6 \end{bmatrix}\begin{bmatrix} 0 & 0 & 1 \\ 1 & 2 & 0 \\ 0 & 0 & 0 \end{bmatrix}$

c. $\begin{bmatrix} 1 & 0 & 0 \\ 2 & 1 & 0 \\ 4 & 5 & 3 \end{bmatrix} \begin{bmatrix} 2 & 0 & 0 \\ 1 & 2 & 0 \\ 0 & 1 & 1 \end{bmatrix}$

d. $\begin{bmatrix} 0 & 1 & 0 & 1 \\ 1 & 0 & 0 & 0 \\ 0 & 0 & 2 & 0 \\ 1 & 1 & 0 & 1 \end{bmatrix} \begin{bmatrix} 1 & 2 & 3 & 4 \\ 5 & 6 & 7 & 8 \\ -1 & 2 & -1 & 1 \\ 1 & 1 & 0 & 1 \end{bmatrix}$

e. $\begin{bmatrix} 1 & 2 & 3 & 4 \\ 1 & 2 & 3 & 4 \\ 1 & 2 & 3 & 4 \\ 1 & 2 & 3 & 4 \end{bmatrix} \begin{bmatrix} 2 & 1 & 1 \\ 1 & 2 & 1 \\ -1 & 1 & 1 \\ 0 & -2 & 1 \end{bmatrix}$

18. The matrix $\mathbf{K} = \begin{bmatrix} 0 & 0 & k \\ 0 & 0 & 0 \end{bmatrix}$ differs from the zero matrix by a single element $k \neq 0$. Calculate **KA** if $\mathbf{A} = \begin{bmatrix} 1 & 2 & 1 \\ 0 & 1 & 5 \\ -1 & 1 & 2 \end{bmatrix}$. Write a matrix $\mathbf{A}_{3\times 3}$ such that $\mathbf{A} \neq \mathbf{0}$ and $\mathbf{KA} = \mathbf{0}_{2\times 3}$.

19. a. Show that $\mathbf{A}^3 - \mathbf{I} = (\mathbf{A} - \mathbf{I})(\mathbf{A}^2 + \mathbf{A} + \mathbf{I})$, where **A** is a square matrix.

b. Calculate the product $(\mathbf{A} - \mathbf{B})(\mathbf{A}^2 + \mathbf{AB} + \mathbf{B}^2)$.

20. a. Since $x^2 - y^2 = (x + y)(x - y)$ in algebra, we might be tempted to write $\mathbf{A}^2 - \mathbf{B}^2 = (\mathbf{A} + \mathbf{B})(\mathbf{A} - \mathbf{B})$ for matrices **A** and **B**. Use $\mathbf{A} = \begin{bmatrix} 2 & -1 \\ 1 & 1 \end{bmatrix}$ and $\mathbf{B} = \begin{bmatrix} 1 & 4 \\ 1 & 2 \end{bmatrix}$ to show that, in general, $\mathbf{A}^2 - \mathbf{B}^2 \neq (\mathbf{A} + \mathbf{B})(\mathbf{A} - \mathbf{B})$.

b. Calculate the product $(\mathbf{A} + \mathbf{B})(\mathbf{A} - \mathbf{B})$ using the distributive law. Is there a particular case in which your answer would be $\mathbf{A}^2 - \mathbf{B}^2$?

21. Write the matrix that counts the paths of length 1 in the network. Calculate the number of paths of length 2. Calculate the number of paths of length 3. What is the total number of paths connecting pairs of points in this network?

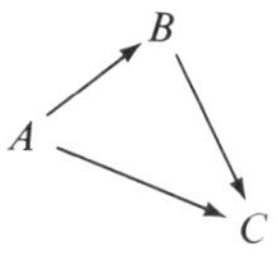

22. The network in the diagram contains paths of length 1 from A to B, from B to A, from A to C, and from C to B. Write the matrix **P** that counts

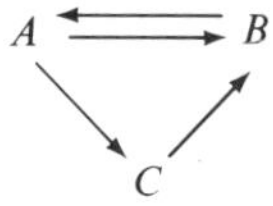

the number of paths of length 1 between each pair of points in the network. Calculate $\mathbf{P}^2$, $\mathbf{P}^3$, $\mathbf{P}^4$, and $\mathbf{P}^5$, and interpret the meaning of each power of $\mathbf{P}$.

23. If $\mathbf{A} = \begin{bmatrix} 1 & 1 & 0 \\ 0 & 1 & 1 \\ 0 & 0 & 1 \end{bmatrix}$, find $\mathbf{A}^2$ and $\mathbf{A}^3$. Can you suggest a formula for $\mathbf{A}^n$?

24. a. Let $\mathbf{A} = \begin{bmatrix} 1 & 1 \\ 0 & 0 \end{bmatrix}$. Calculate $\mathbf{A}^2$, $\mathbf{A}^3$, and $\mathbf{A}^4$. What is $\mathbf{A}^n$ for any integer $n \geqslant 1$?

b. Let $\mathbf{A} = \begin{bmatrix} 1 & 1 \\ 0 & 1 \end{bmatrix}$. Calculate $\mathbf{A}^2$, $\mathbf{A}^3$, and $\mathbf{A}^4$. What is $\mathbf{A}^n$?

c. Let $\mathbf{A} = \begin{bmatrix} 1 & 0 \\ 1 & 1 \end{bmatrix}$. What is $\mathbf{A}^n$?

Supplemental Topics

Idempotent Matrices. A matrix is an **idempotent matrix** if $\mathbf{A}^2 = \mathbf{A}$. An idempotent matrix must be square.

25. Show that $\begin{bmatrix} 1 & 0 & 0 \\ \frac{1}{2} & 0 & \frac{1}{2} \\ 0 & 0 & 1 \end{bmatrix}$ is an idempotent matrix.

26. a. Show that $\begin{bmatrix} -1 & 2 & 4 \\ 1 & -2 & -4 \\ -1 & 2 & 4 \end{bmatrix}$ is idempotent.

b. For what values of m and n is the matrix below idempotent?

$$\begin{bmatrix} -1 & m & n \\ 1 & -m & -n \\ -1 & m & n \end{bmatrix}$$

27. For what values of a, b, c is the matrix below idempotent?

$$\begin{bmatrix} a & b & c \\ a & b & c \\ a & b & c \end{bmatrix}$$

28. If $\mathbf{AB} = \mathbf{A}$ and $\mathbf{BA} = \mathbf{B}$, show that $\mathbf{A}$ and $\mathbf{B}$ are each idempotent matrices.
If $\mathbf{A}$ is an idempotent matrix, show that $\mathbf{I} - \mathbf{A}$ is also idempotent.

Partitioned Matrices. In Example 24, multiplication of matrices was easier when we could think of a row or a column of one of the matrices as an entity. In some cases it helps to think of a subarray of elements in the matrix at one time. The matrix in this case is partitioned into rectangular arrays and these subarrays are treated as elements.

29. The following products are calculated by partitioning the matrices. In each case, study the technique and check the result by multiplying in the usual way.

a. $\mathbf{A} = \begin{bmatrix} 1 & 0 & 3 \\ 0 & 1 & 4 \end{bmatrix}$ and $\mathbf{B} = \begin{bmatrix} 1 & 0 \\ 0 & 1 \\ 2 & 1 \end{bmatrix}$. Think of $\mathbf{A}$ as consisting of two elements, the 2×2 matrix $\mathbf{I}_2$ and the 2×1 matrix $\mathbf{C}_{2\times 1} = \begin{bmatrix} 3 \\ 4 \end{bmatrix}$. $\mathbf{B}$ must also be subdivided appropriately. The partitioning is indicated by dotted lines:

$$\mathbf{A} = \left[\begin{array}{cc|c} 1 & 0 & 3 \\ 0 & 1 & 4 \end{array}\right] = [\mathbf{I}_2 \quad \mathbf{C}_{2\times 1}]$$

and

$$\mathbf{B} = \left[\begin{array}{cc} 1 & 0 \\ 0 & 1 \\ \hline 2 & 1 \end{array}\right] = \begin{bmatrix} \mathbf{I}_2 \\ \mathbf{D}_{1\times 2} \end{bmatrix}$$

where $\mathbf{D} = [2 \quad 1]$. The calculation is then shortened by multiplying the partitioned forms just as we would matrices of numbers:

$$\begin{aligned}
\mathbf{AB} &= [\mathbf{I}_2 \quad \mathbf{C}_{2\times 1}]\begin{bmatrix} \mathbf{I}_2 \\ \mathbf{D}_{1\times 2} \end{bmatrix} \\
&= \mathbf{I}_2\mathbf{I}_2 + \mathbf{C}_{2\times 1}\mathbf{D}_{1\times 2} \\
&= \begin{bmatrix} 1 & 0 \\ 0 & 1 \end{bmatrix}\begin{bmatrix} 1 & 0 \\ 0 & 1 \end{bmatrix} + \begin{bmatrix} 3 \\ 4 \end{bmatrix}[2 \quad 1] \\
&= \begin{bmatrix} 1 & 0 \\ 0 & 1 \end{bmatrix} + \begin{bmatrix} 6 & 3 \\ 8 & 4 \end{bmatrix} = \begin{bmatrix} 7 & 3 \\ 8 & 5 \end{bmatrix}
\end{aligned}$$

Notice that the partitioning must be done so that all the products and sums are defined.

b. As a second example let

$$\mathbf{A} = \left[\begin{array}{cc|cc} 2 & 1 & 0 & 0 \\ -1 & 1 & 0 & 0 \\ \hline 1 & 0 & 1 & 2 \\ 0 & 1 & 1 & 3 \end{array}\right]$$

and

$$\mathbf{B} = \left[\begin{array}{cc|cc} 1 & 0 & 3 & 1 \\ 0 & 1 & 2 & 1 \\ \hline 0 & 0 & 1 & 0 \\ 0 & 0 & 0 & 1 \end{array}\right]$$

be partitioned as shown. Then

$$\mathbf{A} = \begin{bmatrix} \mathbf{C}_{2\times 2} & \mathbf{0}_{2\times 2} \\ \mathbf{I}_2 & \mathbf{D}_{2\times 2} \end{bmatrix}$$

and

$$\mathbf{B} = \begin{bmatrix} \mathbf{I}_2 & \mathbf{E}_{2\times 2} \\ \mathbf{0}_{2\times 2} & \mathbf{I}_2 \end{bmatrix}$$

so that

$$\mathbf{AB} = \begin{bmatrix} \mathbf{C}_{2\times 2}\mathbf{I}_2 + \mathbf{0}_{2\times 2}\mathbf{0}_{2\times 2} & \mathbf{C}_{2\times 2}\mathbf{E}_{2\times 2} + \mathbf{0}_{2\times 2}\mathbf{I}_2 \\ \mathbf{I}_2\mathbf{I}_2 + \mathbf{D}_{2\times 2}\mathbf{0}_{2\times 2} & \mathbf{I}_2\mathbf{E}_{2\times 2} + \mathbf{D}_{2\times 2}\mathbf{I}_2 \end{bmatrix}$$

$$= \begin{bmatrix} \begin{bmatrix} 2 & 1 \\ -1 & 1 \end{bmatrix} + \begin{bmatrix} 0 & 0 \\ 0 & 0 \end{bmatrix} & \begin{bmatrix} 8 & 3 \\ -1 & 0 \end{bmatrix} + \begin{bmatrix} 0 & 0 \\ 0 & 0 \end{bmatrix} \\ \begin{bmatrix} 1 & 0 \\ 0 & 1 \end{bmatrix} + \begin{bmatrix} 0 & 0 \\ 0 & 0 \end{bmatrix} & \begin{bmatrix} 3 & 1 \\ 2 & 1 \end{bmatrix} + \begin{bmatrix} 1 & 2 \\ 1 & 3 \end{bmatrix} \end{bmatrix}$$

$$= \begin{bmatrix} 2 & 1 & 8 & 3 \\ -1 & 1 & -1 & 0 \\ 1 & 0 & 4 & 3 \\ 0 & 1 & 3 & 4 \end{bmatrix}$$

30. Compute the products using the indicated partitioning.

a. $\left[\begin{array}{cc|c} 1 & 2 & 0 \\ -2 & 1 & 0 \\ \hline 0 & 0 & 1 \end{array}\right] \left[\begin{array}{ccc|c} 0 & 0 & 0 & 1 \\ 0 & 0 & 0 & -1 \\ \hline 1 & 0 & 1 & 0 \end{array}\right]$

b. $\left[\begin{array}{c|cc} 1 & 2 & 0 \\ \hline -2 & 1 & 0 \\ 0 & 0 & 1 \end{array}\right] \left[\begin{array}{c|ccc} 0 & 0 & 0 & 1 \\ \hline 0 & 0 & 0 & -1 \\ 1 & 0 & 1 & 0 \end{array}\right]$

c. $\left[\begin{array}{cc|c} 1 & 2 & 0 \\ -2 & 1 & 0 \\ \hline 0 & 0 & 1 \end{array}\right] \left[\begin{array}{c|cc|c} 0 & 0 & 0 & 1 \\ 0 & 0 & 0 & -1 \\ \hline 1 & 0 & 1 & 0 \end{array}\right]$

31. Compute the products using the indicated partitioning.

a. $\left[\begin{array}{cc|cc} 1 & 2 & 0 & 0 \\ 3 & 4 & 0 & 0 \\ \hline 0 & 0 & 1 & 0 \\ 0 & 0 & 2 & 1 \end{array}\right] \left[\begin{array}{cc|cc} 4 & -1 & 0 & 0 \\ 2 & 0 & 0 & 0 \\ \hline 0 & 0 & -2 & 0 \\ 0 & 0 & 1 & 2 \end{array}\right]$

b. $\left[\begin{array}{cc|cc} 3 & 1 & 0 & 0 \\ 5 & 2 & 0 & 0 \\ \hline 0 & 0 & 3 & 1 \\ 0 & 0 & 2 & 1 \end{array}\right] \left[\begin{array}{cc|cc} 2 & -1 & 0 & 0 \\ -5 & 3 & 0 & 0 \\ \hline 0 & 0 & 1 & -1 \\ 0 & 0 & -2 & 3 \end{array}\right]$

32. Find the products using partitioning. The partitioning of one matrix is given. Choose a suitable partitioning for the other.

a. $\left[\begin{array}{cc|ccc} 1 & 1 & 0 & 0 & 0 \\ 0 & 1 & 0 & 0 & 0 \\ \hline 0 & 0 & 1 & 2 & 3 \\ 0 & 0 & 0 & -1 & 2 \\ 0 & 0 & 0 & 0 & 4 \end{array}\right] \begin{bmatrix} 2 & 1 & 0 & 0 & 0 \\ 3 & 2 & 0 & 0 & 0 \\ 0 & 0 & 1 & 0 & 0 \\ 0 & 0 & 0 & 1 & 0 \\ 0 & 0 & 0 & 0 & 1 \end{bmatrix}$

b. $\begin{bmatrix} 1 & 0 & 1 & 0 & 0 \\ 0 & 1 & 0 & 1 & 0 \\ 1 & 1 & 0 & 0 & 1 \\ 0 & 0 & 0 & 1 & 0 \end{bmatrix} \left[\begin{array}{ccc|cc} 0 & 0 & 0 & 1 & 1 \\ 0 & 0 & 0 & 2 & 2 \\ 0 & 0 & 0 & 3 & 3 \\ \hline 1 & 0 & 1 & 4 & 2 \\ 0 & 1 & 0 & 1 & 0 \end{array}\right]$

33. Choose a suitable partitioning and calculate the products.

a. $\begin{bmatrix} 2 & 0 & 4 & 0 & 0 \\ 0 & 3 & 0 & 5 & 0 \\ 0 & 0 & 0 & 0 & 6 \\ 0 & 0 & 0 & 1 & 0 \\ 0 & 0 & 0 & 0 & 1 \end{bmatrix} \begin{bmatrix} 1 & 0 & 0 & 0 & 0 \\ 0 & 2 & 0 & 0 & 0 \\ 1 & 0 & 0 & 1 & 1 \\ 0 & 1 & 0 & -1 & 1 \\ 0 & 0 & 1 & 0 & 2 \end{bmatrix}$

b. $\begin{bmatrix} 1 & 0 & 3 & 0 \\ 0 & 1 & 0 & 3 \\ 2 & 0 & 4 & 0 \\ 0 & 2 & 0 & 4 \end{bmatrix} \begin{bmatrix} 2 & 0 & 1 & 0 \\ 0 & 2 & 0 & 1 \\ 5 & 0 & 6 & 0 \\ 0 & 5 & 0 & 6 \end{bmatrix}$

34. Let $\mathbf{A}_{m\times n}$ and $\mathbf{B}_{n\times r}$ be partitioned as follows:

$$\begin{array}{r} m_1 \text{ rows} \\ m_2 \text{ rows} \\ \\ \\ m_s \text{ rows} \end{array} \begin{bmatrix} \mathbf{A}_{11} & \mathbf{A}_{12} & \cdots & \mathbf{A}_{1k} \\ \mathbf{A}_{21} & \mathbf{A}_{22} & \cdots & \mathbf{A}_{2k} \\ \vdots & \vdots & & \vdots \\ \mathbf{A}_{s1} & \mathbf{A}_{s2} & \cdots & \mathbf{A}_{sk} \end{bmatrix}$$
$$\begin{array}{cccc} n_1 & n_2 & & n_k \\ \text{cols.} & \text{cols.} & & \text{cols.} \end{array}$$

$$\begin{bmatrix} \mathbf{B}_{11} & \mathbf{B}_{12} & \cdots & \mathbf{B}_{1t} \\ \mathbf{B}_{12} & \mathbf{B}_{22} & \cdots & \mathbf{B}_{2t} \\ \vdots & \vdots & & \vdots \\ \mathbf{B}_{k1} & \mathbf{B}_{k2} & \cdots & \mathbf{B}_{kt} \end{bmatrix} \begin{matrix} n_1 \text{ rows} \\ n_2 \text{ rows} \\ \\ n_k \text{ rows} \end{matrix}$$

$$\begin{matrix} r_1 & r_2 & & r_t \\ \text{cols.} & \text{cols.} & & \text{cols.} \end{matrix}$$

Show that each term in the product **AB** is defined. (*Hint*: Consider $\mathbf{A}_{i1}\mathbf{B}_{1j} + \mathbf{A}_{i2}\mathbf{B}_{2j} + \cdots + \mathbf{A}_{ik}\mathbf{B}_{kj}$.)

35. Suppose the sum $\mathbf{A} + \mathbf{B}$ is to be calculated using the method of partitioning. Describe how the partitions chosen in **A** and **B** should be related.

1.4 Geometric Vectors

It is often helpful to have a geometric interpretation of abstract ideas. We therefore introduce geometric vectors.

Think of a plane with coordinate axes Ox and Oy. A point R in this plane has coordinates (a, b). The directed line segment from O to R is a representation of the geometric vector $\mathbf{u} = (a, b)$. (See Figure 1.2.) It is not the only possible representation. Directed line segments do not need to begin at the origin. Suppose P has coordinates (a_1, b_1) and Q has coordinates (a_2, b_2), where $(a_2, b_2) - (a_1, b_1) = (a, b)$. The directed line segment PQ is defined to be equivalent to the directed line segment OR and is an alternative representation of the geometric vector $\mathbf{u} = (a, b)$. (See Figure 1.3.)

From analytic geometry, the length of PQ, written $|PQ|$, is

$$|PQ| = \sqrt{(a_2 - a_1)^2 + (b_2 - b_1)^2} = \sqrt{a^2 + b^2} = |OR|$$

Equivalent directed line segments then have the same length. Define the length of the geometric vector $\mathbf{u} = (a, b)$ to be the length of any of the equivalent line

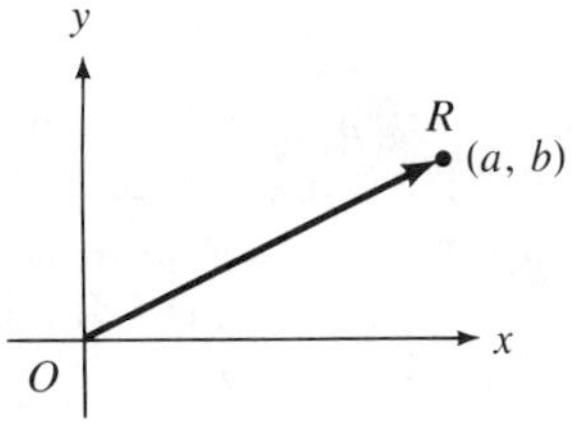

FIGURE 1.2

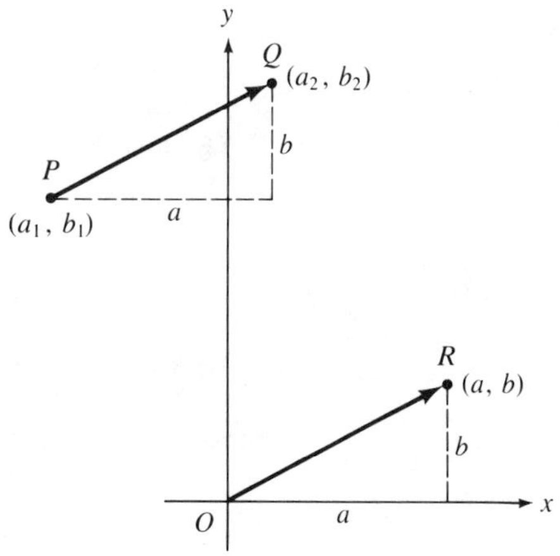

FIGURE 1.3

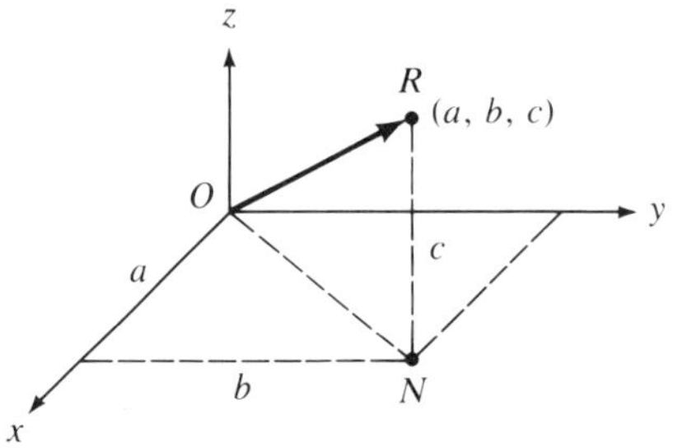

FIGURE 1.4

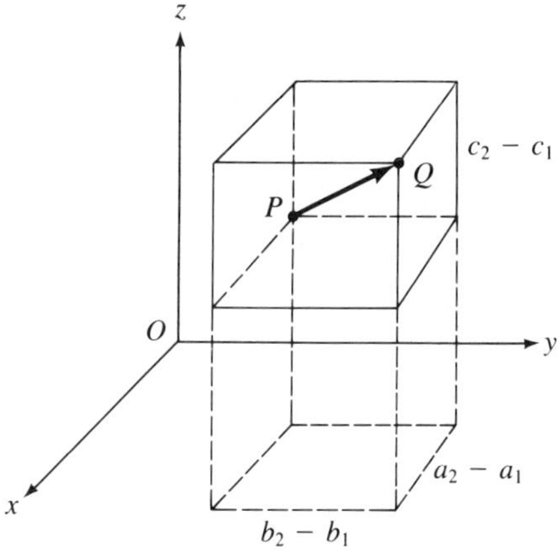

FIGURE 1.5

segments which represent it. The length of **u**, designated by $\|\mathbf{u}\|$, is

$$\|\mathbf{u}\| = \sqrt{a^2 + b^2} = \sqrt{\mathbf{u} \cdot \mathbf{u}}$$

Think of three-dimensional space. Here a coordinate system consists of three fixed coordinate planes, each perpendicular to the other two. The coordinate planes intersect in three perpendicular lines through a point, the origin. If a point R has coordinates (a, b, c), its location is a directed distance a from the yz plane, b from the xz plane, and c from the xy plane. The directed line segment from O to R is a representation of the geometric vector $\mathbf{u} = (a, b, c)$. (See Figure 1.4.) Again, a directed line segment with initial point $P\ (a_1, b_1, c_1)$ and terminal point $Q\ (a_2, b_2, c_2)$ is defined to be equivalent to OR provided that

$$(a_2, b_2, c_2) - (a_1, b_1, c_1) = (a, b, c).$$

The geometric vector $\mathbf{u} = (a, b, c)$ can be represented by any directed line segment equivalent to OR. (See Figure 1.5.)

The length of OR can be calculated by the three-dimensional distance formula or by the Pythagorean theorem. Two steps are required in using the Pythagorean theorem:

$$|ON| = \sqrt{a^2 + b^2}, \qquad |OR| = \sqrt{|ON|^2 + c^2} = \sqrt{a^2 + b^2 + c^2}$$

Why not four-dimensional space? It is not hard to imagine a directed line segment OR from $(0, 0, 0, 0)$ to (a, b, c, d) in four-dimensional space, but it is almost impossible to draw a good representation of one. Still one can imagine calculating the length of OR by an additional application of the Pythagorean theorem:

$$|ON| = \sqrt{a^2 + b^2}; \qquad |OM| = \sqrt{|ON|^2 + c^2}; \qquad |OR| = \sqrt{|OM|^2 + d^2}$$

$$|OR| = \sqrt{a^2 + b^2 + c^2 + d^2}$$

Once we move to four dimensions, it is no greater step to consider any positive integer n and define the concept of length for any n-tuple. The notation R^n is used to represent the set of all n-tuples of real numbers with the operations of addition and scalar multiplication as defined in Section 1.1.

Norm
Unit Vector

Definition 13

Let $\mathbf{u}$ be an element of R^n. The **norm**, or **length**, of $\mathbf{u}$, written $\|\mathbf{u}\|$, is $\sqrt{\mathbf{u} \cdot \mathbf{u}}$. A vector with length 1 is called a **unit vector**.

Example 27 Let $\mathbf{u} = (2, 0, 3, -6)$ and $\mathbf{v} = (-2, 1, -2, 4)$. Then:

$$\begin{aligned} \|\mathbf{u}\| &= \sqrt{2^2 + 0^2 + 3^2 + (-6)^2} = \sqrt{49} = 7 \\ \|\mathbf{v}\| &= \sqrt{(-2)^2 + 1^2 + (-2)^2 + 4^2} = \sqrt{25} = 5 \\ \|2\mathbf{u}\| &= \text{norm of } (4, 0, 6, -12) = \sqrt{4^2 + 0^2 + 6^2 + (-12)^2} \\ &= \sqrt{196} = 14 = 2\|\mathbf{u}\| \\ \mathbf{u} + \mathbf{v} &= (0, 1, 1, -2) \\ \|\mathbf{u} + \mathbf{v}\| &= \sqrt{1 + 1 + 4} = \sqrt{6} < 7 + 5 = \|\mathbf{u}\| + \|\mathbf{v}\| \end{aligned}$$

The vector $(\frac{1}{2}, \frac{1}{2}, \frac{1}{2}, \frac{1}{2})$ is a unit vector since it has norm 1. ■

Theorem 7 $\|\mathbf{u}\| \geqslant 0$, and $\|\mathbf{u}\| = 0$ if and only if $\mathbf{u} = \mathbf{0}$. $\|k\mathbf{u}\| = |k|\,\|\mathbf{u}\|$. If $\mathbf{u} \neq \mathbf{0}$ and $k = 1/\|\mathbf{u}\|$, $k\mathbf{u}$ is a unit vector.

Proof These statements follow directly from Definition 13. You are asked to supply the proof in Exercises 1.4, Problems 7 and 9. □

Look now at the operations of addition and scalar multiplication from the point of view of geometric vectors.

Example 28 Let $\mathbf{u} = (-1, -3, 2)$ and $\mathbf{v} = (1, 2, 1)$. Calculate $\mathbf{u} + \mathbf{v}$, and draw $\mathbf{u}$, $\mathbf{v}$, and $\mathbf{u} + \mathbf{v}$.

$$\mathbf{u} + \mathbf{v} = (-1, -3, 2) + (1, 2, 1) = (0, -1, 3)$$

The directed line segments OP, OR, and OQ, representing $\mathbf{u}$, $\mathbf{v}$, and $\mathbf{u} + \mathbf{v}$, are drawn with initial point at the origin. But OP is equivalent to RQ, since $(0, -1, 3) - (1, 2, 1) = (-1, -3, 2)$. Also, PQ is equivalent to OR. Thus, $OPQR$ is a parallelogram, and the line segment OQ, which represents $\mathbf{u} + \mathbf{v}$, is the diagonal of the parallelogram. This representation of the sum $\mathbf{u} + \mathbf{v}$ illustrates the so-called parallelogram law familiar to students of physics. (See Figure 1.6.) ■

An alternative and useful way to draw the sum of the vectors $\mathbf{u}$ and $\mathbf{v}$ is to draw $\mathbf{u}$ with initial point at the origin and $\mathbf{v}$ with initial point at the terminal point of $\mathbf{u}$.

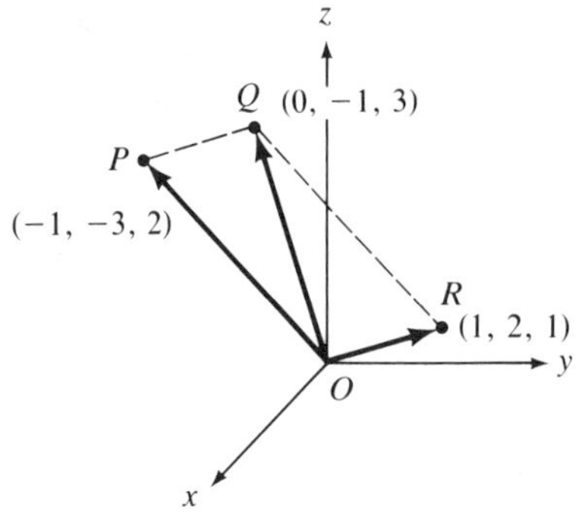

FIGURE 1.6

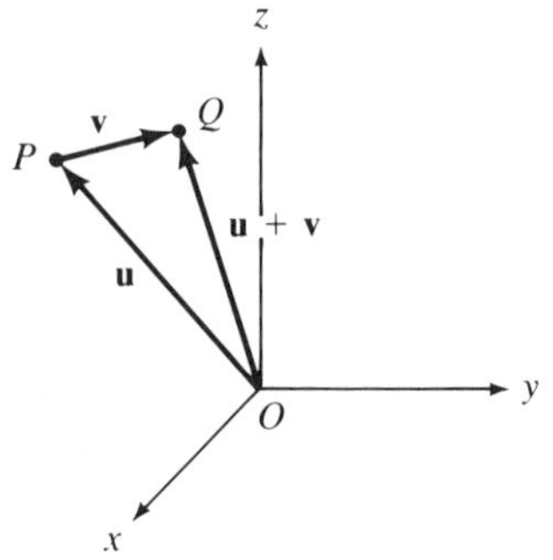

FIGURE 1.7

Then the vector $\mathbf{u} + \mathbf{v}$ will have initial point the origin and terminal point the terminal point of $\mathbf{v}$. (See Figure 1.7.)

This method, frequently referred to as *head to tail*, is useful when several vectors are to be added.

Example 29 Let $\mathbf{u}_1 = (1, 2)$, $\mathbf{u}_2 = (-1, 4)$, $\mathbf{u}_3 = (3, -2)$, $\mathbf{u}_4 = (1, -3)$. Then $\mathbf{w} = \mathbf{u}_1 + \mathbf{u}_2 + \mathbf{u}_3 + \mathbf{u}_4 = (4, 1)$. These vectors are drawn head to tail in Figure 1.8.

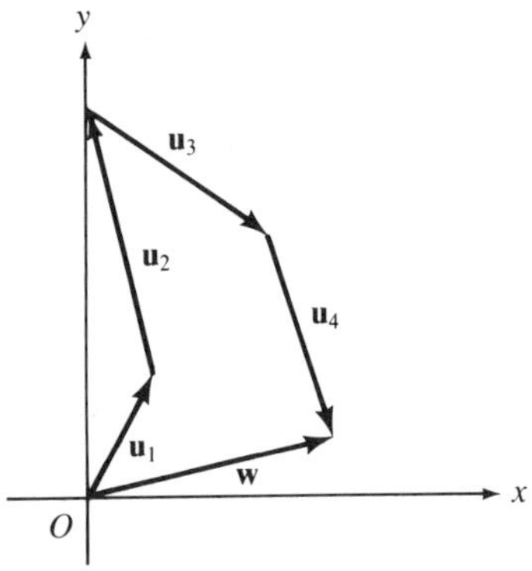

FIGURE 1.8 ■

Example 30 illustrates scalar multiples of vectors and addition of vectors that are multiples of each other.

Example 30 Let $\mathbf{u} = (1, 2)$, $\mathbf{v} = (2, 4)$, and $\mathbf{u} + \mathbf{v} = (3, 6) = 3\mathbf{u}$. These vectors are parallel. Drawn with initial point at the origin, they are collinear; $\|3\mathbf{u}\| = 3\|\mathbf{u}\|$. (See Figure 1.9.)

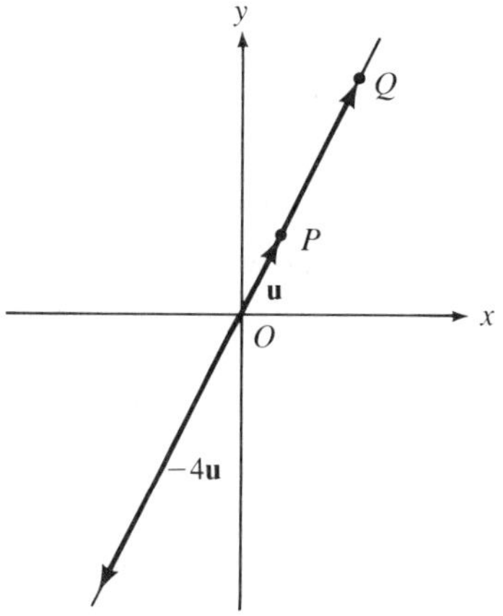

FIGURE 1.9

Let P be the terminal point of **u** and Q be the terminal point of 3**u**. On the line through O, P, and Q, the points P and Q are on the same side of the origin. It is natural to think of OP and OQ as having the same direction.

Now let $k = -4$, so that $k\mathbf{u} = (-4, -8)$. If the initial point is at the origin, the terminal point of $-4\mathbf{u}$ is on the line OPQ but on the opposite side of the origin from P. The vectors **u** and $-4\mathbf{u}$ have opposite direction. ■

In R^2 and R^3, our geometric knowledge lets us define two vectors **u** and **v** to be parallel if $\mathbf{u} = k\mathbf{v}$ for some $k \neq 0$. They have the same direction if k is positive and opposite directions if k is negative. Definition 14 deals with parallel vectors in R^n.

Parallel
Same Direction
Opposite Direction

Definition 14

Two nonzero vectors **u** and **v** in R^n are **parallel** if $\mathbf{u} = k\mathbf{v}$ for some $k \neq 0$. If $k > 0$, **u** and **v** are in the **same direction**. If $k < 0$, **u** and **v** are in **opposite directions**.

Look back at Theorem 7. Given any nonzero vector, **u**, it is quite simple to find a unit vector in the same direction as **u** and a unit vector in the opposite direction. The vector $k\mathbf{u}$ is parallel to **u** and $\|k\mathbf{u}\| = |k|\,\|\mathbf{u}\|$. If k is chosen to be $1/\|\mathbf{u}\|$, $k\mathbf{u}$ has length 1 and is in the same direction as **u**. On the other hand, if $k = -1/\|\mathbf{u}\|$, then $k\mathbf{u}$ has length 1 but is in the direction opposite to that of **u**.

Example 31

$\mathbf{u} = (-1, 4, -2, 2)$ is not a unit vector, since its length is 5.
$(-\frac{1}{5}, \frac{4}{5}, -\frac{2}{5}, \frac{2}{5})$ is a unit vector in the same direction as **u**.
$(\frac{1}{5}, -\frac{4}{5}, \frac{2}{5}, -\frac{2}{5})$ is a unit vector in the direction opposite to that of **u**. ■

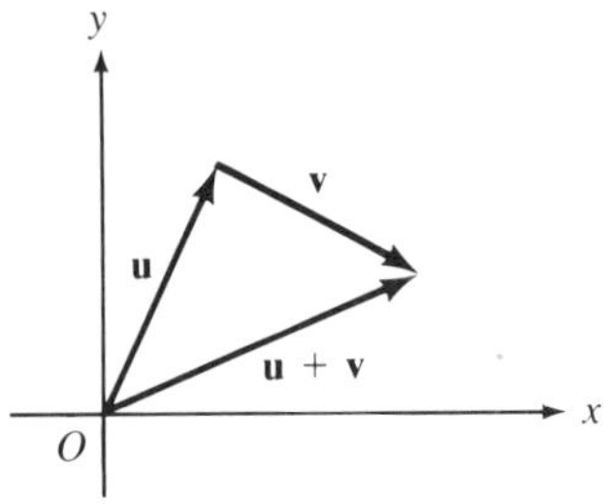

FIGURE 1.10

An important property of the norm of a vector has yet to be discussed. The familiar property of the absolute values of real numbers a and b,

$$|a + b| \leqslant |a| + |b|$$

has its counterpart for the norms of vectors in R^n.

For vectors $\mathbf{u}$ and $\mathbf{v}$ in R^2, we have $\|\mathbf{u} + \mathbf{v}\| \leqslant \|\mathbf{u}\| + \|\mathbf{v}\|$. This inequality is called the *triangle inequality* because it can be explained in R^2 with a simple diagram (Figure 1.10). The length of one side of a triangle cannot exceed the sum of the lengths of the other two sides.

It is an important fact that the triangle inequality is true in R^n. Its proof is based on a famous inequality called the Cauchy-Schwarz Inequality. We state this as Theorem 8.

Theorem 8 The Cauchy-Schwarz Inequality

Let $\mathbf{u}$ and $\mathbf{v}$ be vectors in R^n. Then $|\mathbf{u} \cdot \mathbf{v}| \leqq \|\mathbf{u}\| \, \|\mathbf{v}\|$. Equality holds if and only if $\mathbf{u} = k\mathbf{v}$.

The proof of the Cauchy-Schwarz Inequality illustrates many interesting ideas we have been studying. Its proof is developed in the supplemental topics section of Exercises 1.4. □

Theorem 9 is a direct consequence of the Cauchy-Schwarz Inequality.

Theorem 9 The Triangle Inequality

For vectors $\mathbf{u}$ and $\mathbf{v}$ in R^n, $\|\mathbf{u} + \mathbf{v}\| \leqslant \|\mathbf{u}\| + \|\mathbf{v}\|$.

Proof You will enjoy proving this for yourself. Start out by thinking about $(\mathbf{u} + \mathbf{v}) \cdot (\mathbf{u} + \mathbf{v})$. □

SUMMARY The set of n-tuples R^n can be pictured as a set of directed line segments called geometric vectors. The length, or norm, of $\mathbf{u}$ is defined by $\|\mathbf{u}\| = \sqrt{\mathbf{u} \cdot \mathbf{u}}$. The norm so defined satisfies the conditions:

1. $\|\mathbf{u}\| \geqslant 0$, $\|\mathbf{u}\| = 0$ if and only if $\mathbf{u} = \mathbf{0}$
2. $\|k\mathbf{u}\| = |k| \, \|\mathbf{u}\|$
3. $|\mathbf{u} \cdot \mathbf{v}| \leqslant \|\mathbf{u}\| \, \|\mathbf{v}\|$ (Cauchy-Schwarz Inequality)
4. $\|\mathbf{u} + \mathbf{v}\| \leqslant \|\mathbf{u}\| + \|\mathbf{v}\|$

A unit vector is a vector with norm 1. Nonzero vectors $\mathbf{u}$ and $\mathbf{v}$ are parallel if $\mathbf{v} = k\mathbf{u}$ for some $k \neq 0$. They are in the same direction if $k > 0$ and in opposite directions if $k < 0$.

EXERCISES 1.4

1. Find the lengths of the triples $(1, -1, 3)$ and $(1, 1, 3)$. Write six more triples of the same length.
2. What are the lengths of $(1, 1, 2)$, $(2, 2, 4)$, and $(k, k, 2k)$? Show that $(k, k, 2k)$ has length 1 if $k = 1/\sqrt{6}$.
3. **a.** Choose k so that $(k, 2k, 2k)$ is a unit triple—that is, has length 1.
   b. Choose k so that $k\mathbf{v}$ has norm 1 where $\mathbf{v} = (-1, 1, 1, 3, 6)$.
4. **a.** Find a unit triple that has the same direction as the triple $(-1, 4, 3)$.
   b. Find a unit triple that has the opposite direction to $(0, 2, 5)$.
5. Find the lengths of the 4-tuples $(1, 0, 2, 1)$, $(1, 1, 3, -1)$, and $(1, 2, 0, 2)$.
6. Find the length of the 4-tuple $(1, 1, 2, -1)$. Find the length of $(k, k, 2k, -k)$. Choose k so that $(k, k, 2k, -k)$ is a unit 4-tuple.
7. Show that $\|\mathbf{u}\| = 0$ if and only if $\mathbf{u} = \mathbf{0}$ and that $\|\mathbf{u}\| > 0$ otherwise.
8. Given that $\|\mathbf{u}\| = 5$, write the norm of each of the following vectors: $2\mathbf{u}$, $-2\mathbf{u}$, $6\mathbf{u} + 3\mathbf{u}$, $2\mathbf{u} - 4\mathbf{u}$. Draw a sketch of these vectors, with common initial point.
9. **a.** Show that $\|k\mathbf{u}\| = |k|\,\|\mathbf{u}\|$.
   b. Show that if $\mathbf{u} \neq \mathbf{0}$, and $k = \dfrac{1}{\|\mathbf{u}\|}$, then $k\mathbf{u}$ is a unit vector.
10. Draw geometric vectors $\mathbf{e}_1 = (1, 0)$, $\mathbf{e}_2 = (0, 1)$, $\mathbf{u} = 3\mathbf{e}_1 + 4\mathbf{e}_2$.
11. Draw geometric vectors $\mathbf{u}_1 = (1, 1)$, $\mathbf{u}_2 = (-2, 3)$, $\mathbf{u}_3 = 4\mathbf{u}_1 + \mathbf{u}_2$.
12. Let $\mathbf{u}_1 = (1, -1)$, $\mathbf{u}_2 = (2, 3)$, $\mathbf{u}_3 = (-1, 3)$, and $\mathbf{u}_4 = (3, 1)$. Using the head-to-tail method, draw the linear combination $2\mathbf{u}_1 - \mathbf{u}_2 + 3\mathbf{u}_3 + \mathbf{u}_4$.
13. Let $\mathbf{u}_1 = (1, 1)$, $\mathbf{u}_2 = (-2, 3)$, and $\mathbf{u}_3 = (1, 4)$. Calculate $\mathbf{w} = \mathbf{u}_1 + \mathbf{u}_2 + \mathbf{u}_3$ and draw a geometric representation of this equation.
14. Show that $(\mathbf{u} - \mathbf{v}) \cdot (\mathbf{u} + \mathbf{v}) = \|\mathbf{u}\|^2 - \|\mathbf{v}\|^2$.
15. Show that $\|\mathbf{u} - \mathbf{v}\|^2 = \|\mathbf{u}\|^2 - 2\mathbf{u} \cdot \mathbf{v} + \|\mathbf{v}\|^2$.
16. Prove geometrically in R^3 that $\|\mathbf{u} + \mathbf{v}\| \leqslant \|\mathbf{u}\| + \|\mathbf{v}\|$. (*Hint*: Use the Law of Cosines.)
17. Verify the Cauchy-Schwarz Inequality in the following particular cases.
   a. $\mathbf{u} = (1, -1, 3, 4)$, $\mathbf{v} = (2, 0, 3, 1)$
   b. $\mathbf{u} = (1, 1, -1, -1, 2, 3)$, $\mathbf{v} = (0, 2, 0, 3, 0, 2)$
18. Verify the Cauchy-Schwarz Inequality in the following particular cases.
   a. $\mathbf{u} = (2, 1, 4, 3)$, $\mathbf{v} = (0, 0, 0, 0)$
   b. $\mathbf{u} = (1, 2, 3, 4)$, $\mathbf{v} = (2, 4, 6, 8)$
   c. $\mathbf{u} = (-1, -2, -3, -4)$, $\mathbf{v} = (3, 6, 9, 12)$
   d. $\mathbf{u} = (2, 4, 6, 8)$, $\mathbf{v} = (3, 6, 9, 12)$
19. Show that if $\mathbf{u} = k\mathbf{v}$, equality holds in the Cauchy-Schwarz Inequality.
20. Show that if $\mathbf{u} = k\mathbf{v}$ and $k \geqslant 0$, equality holds in Theorem 9.
21. Carry out the proof of Theorem 9.

Supplemental Topics

Geometric Proofs. Frequently vectors can be used to prove geometric properties.

22. Show that the line joining the midpoints of two sides of a triangle is parallel to the third side and half as long. (*Hint*: Let the vectors $\mathbf{u}$ and $\mathbf{v}$ represent the two sides of the triangle. Then $\frac{1}{2}\mathbf{u}$ and $\frac{1}{2}\mathbf{v}$ are the vector representations of half the sides. See Figure 1.11.)

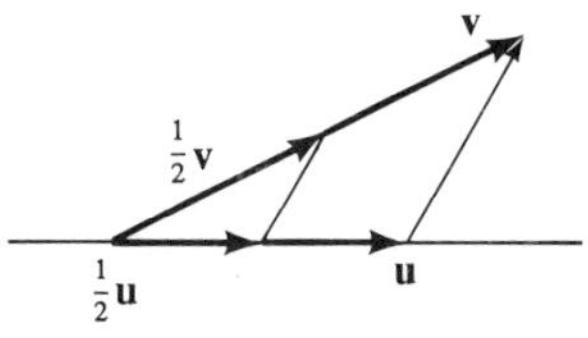

FIGURE 1.11

23. Let $\mathbf{u}$ and $\mathbf{v}$ represent two adjacent sides of a parallelogram. Show that if the diagonals of the parallelogram have the same length, then $\mathbf{u} \cdot \mathbf{v} = 0$.

24. Show that the diagonals of a parallelogram bisect each other.

25. Figure 1.12 shows a quadrilateral. Show that line segments joining midpoints of consecutive sides form a parallelogram.

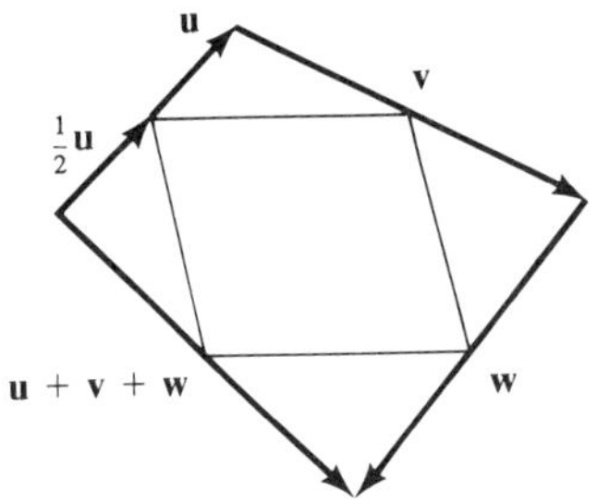

FIGURE 1.12

The Cauchy-Schwarz Inequality. The proof of this inequality can be approached in several ways. The suggestions here make use of the ideas introduced in this chapter.

26. Step 1 of the proof considers the case in which $\mathbf{u} = \mathbf{0}$, $\mathbf{v} = \mathbf{0}$, or both.
    a. Suppose $\|\mathbf{u}\|\,\|\mathbf{v}\| = 0$. What must be true of $\|\mathbf{u}\|$ or $\|\mathbf{v}\|$? What does this imply about $\mathbf{u}$ or $\mathbf{v}$? What does this imply about $\mathbf{u} \cdot \mathbf{v}$? Show that if $\mathbf{u}$ or $\mathbf{v}$ is zero, the inequality is true.
    b. Show that if $\mathbf{u} \neq \mathbf{0}$ and $\mathbf{v} \neq \mathbf{0}$, the inequality can be written in the form $\left| \dfrac{\mathbf{u}}{\|\mathbf{u}\|} \cdot \dfrac{\mathbf{v}}{\|\mathbf{v}\|} \right| \leqslant 1$.

27. Step 2 proves a useful inequality. Let $\mathbf{s}$ and $\mathbf{t}$ be unit vectors defined by $\mathbf{s} = \dfrac{\mathbf{u}}{\|\mathbf{u}\|}$, $\mathbf{t} = \dfrac{\mathbf{v}}{\|\mathbf{v}\|}$.
    a. Show that $(\mathbf{s} - \mathbf{t}) \cdot (\mathbf{s} - \mathbf{t}) = 2 - 2\mathbf{s} \cdot \mathbf{t}$.
    b. Use the fact that $(\mathbf{s} - \mathbf{t}) \cdot (\mathbf{s} - \mathbf{t}) \geqslant 0$ to show that $1 \geqslant \mathbf{s} \cdot \mathbf{t}$.

28. Step 3 derives another inequality.
    a. Show that $(\mathbf{s} + \mathbf{t}) \cdot (\mathbf{s} + \mathbf{t}) = 2 + 2\mathbf{s} \cdot \mathbf{t}$.
    b. Show that $\mathbf{s} \cdot \mathbf{t} \geqslant -1$.

29. Use 27 and 28 to show the following:
    a. $-1 \leqslant \mathbf{s} \cdot \mathbf{t} \leqslant 1$
    b. $-\|\mathbf{u}\|\,\|\mathbf{v}\| \leqslant \mathbf{u} \cdot \mathbf{v} \leqslant \|\mathbf{u}\|\,\|\mathbf{v}\|$
    c. $|\mathbf{u} \cdot \mathbf{v}| \leqslant \|\mathbf{u}\|\,\|\mathbf{v}\|$

30. Show that if $\mathbf{u} = k\mathbf{v}$, then $|\mathbf{u} \cdot \mathbf{v}| = \|\mathbf{u}\|\,\|\mathbf{v}\|$.

1.5 Orthogonal Vectors, Planes, Lines

We have defined parallel vectors (Definition 14). How can we characterize perpendicular vectors, or, more generally, how can we define the angle between two vectors? They must be nonzero vectors for such a definition to be possible.

Given two nonzero geometric vectors $\mathbf{u}$ and $\mathbf{v}$, we can draw them with a common initial point. They form two sides of a triangle in which the third side is a representation of the geometric vector $\mathbf{u} - \mathbf{v}$. (See Figure 1.13.)

The Law of Cosines for triangles in R^2 or R^3 says

$$\|\mathbf{u} - \mathbf{v}\|^2 = \|\mathbf{u}\|^2 + \|\mathbf{v}\|^2 - 2\|\mathbf{u}\|\,\|\mathbf{v}\| \cos \theta$$

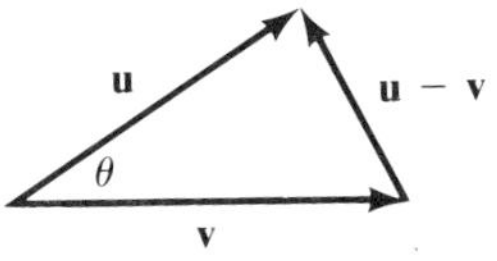

FIGURE 1.13

where θ is the angle between the vectors **u** and **v**. From this,

$$\cos\theta = \frac{\|\mathbf{u}\|^2 + \|\mathbf{v}\|^2 - \|\mathbf{u} - \mathbf{v}\|^2}{2\|\mathbf{u}\|\,\|\mathbf{v}\|}$$

In Exercises 1.4, Problem 15, you were asked to show that

$$\|\mathbf{u} - \mathbf{v}\|^2 = \|\mathbf{u}\|^2 + \|\mathbf{v}\|^2 - 2\mathbf{u}\cdot\mathbf{v}$$

This implies that

$$\cos\theta = \frac{\mathbf{u}\cdot\mathbf{v}}{\|\mathbf{u}\|\,\|\mathbf{v}\|}$$

In R^2 and R^3 nonzero geometric vectors are perpendicular if and only if $\theta = 90°$—that is, $\cos\theta = 0$, which implies $\mathbf{u}\cdot\mathbf{v} = 0$.

We would like to define the concepts of perpendicularity and the angle between two vectors in R^n by expressions similar to those for R^2 and R^3. First we must be sure that the equation $\cos\theta = \dfrac{\mathbf{u}\cdot\mathbf{v}}{\|\mathbf{u}\|\,\|\mathbf{v}\|}$ really defines an angle. By Theorem 8, we have the inequality $|\mathbf{u}\cdot\mathbf{v}| \leqslant \|\mathbf{u}\|\,\|\mathbf{v}\|$, so that $\left|\dfrac{\mathbf{u}\cdot\mathbf{v}}{\|\mathbf{u}\|\,\|\mathbf{v}\|}\right| \leqslant 1$. This means that given **u** and **v** both not **0**, an angle θ is defined by $\cos\theta = \dfrac{\mathbf{u}\cdot\mathbf{v}}{\|\mathbf{u}\|\,\|\mathbf{v}\|}$. In referring to vectors in R^n for $n > 3$, the word **orthogonal** is used in preference to the word **perpendicular** when the angle between two vectors is 90°. The use of the word orthogonal emphasizes the fact that this is a property of n-tuples, not just of their geometric representation.

Angle between Two Vectors

Definition 15

If **u** and **v** are nonzero elements of R^n, the cosine of the **angle** θ **between u and v** is defined by

$$\cos\theta = \frac{\mathbf{u}\cdot\mathbf{v}}{\|\mathbf{u}\|\,\|\mathbf{v}\|}$$

Orthogonal Vectors

In particular, **u** and **v** are **orthogonal vectors** if $\mathbf{u}\cdot\mathbf{v} = 0$. The vector **0** in R^n is orthogonal to every element of R^n.

Example 32

Let $\mathbf{u} = (-1, 4, 3, 1)$, $\mathbf{v} = (1, -1, 2, -1)$, $\mathbf{w} = (1, 0, 0, 1)$. Since $\mathbf{u}\cdot\mathbf{v} = -1 - 4 + 6 - 1 = 0$, the vectors **u** and **v** are orthogonal. A similar calculation shows that $\mathbf{u}\cdot\mathbf{w} = 0$ and $\mathbf{v}\cdot\mathbf{w} = 0$. The set of vectors $\{\mathbf{u}, \mathbf{v}, \mathbf{w}\}$ has the property that each of its vectors is orthogonal to each of the other two vectors. This set is called an orthogonal set. ■

The vectors in Example 32 are not unit vectors. We can find unit vectors in the same direction as the given vectors by multiplying each by the reciprocal of its norm (see Example 31). The process of replacing $\mathbf{u}$ by $\dfrac{\mathbf{u}}{\|\mathbf{u}\|}$ is called **normalization**.

Example 33 Let $\mathbf{u} = (-1, 4, 3, 1)$, $\mathbf{v} = (1, -1, 2, -1)$, and $\mathbf{w} = (1, 0, 0, 1)$. Then $\|\mathbf{u}\| = 3\sqrt{3}$, $\|\mathbf{v}\| = \sqrt{7}$, and $\|\mathbf{w}\| = \sqrt{2}$. The vectors

$$\mathbf{u}_1 = \left(\frac{-1}{3\sqrt{3}}, \frac{4}{3\sqrt{3}}, \frac{1}{\sqrt{3}}, \frac{1}{3\sqrt{3}}\right), \qquad \mathbf{v}_1 = \left(\frac{1}{\sqrt{7}}, \frac{-1}{\sqrt{7}}, \frac{2}{\sqrt{7}}, \frac{-1}{\sqrt{7}}\right),$$

$$\mathbf{w}_1 = \left(\frac{1}{\sqrt{2}}, 0, 0, \frac{1}{\sqrt{2}}\right)$$

are unit vectors in the same direction as $\mathbf{u}$, $\mathbf{v}$, $\mathbf{w}$. The set of vectors $\{\mathbf{u}_1, \mathbf{v}_1, \mathbf{w}_1\}$ is also an orthogonal set. Since these vectors are each unit vectors and form an orthogonal set, the set is called an **orthonormal** set. The word *orthonormal* is a combination of the words *orthogonal* and *normalized.* ■

Example 34 One of the simplest examples of an orthonormal set is the set of standard n-tuples $\{\mathbf{e}_1, \mathbf{e}_2, \ldots, \mathbf{e}_n\}$. For any n,

$$\mathbf{e}_i \cdot \mathbf{e}_i = 1, \qquad \text{for } i = 1, 2, \ldots, n$$

$$\mathbf{e}_i \cdot \mathbf{e}_j = 0, \qquad i \neq j, \quad i, j = 1, 2, \ldots, n.$$

In R^3 the geometric vectors representing the standard 3-tuples are (1, 0, 0), (0, 1, 0), and (0, 0, 1). These lie on the rectangular coordinate axes. (See Figure 1.14.)

There are many examples of orthonormal sets. In R^4, for example, the set $\{\mathbf{u}_1, \mathbf{u}_2, \mathbf{u}_3, \mathbf{u}_4\}$ is orthonormal where $\mathbf{u}_1 = \left(\frac{1}{\sqrt{2}}, 0, \frac{1}{\sqrt{2}}, 0\right)$, $\mathbf{u}_2 = (\frac{1}{2}, \frac{1}{2}, -\frac{1}{2}, \frac{1}{2})$, $\mathbf{u}_3 = \left(0, \frac{1}{\sqrt{2}}, 0, \frac{-1}{\sqrt{2}}\right)$, and $\mathbf{u}_4 = (-\frac{1}{2}, \frac{1}{2}, \frac{1}{2}, \frac{1}{2})$. What about the set $\{\mathbf{u}_1, \mathbf{u}_2, \mathbf{u}_3\}$? This is also an orthonormal set. In fact, any nonempty subset of an orthonormal set is an orthonormal set. (See Exercises 1.5, Problem 15.) ■

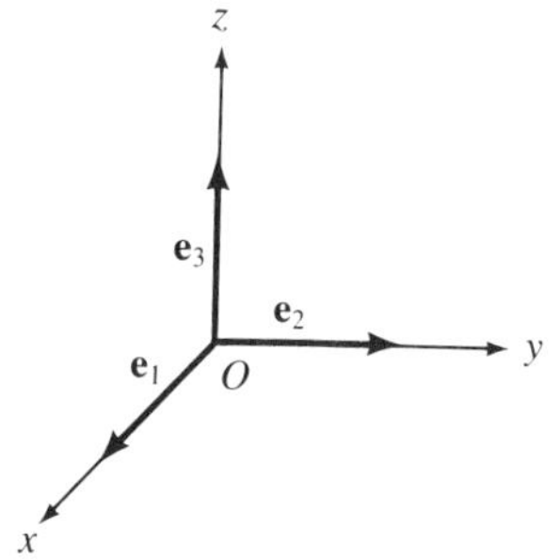

FIGURE 1.14

Orthogonal Set

Orthonormal Set

Definition 16

A set of vectors $\{\mathbf{u}_1, \mathbf{u}_2, \ldots, \mathbf{u}_s\}$ in R^n is an **orthogonal set** if $\mathbf{u}_i \cdot \mathbf{u}_j = 0$ for $i, j = 1, 2, \ldots, s$, $i \neq j$. If, in addition, $\mathbf{u}_1, \mathbf{u}_2, \ldots, \mathbf{u}_s$ are each unit vectors, the set $\{\mathbf{u}_1, \mathbf{u}_2, \ldots, \mathbf{u}_s\}$ is an **orthonormal** set.

If the vectors **u** and **v** are not orthogonal, it is often useful to consider the projection of **u** on **v** and the projection of **u** orthogonal to **v**. This is closely related to the idea of components of a vector in the direction of **v**, and orthogonal to **v**.

Example 35

Let $\mathbf{u} = (10, 5)$ and $\mathbf{v} = (3, 4)$. (See Figure 1.15.) We wish to write **u** as the sum of two vectors, one a multiple of **v** and the other orthogonal to **v**. That is, $\mathbf{u} = k\mathbf{v} + \mathbf{w}$ where **w** is orthogonal to **v**. Let θ be the angle between **u** and **v**. Then

$$\cos\theta = \frac{\mathbf{u}\cdot\mathbf{v}}{\|\mathbf{u}\|\,\|\mathbf{v}\|} = \frac{50}{(5\sqrt{5})(5)} = \frac{2}{\sqrt{5}}$$

The length of OQ is $(5\sqrt{5})(2/\sqrt{5}) = 10$. The vector $k\mathbf{v}$ is $10(\frac{3}{5}, \frac{4}{5}) = (6, 8)$. The vector **w** is $(10, 5) - (6, 8) = (4, -3)$. The vector $k\mathbf{v}$ is called the projection of **u** on **v**; the vector **w** is the projection of **u** orthogonal to **v**.

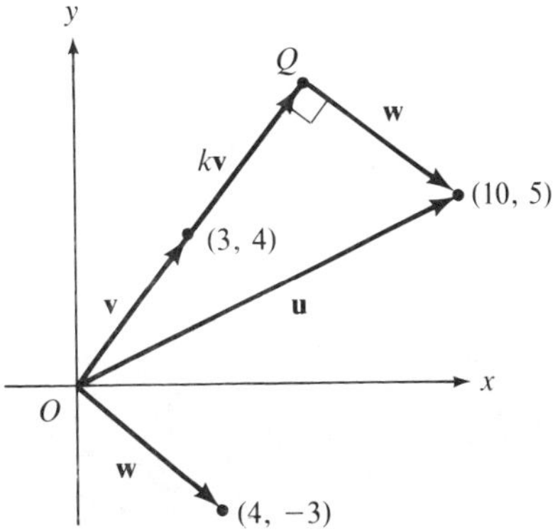

FIGURE 1.15 ■

Projection of u on v

Projection of u Orthogonal to v

Definition 17

If $\mathbf{v} \neq \mathbf{0}$, the **projection of u on v** is the vector $k\mathbf{v}$ with the property that $k\mathbf{v} + \mathbf{w} = \mathbf{u}$, where **w** is orthogonal to **v**. The **projection of u orthogonal to v** is the vector **w** such that **w** is orthogonal to **v** and $k\mathbf{v} + \mathbf{w} = \mathbf{u}$ for some k.

Theorem 10 The projection of $\mathbf{u}$ on $\mathbf{v}$ is $\dfrac{\mathbf{u} \cdot \mathbf{v}}{\mathbf{v} \cdot \mathbf{v}}\mathbf{v}$. Its length is $\dfrac{|\mathbf{u} \cdot \mathbf{v}|}{\|\mathbf{v}\|}$.

Proof By definition, $\mathbf{u} = k\mathbf{v} + \mathbf{w}$, so that $\mathbf{u} \cdot \mathbf{v} = k\mathbf{v} \cdot \mathbf{v} + \mathbf{w} \cdot \mathbf{v}$. But $\mathbf{w}$ is orthogonal to $\mathbf{v}$, so $\mathbf{w} \cdot \mathbf{v} = 0$. This implies $k = \dfrac{\mathbf{u} \cdot \mathbf{v}}{\mathbf{v} \cdot \mathbf{v}}$. Thus, the projection of $\mathbf{u}$ on $\mathbf{v}$ is $\dfrac{\mathbf{u} \cdot \mathbf{v}}{\mathbf{v} \cdot \mathbf{v}}\mathbf{v}$, and its length is $\dfrac{|\mathbf{u} \cdot \mathbf{v}|}{\|\mathbf{v}\|^2}\|\mathbf{v}\| = \dfrac{|\mathbf{u} \cdot \mathbf{v}|}{\|\mathbf{v}\|}$.

Corollary The projection of $\mathbf{u}$ orthogonal to $\mathbf{v}$ is $\mathbf{w} = \mathbf{u} - \dfrac{\mathbf{u} \cdot \mathbf{v}}{\mathbf{v} \cdot \mathbf{v}}\mathbf{v}$. □

The ideas of parallelism and perpendicularity enable us to define planes in spaces of n-tuples. Consider first lines and planes in R^2 and R^3. A line in R^2 or R^3 is determined by a direction and a point on the line.

Example 36 We wish to find the equation of a line through the fixed point $P_0 = (2, -1, 3)$ and parallel to $\mathbf{u} = (1, 3, 5)$. The point $P\,(x, y, z)$ is on the line if PP_0 is parallel to $\mathbf{u}$. Since PP_0 is the vector $(x - 2, y + 1, z - 3)$, PP_0 is parallel to $\mathbf{u}$ provided $(x - 2, y + 1, z - 3) = k(1, 3, 5)$, where k is a real number. We can write this as three separate equations:

$$\begin{aligned} x - 2 &= k \\ y + 1 &= 3k \\ z - 3 &= 5k \end{aligned}$$

These equations are called the parametric equations of the line. When k is set equal to any real number, these equations give the coordinates of a point on the line. ■

We make the convention that $P\,(x, y, z)$ represents a point and $\mathbf{x}$ represents the vector OP, where O is the point $(0, 0, 0)$. Similarly, if $P_0\,(x_0, y_0, z_0)$ is a fixed point $\mathbf{x}_0$ represents the vector OP_0. The equation of a line containing the fixed point P_0 and parallel to the vector $\mathbf{u}$ can be written in vector form as the set of all $P\,(x, y, z)$ such that $\mathbf{x} - \mathbf{x}_0 = k\mathbf{u}$. Thus the line consists of the endpoints of all vectors $\mathbf{x} = \mathbf{x}_0 + k\mathbf{u}$. (See Figure 1.16.)

A plane in R^3 is determined by a point in the plane and a vector perpendicular to the plane called a normal vector. If $P_0\,(x_0, y_0, z_0)$ is the fixed point and $\mathbf{u}$ is a normal vector, the point $P(x, y, z)$ lies in the plane if and only if the vector $\mathbf{x} - \mathbf{x}_0$ is perpendicular to $\mathbf{u}$—that is, $(\mathbf{x} - \mathbf{x}_0) \cdot \mathbf{u} = 0$. (See Figure 1.17.)

This is often written $(x - x_0, y - y_0, z - z_0) \cdot (a, b, c) = 0$, where $\mathbf{u} = (a, b, c)$, or $ax + by + cz = d$, where $d = \mathbf{x}_0 \cdot \mathbf{u}$, the customary linear equation in three unknowns. We get exactly the same set of points and an equivalent equation if $\mathbf{u}$ is replaced by any nonzero multiple of $\mathbf{u}$.

The idea of a plane can be extended to R^n. If $n \geqslant 4$, the word *hyperplane* is usually used rather than plane, but the equation has the same form.

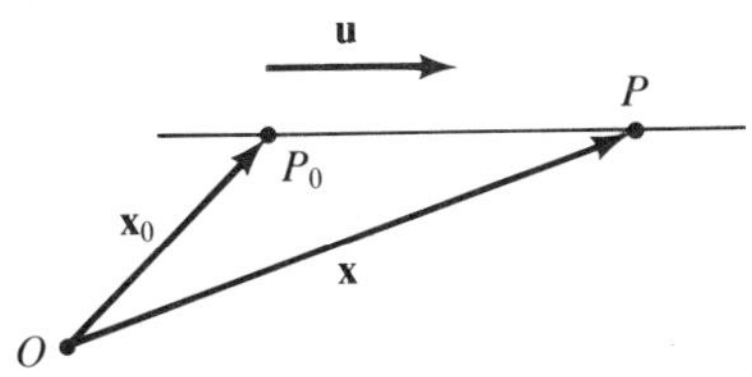

FIGURE 1.16

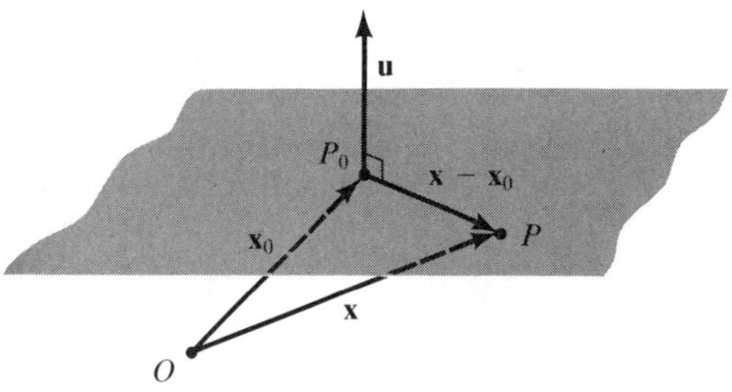

FIGURE 1.17

Hyperplane

Definition 18

A **hyperplane** is determined by a point P_0 in the hyperplane and a vector $\mathbf{u}$ orthogonal to the hyperplane. Its equation in vector form is $(\mathbf{x} - \mathbf{x}_0) \cdot \mathbf{u} = 0$.

If $\mathbf{u} = (a_1, a_2, \ldots, a_n)$ and $\mathbf{x} = (x_1, x_2, \ldots, x_n)$, this equation can also be written in the form

$$a_1 x_1 + a_2 x_2 + \cdots + a_n x_n = d, \qquad \text{where } d = \mathbf{x}_0 \cdot \mathbf{u}$$

The equation $a_1x_1 + a_2x_2 + \cdots + a_nx_n = d$ is a linear equation in n unknowns, an obvious generalization of the equation of a plane in R^3.

Example 37 The equation of a plane through $(1, -1, 3)$ and perpendicular to the vector $(3, 1, -2)$ is

$$\begin{aligned} (x - 1, y + 1, z - 3) \cdot (3, 1, -2) &= 0 \\ 3x - 3 + y + 1 - 2z + 6 &= 0 \\ 3x + y - 2z &= -4 \end{aligned}$$

Similarly, the equation of a hyperplane through $(2, 1, -1, 3, -2)$ and orthogonal to the vector $(1, 2, -1, -3, 1)$ is $(\mathbf{x} - \mathbf{x}_0) \cdot \mathbf{u} = 0$, or

$$(x_1 - 2, x_2 - 1, x_3 + 1, x_4 - 3, x_5 + 2) \cdot (1, 2, -1, -3, 1) = 0$$

This yields $x_1 + 2x_2 - x_3 - 3x_4 + x_5 = -6$.

The equation $3x_1 - 5x_2 + 3x_3 + x_4 = 11$ can be thought of as the equation of a hyperplane in R^4 normal to the vector $\mathbf{u} = (3, -5, 3, 1)$. ■

Now suppose $n = 2$—that is, $\mathbf{x} = (x, y)$, $\mathbf{u} = (a, b)$ and $\mathbf{x}_0 = (x_0, y_0)$. The equation $(\mathbf{x} - \mathbf{x}_0) \cdot \mathbf{u} = 0$ yields $ax + by = d$, where $d = ax_0 + by_0$. We are accustomed to thinking of this as a line. However, since the space itself (a plane) has only two dimensions, the concept of a hyperplane and a line coincide. This is discussed in the following example.

Example 38 Let $P = (-1, 2)$ be a fixed point and $\mathbf{u} = (3, 4)$ be a vector in R^2. Write an equation of the line through P parallel to $\mathbf{u}$.

The parametric form of the equation is $x = -1 + 3k$, $y = 2 + 4k$. Now eliminate k from these two expressions; $k = (x + 1)/3$; $y = 2 + 4(x + 1)/3$. After simplification this equation becomes

$$4x - 3y = -10$$

The vector $(4, -3)$ is perpendicular to the vector $(3, 4)$. This equation is the equation of a "plane" through $(-1, 2)$ and normal to $(4, -3)$. Notice that $(-1, 2) \cdot (4, -3) = -10$. ■

The following theorem sums up this discussion.

Theorem 11 Let P_0 be a fixed point, $\mathbf{x}_0$ be the vector OP_0, and $\mathbf{u}$ be a fixed vector. The equation

$$(\mathbf{x} - \mathbf{x}_0) \cdot \mathbf{u} = 0$$

or

$$a_1x_1 + a_2x_2 + \cdots + a_nx_n = d$$

represents a line in R^2, a plane in R^3, or a hyperplane in R^n, $n \geqslant 4$, passing through P_0 and orthogonal to $\mathbf{u}$.

Proof The points $\mathbf{x}$ in the plane are terminal points of the vector $\mathbf{x}$ with initial point the origin and such that the vector $\mathbf{x} - \mathbf{x}_0$ is orthogonal to $\mathbf{u}$. The equation states the orthogonality condition. □

The interpretation of the linear equation $a_1x_1 + a_2x_2 + \cdots + a_nx_n = d$ as a line, plane, or hyperplane will be useful in the next chapter in discussing the solution set of a system of linear equations.

Example 39 illustrates the use of the ideas of this section in a practical situation.

Example 39 In searching for oil it is important to obtain as much information as possible about the position of the subsurface bedding planes, since this is helpful in choosing new well locations. An electronic instrument called a *dipmeter* is lowered into the well to take resistivity readings on the surrounding rock. From the information obtained in this way, it is possible to estimate an equation of a potential oil-bearing rock formation. From this equation the dip and azimuth of the rock formation must be derived. (See Figure 1.18.) Assume that the well bore is vertical. In Figure 1.18 the positive x-axis is in the south direction, the positive y-axis in the east direction, and the z-axis is vertical. Assume that an equation of the potential rock-bearing plane at a certain depth is found to be $x - 2y + 12z = -36$. Calculate the dip angle and the azimuth.

The dip angle is the angle between the vector $(0, 0, 1)$ and the vector normal to the bedding plane. In this case $\mathbf{n} = (1, -2, 12)$. The dip angle θ is found from $\cos\theta = 12/\sqrt{149} = 0.98$, so that $\theta = 10.64°$.

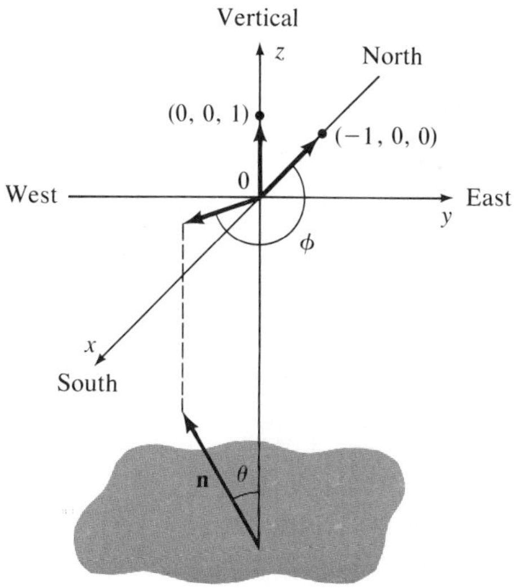

FIGURE 1.18

The azimuth, ϕ, is the angle measured from the north direction in a clockwise direction to the projection of the normal onto the xy-plane. The projection of $(1, -2, 12)$ onto the plane $z = 0$ is $(1, -2, 0)$. The north direction is $(-1, 0, 0)$, thus $\cos \phi = \dfrac{(1, -2, 0) \cdot (-1, 0, 0)}{\sqrt{5}} = -0.447$. The azimuth, ϕ, is 243.43°. ■

SUMMARY Two vectors **u** and **v** are orthogonal if $\mathbf{u} \cdot \mathbf{v} = 0$. If **u** and **v** are nonzero vectors, the angle between them is defined by

$$\cos \theta = \frac{\mathbf{u} \cdot \mathbf{v}}{\|\mathbf{u}\| \, \|\mathbf{v}\|}$$

A set of vectors $\{\mathbf{u}_1, \mathbf{u}_2, \ldots, \mathbf{u}_n\}$ is an orthonormal set if $\mathbf{u}_i \cdot \mathbf{u}_j = 0$, $i, j = 1, 2, \ldots, n$, $i \neq j$, and $\mathbf{u}_i \cdot \mathbf{u}_i = 1$, $i = 1, 2, \ldots, n$.

If the vector **u** is written in the form

$$\mathbf{u} = k\mathbf{v} + \mathbf{w}$$

where **v** is a nonzero vector and $\mathbf{v} \cdot \mathbf{w} = 0$, $k\mathbf{v}$ is the projection of **u** on **v**, and **w** is the projection of **u** orthogonal to **v**.

A linear equation of the form $a_1x_1 + a_2x_2 + \cdots + a_nx_n = d$ represents a line in R^2, a plane in R^3, or a hyperplane in R^n. The vector $\mathbf{u} = (a_1, a_2, \ldots, a_n)$ is orthogonal to the line, plane, or hyperplane.

EXERCISES 1.5

1. Find $\cos\theta$, where θ is the angle between the vectors **u** and **v**.
   a. $\mathbf{u} = (1, 0, 1)$, $\mathbf{v} = (1, 1, 0)$
   b. $\mathbf{u} = (1, -1, 1)$, $\mathbf{v} = (1, 1, 1)$
   c. $\mathbf{u} = (2, 1, 2)$, $\mathbf{v} = (1, 1, 0)$
   d. $\mathbf{u} = (1, 3, -1, 4)$, $\mathbf{v} = (0, 1, 0, 1)$

2. Let $\mathbf{u} = (1, 1, 2)$ and $\mathbf{v} = (k, 0, 3)$.
   a. Choose k so that **u** and **v** are orthogonal.
   b. Choose k so that the angle between **u** and **v** is 30°.

3. In R^2 draw the geometric vectors $\mathbf{u} = (1, 3)$, $\mathbf{v} = (3, 1)$, and $\mathbf{w} = (-3, 1)$. Of these three vectors, which two are orthogonal to each other?

4. Let $\mathbf{u} = (1, 1, 1, 1)$, $\mathbf{v} = (1, -1, 2, -2)$, $\mathbf{w} = (1, 1, -1, 2)$, $\mathbf{x} = (1, 1, 2, -2)$, and $\mathbf{y} = (1, 0, -1, 0)$. Among these 4-tuples find all orthogonal pairs.

5. a. Write the parametric equations of a line passing through $(1, 2)$ and parallel to the vector $(3, -1)$.
   b. Write the equation of a line through $(1, 2)$ and perpendicular to the vector $(1, 3)$. Show that the lines in (a) and (b) are the same.

6. Write the parametric equations of the line in R^3 containing the point $(1, 1, 1)$ and parallel to the vector $\mathbf{u} = (1, 3, -2)$.

7. a. Let $P_1 = (1, 2, -1)$ and $P_2 = (2, 1, 5)$. Write an equation of the plane passing through P_1 and normal to the vector P_1P_2.
   b. Write an equation of the plane passing through the origin and normal to the vector P_1P_2.

8. a. Write an equation of the line containing $P_1 = (1, 2, -1)$ and $P_2 = (2, 1, 5)$.
   b. Write an equation of the line containing the origin and parallel to the vector P_1P_2.

9. A plane in R^3 has equation $2x + y - 7z = 13$.
   a. Write an equation of a plane parallel to this plane and passing through the origin.
   b. Write an equation of a plane parallel to this plane and passing through $(1, -1, 4)$.
   c. Write an equation of the line perpendicular to this plane and passing through $(1, -1, 4)$.

10. The angle between planes or hyperplanes is defined to be the angle between their normal vectors. Find the cosine of the angle between the hyperplanes $2x_1 + 3x_2 + x_3 - x_4 = 4$ and $x_1 - 2x_2 + x_3 - 3x_4 = 7$.

11. Of the four hyperplanes, which are parallel to each other? Which are orthogonal to each other? (See Problem 10.)
    Plane 1: $3x_1 - 2x_2 + 4x_3 - x_4 = 7$
    Plane 2: $2x_1 + 3x_2 - x_3 - 4x_4 = 2$
    Plane 3: $3x_1 + 2x_2 + 4x_3 - x_4 = 3$
    Plane 4: $3x_1 - 2x_2 + 4x_3 - x_4 = 1$

12. a. Show that $\{\mathbf{u}_1, \mathbf{u}_2, \mathbf{u}_3\}$ is an orthonormal set, where $\mathbf{u}_1 = (\frac{2}{3}, -\frac{2}{3}, \frac{1}{3})$, $\mathbf{u}_2 = (\frac{1}{3}, \frac{2}{3}, \frac{2}{3})$, $\mathbf{u}_3 = (\frac{2}{3}, \frac{1}{3}, -\frac{2}{3})$.
    b. Let **A** be the matrix with columns the triples $\mathbf{u}_1, \mathbf{u}_2, \mathbf{u}_3$. Calculate $\mathbf{AA}^T$.

13. a. Show that the set $\{\mathbf{v}_1, \mathbf{v}_2, \mathbf{v}_3\}$ is an orthogonal set but not an orthonormal set, where $\mathbf{v}_1 = (1, 1, 1)$, $\mathbf{v}_2 = (2, -1, -1)$, $\mathbf{v}_3 = (0, 1, -1)$.
    b. Let **B** be the matrix
    $$\begin{bmatrix} 1 & 1 & 1 \\ 2 & -1 & -1 \\ 0 & 1 & -1 \end{bmatrix}$$
    Calculate $\mathbf{BB}^T$.
    c. What is the geometric meaning of the diagonal elements in the product $\mathbf{BB}^T$?

14. Write an orthonormal set consisting of vectors parallel to the vectors in Problem 13.

15. Show that any nonempty subset of an orthonormal set is also an orthonormal set.

16. In Section 1.2 the matrix $\begin{bmatrix} \cos\theta & -\sin\theta \\ \sin\theta & \cos\theta \end{bmatrix}$ was used to rotate axes in R^2 through an angle of θ. Show that the rows of this matrix form an orthonormal set. Do the columns also form an orthonormal set?

17. a. Let $\mathbf{u} = (a_1, a_2, a_3)$ and $\mathbf{v} = (b_1, b_2, b_3)$. The vector $\mathbf{u} \times \mathbf{v} = (a_2b_3 - a_3b_2, a_3b_1 - a_1b_3, a_1b_2 - a_2b_1)$. Show that $\mathbf{u} \cdot \mathbf{u} \times \mathbf{v} = 0$ and that $\mathbf{v} \cdot \mathbf{u} \times \mathbf{v} = 0$.
    b. Write a vector perpendicular to $(1, 1, -1)$ and $(2, 0, 3)$.

18. Use the preceding problem to find an equation of a plane containing the three points $P_1 = (1, 2, -1)$, $P_2 = (3, 0, 4)$, and $P_3 = (-1, -1, 5)$.

19. Let $\mathbf{u} = (a, b, c)$. Let α be the angle between $\mathbf{u}$ and $\mathbf{e}_1$, β the angle between $\mathbf{u}$ and $\mathbf{e}_2$, and γ the angle between $\mathbf{u}$ and $\mathbf{e}_3$. Calculate $\cos\alpha$, $\cos\beta$, and $\cos\gamma$. These are referred to as the *direction cosines* of OP, where $P = (a, b, c)$.

20. Show that the direction cosines of OP have the property that $\cos^2\alpha + \cos^2\beta + \cos^2\gamma = 1$.

21. In Example 39, the dip and azimuth of a bedding plane were defined. Find the dip and azimuth for bedding planes with the following equations:
  a. $5x + 12z = -30$
  b. $3x - 2y + 3z = -18$

Supplemental Topic

Geometric Proofs

22. Find the perpendicular distance from a point to a plane. (*Hint*: Let P_0 be a point in the plane, and $\mathbf{n}$ be a normal vector. Let W be the end point of the vector $\mathbf{w}$. We wish to find the perpendicular distance from W to the plane.
  a. Find the projection of the vector $\mathbf{w} - \mathbf{x}_0$ on the normal vector $\mathbf{n}$.
  b. Use this projection to obtain the distance from W to the plane. (See Figure 1.19.)

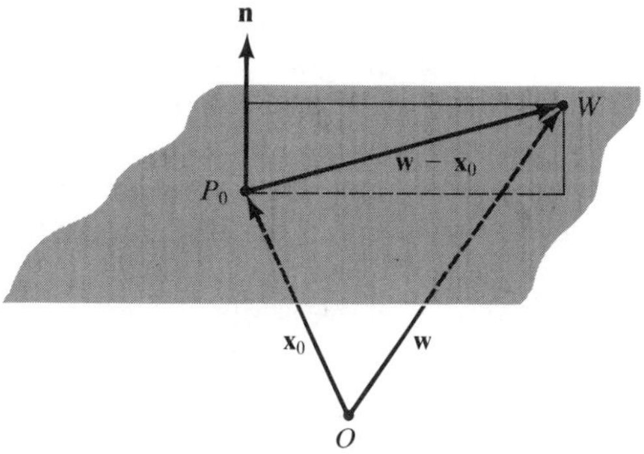

FIGURE 1.19

  c. Derive the usual formula for the distance from a point to a plane in R^3, using $\mathbf{n} = (a, b, c)$, $\mathbf{x}_0 = (x_0, y_0, z_0)$, and $\mathbf{w} = (x, y, z)$.

23. Show that a parallelogram is a rectangle if and only if the diagonals are the same length.

24. Show that the diagonals of a rhombus are perpendicular to each other.

25. The area of a trapezoid is half the sum of the lengths of the parallel sides times the distance between them. Find a formula for the area of the parallelogram with sides $\mathbf{u}$ and $\mathbf{v}$.

1.6 *Applications: You and the Computer*

In this section we discuss further examples and applications with one important addition: the use of software that makes solving realistic linear algebra problems possible. In many applications, computations with matrices cannot be completed without the help of computers. When digital computers became generally available in the early 1950s, some of the most significant problems they solved involved matrix methods in statistics, linear programming, and solutions of systems of equations. Over the course of many years, professionally written routines for handling matrix operations have become available in a variety of computer languages. You are the ultimate benefactor of over 40 years of effort in developing good matrix-handling programs that will run on today's modern microcomputers.

Our point of view is that it is not so important that you write each and every program yourself (although we encourage you to try your hand at writing a few). We want you to know that programs do exist for making matrix operations easy to undertake. Some useful programs are included at the end of this book. You might want to study them or even modify them if you wish. Be warned, however, that producing truly user-friendly software is a time-consuming and exacting task. The reward is an elegant program that performs quickly, accurately, and without unpleasant surprises.

Example 40

Matrix Products

One of the most far-reaching definitions of this chapter is that of matrix multiplication. What better program to have at hand than one that will multiply matrices? The following program outline illustrates what we need to consider before coding such a program. The symbol := is read "becomes" or "is given the value of." In deference to the widely used terminology in programming, a matrix in computer memory is a two-dimensional array.

```
 INPUT DATA:        ARRAY  A[1..M,  1..N] of real numbers;
                    ARRAY  B[1..P,  1..Q] of real numbers;
OUTPUT DATA:        ARRAY  C[1..R,  1..S] of real numbers.

<Start of Program>
      If N <> P Then report "Matrices are not compatible for
                             multiplication"
      Else
        Begin
          R := M
          S := Q
          For J := 1 to R Do
            For K := 1 to S Do
              Begin
                Sum := Ø.Ø
                For I := 1 to N Do
                  Sum := Sum  +  A[J,I] * B[I,K]
                C[J,K] := Sum
              End   { Do }
          Write C
        End  { Else }
<End of Program>
```

At this point, this outline can be coded into whatever language is most convenient, such as, BASIC, FORTRAN, or Pascal. Some languages—for example, APL—are designed for doing matrix manipulations and would reduce much of this outline to a few simple commands. But no matter how the outline is actually *implemented* into some computer code, it is important *first* to be sure of the soundness of the logic behind it. ■

Example 41

Matrix Powers

Now that we know how to multiply compatible matrices, we can solve surprisingly useful problems by raising a *square* matrix to powers. Thus, if $\mathbf{A} = [a_{ij}]_{n \times n}$ is a given matrix, we can find $\mathbf{A}^2 = \mathbf{AA}$ by using the previous program. Higher powers of $\mathbf{A}$ are then found iteratively; that is, by building up through higher and higher exponents. To find $\mathbf{A}^{10}$, for example, we find $\mathbf{A}^{10} = \mathbf{A}^9\mathbf{A}$, $\mathbf{A}^9 = \mathbf{A}^8\mathbf{A}$, and so on. It is also useful to find sums of the form $\mathbf{A} + \mathbf{A}^2 + \mathbf{A}^3 + \cdots + \mathbf{A}^n$, certainly a formidable computational task.

How would we approach such a problem? Study the following outline to see one possibility. A completely coded program is provided for your use in the appendix.

```
   INPUT DATA:       ARRAY  A[1..N,  1..N] of real numbers;
                     HIGHESTPOWER, an integer;
  OUTPUT DATA:       ARRAY  P[1..N,  1..N] of real numbers;
                     ARRAY  S[1..N,  1..N] of real numbers;
NEEDED STORAGE:      ARRAY  C[1..N,  1..N] of real numbers.

<Start of Program>
      P := A         {Initialize P equal to A; P is current power
                      of A}
      S := A         {Initialize S equal to A; S is the sum of
                      all powers of A}
      If HIGHESTPOWER = 1 Then EXIT
        ELSE
          BEGIN
            FOR  J := 2 to HIGHESTPOWER Do
              BEGIN
                C := P * A    {Multiply previous power of A by A}
                P := C
                S := S + C    {Add current power of A to S}
              END  { DO }
            Write matrices P and S
          END  { ELSE }
<End of Program>
```

■

Example 42

There are many good, professionally written programs available to perform matrix arithmetic. Some will even carry out the computations used in several concepts that we examine in later chapters. Most of these programs are *command-driven*; that is, the user enters English words that describe what action or actions are desired, such as *change*, *display*, *edit*, *add*, *multiply*, or *compute*. We might wonder how we could expect a typical program of this kind to find $\mathbf{A}^2$, $\mathbf{A}^3$, $\mathbf{A}^4$, $\mathbf{A}^5$, and the sum of these powers when

$$\mathbf{A} = \begin{bmatrix} 1 & 2 & 1 \\ -1 & 2 & -1 \\ 3 & 2 & 1 \end{bmatrix}$$

The following example shows how we could carry out this computation with a command driven program that performs matrix arithmetic. Keep in mind that any program needs to know not only the entries in a matrix, but also what its size must be and by what symbol we would like the matrix called. Also, most programs can repeat back to the user the most recent command. The following example was run on MAX, a matrix algebra calculator available from Brooks/Cole. Everything written by the program is in italics, but commands written by the user are in normal type.

```
Command:  ZERO 3 3 A
Zero -- store the 3 by 3 zero matrix in A

      0.          0.          0.
      0.          0.          0.
      0.          0.          0.

Command:  CHANGE A
Change the entries in A

A( 1, 1): <      0.    > 1
A( 2, 1): <      0.    > -1
A( 3, 1): <      0.    > 3
A( 1, 2): <      0.    > 2
A( 2, 2): <      0.    > 2
A( 3, 2): <      0.    > 2
A( 1, 3): <      0.    > 1
A( 2, 3): <      0.    > -1
A( 3, 3): <      0.    > 1
If you are done making changes, type EXIT
A( 3, 3): <      1.    > EXIT

      1.          2.          1.
     -1.          2.         -1.
      3.          2.          1.

Command:  COMPUTE A + A^2 + A^3 + A^4 + A^5 SUM
Compute ((((A + (A^2)) + (A^3)) + (A^4)) + (A^5)) and store
in SUM

   -203.        -74.       -129.
     -9.       -378.         37.
   -295.         18.       -203.

Command:  QUIT
Exit

Do you really want to leave the program? <Yes> YES
```
■

With such a program at hand to find matrix powers and their sums, the next example is a pleasure to solve.

Example 43

Domination Matrices

The coach of State University's tennis team feels that the better players are ready for competition. However, she must rank her players from the strongest to the weakest within the group. She decides on the following scheme: all the players will compete against each other in such a way that each one is pitted against each of the others exactly once. She then defines

$$a_{ij} = \begin{cases} 1 & \text{if player } i \text{ beats player } j \\ 0 & \text{if this is not true} \end{cases}$$

She then constructs a *domination matrix* **D** for the eight players:

Player number	1	2	3	4	5	6	7	8
1	0	1	0	1	1	0	1	1
2	0	0	0	1	1	0	1	0
3	1	1	0	0	1	0	0	1
4	0	0	1	0	1	0	1	1
5	0	0	0	0	0	1	0	1
6	1	1	1	1	0	0	1	0
7	0	0	1	0	1	0	0	1
8	0	1	0	0	0	1	0	0

Luckily, the coach and some of her players are students of linear algebra. They define the *strength* of player i to be the sum of the entries in the ith row of $\mathbf{D} + \mathbf{D}^2$. They are measuring how many people player i has beaten directly or through one other player.*

$$\textbf{Sum} = \mathbf{D} + \mathbf{D}^2 = \begin{bmatrix} 0 & 2 & 2 & 2 & 4 & 2 & 3 & 4 \\ 0 & 0 & 2 & 1 & 3 & 1 & 2 & 3 \\ 1 & 3 & 0 & 2 & 3 & 2 & 2 & 3 \\ 1 & 2 & 2 & 0 & 3 & 2 & 1 & 4 \\ 1 & 2 & 1 & 1 & 0 & 2 & 1 & 1 \\ 2 & 3 & 3 & 3 & 5 & 0 & 4 & 4 \\ 1 & 2 & 1 & 0 & 2 & 2 & 0 & 3 \\ 1 & 2 & 1 & 2 & 1 & 1 & 2 & 0 \end{bmatrix} \qquad \begin{matrix} \text{Row Sums} \\ \text{(strength)} \\ 19 \\ 12 \\ 16 \\ 15 \\ 9 \\ 24 \\ 11 \\ 10 \end{matrix}$$

Thus, player 6 is judged to be the strongest of the eight. This might not seem obvious at first, since both players 1 and 6 have five wins apiece. But intuitively player 6 has beaten more of the "tougher" competition. ■

Example 44 **Computer Graphics**

One interesting application of linear algebra lies in computer graphics. A modern digital computer can store and update (that is, alter or modify) thousands of data values. Also, most microcomputers with sufficiently large memories can update

*MAX can find $\mathbf{D} + \mathbf{D}^2$ with a single command: COMPUTE D + D * D SUM.

pictures or drawings, incorporating these values on a video terminal. Computer graphics is essentially the study of how a computer can be used to store, change, and show pictorial information. To do this, each picture element (or *pixel*) on the video screen is represented as a coordinate (x, y), which we can write as a column matrix $\begin{bmatrix} x \\ y \end{bmatrix}$. When a computer's output is a graphics screen, sets of points represented by matrices $\begin{bmatrix} x \\ y \end{bmatrix}$ will be altered on the video terminal.

How can this be done? First we need to know what kind of action we wish the computer to take as it prepares a video image. We have already seen one: the general rotation of the axes around the origin. We can express the effect of a rotation through an angle θ by the matrix product

$$\begin{bmatrix} \cos\theta & -\sin\theta \\ \sin\theta & \cos\theta \end{bmatrix} \begin{bmatrix} x \\ y \end{bmatrix}$$

Thus it would seem reasonable that other changes to a point or set of points can be represented using a matrix product. For example, the matrix $\begin{bmatrix} 1 & -1 \\ -1 & 2 \end{bmatrix}$ could be thought of as representing a change (or transformation) to the set of points in the plane. What change results when the transformation acts on the point $(2, -1)$? Since $\begin{bmatrix} 1 & -1 \\ -1 & 2 \end{bmatrix}\begin{bmatrix} 2 \\ -1 \end{bmatrix} = \begin{bmatrix} 3 \\ -4 \end{bmatrix}$, the point $(2, -1)$ becomes point $(3, -4)$. In general the image of any point (x, y) under this transformation is given by the product

$$\begin{bmatrix} 1 & -1 \\ -1 & 2 \end{bmatrix} \begin{bmatrix} x \\ y \end{bmatrix} = \begin{bmatrix} x - y \\ -x + 2y \end{bmatrix}$$

The image is the point $(x - y, -x + 2y)$. ■

There are many transformations that can be represented by 2×2 matrices. The following table lists several of them. Test some of them as you study the table; you will be asked to work with them in the exercises.

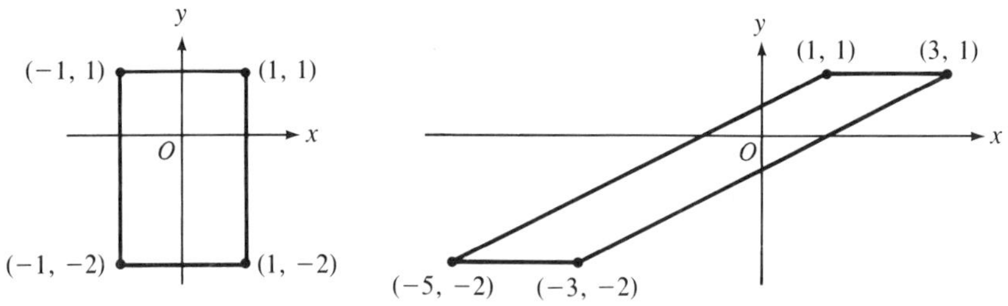

FIGURE 1.20

Transformation	*Explanation*	*2 × 2 Matrix*
Identity	All points remain unchanged	$\begin{bmatrix} 1 & 0 \\ 0 & 1 \end{bmatrix}$
Zero	All points removed to (0, 0)	$\begin{bmatrix} 0 & 0 \\ 0 & 0 \end{bmatrix}$
Scale change in x-direction	Stretch by a factor of a only in x-direction	$\begin{bmatrix} a & 0 \\ 0 & 1 \end{bmatrix}$
Reflect in y-axis	Exchange points (x, y) and $(-x, y)$	$\begin{bmatrix} -1 & 0 \\ 0 & 1 \end{bmatrix}$
Rotate 90° about origin	Send (x, y) to $(-y, x)$	$\begin{bmatrix} 0 & -1 \\ 1 & 0 \end{bmatrix}$
Shear in x-direction	Send (x, y) to $(x + by, y)$	$\begin{bmatrix} 1 & b \\ 0 & 1 \end{bmatrix}$

The effect of a shear in the x-direction is to add a multiple of the y-coordinate to the x-coordinate. The effect of the shear $\begin{bmatrix} 1 & 2 \\ 0 & 1 \end{bmatrix}$ on parallelogram P with vertices $(-1, 1)$, $(1, 1)$, $(1, -2)$ and $(-1, -2)$ is shown in Figure 1.20. Notice that the effect of the shear on each of the coordinates of P can be found in the single matrix product

$$\begin{bmatrix} 1 & 2 \\ 0 & 1 \end{bmatrix} \begin{bmatrix} -1 & 1 & 1 & -1 \\ 1 & 1 & -2 & -2 \end{bmatrix} = \begin{bmatrix} 1 & 3 & -3 & -5 \\ 1 & 1 & -2 & -2 \end{bmatrix}.$$

There is one transformation that cannot be represented by multiplication by a 2×2 matrix: a translation (or sliding) of points in the plane. Every such transformation can be defined by a motion in the x- and y-directions. For example, sliding from (1, 3) to (6, −8) can be described by *first* moving right 5 units from (1, 3) to (6, 3) and then moving down 11 units from (6, 3) to (6, −8). Any point (x, y) moved by this translation would have its image at $(x + 5, y - 11)$. Thus, if a matrix $\begin{bmatrix} a & b \\ c & d \end{bmatrix}$ represents such a translation, then

$$\begin{bmatrix} a & b \\ c & d \end{bmatrix} \begin{bmatrix} x \\ y \end{bmatrix} = \begin{bmatrix} x + 5 \\ y - 11 \end{bmatrix}$$

This must be true for *all* choices of points (x, y) if indeed we are moving the entire plane. However, this matrix equation cannot be solved for any choices of a, b, c, or d when $x = 0$ and $y = 0$. (Why?)

In Chapter 4 we will see a method for resolving this difficulty.

SUMMARY There are many important concepts applied in this chapter. Matrices can be defined whose entries measure the number of *connections* between objects, ideas, or even people. These connections mean different things in various contexts:

circuits, dominations, transition between states, and so on. Powers of these matrices are then seen to have many interesting interpretations and can be used to make predictions of the situation under study. More important, a matrix can be viewed as a transformation of the plane—that is, a function that describes how points can be uniformly moved. This interpretation of matrices is extremely useful in computer graphics. There are several easy-to-use computer programs available that will accurately carry out matrix calculations.

EXERCISES 1.6

1. Write a program in a language of your choice (or use an available program) that will read a given $m \times n$ matrix and print its transpose.

2. Use your program from Problem 1 to read the following matrices and print their transposes:

a. $\begin{bmatrix} 3 & 2 & 1 \\ 0 & 1 & -1 \end{bmatrix}$ **b.** $\begin{bmatrix} 2 & 1 \\ 3 & -2 \end{bmatrix}$

c. $\begin{bmatrix} 1 & 3 & -1 \\ 0 & 4 & 0 \\ 1 & 2 & -1 \end{bmatrix}$ **d.** $\begin{bmatrix} 0 & 1 & 3 \\ 1 & 2 & 8 \\ 3 & 8 & -1 \end{bmatrix}$

3. Write a program in a language of your choice (or use an available program) that will read a given $m \times n$ matrix $\mathbf{A}$ and then compute and print $\mathbf{A}^T\mathbf{A}$ and $\mathbf{A}\mathbf{A}^T$.

4. Use an available program of your choice to find $\mathbf{A}\mathbf{A}^T$ and $\mathbf{A}^T\mathbf{A}$ for each $\mathbf{A}$:

a. $\begin{bmatrix} 3 & 1 \\ 0 & -1 \end{bmatrix}$ **b.** $\begin{bmatrix} 2 & 1 \\ 3 & -2 \\ 0 & 1 \end{bmatrix}$

c. $[1 \quad -1 \quad 3]$ **d.** $\begin{bmatrix} 4 \\ -1 \end{bmatrix}$

5. Use the matrices in Problem 4 to verify the results in Theorem 6, part 3. Illustrate the other statements in Theorem 6 using the matrices in Problem 4 or other suitable matrices.

6. Write a program in a language of your choice (or use an existing program) that will read two nonzero n-tuples $\mathbf{v} = (x_1, x_2, \ldots, x_n)$ and $\mathbf{w} = (y_1, y_2, \ldots, y_n)$ and find their dot product $\mathbf{v} \cdot \mathbf{w}$, norms $\|\mathbf{v}\|$, $\|\mathbf{w}\|$, and the measure in radians of the angle θ between them.

7. Use a matrix arithmetic program of your choice to find $\mathbf{T}^3$ through $\mathbf{T}^{20}$ for

$$\mathbf{T} = \begin{bmatrix} 0.63 & 0.17 & 0.14 \\ 0.29 & 0.55 & 0.05 \\ 0.08 & 0.28 & 0.81 \end{bmatrix}$$

Describe the apparent behavior of $\mathbf{T}^j$ as j becomes large.

8. Suppose there are 10 ham radio operators around the country who decide to organize a private network among themselves to relay calls. Because of differences in equipment, the distances involved, unreliable weather conditions, and so on, not all of the operators can talk directly to all of the others. Let us create a *communications matrix* $\mathbf{A} = [a_{ij}]_{10 \times 10}$ by saying that

$$a_{ij} = \begin{cases} 1 & \text{if operator } \#i \text{ can talk directly to operator } \#j\ (i \neq j) \\ 0 & \text{if this is not possible} \end{cases}$$

Thus $a_{ii} = 0$ means that each operator cannot simultaneously send and receive his own signal. Let us assume that for this club, $\mathbf{A}$ is

$$\mathbf{A} = \begin{bmatrix} 0 & 1 & 0 & 1 & 0 & 0 & 0 & 0 & 0 & 1 \\ 1 & 0 & 0 & 0 & 1 & 1 & 1 & 0 & 0 & 0 \\ 0 & 0 & 0 & 0 & 0 & 1 & 0 & 0 & 1 & 0 \\ 0 & 0 & 1 & 0 & 0 & 1 & 0 & 0 & 0 & 0 \\ 1 & 0 & 0 & 0 & 0 & 0 & 1 & 0 & 1 & 1 \\ 1 & 0 & 0 & 0 & 1 & 0 & 1 & 1 & 0 & 0 \\ 1 & 0 & 1 & 0 & 0 & 0 & 0 & 1 & 1 & 0 \\ 0 & 1 & 0 & 1 & 0 & 0 & 0 & 0 & 0 & 1 \\ 0 & 0 & 0 & 1 & 1 & 0 & 1 & 0 & 0 & 0 \\ 0 & 0 & 0 & 1 & 1 & 0 & 1 & 0 & 1 & 0 \end{bmatrix}$$

a. Use the matrix power program (or a program of your choice) to compute $\mathbf{A}^2$, $\mathbf{A}^3$, $\mathbf{A}^4$, and $\mathbf{A} + \mathbf{A}^2 + \mathbf{A}^3 + \mathbf{A}^4$.
b. Give interpretations for $\mathbf{A}^2$ and $\mathbf{A}^3$.
c. What is the smallest value of **k** so that $\mathbf{A} + \mathbf{A}^2 + \mathbf{A}^3 + \cdots + \mathbf{A}^k$ has no zero entries (except possibly on the major diagonal)? What does this say about the effectiveness of the network?

9. Five friends, F_1, F_2, F_3, F_4, and F_5, always keep up on the latest gossip. If F_1 hears a piece of gossip, it gets passed on to F_2, F_3, and F_5; F_2 passes gossip on to F_3 and F_4; F_3 passes gossip to F_1 and F_5; F_4 passes gossip to everyone else; and F_5 repeats no gossip.
a. Let

$$a_{ij} = \begin{cases} 1 & \text{if } F_i \text{ passes gossip to } F_j \\ 0 & \text{if this is not true} \end{cases}$$

Write the matrix representing this state of affairs.
b. Suppose F_2 has just heard a tidbit and passes it on as described above. Who knows the gosssip after one step? Who finds out with one intermediary? Will all five friends know the gossip either directly from F_2 or second-hand?
c. Suppose F_3 hears a new piece of gossip. How many steps does it take for everyone to have heard it?

10. A matrix $\mathbf{S} = [a_{ij}]_{m \times m}$, in which all entries are nonnegative and all the column sums equal one, is called a *stochastic matrix*. For example, consider

$$\mathbf{S} = \begin{bmatrix} 0.19 & 0.11 & 0.24 \\ 0.63 & 0.07 & 0.39 \\ 0.18 & 0.82 & 0.37 \end{bmatrix}$$

Use a program of your choice to investigate the following facts about stochastic matrices.
a. Powers of stochastic matrices are stochastic matrices.
b. Powers of stochastic matrices eventually stabilize. This means that the entries of $\mathbf{S}^n$ approach limiting values as n becomes arbitrarily large. Based on your computations, can you conjecture what else may be true about these limiting values?

11. Five legislators are constantly influencing each other as shown by the following sociogram:

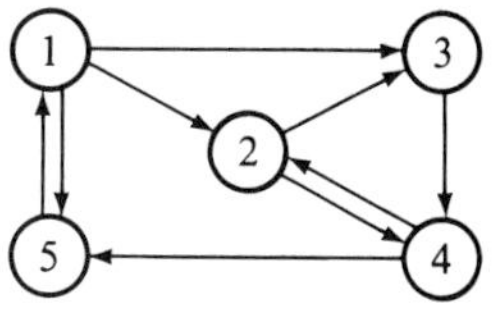

The arrows indicate the flow of direct influence between individuals.
a. Let

$$a_{ij} = \begin{cases} 1 & \text{if there is a direct influence from legislator } i \text{ to legislator } j \\ 0 & \text{if this is not true} \end{cases}$$

Write the matrix that corresponds to the diagram.
b. Find the matrix that shows the number of ways in which any one legislator can influence another using at most one intermediary.
c. Based on the ideas of Example 43, which legislator would you say is most influential among the five?

12. The concept of a *domination matrix* can be applied to the study of professional sports. For example, Rick Merrill of Houston, Texas, has extensively studied the National Football League's seasons from 1980 to 1985 to see if winners can be predicted using the ideas in Example 43. He numbered the 28 teams involved and created sequential files of team identification numbers and scores for each game played during each week of the 16-week season. The team-numbering scheme and the score matrix for the 1985 season are from Mr. Merrill's analysis. Each row and column number 1–28 in the matrix matches the corresponding team number. Because teams in the same conference can play each other more than once, the entries in the matrix are *total game scores*. Use the score matrix to decide which of the teams was the most dominant in that season.

NFL TEAMS

Num	*Team*	*Num*	*Team*	*Num*	*Team*	*Num*	*Team*	*Num*	*Team*	*Num*	*Team*
01	Buffalo	06	Bengals	10	Chargers	15	Redskins	20	Detroit	25	Falcons
02	Patriots	07	Browns	11	Raiders	16	St. Louis	21	Packers	26	49'ers
03	Miami	08	Steelers	12	Denver	17	Dallas	22	Vikings	27	LA Rams
04	NY Jets	09	Houston	13	Seattle	18	Eagles	23	Chicago	28	Saints
05	Colts			14	Chiefs	19	Giants	24	Tampa Bay		

1985 GAME SCORE MATRIX

0	17	14	10	38	17	7	24	20	16	0	0	0	0	0	0	0	17	0	0	0	20	0	0	0	0	0	0
31	0	44	33	72	34	20	0	0	0	20	0	20	0	0	0	0	0	0	23	26	0	7	32	0	0	0	0
51	43	0	28	64	0	0	24	23	0	0	30	0	31	0	0	0	0	0	21	34	0	38	41	0	0	0	0
69	29	40	0	60	29	37	0	0	0	0	0	17	0	0	0	0	0	0	20	24	0	6	62	0	0	0	0
58	46	33	37	0	0	0	3	34	0	0	10	0	7	0	0	0	0	0	14	37	0	10	31	0	0	0	0
23	23	0	20	0	0	33	63	72	41	6	0	24	0	24	27	50	0	35	0	0	0	0	0	0	0	0	0
17	24	0	10	0	34	0	26	49	21	20	0	13	0	7	24	7	0	35	0	0	0	0	0	0	0	0	0
30	0	20	0	45	45	17	0	50	44	0	23	0	36	23	23	13	0	10	0	0	0	0	0	0	0	0	0
0	0	26	0	16	71	27	7	0	37	0	20	0	23	13	20	10	0	14	0	0	0	0	0	0	0	0	0
54	0	0	0	0	44	7	54	35	0	61	54	56	65	0	0	0	20	0	0	0	17	0	0	0	0	0	0
0	35	0	31	0	13	21	0	0	68	0	48	16	39	0	0	0	0	0	0	0	0	0	0	34	10	16	23
0	0	26	0	15	0	0	31	31	40	42	0	40	44	0	0	0	0	0	0	0	0	0	0	44	17	16	34
0	13	0	14	0	28	31	0	0	75	36	34	0	31	0	0	0	0	0	0	0	0	0	0	30	6	24	27
0	0	0	0	20	0	0	28	20	58	46	23	34	0	0	0	0	0	0	0	0	0	0	0	38	3	0	47
0	0	0	0	0	27	14	30	16	0	0	0	0	0	0	54	21	23	26	24	0	0	10	0	44	8	0	0
0	0	0	0	0	41	27	10	10	0	0	0	0	0	26	0	38	21	20	0	43	0	0	0	0	0	14	28
0	0	0	0	0	24	20	27	17	0	0	0	0	0	57	45	0	48	58	21	0	0	0	0	24	16	0	0
21	0	0	0	0	0	0	0	0	14	0	0	0	0	31	54	33	0	10	0	0	60	0	0	23	13	6	21
0	0	0	0	0	30	33	28	35	0	0	0	0	0	38	61	50	37	0	0	20	0	0	22	0	0	24	21
0	6	31	31	6	0	0	0	0	0	0	0	0	0	3	0	26	0	0	0	33	54	20	46	28	23	0	0
0	20	24	3	10	0	0	0	0	0	0	0	0	0	0	28	0	0	23	69	0	47	17	41	0	0	17	38
27	0	0	0	0	0	0	0	0	21	0	0	0	0	0	0	0	63	0	37	34	0	33	57	13	28	10	23
0	20	24	19	17	0	0	0	0	0	0	0	0	0	45	0	44	0	0	61	39	60	0	65	36	26	0	0
0	14	38	28	23	0	0	0	0	0	0	0	0	0	0	16	0	0	20	28	17	23	47	0	0	0	27	13
0	0	0	0	0	0	0	0	0	0	24	28	26	10	10	0	10	17	0	27	0	14	0	0	0	33	36	47
0	0	0	0	0	0	0	0	0	0	34	16	19	31	35	0	31	24	0	21	0	21	10	0	73	0	48	48
0	0	0	0	0	0	0	0	0	0	6	20	35	16	0	46	0	17	19	0	34	13	0	31	31	41	0	31
0	0	0	0	0	0	0	0	0	0	13	23	3	27	0	16	0	23	13	0	14	30	0	20	34	39	39	0

13. Find the image of the given point using the given transformation.

a. $(-2, 4)$; $\begin{bmatrix} 1 & 0 \\ 0 & 1 \end{bmatrix}$

b. $(3, -1)$; $\begin{bmatrix} 3 & 0 \\ 0 & 1 \end{bmatrix}$

c. $(2, 2)$; $\begin{bmatrix} \frac{1}{2} & 0 \\ 0 & 2 \end{bmatrix}$

d. $(-4, -3)$; $\begin{bmatrix} 1 & 2 \\ 0 & 1 \end{bmatrix}$

e. $(1, -1)$; $\begin{bmatrix} \frac{1}{2}\sqrt{2} & -\frac{1}{2}\sqrt{2} \\ \frac{1}{2}\sqrt{2} & \frac{1}{2}\sqrt{2} \end{bmatrix}$

14. Find the image of the given point using the given transformation.

a. $(4, \frac{1}{2})$; $\begin{bmatrix} 1 & 0 \\ 0 & 2 \end{bmatrix}$

b. $(-1, 3)$; $\begin{bmatrix} 0 & 1 \\ 1 & 0 \end{bmatrix}$

c. $(-3, -5)$; $\begin{bmatrix} 1 & 0 \\ 3 & 1 \end{bmatrix}$

d. $(-1, 2)$; $\begin{bmatrix} 1 & 3 \\ 2 & 1 \end{bmatrix}$

e. $(-2, 1)$; $\begin{bmatrix} -1 & 0 \\ 0 & -1 \end{bmatrix}$

15. Describe the action of the following transformations. The first problem is worked as an example.

a. $\begin{bmatrix} 1 & 0 \\ 0 & -2 \end{bmatrix}$

Answer:

$$\begin{bmatrix} 1 & 0 \\ 0 & -2 \end{bmatrix}\begin{bmatrix} x \\ y \end{bmatrix} = \begin{bmatrix} x \\ -2y \end{bmatrix}$$

Rescale by factor of 2 in the negative direction of the y-axis.

b. $\begin{bmatrix} 2 & 0 \\ 0 & 1 \end{bmatrix}$ c. $\begin{bmatrix} 2 & 0 \\ 0 & 3 \end{bmatrix}$

d. $\begin{bmatrix} 1 & 0 \\ 0 & -1 \end{bmatrix}$ e. $\begin{bmatrix} -1 & 0 \\ 0 & 1 \end{bmatrix}$

f. $\begin{bmatrix} 0 & 1 \\ 1 & 0 \end{bmatrix}$ g. $\begin{bmatrix} 1 & 3 \\ 0 & 1 \end{bmatrix}$

h. $\begin{bmatrix} 1 & 0 \\ 2 & 1 \end{bmatrix}$ i. $\begin{bmatrix} 1 & 3 \\ 2 & 1 \end{bmatrix}$

j. $\begin{bmatrix} \frac{1}{2}\sqrt{3} & -\frac{1}{2} \\ \frac{1}{2} & \frac{1}{2}\sqrt{3} \end{bmatrix}$ k. $\begin{bmatrix} 0 & 1 \\ -1 & 0 \end{bmatrix}$

16. Use the product of two 2×2 matrices to describe the effect of a 90° rotation of the line segment joining $(-1, 2)$ and $(3, 4)$.

17. Use the product of two 2×2 matrices to describe the effect of a 60° rotation of the line segment joining $(2, 0)$ and $(0, 4)$.

18. Use the product of the column matrix $\begin{bmatrix} x \\ 2x - 1 \end{bmatrix}$ and a 2×2 matrix to describe the change to the line $y = 2x - 1$ when rotated $+45°$.

19. Describe the change to the line $y = -x + 1$ when subjected to the shear $\begin{bmatrix} 1 & 0 \\ 2 & 1 \end{bmatrix}$.

20. Design a 2×2 matrix to represent a transformation that will contract all x-values by a factor of $\frac{1}{2}$ and expand all y-values by a factor of $\frac{3}{2}$.

21. Design a 2×2 matrix to represent a shear transformation with a multiple of 3 in both the x- and y-directions.

22. What two matrices, when multiplied together, describe a transformation that is *first* a rotation of $+90°$ and *second* a shear in the x-direction by a factor of 2? Pay close attention to the order in which the matrices are to be multiplied. What happens if the transformations are performed in the opposite order?

23. What two matrices, when multiplied together, describe a transformation that is *first* a shear in the y-direction by a factor of 3 *followed* by a rotation of $-135°$? Pay close attention to the order in which the matrices are to be multiplied.

2 Systems of Linear Equations

2.1 Equivalent Systems of Equations

In almost every area of activity there are situations that can be analyzed by examining a system of equations. Simple systems of equations are familiar from elementary algebra. Systems arising in such areas as engineering, economics, and business may involve many variables and require a computer to carry out the analysis. (See Section 2.5.) We begin by examining a systematic approach to solving a system of linear equations.

Suppose a set of equations involves n unknown quantities represented by $x_1, x_2, \ldots, x_n$. Let a_{ij} represent the real number that is the coefficient of x_j in the ith equation. Let $b_1, b_2, \ldots, b_m$ be given real numbers. The system of equations

$$\begin{array}{ccccccccc} a_{11}x_1 & + & a_{12}x_2 & + & \cdots & + & a_{1n}x_n & = & b_1 \\ a_{21}x_1 & + & a_{22}x_2 & + & \cdots & + & a_{2n}x_n & = & b_2 \\ \vdots & & \vdots & & & & \vdots & & \vdots \\ a_{m1}x_1 & + & a_{m2}x_2 & + & \cdots & + & a_{mn}x_n & = & b_m \end{array}$$

is a system of **simultaneous linear algebraic equations**. A **solution** of this system is a set of n numbers that, when substituted for the unknowns, make each of the m statements in the equations true. Such a set is said to **satisfy** the system. Each solution is an n-tuple of real numbers.

Some systems of equations are written in such a way that it is simple to read the solution.

Example 1 a. The system of equations

$$\begin{aligned} x_1 &= 1 \\ x_2 &= 3 \\ x_3 &= 5 \end{aligned}$$

is completely trivial. The only solution is obviously the triple $(1, 3, 5)$.

b. The system of equations

$$\begin{aligned} x_1 + x_2 - x_3 &= 7 \\ x_2 + x_3 &= 3 \\ x_3 &= 2 \end{aligned}$$

is triangular and can be solved by substituting from the third into the second ($x_2 + 2 = 3$, so $x_2 = 1$) and then from the third and second into the first ($x_1 + 1 - 2 = 7$, so $x_1 = 8$). This system also has only one solution, the triple $(8, 1, 2)$.

c. The system

$$\begin{aligned} x_1 - 2x_3 &= 1 \\ x_2 + x_3 &= 3 \end{aligned}$$

can be written as

$$\begin{aligned} x_1 + 0x_2 - 2x_3 &= 1 \\ x_2 + x_3 &= 3 \end{aligned}$$

If we assign x_3 an arbitrary value, $x_3 = k$, the system can be solved by substitution as if it were triangular: $x_3 = k$, $x_2 = 3 - k$, $x_1 = 1 + 2k$. In this case the solution is not unique. The solution set consists of all triples of the form $(1 + 2k, 3 - k, k)$, where k is any real number.

d. The system of equations

$$\begin{aligned} 2x_1 + 5x_2 + x_3 &= 5 \\ x_1 + 4x_2 + 2x_3 &= 1 \\ 4x_1 + 10x_2 - x_3 &= 1 \end{aligned}$$

cannot be solved by inspection. We must look for a system of equations with the same solution set but in a more suitable form. ■

Equivalent Systems of Equations

Definition 1

Two systems of equations are **equivalent** if they have the same solution set.

Our goal is to derive a system of equations that is simpler than the original system but equivalent to it. To do this we need the following theorem.

Theorem 1 Systems of equations are equivalent if each can be obtained from the other by one or more of the following operations:

1. Interchange the order of the equations.
2. Multiply one equation by a nonzero scalar.
3. Add a multiple of one equation to another.

Proof Writing the equations in a different order cannot change the solutions. Neither can multiplying (or dividing) both sides of an equation by a nonzero constant. Not so obvious is the fact that applying the third operation also does not affect the solution set.

Let system 1 be a system of m equations in n unknowns. Use the notation $\mathbf{u}_i = (a_{i1}, a_{i2}, \ldots, a_{in})$ and $\mathbf{x} = (x_1, x_2, \ldots, x_n)$. System 1 can be written $\mathbf{u}_i \cdot \mathbf{x} = b_i$, $i = 1, 2, \ldots, m$. A particular n-tuple $\mathbf{x}_0$ is a solution of the system if

$$\mathbf{u}_i \cdot \mathbf{x}_0 = b_i \quad \text{for } i = 1, 2, \ldots, m.$$

We have then:

$$\text{System 1:} \quad \mathbf{u}_i \cdot \mathbf{x} = b_i, \quad i = 1, 2, \ldots, m; \qquad \text{solution set } S_1.$$

Add k times equation i to equation j. Then

$$\begin{aligned} \text{System 2:} \quad \mathbf{u}_i \cdot \mathbf{x} &= b_i, \quad i \neq j \\ (\mathbf{u}_j + k\mathbf{u}_i) \cdot \mathbf{x} &= b_j + kb_i; \qquad \text{solution set } S_2. \end{aligned}$$

Let $\mathbf{x}_0$ be a member of S_1. Then $\mathbf{u}_i \cdot \mathbf{x}_0 = b_i$ is a true statement for all i, $i = 1, 2, \ldots, m$. But $(\mathbf{u}_j + k\mathbf{u}_i) \cdot \mathbf{x}_0 = \mathbf{u}_j \cdot \mathbf{x}_0 + k\mathbf{u}_i \cdot \mathbf{x}_0$ so that, if $\mathbf{u}_j \cdot \mathbf{x}_0 = b_j$, and $\mathbf{u}_i \cdot \mathbf{x}_0 = b_i$, then $(\mathbf{u}_j + k\mathbf{u}_i) \cdot \mathbf{x}_0 = b_j + kb_i$ is a true statement. This means that $\mathbf{x}_0$ belongs to S_2 so that S_1 is contained in S_2.

Now suppose $\mathbf{x}_0$ is an element of S_2. Then the statements $\mathbf{u}_i \cdot \mathbf{x}_0 = b_i, i \neq j$ and $(\mathbf{u}_j + k\mathbf{u}_i) \cdot \mathbf{x}_0 = b_j + kb_i$ are true. Since $(\mathbf{u}_j + k\mathbf{u}_i) \cdot \mathbf{x}_0 + (-k)\mathbf{u}_i \cdot \mathbf{x}_0 = \mathbf{u}_j \cdot \mathbf{x}_0$ and $b_j + kb_i + (-k)b_i = b_j$, we see that $\mathbf{u}_j \cdot \mathbf{x}_0 = b_j$ is also true and $\mathbf{x}_0$ belongs to S_1. This implies that S_2 is contained in S_1. Thus S_2 and S_1 are the same set. □

The creation of equivalent systems is illustrated in Example 2.

Example 2 Find the solution set of the system of equations

$$\begin{aligned} 2x_1 + 5x_2 + x_3 &= 5 \\ x_1 + 4x_2 + 2x_3 &= 1 \\ 4x_1 + 10x_2 - x_3 &= 1 \end{aligned}$$

Solution

1. $\left.\begin{aligned} x_1 + 4x_2 + 2x_3 &= 1 \\ 2x_1 + 5x_2 + x_3 &= 5 \\ 4x_1 + 10x_2 - x_3 &= 1 \end{aligned}\right\}$

Write the second equation first.

The coefficient of x_1 in the new first equation is 1.

2. $\left.\begin{aligned} x_1 + 4x_2 + 2x_3 &= 1 \\ - 3x_2 - 3x_3 &= 3 \\ 4x_1 + 10x_2 - x_3 &= 1 \end{aligned}\right\}$

Add -2 times the first equation to the second.

Steps 2 and 3 replace the second equation and the third equation by equations in which the coefficient of x_1 is 0.

3. $\left.\begin{aligned} x_1 + 4x_2 + 2x_3 &= 1 \\ - 3x_2 - 3x_3 &= 3 \\ - 6x_2 - 9x_3 &= -3 \end{aligned}\right\}$

Add -4 times the first equation to the third.

These two steps could be combined.

4. $\left.\begin{aligned} x_1 + 4x_2 + 2x_3 &= 1 \\ x_2 + x_3 &= -1 \\ -6x_2 - 9x_3 &= -3 \end{aligned}\right\}$	Multiply the second equation by $-\frac{1}{3}$.	In the new second equation the coefficient of x_2 is 1.
5. $\left.\begin{aligned} x_1 + 4x_2 + 2x_3 &= 1 \\ x_2 + x_3 &= -1 \\ -3x_3 &= -9 \end{aligned}\right\}$	Add 6 times the second equation to the third.	Step 5 changes the third equation into one in which the coefficients of x_1 and x_2 are 0.
6. $\left.\begin{aligned} x_1 + 4x_2 + 2x_3 &= 1 \\ x_2 + x_3 &= -1 \\ x_3 &= 3 \end{aligned}\right\}$	Multiply the third equation by $-\frac{1}{3}$.	The coefficient of x_3 in the third equation is now 1.

The six steps have created a system of equations equivalent to the original system but with the triangular form of Example 1, part b. Back substitution could now give us the solution, consisting of the single triple $(11, -4, 3)$. Back substitution can be done more formally by continuing to use the operations described in Theorem 1.

7. $\left.\begin{aligned} x_1 + 4x_2 &= -5 \\ x_2 &= -4 \\ x_3 &= 3 \end{aligned}\right\}$	Add -2 times equation 3 to equation 1 and -1 times equation 3 to equation 2.	Step 7 eliminates x_3 from equations 1 and 2.
8. $\left.\begin{aligned} x_1 &= 11 \\ x_2 &= -4 \\ x_3 &= 3 \end{aligned}\right\}$	Add -4 times equation 2 to equation 1.	Step 8 eliminates x_2 from equation 1.

■

Systems of linear equations can be conveniently expressed using matrix notation.

Example 3 The system

$$\begin{aligned} 2x_1 + 5x_2 + x_3 &= 5 \\ x_1 + 4x_2 + 2x_3 &= 1 \\ 4x_1 + 10x_2 - x_3 &= 1 \end{aligned}$$

is a statement of equality between the 3×1 arrays

$$\begin{bmatrix} 2x_1 + 5x_2 + x_3 \\ x_1 + 4x_2 + 2x_3 \\ 4x_1 + 10x_2 - x_3 \end{bmatrix} = \begin{bmatrix} 5 \\ 1 \\ 1 \end{bmatrix}$$

Moreover, the matrix on the left is itself the matrix product

$$\begin{bmatrix} 2 & 5 & 1 \\ 1 & 4 & 2 \\ 4 & 10 & -1 \end{bmatrix} \begin{bmatrix} x_1 \\ x_2 \\ x_3 \end{bmatrix}$$

Thus the system of three equations in three unknowns can be written as the single matrix equation

$$\begin{bmatrix} 2 & 5 & 1 \\ 1 & 4 & 2 \\ 4 & 10 & -1 \end{bmatrix} \begin{bmatrix} x_1 \\ x_2 \\ x_3 \end{bmatrix} = \begin{bmatrix} 5 \\ 1 \\ 1 \end{bmatrix}$$

or $\mathbf{AX} = \mathbf{B}$, where $\mathbf{A}$ is a matrix of scalars (the coefficients of the unknowns), $\mathbf{X}$ is a 3×1 array to be determined (the array of unknowns), and $\mathbf{B}$ is a 3×1 array of scalars (the constants on the right-hand side of the equations). Given $\mathbf{A}$ and $\mathbf{B}$, the solution of $\mathbf{AX} = \mathbf{B}$ is the collection of triples that, when written as the 3×1 array $\mathbf{X}$, make the statement $\mathbf{AX} = \mathbf{B}$ true. The solution of this system was found in Example 2 to be the triple $(11, -4, 3)$, or $\mathbf{X} = \begin{bmatrix} 11 \\ -4 \\ 3 \end{bmatrix}$. ■

The system of m linear equations in n unknowns

$$\begin{aligned} a_{11}x_1 + a_{12}x_2 + \cdots + a_{1n}x_n &= b_1 \\ a_{21}x_1 + a_{22}x_2 + \cdots + a_{2n}x_n &= b_2 \\ \vdots \qquad\quad \vdots \qquad\qquad\quad \vdots \quad &\quad\ \vdots \\ a_{m1}x_1 + a_{m2}x_2 + \cdots + a_{mn}x_n &= b_m \end{aligned}$$

becomes, in matrix form,

$$\begin{bmatrix} a_{11} & a_{12} & \cdots & a_{1n} \\ a_{21} & a_{22} & \cdots & a_{2n} \\ \vdots & \vdots & & \vdots \\ a_{m1} & a_{m2} & \cdots & a_{mn} \end{bmatrix} \begin{bmatrix} x_1 \\ x_2 \\ \vdots \\ x_n \end{bmatrix} = \begin{bmatrix} b_1 \\ b_2 \\ \vdots \\ b_m \end{bmatrix}$$

or $\mathbf{AX} = \mathbf{B}$. The matrix $\mathbf{A}$ is the **coefficient matrix**. The number of rows of $\mathbf{A}$ is the number of equations in the system, and the number of columns is the number of unknowns. In writing $\mathbf{A}$ be sure that the unknowns are in the same order in each equation, and insert a zero coefficient if a particular unknown does not appear.

Example 4 The system

$$\begin{aligned} x_1 + x_2 &= x_4 - 5 \\ x_2 + x_4 &= x_1 - x_3 + 2 \end{aligned}$$

is written

$$\begin{aligned} x_1 + x_2 + 0x_3 - x_4 &= -5 \\ -x_1 + x_2 + x_3 + x_4 &= 2 \end{aligned}$$

In matrix form this is

$$\begin{bmatrix} 1 & 1 & 0 & -1 \\ -1 & 1 & 1 & 1 \end{bmatrix} \begin{bmatrix} x_1 \\ x_2 \\ x_3 \\ x_4 \end{bmatrix} = \begin{bmatrix} -5 \\ 2 \end{bmatrix}$$

The matrix equation **AX** = **B**, where $\mathbf{A} = \begin{bmatrix} 1 & 5 & 1 \\ 0 & 1 & 1 \\ 1 & 0 & -1 \end{bmatrix}$ and $\mathbf{B} = \begin{bmatrix} 3 \\ 2 \\ 0 \end{bmatrix}$ is the same as the linear system of three equations in three unknowns

$$\begin{aligned} x_1 + 5x_2 + x_3 &= 3 \\ x_2 + x_3 &= 2 \\ x_1 \qquad - x_3 &= 0 \end{aligned}$$

■

Each of the operations listed in Theorem 1 involves working with entire equations. Moreover, the operation has the same effect on an entire row of the coefficient matrix and the element of **B** that corresponds to that row. We enlarge the coefficient matrix by including **B** as an additional column. The matrix formed in this way is called the **augmented matrix** of the system because the matrix includes another column. The augmented matrix is usually written [**A**|**B**].

Example 5 For the system of equations

$$\begin{aligned} 2x + 5y + z &= 5 \\ x + 4y + 2z &= 1 \\ 4x + 10y - z &= 1 \end{aligned}$$

the augmented matrix is

$$[\mathbf{A}|\mathbf{B}] = \left[\begin{array}{ccc|c} 2 & 5 & 1 & 5 \\ 1 & 4 & 2 & 1 \\ 4 & 10 & -1 & 1 \end{array}\right]$$

The line placed between the matrix **A** and the column **B** emphasizes the fact that in interpreting the results the matrix **A** plays a different role from that played by the column **B**.

If the augmented matrix is

$$[\mathbf{A}|\mathbf{B}] = \left[\begin{array}{ccc|c} 2 & 1 & 0 & 4 \\ 1 & -1 & 2 & 1 \end{array}\right]$$

the corresponding system of equations is

$$\begin{aligned} 2x_1 + x_2 \qquad &= 4 \\ x_1 - x_2 + 2x_3 &= 1 \end{aligned}$$

■

The following example repeats Example 2 in matrix form. We use the notation:

1. $R_i \leftrightarrow R_j$ Interchange rows i and j.
2. $kR_i \rightarrow R_i$ The new ith row is k times the old ith row.
3. $kR_i + R_j \rightarrow R_j$ The new jth row is found by adding k times row i to row j.

Example 6 The given system of equations

$$\begin{aligned} 2x_1 + 5x_2 + x_3 &= 5 \\ x_1 + 4x_2 + 2x_3 &= 1 \\ 4x_1 + 10x_2 - x_3 &= 1 \end{aligned}$$

The augmented matrix of the given system

$$\left[\begin{array}{ccc|c} 2 & 5 & 1 & 5 \\ 1 & 4 & 2 & 1 \\ 4 & 10 & -1 & 1 \end{array}\right]$$

$R_1 \leftrightarrow R_2$
$$\left[\begin{array}{ccc|c} 1 & 4 & 2 & 1 \\ 2 & 5 & 1 & 5 \\ 4 & 10 & -1 & 1 \end{array}\right]$$

$-2R_1 + R_2 \rightarrow R_2$
$-4R_1 + R_3 \rightarrow R_3$
$$\left[\begin{array}{ccc|c} 1 & 4 & 2 & 1 \\ 0 & -3 & -3 & 3 \\ 0 & -6 & -9 & -3 \end{array}\right]$$
This corresponds to the system in step 3 of Example 2.

$-\frac{1}{3}R_2 \rightarrow R_2$
$$\left[\begin{array}{ccc|c} 1 & 4 & 2 & 1 \\ 0 & 1 & 1 & -1 \\ 0 & -6 & -9 & -3 \end{array}\right]$$
See step 4 of Example 2.

$6R_2 + R_3 \rightarrow R_3$
$$\left[\begin{array}{ccc|c} 1 & 4 & 2 & 1 \\ 0 & 1 & 1 & -1 \\ 0 & 0 & -3 & -9 \end{array}\right]$$
See step 5 of Example 2.

$-\frac{1}{3}R_3 \rightarrow R_3$
$$\left[\begin{array}{ccc|c} 1 & 4 & 2 & 1 \\ 0 & 1 & 1 & -1 \\ 0 & 0 & 1 & 3 \end{array}\right]$$
See step 6 of Example 2.

$-2R_3 + R_1 \rightarrow R_1$
$-R_3 + R_2 \rightarrow R_2$
$$\left[\begin{array}{ccc|c} 1 & 4 & 0 & -5 \\ 0 & 1 & 0 & -4 \\ 0 & 0 & 1 & 3 \end{array}\right]$$
See step 7 of Example 2.

$-4R_2 + R_1 \rightarrow R_1$
$$\left[\begin{array}{ccc|c} 1 & 0 & 0 & 11 \\ 0 & 1 & 0 & -4 \\ 0 & 0 & 1 & 3 \end{array}\right]$$
See step 8 of Example 2.

The system of equations corresponding to this augmented matrix is

$$\begin{aligned} x_1 &= 11 \\ x_2 &= -4 \\ x_3 &= 3 \end{aligned}$$

The unique solution is $\mathbf{X} = \begin{bmatrix} 11 \\ -4 \\ 3 \end{bmatrix}$. ■

Definition 2

Row Operations

The following operations are called **row operations on a matrix.**

1. Interchange two rows.
2. Multiply a row by a nonzero scalar.
3. Add a multiple of one row to another row.

Row-Equivalent Matrices

Matrices **M** and **N** are **row-equivalent** if each matrix can be obtained from the other by a sequence of row operations. The notation $\mathbf{M} \Leftrightarrow \mathbf{N}$ means that the matrices **M** and **N** are row-equivalent.

Clearly, row-equivalent matrices must be of the same size. Compare the row operations listed in Definition 2 with the operations used to produce an equivalent system of equations. If the augmented matrices of two systems of equations are row-equivalent, then the systems of equations are equivalent.

The operations in Definition 2 are reversible. If a row operation changes **A** to **B**, then a row operation of the same type changes **B** to **A**. In the following section, row operations and their use will be explored further.

The system of equations in Example 6 has a unique solution. This is not necessarily true for all systems. A simple geometric example will illustrate some possibilities.

Example 7

a. Consider the system of three equations in two unknowns:

$$\begin{aligned} x + 3y &= 5 \\ 2x - y &= 3 \\ -x + 2y &= 0 \end{aligned}$$

We use row operations on the augmented matrix to get a simpler system of equations:

$$\left[\begin{array}{rr|r} 1 & 3 & 5 \\ 2 & -1 & 3 \\ -1 & 2 & 0 \end{array}\right] \Leftrightarrow \left[\begin{array}{rr|r} 1 & 3 & 5 \\ 0 & -7 & -7 \\ 0 & 5 & 5 \end{array}\right] \Leftrightarrow \left[\begin{array}{rr|r} 1 & 3 & 5 \\ 0 & 1 & 1 \\ 0 & 1 & 1 \end{array}\right] \Leftrightarrow \left[\begin{array}{rr|r} 1 & 0 & 2 \\ 0 & 1 & 1 \\ 0 & 0 & 0 \end{array}\right]$$

The new system is $x = 2$, $y = 1$. The system represents three distinct lines passing through the point (2, 1). (See Figure 2.1.)

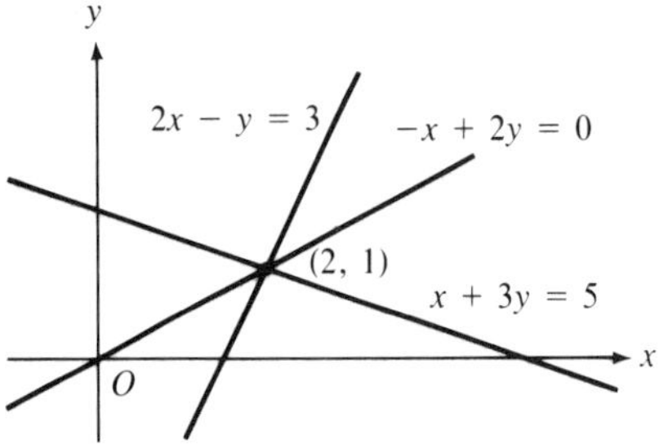

FIGURE 2.1

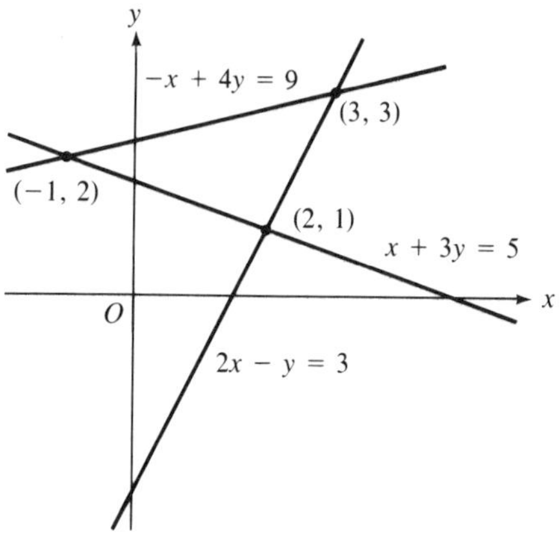

FIGURE 2.2

b. Now apply the same technique to the system

$$\begin{aligned} x + 3y &= 5 \\ 2x - y &= 3 \\ -x + 4y &= 9 \end{aligned}$$

The augmented matrix is

$$\left[\begin{array}{rr|r} 1 & 3 & 5 \\ 2 & -1 & 3 \\ -1 & 4 & 9 \end{array}\right] \Leftrightarrow \left[\begin{array}{rr|r} 1 & 3 & 5 \\ 0 & -7 & -7 \\ 0 & 7 & 14 \end{array}\right] \Leftrightarrow \left[\begin{array}{rr|r} 1 & 3 & 5 \\ 0 & 1 & 1 \\ 0 & 1 & 2 \end{array}\right] \Leftrightarrow \left[\begin{array}{rr|r} 1 & 0 & 2 \\ 0 & 1 & 1 \\ 0 & 0 & 1 \end{array}\right]$$

The new system of equations says:

$$x = 2, \qquad y = 1, \qquad 0y = 1.$$

Since there is no value of y for which $0y = 1$, this system has no solution. Geometrically, the system is a set of lines that intersect in pairs, but the three points of intersection are different. (See Figure 2.2.)

c. Consider the following system of equations in three unknowns. This system represents three planes in R^3.

$$\begin{aligned} x + 2y - z &= 1 \\ x \qquad + z &= 3 \\ x - y \qquad &= 2 \end{aligned}$$

The vectors normal to the planes are $(1, 2, -1)$, $(1, 0, 1)$, and $(1, -1, 0)$. No two of these vectors are parallel, so no two of the planes are parallel. To find out whether these planes have a common point, we again look at the augmented matrix. Row operations applied as before reduce the augmented matrix

$$\left[\begin{array}{rrr|r} 1 & 2 & -1 & 1 \\ 1 & 0 & 1 & 3 \\ 1 & -1 & 0 & 2 \end{array}\right] \quad \text{to} \quad \left[\begin{array}{rrr|r} 1 & 0 & 0 & 2 \\ 0 & 1 & 0 & 0 \\ 0 & 0 & 1 & 1 \end{array}\right]$$

The equations have a unique solution $x = 2$, $y = 0$, $z = 1$. The three planes have the single point $(2, 0, 1)$ in common.

d. Three planes with equations

$$\begin{aligned} x + 2y - z &= 1 \\ x \qquad + z &= 3 \\ x + y \qquad &= 2 \end{aligned}$$

also have the property that no two are parallel. Row operations on the augmented matrix change

$$\left[\begin{array}{rrr|r} 1 & 2 & -1 & 1 \\ 1 & 0 & 1 & 3 \\ 1 & 1 & 0 & 2 \end{array}\right] \quad \text{to} \quad \left[\begin{array}{rrr|r} 1 & 0 & 1 & 3 \\ 0 & 1 & -1 & -1 \\ 0 & 0 & 0 & 0 \end{array}\right]$$

The new system of equations is

$$\begin{aligned} x \qquad + z &= 3 \\ y - z &= -1 \\ 0z &= 0. \end{aligned}$$

The third equation is true for all z. The first and second equations make it possible to express x and y in terms of z for any arbitrary choice of z. This system of equations has an infinite set of solutions. Let $z = k$. Then the solutions of this system of equations are $x = 3 - k$, $y = -1 + k$, $z = k$. Written in vector form, the solution is

$$(x, y, z) = (3, -1, 0) + k(-1, 1, 1).$$

Recall from Section 1.5, Example 36, that this equation is the equation of a line through the point $(3, -1, 0)$ and in the direction parallel to $(-1, 1, 1)$. The three planes all pass through the same line. Notice that each of the vectors $(1, 2, -1)$, $(1, 0, 1)$, and $(1, 1, 0)$ is orthogonal to $(-1, 1, 1)$.

e. Now consider the three planes

$$\begin{aligned} x + 2y - z &= 1 \\ x \qquad + z &= 3 \\ x + y \qquad &= 4 \end{aligned}$$

In this case we have

$$\left|\begin{array}{rrr|r} 1 & 2 & -1 & 1 \\ 1 & 0 & 1 & 3 \\ 1 & 1 & 0 & 4 \end{array}\right| \Leftrightarrow \left|\begin{array}{rrr|r} 1 & 0 & 1 & 3 \\ 0 & 1 & -1 & 1 \\ 0 & 0 & 0 & -2 \end{array}\right|$$

The third equation here is $0z = -2$, which is impossible, so the system of equations has no solution. Although no two planes of the system are parallel, the three planes represented by this system of equations have no point in common. In this case each pair of planes intersects in a line but the three lines so determined do not pass through a common point. ■

Consistent
Inconsistent

Definition 3

A system of equations is **consistent** if it has a solution and **inconsistent** if it does not have a solution.

In Example 7, the systems in (a), (c), and (d) are consistent, but (b) and (e) are inconsistent.

In the remainder of this chapter, we will define the row-reduced form of a matrix and use it to derive some important results about the solution sets of systems of equations.

SUMMARY Two systems of equations are equivalent if and only if they have the same solution set. Systems of linear equations are equivalent if each can be obtained from the other by one or more of the following operations:

1. Interchange the order of the equations.
2. Multiply one equation by a nonzero scalar.
3. Add a multiple of one equation to another.

A system of equations is consistent if it has a solution. Otherwise it is inconsistent.

A system of m linear equations in n unknowns can be written in the form $\mathbf{AX} = \mathbf{B}$, where $\mathbf{A}$ is an $m \times n$ matrix called the coefficient matrix, $\mathbf{X}$ is an $n \times 1$ matrix of unknowns, and $\mathbf{B}$ is an $m \times 1$ matrix of scalars. The $m \times (n+1)$ matrix $[\mathbf{A}|\mathbf{B}]$ is called the augmented matrix. The three operations on systems of equations correspond to row operations on the matrix $[\mathbf{A}|\mathbf{B}]$.

EXERCISES 2.1

1. a. Verify that $(2, 3, -1)$ is a solution of the system of equations

$$\begin{aligned} x_1 + 2x_2 + x_3 &= 7 \\ x_1 \qquad\quad - x_3 &= 3 \\ 4x_1 + x_2 + x_3 &= 10 \end{aligned}$$

b. Write the system in (**a**) in the form $\mathbf{AX} = \mathbf{B}$.

c. Verify that

$$\begin{bmatrix} 1 & 2 & 1 \\ 1 & 0 & -1 \\ 4 & 1 & 1 \end{bmatrix} \begin{bmatrix} 2 \\ 3 \\ -1 \end{bmatrix} = \begin{bmatrix} 7 \\ 3 \\ 10 \end{bmatrix}$$

and thus show that $\mathbf{X} = \begin{bmatrix} 2 \\ 3 \\ -1 \end{bmatrix}$ is a solution of the equation $\mathbf{AX} = \mathbf{B}$ in (**b**).

2. a. Verify that every triple of the form $(7 - 2k, 8 + 6k, k)$ is a solution of the system

$$\begin{aligned} x_1 + 2x_3 &= 7 \\ x_2 - 6x_3 &= 8 \end{aligned}$$

b. Write the system of equations in (**a**) in the form $\mathbf{AX} = \mathbf{B}$ and show that

$$\mathbf{X} = \begin{bmatrix} 7 - 2k \\ 8 + 6k \\ k \end{bmatrix}$$

is a solution of $\mathbf{AX} = \mathbf{B}$.

3. a. Verify that $(1, -1, 0, 2)$ is a solution of the system of equations

$$\begin{aligned} 2x_1 + 4x_2 + x_3 + 3x_4 &= 4 \\ -x_1 + 2x_2 + 5x_3 + 6x_4 &= 9 \end{aligned}$$

b. Write the system of equations in (**a**) in the form $\mathbf{AX} = \mathbf{B}$ and show that

$$\mathbf{X} = \begin{bmatrix} 1 \\ -1 \\ 0 \\ 2 \end{bmatrix}$$

is a solution of $\mathbf{AX} = \mathbf{B}$.

4. a. Find the solution set of the system of equations

$$\begin{aligned} x_1 - 3x_3 &= 5 \\ x_2 + 2x_3 &= 4 \end{aligned}$$

b. Write the system in (**a**) in the form $\mathbf{AX} = \mathbf{B}$. What values of $\mathbf{X}$ are solutions of this system?

5. a. Describe the operations that have been performed to produce an equivalent system of equations:

$$\left.\begin{aligned} x_1 - x_2 + x_3 &= 3 \\ 2x_1 + 3x_2 - 4x_3 &= 9 \\ -x_1 + 3x_2 + 8x_3 &= 1 \end{aligned}\right\}$$

becomes

$$\left\{\begin{aligned} x_1 - x_2 + x_3 &= 3 \\ 5x_2 - 6x_3 &= 3 \\ 2x_2 + 9x_3 &= 4 \end{aligned}\right.$$

b. Write the augmented matrices of the two systems of equations in (**a**). Show that these two matrices are row-equivalent.

6. a. Let

$$\left[\begin{array}{rrr|r} 1 & 2 & -4 & 7 \\ 3 & -2 & 5 & 9 \\ 1 & 4 & -1 & 3 \end{array}\right]$$

be the augmented matrix of a system of equations. What matrix is obtained when row 1 is replaced by itself plus row 2, and row 3 is replaced by itself plus row 2?

b. Write the original system of equations and the resulting equivalent system corresponding to the new matrix formed in (**a**).

7. The matrix

$$\left[\begin{array}{rrr|r} 1 & 2 & -1 & 6 \\ -2 & 1 & 7 & -7 \\ 3 & -2 & -1 & 0 \end{array}\right]$$

is the augmented matrix of a system of equations. Perform row operations on this matrix to obtain a matrix in which the first element in row 2 is 0 and the first element in row 3 is 0. Write the corresponding system of equations.

8. a. Show that $(1, -1, 2)$ is a solution of the system of equations

$$\begin{aligned} x_1 + x_2 + x_3 &= 2 \\ 2x_1 - x_2 - x_3 &= 1 \end{aligned}$$

b. The system

$$\begin{aligned} x_1 + x_2 + x_3 &= 2 \\ 3x_1 \qquad\qquad &= 3 \end{aligned}$$

is formed by adding the first equation to the second. Show that $(1, -1, 2)$ is still a solution.

c. The system

$$\begin{aligned} 5x_1 - x_2 - x_3 &= 4 \\ 2x_1 - x_2 - x_3 &= 1 \end{aligned}$$

is formed from the system in (**a**) by adding two times the second equation to the first. Is $(1, -1, 2)$ still a solution of the system?

9. Write the linear equations that ask the following question: Is the pair $(3, 1)$ a linear combination of $(1, 5)$ and $(-1, 1)$? Solve them.

10. Let $\mathbf{u}_1 = (1, 1, 3)$, $\mathbf{u}_2 = (1, -1, 4)$, and $\mathbf{u}_3 = (1, 0, 1)$. Is there a linear combination of $\mathbf{u}_1$, $\mathbf{u}_2$, $\mathbf{u}_3$ that is the zero triple? Is there more than one such combination?

11. Does there exist a pair (x_1, x_2) such that the following is true?

$$\begin{bmatrix} 2 & 1 \\ 1 & 2 \end{bmatrix} \begin{bmatrix} x_1 \\ x_2 \end{bmatrix} = \begin{bmatrix} x_1 \\ x_2 \end{bmatrix}$$

12. For what values of a, b, c, and d is $\mathbf{AB} = \mathbf{BA}$ if

$$\mathbf{A} = \begin{bmatrix} 2 & 1 \\ 3 & 4 \end{bmatrix} \quad \text{and} \quad \mathbf{B} = \begin{bmatrix} a & b \\ c & d \end{bmatrix}?$$

13. **a.** Is a diagonal matrix always row-equivalent to an identity matrix? Discuss the possible cases.
b. Is a triangular matrix row-equivalent to an identity matrix? Discuss.

14. What matrices are row-equivalent to the zero matrix $\mathbf{0}_{m \times n}$?

15. Write the augmented matrix for the system of equations

$$\begin{aligned} x + y + 2z &= 1 \\ x \quad\;\; - z &= 1 \\ 2x + 3y + 5z &= 4 \end{aligned}$$

What is the solution of this system? What does this solution imply about the three planes represented by these three equations?

16. The system of equations

$$\begin{aligned} x_1 + 2x_2 + x_3 &= 4 \\ 2x_1 \quad\;\; + x_3 &= 5 \\ 4x_1 + 4x_2 + 3x_3 &= 13 \end{aligned}$$

represents three planes. Solve the system. Is it consistent? Is the solution unique? What does this solution tell us about the three planes?

17. Consider the system of equations

$$\begin{aligned} x_1 + x_2 - x_3 &= 4 \\ 2x_1 - x_2 \quad\;\; &= 3 \\ 5x_1 - x_2 - x_3 &= 6 \end{aligned}$$

This system represents three planes. Is the system consistent? What does this mean about the three planes?

18. For the system of equations

$$\begin{aligned} x_1 + x_2 + 2x_3 + x_4 &= 8 \\ x_1 \quad\;\; + x_3 + x_4 &= 6 \\ x_2 \quad\;\; + x_4 &= 4 \\ x_1 - x_2 - x_3 + 2x_4 &= 6 \end{aligned}$$

use row operations on the augmented matrix to solve the system. Is the system consistent? Is the solution set finite or infinite?

19. An estate of \$220,000 is to be divided among three sons. The oldest is to receive 50% more than the second son because of extra care given to the parents. Since the youngest son has two children, his share of the estate is to be \$10,000 more than that of the second son. How much is each son's share?

20. A system of water pipes is connected at A, B, C, and D as shown. Water flows in at A, B, and D at the rate of 20 liters per minute, 10 liters per minute, and 20 liters per minute, respectively. Let r_1, r_2, r_3, r_4, r_5 be the number of liters per minute of flow through the remaining sections of the pipes in the directions indicated. A steady flow requires that the amount of water entering at any connecting point should be the same as the amount leaving. This leads to a system of four equations, one for each connecting point. At A we have $r_1 + r_2 = 20$; at B, $r_2 + 10 = r_4$; at C, $r_3 + r_4 = r_5$; at D, $r_1 + 20 = r_3$.
Find the possible values of each flow rate.

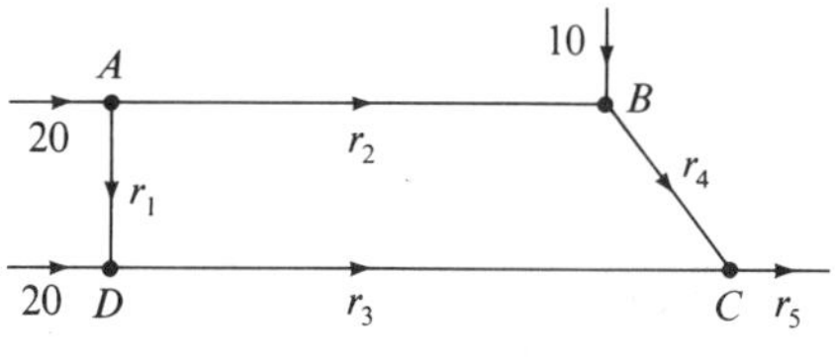

21. A system of water pipes is connected at A, B, and C, as shown. Water flows in at A at 40 liters per minute, and at B at 20 liters per minute. A steady flow requires that the amount of water entering at any connecting point should be the same as the amount leaving.

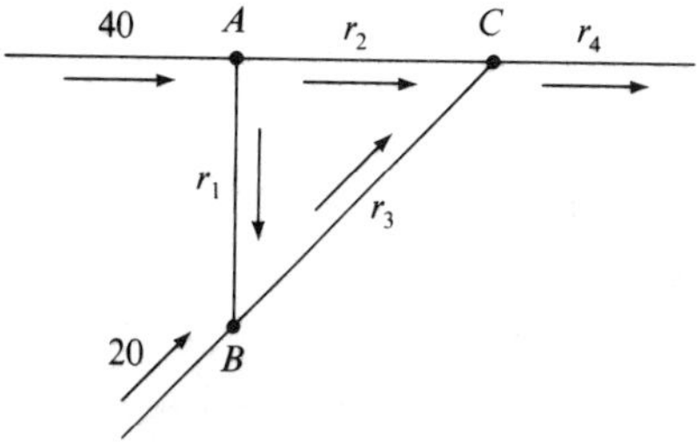

a. Write the conditions that must be satisfied by the rates of flow at each of the three connecting points.

b Show that for the situation to be possible, r_4 must equal 60 liters per minute.

c. If $r_4 = 60$, show that the system has an infinite set of solutions.

2.2 *The Row-Reduced Form of a Matrix; Rank*

For any matrix **A** many different sequences of row operations can be done. Therefore, many different matrices are row-equivalent to **A**. In this section we identify a particular form called the **row-reduced** form of a matrix.

Example 8 Consider the following matrix **A**. The row operations carried out on this matrix illustrate an algorithm for finding the row-reduced form of the matrix.

$$\mathbf{A} = \begin{bmatrix} 1 & 2 & 1 & 2 & 1 & 0 & 7 \\ 1 & 2 & 4 & -1 & 4 & 3 & 1 \\ 2 & 4 & 5 & 1 & 5 & -2 & 3 \\ 2 & 4 & 8 & -2 & 8 & 6 & 2 \\ 1 & 2 & 1 & 2 & 6 & 0 & 7 \end{bmatrix}$$

Column 1 is the first column with nonzero elements. It is a **leading column**. Use row operations to make its first element 1 and the elements below the first element zero.

$$\begin{bmatrix} 1 & 2 & 1 & 2 & 1 & 0 & 7 \\ 0 & 0 & 3 & -3 & 3 & 3 & -6 \\ 0 & 0 & 3 & -3 & 3 & -2 & -11 \\ 0 & 0 & 6 & -6 & 6 & 6 & -12 \\ 0 & 0 & 0 & 0 & 5 & 0 & 0 \end{bmatrix} \qquad \begin{matrix} -R_1 + R_2 \to R_2 \\ -2R_1 + R_3 \to R_3 \\ -2R_1 + R_4 \to R_4 \\ -R_1 + R_5 \to R_5 \end{matrix}$$

Move to the right. Column 3 is the first column with a nonzero element in row 2 or lower. Column 3 is a leading column. Use row operations so that the entry in column 3 row 2 becomes a 1 and the entries below it become 0.

$$\begin{bmatrix} 1 & 2 & 1 & 2 & 1 & 0 & 7 \\ 0 & 0 & 1 & -1 & 1 & 1 & -2 \\ 0 & 0 & 3 & -3 & 3 & -2 & -11 \\ 0 & 0 & 6 & -6 & 6 & 6 & -12 \\ 0 & 0 & 0 & 0 & 5 & 0 & 0 \end{bmatrix} \qquad (\tfrac{1}{3})R_2 \to R_2$$

$$\begin{bmatrix} 1 & 2 & 1 & 2 & 1 & 0 & 7 \\ 0 & 0 & 1 & -1 & 1 & 1 & -2 \\ 0 & 0 & 0 & 0 & 0 & -5 & -5 \\ 0 & 0 & 0 & 0 & 0 & 0 & 0 \\ 0 & 0 & 0 & 0 & 5 & 0 & 0 \end{bmatrix} \qquad \begin{matrix} -3R_2 + R_3 \to R_3 \\ -6R_2 + R_4 \to R_4 \end{matrix}$$

Move to the right. Column 5 is the next column with a nonzero element in row 3 or lower. Column 5 is a leading column. Interchange rows 3 and 5, and then continue as above.

$$\begin{bmatrix} 1 & 2 & 1 & 2 & 1 & 0 & 7 \\ 0 & 0 & 1 & -1 & 1 & 1 & -2 \\ 0 & 0 & 0 & 0 & 5 & 0 & 0 \\ 0 & 0 & 0 & 0 & 0 & 0 & 0 \\ 0 & 0 & 0 & 0 & 0 & -5 & -5 \end{bmatrix} \qquad R_3 \leftrightarrow R_5$$

$$\begin{bmatrix} 1 & 2 & 1 & 2 & 1 & 0 & 7 \\ 0 & 0 & 1 & -1 & 1 & 1 & -2 \\ 0 & 0 & 0 & 0 & 1 & 0 & 0 \\ 0 & 0 & 0 & 0 & 0 & -5 & -5 \\ 0 & 0 & 0 & 0 & 0 & 0 & 0 \end{bmatrix} \qquad \begin{matrix} R_4 \leftrightarrow R_5 \\ (\tfrac{1}{5})R_3 \to R_3 \end{matrix}$$

Move to the right. Column 6 is the first column with a nonzero element in row 4 or lower. Column 6 is a leading column.

$$\begin{bmatrix} 1 & 2 & 1 & 2 & 1 & 0 & 7 \\ 0 & 0 & 1 & -1 & 1 & 1 & -2 \\ 0 & 0 & 0 & 0 & 1 & 0 & 0 \\ 0 & 0 & 0 & 0 & 0 & 1 & 1 \\ 0 & 0 & 0 & 0 & 0 & 0 & 0 \end{bmatrix} \qquad (-\tfrac{1}{5})R_4 \to R_4$$

Column 7 is not a leading column. This matrix has four leading columns: columns 1, 3, 5, and 6.

The second phase of the algorithm moves from right to left. It concerns itself with the leading columns and uses row operations to create zeros in the upper part of each of the leading columns.

$$\begin{bmatrix} 1 & 2 & 1 & 2 & 1 & 0 & 7 \\ 0 & 0 & 1 & -1 & 1 & 0 & -3 \\ 0 & 0 & 0 & 0 & 1 & 0 & 0 \\ 0 & 0 & 0 & 0 & 0 & 1 & 1 \\ 0 & 0 & 0 & 0 & 0 & 0 & 0 \end{bmatrix} \qquad -R_4 + R_2 \to R_2$$

$$\begin{bmatrix} 1 & 2 & 1 & 2 & 0 & 0 & 7 \\ 0 & 0 & 1 & -1 & 0 & 0 & -3 \\ 0 & 0 & 0 & 0 & 1 & 0 & 0 \\ 0 & 0 & 0 & 0 & 0 & 1 & 1 \\ 0 & 0 & 0 & 0 & 0 & 0 & 0 \end{bmatrix} \qquad \begin{matrix} -R_3 + R_1 \to R_1 \\ -R_3 + R_2 \to R_2 \end{matrix}$$

$$\begin{bmatrix} 1 & 2 & 0 & 3 & 0 & 0 & 10 \\ 0 & 0 & 1 & -1 & 0 & 0 & -3 \\ 0 & 0 & 0 & 0 & 1 & 0 & 0 \\ 0 & 0 & 0 & 0 & 0 & 1 & 1 \\ 0 & 0 & 0 & 0 & 0 & 0 & 0 \end{bmatrix} \qquad -R_2 + R_1 \to R_1$$

Notice that there are four nonzero rows, and these are the first four rows of the matrix. The first nonzero element in each nonzero row is 1. The column containing this 1 has all other elements zero. ■

The sequence of steps used in Example 8 is called *Gaussian reduction* modified by a backward pass through the matrix, or *Gauss-Jordan reduction.* The steps are described below.

The first part of the process involves moving from left to right, creating an array of zero elements in the lower left portion of the matrix.

1. Begin at the left. Find the first nonzero column (call it j_1). Interchange rows so that a nonzero element is in the first row of this column. Use row operations of types 2 and 3 to make the first element in this column 1 and the remaining elements zero. This is the first **leading column** in the row-reduced form of the matrix.
2. Move to the right and find the next column (j_2) with nonzero element in rows 2 or lower. Use row operations so that the new column j_2 has a 1 in row 2 and zeros below it. Note that these row operations do not affect the elements in any column to the left of column j_2 since in these columns all the elements below row 1 are zero.
3. Move to the right. Find the next column (j_3) that has a nonzero element in rows 3 or lower. Use row operations so that, in the resulting matrix, column j_3 has a 1 in row 3 and zeros below it.
4. Continue in this way until r leading columns are identified: $j_1, j_2, \ldots, j_r$, and there are only zero elements in rows $r + 1, r + 2, \ldots, m$.

   The second part of the process moves from right to left and has as its purpose to create zeros in the upper part of the leading columns.
5. Use row r and row operations of type 3 so that column j_r has zero elements in rows $1, 2, \ldots, r - 1$. No columns to the left of column j_r are affected by these operations since the first $j_r - 1$ elements of row r are zero.
6. Use row $r - 1$ and row operations of type 3 so that column j_{r-1} has zero elements in rows $1, 2, \ldots, r - 2$. Continue in this way so that each leading column j_i has zero elements in the first $i - 1$ rows.

The final form of the row-reduced matrix is

$$\left[\begin{array}{cccccccccc}
\cdots & 0 & \overset{j_1}{1} & \cdots & \overset{j_2}{0} & \cdots & \overset{j_3}{0} & \cdots & \overset{j_r}{0} & \cdots \\
\cdots & 0 & 0 & \cdots & 1 & \cdots & 0 & \cdots & 0 & \cdots \\
\cdots & 0 & 0 & \cdots & 0 & \cdots & 1 & \cdots & 0 & \cdots \\
 & \vdots & \vdots & & \vdots & & \vdots & & \vdots & \\
\cdots & 0 & 0 & \cdots & 0 & \cdots & 0 & \cdots & 1 & \cdots \\
 & & & & \multicolumn{3}{c}{\text{(all zeros)}} & & & \\
\cdots & 0 & 0 & \cdots & 0 & \cdots & 0 & \cdots & 0 & \cdots
\end{array}\right]
\begin{array}{l} \\ \\ \\ \\ \text{row } r \\ \\ \text{row } m \end{array}$$

The steps outlined describe the most direct way of arriving at the row-reduced form of a matrix. However, other sequences of row operations could be used to achieve the same result. The row-reduced form is unique and has the following properties:

1. There are r nonzero rows and these are the first r rows of the matrix.
2. The first nonzero element in each nonzero row is 1. The column containing this 1 has all other elements zero. It is called a **leading column**. There are r leading columns.
3. The leading columns need not be the first r columns but the leading column j_i is to the left of j_k if and only if $i < k$.

The number r is of considerable importance. It is called the **rank** of the matrix.

Rank

Definition 4

The **rank** of a matrix is the number of nonzero rows in the row-reduced form of the matrix. It is also the number of leading columns.

Sometimes we do not need to complete the row reduction of a matrix. The rank is known as soon as the number of leading columns can be identified. A matrix is said to be in *echelon form* if it has been row-reduced until it is triangular or as nearly triangular as possible. It will be in echelon form if:

1. Its r nonzero rows are in the upper part of the matrix.
2. In the ith leading column, the elements below the ith row are all zero.

Example 9

In each case identify whether the matrix is in echelon form, row-reduced form, or neither. State the rank of the matrix.

a. $\begin{bmatrix} 0 & 1 & 2 & 0 & 3 \\ 0 & 0 & 0 & 1 & 2 \\ 0 & 0 & 0 & 0 & 0 \end{bmatrix}$

This matrix is in row-reduced form. Its leading columns are 2 and 4. It has rank 2.

b. $\begin{bmatrix} 0 & 0 & 0 & 1 & 2 \\ 0 & 1 & 2 & 0 & 3 \\ 1 & 0 & 0 & 2 & 1 \\ 0 & 0 & 0 & 0 & 0 \end{bmatrix}$ This matrix is in neither form. If rows 3 and 1 were interchanged it would be in echelon form. Columns 1, 2, and 4 would be leading columns.

$\begin{bmatrix} 1 & 0 & 0 & 2 & 1 \\ 0 & 1 & 2 & 0 & 3 \\ 0 & 0 & 0 & 1 & 2 \\ 0 & 0 & 0 & 0 & 0 \end{bmatrix}$ To put it in row-reduced form, add -2 times row 3 to row 1. The matrix has rank 3.

c. $\begin{bmatrix} 5 & 3 & 2 & 1 & 4 \\ 0 & 0 & 3 & 2 & 1 \\ 0 & 0 & 0 & 0 & 7 \end{bmatrix}$ This matrix is in echelon form. The columns 1, 3, and 5 are leading columns. It has rank 3. ■

The algorithm described here is a sure path to the row-reduced form of a matrix. It is easily understood. It is easy to program, but it is not the most efficient numerical method for solving systems of equations. This will be discussed in Section 5. If you are working with no more than a hand calculator, the method may be quite tedious, especially if there is a good deal of arithmetic involved. The steps described in the algorithm are not the only path that can be followed, and you should feel free to look for shortcuts. Be careful not to combine too many steps, lest you produce an incorrect combination of row operations.

Example 10

Let $\mathbf{A} = \begin{bmatrix} 5 & 2 & 2 & 1 \\ 7 & 3 & 4 & 4 \\ 6 & 1 & 2 & 1 \end{bmatrix}$. A straightforward application of the algorithm yields the following sequence of matrices.

$$\tfrac{1}{5}R_1 \to R_1 \begin{bmatrix} 1 & \frac{2}{5} & \frac{2}{5} & \frac{1}{5} \\ 7 & 3 & 4 & 4 \\ 6 & 1 & 2 & 1 \end{bmatrix} \qquad \begin{matrix} -7R_1 + R_2 \to R_2 \\ -6R_1 + R_3 \to R_3 \end{matrix} \begin{bmatrix} 1 & \frac{2}{5} & \frac{2}{5} & \frac{1}{5} \\ 0 & \frac{1}{5} & \frac{6}{5} & \frac{13}{5} \\ 0 & -\frac{7}{5} & -\frac{2}{5} & -\frac{1}{5} \end{bmatrix}$$

$$5R_2 \to R_2 \begin{bmatrix} 1 & \frac{2}{5} & \frac{2}{5} & \frac{1}{5} \\ 0 & 1 & 6 & 13 \\ 0 & -\frac{7}{5} & -\frac{2}{5} & -\frac{1}{5} \end{bmatrix} \qquad \tfrac{7}{5}R_2 + R_3 \to R_3 \begin{bmatrix} 1 & \frac{2}{5} & \frac{2}{5} & \frac{1}{5} \\ 0 & 1 & 6 & 13 \\ 0 & 0 & \frac{40}{5} & \frac{90}{5} \end{bmatrix}$$

$$\tfrac{5}{40}R_3 \to R_3 \begin{bmatrix} 1 & \frac{2}{5} & \frac{2}{5} & \frac{1}{5} \\ 0 & 1 & 6 & 13 \\ 0 & 0 & 1 & \frac{9}{4} \end{bmatrix} \qquad \begin{matrix} -\frac{2}{5}R_3 + R_1 \to R_1 \\ -6R_3 + R_2 \to R_2 \end{matrix} \begin{bmatrix} 1 & \frac{2}{5} & 0 & -\frac{14}{20} \\ 0 & 1 & 0 & -\frac{2}{4} \\ 0 & 0 & 1 & \frac{9}{4} \end{bmatrix}$$

$$-\tfrac{2}{5}R_2 + R_1 \to R_1 \begin{bmatrix} 1 & 0 & 0 & -\frac{1}{2} \\ 0 & 1 & 0 & -\frac{1}{2} \\ 0 & 0 & 1 & \frac{9}{4} \end{bmatrix}$$

As an alternative approach, try to obtain a 1 without introducing fractions. Get 0 above and below the 1 in a leading column in the same set of operations. Settle for a nonzero integer in place of a 1 if that seems easier until the very end. A possible set of operations on the same matrix **A** is given next. See if you can follow the steps that were taken. Can you find other ways to row-reduce **A**?

$$\begin{bmatrix} 6 & 1 & 2 & 1 \\ 7 & 3 & 4 & 4 \\ 5 & 2 & 2 & 1 \end{bmatrix} \Leftrightarrow \begin{bmatrix} 1 & -1 & 0 & 0 \\ 7 & 3 & 4 & 4 \\ 5 & 2 & 2 & 1 \end{bmatrix} \Leftrightarrow \begin{bmatrix} 1 & -1 & 0 & 0 \\ 0 & 10 & 4 & 4 \\ 0 & 7 & 2 & 1 \end{bmatrix}$$

$$\Leftrightarrow \begin{bmatrix} 1 & -1 & 0 & 0 \\ 0 & 15 & 6 & 6 \\ 0 & 14 & 4 & 2 \end{bmatrix} \Leftrightarrow \begin{bmatrix} 1 & -1 & 0 & 0 \\ 0 & 1 & 2 & 4 \\ 0 & 14 & 4 & 2 \end{bmatrix} \Leftrightarrow \begin{bmatrix} 1 & 0 & 2 & 4 \\ 0 & 1 & 2 & 4 \\ 0 & 0 & -24 & -54 \end{bmatrix}$$

$$\Leftrightarrow \begin{bmatrix} 1 & 0 & 2 & 4 \\ 0 & 1 & 2 & 4 \\ 0 & 0 & 4 & 9 \end{bmatrix} \Leftrightarrow \begin{bmatrix} 2 & 0 & 4 & 8 \\ 0 & 2 & 4 & 8 \\ 0 & 0 & 4 & 9 \end{bmatrix} \Leftrightarrow \begin{bmatrix} 2 & 0 & 0 & -1 \\ 0 & 2 & 0 & -1 \\ 0 & 0 & 4 & 9 \end{bmatrix}$$

$$\Leftrightarrow \begin{bmatrix} 1 & 0 & 0 & -\frac{1}{2} \\ 0 & 1 & 0 & -\frac{1}{2} \\ 0 & 0 & 1 & \frac{9}{4} \end{bmatrix}$$

■

Row reduction involves only row operations and proceeds first from left to right and then from right to left. Let **A** be the matrix consisting of the first s columns of a matrix **C**. The row-reduced form of **A** will be the first s columns of the row-reduced form of **C**. The following example illustrates this.

Example 11 Compare the steps in row-reducing the matrices **A** and **C**. Notice that the columns of **A** are the first four columns of **C**.

$$\mathbf{A} = \begin{bmatrix} 1 & 1 & 2 & 1 \\ 1 & 4 & -1 & 4 \\ 2 & 5 & 1 & 5 \\ 1 & 1 & 2 & 6 \end{bmatrix} \qquad \mathbf{C} = \begin{bmatrix} 1 & 1 & 2 & 1 & 0 & 7 \\ 1 & 4 & -1 & 4 & 3 & 1 \\ 2 & 5 & 1 & 5 & -2 & 3 \\ 1 & 1 & 2 & 6 & 0 & 7 \end{bmatrix}$$

$$\begin{bmatrix} 1 & 1 & 2 & 1 \\ 0 & 3 & -3 & 3 \\ 0 & 3 & -3 & 3 \\ 0 & 0 & 0 & 5 \end{bmatrix} \qquad \begin{bmatrix} 1 & 1 & 2 & 1 & 0 & 7 \\ 0 & 3 & -3 & 3 & 3 & -6 \\ 0 & 3 & -3 & 3 & -2 & -11 \\ 0 & 0 & 0 & 5 & 0 & 0 \end{bmatrix}$$

$$\begin{bmatrix} 1 & 1 & 2 & 1 \\ 0 & 1 & -1 & 1 \\ 0 & 0 & 0 & 0 \\ 0 & 0 & 0 & 5 \end{bmatrix} \qquad \begin{bmatrix} 1 & 1 & 2 & 1 & 0 & 7 \\ 0 & 1 & -1 & 1 & 1 & -2 \\ 0 & 0 & 0 & 0 & -5 & -5 \\ 0 & 0 & 0 & 5 & 0 & 0 \end{bmatrix}$$

$$\begin{bmatrix} 1 & 1 & 2 & 1 \\ 0 & 1 & -1 & 1 \\ 0 & 0 & 0 & 1 \\ 0 & 0 & 0 & 0 \end{bmatrix} \qquad \begin{bmatrix} 1 & 1 & 2 & 1 & 0 & 7 \\ 0 & 1 & -1 & 1 & 1 & -2 \\ 0 & 0 & 0 & 1 & 0 & 0 \\ 0 & 0 & 0 & 0 & 1 & 1 \end{bmatrix}$$

$$\begin{bmatrix} 1 & 1 & 2 & 1 & 0 & 7 \\ 0 & 1 & -1 & 1 & 0 & -3 \\ 0 & 0 & 0 & 1 & 0 & 0 \\ 0 & 0 & 0 & 0 & 1 & 1 \end{bmatrix}$$

$$\begin{bmatrix} 1 & 1 & 2 & 0 \\ 0 & 1 & -1 & 0 \\ 0 & 0 & 0 & 1 \\ 0 & 0 & 0 & 0 \end{bmatrix} \qquad \begin{bmatrix} 1 & 1 & 2 & 0 & 0 & 7 \\ 0 & 1 & -1 & 0 & 0 & -3 \\ 0 & 0 & 0 & 1 & 0 & 0 \\ 0 & 0 & 0 & 0 & 1 & 1 \end{bmatrix}$$

$$\begin{bmatrix} 1 & 0 & 3 & 0 \\ 0 & 1 & -1 & 0 \\ 0 & 0 & 0 & 1 \\ 0 & 0 & 0 & 0 \end{bmatrix} \qquad \begin{bmatrix} 1 & 0 & 3 & 0 & 0 & 10 \\ 0 & 1 & -1 & 0 & 0 & -3 \\ 0 & 0 & 0 & 1 & 0 & 0 \\ 0 & 0 & 0 & 0 & 1 & 1 \end{bmatrix}$$

The leading columns of **A** are columns 1, 2, and 4. Those of **C** are 1, 2, 4, and 5. The rank of **A** is 3; the rank of **C** is 4. ■

An important special case of the situation illustrated in Example 11 occurs in solving systems of equations $\mathbf{AX} = \mathbf{B}$. Here the coefficient matrix is the first n columns of the augmented matrix.

$$\mathbf{A} = \begin{bmatrix} a_{11} & a_{12} & \cdots & a_{1n} \\ a_{21} & a_{22} & \cdots & a_{2n} \\ \vdots & \vdots & & \vdots \\ a_{m1} & a_{m2} & \cdots & a_{mn} \end{bmatrix} \quad \text{and} \quad [\mathbf{A}|\mathbf{B}] = \left[\begin{array}{cccc|c} a_{11} & a_{12} & \cdots & a_{1n} & b_1 \\ a_{21} & a_{22} & \cdots & a_{2n} & b_2 \\ \vdots & \vdots & & \vdots & \vdots \\ a_{m1} & a_{m2} & \cdots & a_{mn} & b_m \end{array}\right]$$

Since row reduction proceeds first from left to right, the row-reduced form of **A** agrees with the first n columns of the row-reduced form of $[\mathbf{A}|\mathbf{B}]$. This implies that the rank of the coefficient matrix **A** is less than or equal to the rank of the augmented matrix. It also makes it possible to describe the solution set of a system of equations and relate the solution set to the ranks of the coefficient matrix and the augmented matrix. The following example illustrates this.

Example 12

Augmented Matrix	*System of Equations*	*Solution Set*
a. $\left[\begin{array}{ccc\|c} 1 & 0 & 0 & 2 \\ 0 & 1 & 0 & 5 \\ 0 & 0 & 1 & 1 \end{array}\right]$	$x_1 = 2$ $x_2 = 5$ $x_3 = 1$	The unique triple (2, 5, 1)

b. $\left[\begin{array}{ccc|c} 1 & 0 & 0 & 0 \\ 0 & 1 & 0 & 3 \\ 0 & 0 & 1 & 1 \\ 0 & 0 & 0 & 0 \\ 0 & 0 & 0 & 0 \end{array}\right]$ $\quad \begin{aligned} x_1 &= 0 \\ x_2 &= 3 \\ x_3 &= 1 \\ 0 &= 0 \\ 0 &= 0 \end{aligned}$ The unique triple $(0, 3, 1)$

c. $\left[\begin{array}{ccc|c} 1 & 0 & 0 & 0 \\ 0 & 1 & 0 & 3 \\ 0 & 0 & 1 & 1 \\ 0 & 0 & 0 & 1 \\ 0 & 0 & 0 & 0 \end{array}\right]$ $\quad \begin{aligned} x_1 &= 0 \\ x_2 &= 3 \\ x_3 &= 1 \\ 0 &= 1 \\ 0 &= 0 \end{aligned}$ Empty set. There is no choice of x_1, x_2, x_3 that can make $0 = 1$.

d. $\left[\begin{array}{ccc|c} 1 & 0 & 2 & 3 \\ 0 & 1 & 1 & 4 \\ 0 & 0 & 0 & 0 \\ 0 & 0 & 0 & 0 \end{array}\right]$ $\quad \begin{aligned} x_1 + 2x_3 &= 3 \\ x_2 + x_3 &= 4 \\ 0 &= 0 \\ 0 &= 0 \end{aligned}$ An infinite set in which x_3 can be assigned an arbitrary value.

e. $\left[\begin{array}{ccc|c} 1 & 2 & 3 & 1 \\ 0 & 0 & 0 & 0 \\ 0 & 0 & 0 & 0 \end{array}\right]$ $\quad \begin{aligned} x_1 + 2x_2 + 3x_3 &= 1 \\ 0 &= 0 \\ 0 &= 0 \end{aligned}$ An infinite set in which x_2 and x_3 can be assigned arbitrary values.

In part (c), the impossible condition $0 = 1$ arises because the rank of the augmented matrix is 4 and the rank of the coefficient matrix is 3. A situation like this is bound to arise unless the rank of the coefficient matrix equals the rank of the augmented matrix. The system in (c) is inconsistent.

In the other four cases compare the rank of the coefficient matrix and the number of unknowns. The number of unknowns is the same as the number of columns of **A**. In (a) and (b) the rank of **A** is 3, the number of unknowns. The system has a unique solution, since every column must be a leading column. In case (d) the rank of **A** is 2, the number of columns is 3, and there is one column that is not a leading column so that one unknown can be assigned arbitrarily. In (e) the rank of **A** is 1, the number of columns is 3, and there are two columns that are not leading columns so that two unknowns can be assigned arbitrarily. The solution set can be written as triples or as arrays. In (d) the solution set is

$$\begin{aligned} x_1 &= 3 - 2k \\ x_2 &= 4 - k \\ x_3 &= k \end{aligned} \quad \text{or} \quad \mathbf{X} = \begin{bmatrix} 3 - 2k \\ 4 - k \\ k \end{bmatrix} = \begin{bmatrix} 3 \\ 4 \\ 0 \end{bmatrix} + k \begin{bmatrix} -2 \\ -1 \\ 1 \end{bmatrix} \quad k \text{ a real number.}$$

Written as triples, the solution set is $\{(3, 4, 0) + k(-2, -1, 1), k \text{ a real number}\}$.

In (e) we have

$$\begin{aligned} x_1 &= 1 - 2k_1 - 3k_2 \\ x_2 &= 0 + k_1 + 0k_2 \\ x_3 &= 0 + 0k_1 + k_2 \end{aligned} \quad \text{or} \quad \mathbf{X} = \begin{bmatrix} 1 \\ 0 \\ 0 \end{bmatrix} + k_1 \begin{bmatrix} -2 \\ 1 \\ 0 \end{bmatrix} + k_2 \begin{bmatrix} -3 \\ 0 \\ 1 \end{bmatrix}, \quad k_1, k_2 \text{ real numbers.}$$

Written as triples, the solution set is $\{(1, 0, 0) + k_1(-2, 1, 0) + k_2(-3, 0, 1), k_1, k_2$ real numbers$\}$. ■

Example 13 gives a detailed discussion of the process of writing the solution set for a system of equations with seven unknowns, assuming that the augmented matrix of the system is already in row-reduced form.

Example 13

Augmented Matrix

$$\left[\begin{array}{ccccccc|c} 1 & 0 & 2 & -1 & 0 & 0 & 2 & 8 \\ 0 & 1 & 1 & 3 & 0 & 0 & 5 & 1 \\ 0 & 0 & 0 & 0 & 1 & 0 & -1 & 2 \\ 0 & 0 & 0 & 0 & 0 & 1 & 1 & 4 \\ 0 & 0 & 0 & 0 & 0 & 0 & 0 & 0 \\ 0 & 0 & 0 & 0 & 0 & 0 & 0 & 0 \end{array}\right]$$

The rank of the augmented matrix is 4. The rank of the coefficient matrix is 4. The leading columns are the first, second, fifth, and sixth. Therefore, the coefficient of x_1, x_2, x_5, and x_6 must be 1. These four variables can be expressed in terms of the other three, and arbitrary values can be assigned as follows: $x_3 = k_1$, $x_4 = k_2$, $x_7 = k_3$.

System of Equations

$$\begin{array}{l} x_1 + 2x_3 - x_4 + 2x_7 = 8 \\ x_2 + x_3 + 3x_4 + 5x_7 = 1 \\ x_5 - x_7 = 2 \\ x_6 + x_7 = 4 \end{array} \quad \text{or} \quad \begin{array}{l} x_1 = 8 - 2x_3 + x_4 - 2x_7 \\ x_2 = 1 - x_3 - 3x_4 - 5x_7 \\ x_5 = 2 + x_7 \\ x_6 = 4 - x_7 \end{array}$$

To obtain **X** as a sum of 7×1 arrays, we write

$$\begin{aligned} x_1 &= 8 + -2k_1 + k_2 + -2k_3 \\ x_2 &= 1 + -k_1 + -3k_2 + -5k_3 \\ x_3 &= 0 + k_1 + 0k_2 + 0k_3 \\ x_4 &= 0 + 0k_1 + k_2 + 0k_3 \\ x_5 &= 2 + 0k_1 + 0k_2 + k_3 \\ x_6 &= 4 + 0k_1 + 0k_2 + -k_3 \\ x_7 &= 0 + 0k_1 + 0k_2 + k_3 \end{aligned}$$

or

$$\begin{bmatrix} x_1 \\ x_2 \\ x_3 \\ x_4 \\ x_5 \\ x_6 \\ x_7 \end{bmatrix} = \begin{bmatrix} 8 \\ 1 \\ 0 \\ 0 \\ 2 \\ 4 \\ 0 \end{bmatrix} + k_1 \begin{bmatrix} -2 \\ -1 \\ 1 \\ 0 \\ 0 \\ 0 \\ 0 \end{bmatrix} + k_2 \begin{bmatrix} 1 \\ -3 \\ 0 \\ 1 \\ 0 \\ 0 \\ 0 \end{bmatrix} + k_3 \begin{bmatrix} -2 \\ -5 \\ 0 \\ 0 \\ 1 \\ -1 \\ 1 \end{bmatrix}$$

■

The following theorem summarizes the previous discussion.

Theorem 2 Fundamental Theorem of Linear Systems

A system of m linear algebraic equations in n unknowns can be written in the form $\mathbf{AX} = \mathbf{B}$, where $\mathbf{A}$ is $m \times n$, $\mathbf{X}$ is $n \times 1$, and $\mathbf{B}$ is $m \times 1$. Let r be the rank of $\mathbf{A}$ and r_a the rank of $[\mathbf{A}|\mathbf{B}]$.

If $r < r_a$, the system is inconsistent.
If $r = r_a = n$, the solution set consists of a single n-tuple.
If $r = r_a < n$, then the solution set is infinite and has the form

$$\{\mathbf{d} + k_1\mathbf{u}_1 + k_2\mathbf{u}_2 + \cdots + k_{n-r}\mathbf{u}_{n-r}\},$$

where $\mathbf{d}, \mathbf{u}_1, \mathbf{u}_2, \ldots, \mathbf{u}_{n-r}$ are n-tuples and $k_1, k_2, \ldots, k_{n-r}$ are arbitrary scalars.

Proof This theorem follows from a consideration of the row-reduced form of the matrices $\mathbf{A}$ and $[\mathbf{A}|\mathbf{B}]$. First note that if the row-reduced form of $[\mathbf{A}|\mathbf{B}]$ is $[\mathbf{C}|\mathbf{D}]$, then the row-reduced form of $\mathbf{A}$ is $\mathbf{C}$, and $r \leqslant r_a$.

Suppose $r < r_a$. This means that the first r rows of $\mathbf{C}$ are not zero and that $[\mathbf{C}|\mathbf{D}]$ has $r + 1$ nonzero rows. Row $r + 1$ of $[\mathbf{C}|\mathbf{D}]$ corresponds to the equation $0 = 1$. Since this cannot be true for any choice of $(x_1, x_2, \ldots, x_n)$, the equations are inconsistent.

Suppose $r = r_a = n$. Since $r = r_a$, rows $r + 1, r + 2, \ldots, m$ of $[\mathbf{C}|\mathbf{D}]$ are all zero. The fact that $r = n$ implies that all the columns of $\mathbf{A}$ are leading columns and the submatrix in the first n rows of $\mathbf{A}$ is $\mathbf{I}_n$. The row-reduced form of $[\mathbf{A}|\mathbf{B}]$ is thus

$$\left[\begin{array}{cccc|c} 1 & 0 & \cdots & 0 & d_1 \\ 0 & 1 & \cdots & 0 & d_2 \\ \vdots & \vdots & & \vdots & \vdots \\ 0 & 0 & \cdots & 1 & d_n \\ 0 & 0 & \cdots & 0 & 0 \\ 0 & 0 & \cdots & 0 & 0 \end{array}\right]$$

which implies a unique solution $(x_1, x_2, \ldots, x_n) = (d_1, d_2, \ldots, d_n)$.

Suppose $r = r_a < n$. Since $r = r_a$, again rows $r + 1, r + 2, \ldots, m$ are all zero. Since $r < n$, there are exactly r leading columns and $n - r$ nonleading columns, where $n - r > 0$. Each unknown corresponding to a leading column can be written as a linear combination of the unknowns corresponding to nonleading columns. This leads to the representation

$$\mathbf{x} = \mathbf{d} + k_1\mathbf{u}_1 + k_2\mathbf{u}_2 + \cdots + k_{n-r}\mathbf{u}_{n-r}. \qquad \square$$

Corollary In the case of an $n \times n$ square matrix $\mathbf{A}$, the following statements are equivalent:

a) $\mathbf{A}$ is row equivalent to $\mathbf{I}$.
b) $\mathbf{AX} = \mathbf{B}$ has a unique solution.
c) $\mathbf{AX} = \mathbf{0}$ has only the trivial solution.
d) The rank of $\mathbf{A}$ is n. $\square$

SUMMARY Row operations on a matrix **A** produce a unique matrix with the following properties: There are r nonzero rows and these are the first r rows of the matrix; the first nonzero element in each nonzero row is 1; the column containing this 1 is a leading column and has all other elements zero; there are r leading columns; if $a_{ij} = 1$ and $a_{i+1,k} = 1$, then $j < k$. This unique matrix is called the Row-Reduced Form of **A**. The number r is the rank of **A**.

A system of m linear equations in n unknowns is equivalent to the single equation $\mathbf{A}_{m\times n}\mathbf{X}_{n\times 1} = \mathbf{B}_{m\times 1}$. Let r be the rank of the coefficient matrix **A**, and r_a the rank of the augmented matrix $[\mathbf{A}|\mathbf{B}]$. It is not possible to have $r > r_a$ or to have $r > n$. The Fundamental Theorem of Linear Systems states that:

If $r < r_a$, there is no solution; the system is inconsistent.
If $r = r_a = n$, there is one solution.
If $r = r_a < n$, there is an infinite set of solutions.

A system of linear equations can be solved by the following steps: Write the augmented matrix of the system; use row operations to find the row-reduced form; write the system of equations corresponding to the row-reduced form; write the solution if there is one.

EXERCISES 2.2

1. Write each of the following matrices in row-reduced form and find its rank.

a. $\mathbf{A} = \begin{bmatrix} 3 & 4 \\ 1 & 2 \\ -1 & 6 \end{bmatrix}$

b. $\mathbf{A} = \begin{bmatrix} 3 & 1 & -1 \\ 4 & 2 & 6 \end{bmatrix}$

c. $\mathbf{A} = \begin{bmatrix} -1 & 4 & 1 \\ 0 & 7 & 5 \\ -2 & 3 & -1 \end{bmatrix}$

d. $\mathbf{A} = \begin{bmatrix} 2 & 1 & 1 \\ 0 & 0 & 0 \\ 3 & 1 & 2 \end{bmatrix}$

2. Write each of the following matrices in row-reduced form and find the rank of each matrix.

a. $\mathbf{A} = \begin{bmatrix} 1 & 3 & 1 & 7 \\ 3 & -2 & 4 & 1 \\ 4 & 1 & 9 & 6 \end{bmatrix}$

b. $\mathbf{A} = \begin{bmatrix} 1 & 2 & 1 \\ 1 & 3 & 5 \\ 2 & 5 & 6 \\ 3 & 7 & 7 \end{bmatrix}$

c. $\mathbf{A} = \begin{bmatrix} 1 & 1 & 3 & 1 \\ 1 & 2 & 1 & 4 \\ 2 & 3 & 4 & 6 \\ 3 & 4 & 7 & 7 \end{bmatrix}$

3. a. What is the rank of a zero matrix whose size is 3×4? What is the rank of a zero matrix of size $m \times n$?

b. What is the rank of a 2×2 identity matrix? What is the rank of a 3×3 identity matrix? What is the rank of an $n \times n$ identity matrix?

4. a. Show that the possible row-reduced forms of a 2×2 matrix are

$$\begin{bmatrix} 0 & 0 \\ 0 & 0 \end{bmatrix}, \begin{bmatrix} 0 & 1 \\ 0 & 0 \end{bmatrix}, \begin{bmatrix} 1 & c \\ 0 & 0 \end{bmatrix}, \begin{bmatrix} 1 & 0 \\ 0 & 1 \end{bmatrix}$$

where c stands for any number not necessarily 0 or 1. In each case, what is the rank of the matrix?

b. Write the possible row-reduced forms of a 2×3 matrix. What are the possible values of the rank of a 2×3 matrix?

5. What is the largest possible rank of a 3×4 matrix? Of a 5×2 matrix? Of a 2×5 matrix? Of a 4×4 matrix? Of an $m \times n$ matrix? Justify your answers.

6. Let

$$\mathbf{A} = \begin{bmatrix} 1 & 1 & 0 \\ 2 & 2 & 3 \\ 1 & 1 & 3 \end{bmatrix} \quad \text{and} \quad \mathbf{B} = \begin{bmatrix} 0 & 0 & 3 \\ -1 & -1 & 0 \\ 0 & 0 & 0 \end{bmatrix}$$

Find $\mathbf{A} + \mathbf{B}$. What is the rank of $\mathbf{A}$, the rank of $\mathbf{B}$, and the rank of $\mathbf{A} + \mathbf{B}$?

7. a. Give an example of a matrix $\mathbf{A}$ of rank 1 and a matrix $\mathbf{B}$ of rank 1 such that the matrix $\mathbf{A} + \mathbf{B}$ has rank 2.

b. Give an example of a matrix $\mathbf{A}$ of rank 3 and a matrix $\mathbf{B}$ of rank 3 such that the matrix $\mathbf{A} + \mathbf{B}$ has rank 0.

c. Give an example of a matrix $\mathbf{A}$ of rank 3 and a matrix $\mathbf{B}$ of rank 3 such that the matrix $\mathbf{A} + \mathbf{B}$ has rank 1.

8. The system of equations $\mathbf{AX} = \mathbf{B}$ has augmented matrix

$$\left[\begin{array}{cccc|c} 1 & 1 & 2 & 1 & 3 \\ 1 & -1 & 2 & 1 & 1 \\ 1 & 2 & 3 & 4 & 5 \end{array}\right]$$

Find the row-reduced form of the augmented matrix and the row-reduced form of the coefficient matrix. Compare the rank of the augmented matrix and the rank of the coefficient matrix.

9. In each case solve the system of equations by reducing the augmented matrix to row-reduced form. Write the solution set of the system.

a.
$$\begin{aligned} x_1 + 2x_2 + x_3 + x_4 &= 2 \\ x_1 - x_2 + 4x_3 + 2x_4 &= -2 \\ 2x_1 + x_2 + 3x_3 + x_4 &= 2 \\ -3x_1 + x_2 + x_3 + 4x_4 &= -6 \end{aligned}$$

b.
$$\begin{aligned} x_1 + 2x_2 + x_3 + x_4 &= 2 \\ x_1 - x_2 + 4x_3 + 4x_4 &= -4 \\ 2x_1 + x_2 + 5x_3 + 5x_4 &= -2 \\ 3x_1 \qquad + 9x_3 + 9x_4 &= -6 \end{aligned}$$

10. The matrix

$$\left[\begin{array}{ccc|c} 1 & 1 & 2 & 1 \\ 1 & 0 & -1 & 1 \\ 2 & 3 & 5 & 4 \end{array}\right]$$

is the augmented matrix of a system of equations. Find the row-reduced form of this matrix. What is the corresponding system of equations and its solution?

11. Three types of row operations are defined in Definition 2. Let

$$\mathbf{E}_1 = \begin{bmatrix} 1 & 0 & 0 \\ 0 & 0 & 1 \\ 0 & 1 & 0 \end{bmatrix}, \quad \mathbf{E}_2 = \begin{bmatrix} 1 & 0 & 0 \\ 0 & k & 0 \\ 0 & 0 & 1 \end{bmatrix},$$

$$\mathbf{E}_3 = \begin{bmatrix} 1 & 0 & 0 \\ 0 & 1 & 0 \\ k & 0 & 1 \end{bmatrix},$$

$$\mathbf{A} = \begin{bmatrix} a_{11} & a_{12} & \cdots & a_{1n} \\ a_{21} & a_{22} & \cdots & a_{2n} \\ a_{31} & a_{32} & \cdots & a_{3n} \end{bmatrix}$$

Show that: $\mathbf{E}_1\mathbf{A}$ performs an operation of type 1 on the matrix $\mathbf{A}$, $\mathbf{E}_2\mathbf{A}$ performs an operation of type 2 on matrix $\mathbf{A}$, and $\mathbf{E}_3\mathbf{A}$ performs an operation of type 3 on matrix $\mathbf{A}$. In each case describe the operation performed.

12. Let $\mathbf{A}$ be a 4×5 matrix.

a. Write a matrix $\mathbf{E}$ such that $\mathbf{EA}$ has rows 2 and 4 of $\mathbf{A}$ interchanged.

b. Write a matrix $\mathbf{E}$ such that $\mathbf{EA}$ has row 3 of $\mathbf{A}$ multiplied by 5.

c. Write a matrix $\mathbf{E}$ such that $\mathbf{EA}$ has -2 times row 4 added to row 2.

13. Let $\mathbf{A} = \begin{bmatrix} 1 & 2 & 1 \\ -1 & 1 & 0 \\ 1 & 2 & 4 \end{bmatrix}$. Let $\mathbf{B}_1 = \begin{bmatrix} 1 & 0 & 0 \\ 1 & 1 & 0 \\ 0 & 0 & 1 \end{bmatrix}$, $\mathbf{B}_2 =$

$$\begin{bmatrix} 1 & 0 & 0 \\ 0 & 1 & 0 \\ -1 & 0 & 1 \end{bmatrix}, \mathbf{B}_3 = \begin{bmatrix} 1 & 0 & 0 \\ 0 & 1 & 0 \\ 0 & 0 & \frac{1}{3} \end{bmatrix}, \mathbf{B}_4 = \begin{bmatrix} 1 & 0 & -1 \\ 0 & 1 & 0 \\ 0 & 0 & 1 \end{bmatrix},$$

$$\mathbf{B}_5 = \begin{bmatrix} 1 & 0 & 0 \\ 0 & 1 & -1 \\ 0 & 0 & 1 \end{bmatrix}, \mathbf{B}_6 = \begin{bmatrix} 1 & 0 & 0 \\ 0 & \frac{1}{3} & 0 \\ 0 & 0 & 1 \end{bmatrix}, \text{ and}$$

$$\mathbf{B}_7 = \begin{bmatrix} 1 & -2 & 0 \\ 0 & 1 & 0 \\ 0 & 0 & 1 \end{bmatrix}, \text{ and let } \mathbf{A}_i = \mathbf{B}_i\mathbf{A}_{i-1},$$

$i = 1, 2, \ldots, 7$, where $\mathbf{A}_0 = \mathbf{A}$. Show that $\mathbf{A}_7$ is the row-reduced form of $\mathbf{A}$.

14. Write the sequence of matrices $\mathbf{B}_i$ needed to produce the row-reduced form of

$$\mathbf{A} = \begin{bmatrix} 1 & 2 & -6 \\ 1 & 4 & 4 \\ 3 & 10 & 2 \end{bmatrix}$$ by a method similar to Problem 13.

15. Let $\mathbf{A} = [\mathbf{A}_1\ \mathbf{A}_2\ \mathbf{A}_3] = \begin{bmatrix} 1 & 3 & 1 \\ 2 & 1 & 1 \\ 0 & 1 & 5 \end{bmatrix}$ and $\mathbf{B} =$

$[\mathbf{A}_3\ \mathbf{A}_1\ \mathbf{A}_2] = \begin{bmatrix} 1 & 1 & 3 \\ 1 & 2 & 1 \\ 5 & 0 & 1 \end{bmatrix}$. Let $\mathbf{C} = [\mathbf{C}_1\ \mathbf{C}_2\ \mathbf{C}_3]$ be the matrix obtained from $\mathbf{A}$ by adding -2 times row 1 to row 2, and $\mathbf{D}$ be the matrix obtained from $\mathbf{B}$ by the same row operation. Show that the columns of $\mathbf{D}$ are $\mathbf{C}_3$, $\mathbf{C}_1$, $\mathbf{C}_2$.

16. The $m \times n$ matrix $\mathbf{B}$ is obtained from $\mathbf{A}$ by arranging the columns of $\mathbf{A}$ in the order $j_1, j_2, \ldots, j_n$. If $\mathbf{A}$ is row-equivalent to $\mathbf{C}$, show that $\mathbf{B}$ is row-equivalent to the matrix obtained from $\mathbf{C}$ by arranging the columns of $\mathbf{C}$ in the order $j_1, j_2, \ldots, j_n$.

17. In each case the augmented matrix of a system of equations is given in row-reduced form. Compare the rank of the coefficient matrix and the rank of the augmented matrix. Does a solution exist? If so write the solution.

a. $\left[\begin{array}{cccc|c} 1 & 3 & 0 & 0 & 0 \\ 0 & 0 & 1 & 2 & 0 \\ 0 & 0 & 0 & 0 & 3 \end{array}\right]$

b. $\left[\begin{array}{cccc|c} 1 & 2 & 0 & 0 & 0 \\ 0 & 0 & 1 & 1 & 0 \\ 0 & 0 & 0 & 0 & 0 \end{array}\right]$

c. $\left[\begin{array}{ccccc|c} 1 & 2 & 0 & 0 & 4 & 3 \\ 0 & 0 & 1 & 0 & 2 & 5 \\ 0 & 0 & 0 & 1 & 3 & 7 \\ 0 & 0 & 0 & 0 & 0 & 0 \end{array}\right]$

18. In each case the augmented matrix of a system of equations is given in row-reduced form. Write the solution of the system as $n \times 1$ arrays.

a. $\left[\begin{array}{ccc|c} 1 & 0 & 1 & 2 \\ 0 & 1 & 2 & 3 \\ 0 & 0 & 0 & 0 \end{array}\right]$

b. $\left[\begin{array}{cccc|c} 1 & 2 & 0 & 0 & 5 \\ 0 & 0 & 1 & 0 & 3 \\ 0 & 0 & 0 & 1 & 1 \end{array}\right]$

c. $\left[\begin{array}{ccccc|c} 1 & 2 & 0 & 0 & 4 & 0 \\ 0 & 0 & 1 & 0 & 2 & 0 \\ 0 & 0 & 0 & 1 & 3 & 0 \\ 0 & 0 & 0 & 0 & 0 & 0 \end{array}\right]$

In each case compare the rank of the coefficient matrix and the rank of the augmented matrix.

19. In each case below, the augmented matrix of a system of equations is given not quite in row-reduced form. For each decide whether a solution will exist, whether the solution will be unique, and if the solution is not unique, how many of the unknowns can be given arbitrary values. Compare the rank of the coefficient matrix with the rank of the augmented matrix and with the number of unknowns.

a. $\left[\begin{array}{cccc|c} 1 & 2 & 3 & 4 & 5 \\ 0 & 1 & 1 & 3 & 2 \\ 0 & 0 & 0 & 1 & 1 \end{array}\right]$

b. $\left[\begin{array}{cccc|c} 1 & 2 & 3 & 4 & 5 \\ 0 & 1 & 1 & 3 & 2 \\ 0 & 1 & 1 & 3 & 2 \end{array}\right]$

c. $\left[\begin{array}{cccc|c} 1 & 2 & 3 & 4 & 5 \\ 0 & 1 & 1 & 3 & 2 \\ 0 & 0 & 0 & 0 & 2 \end{array}\right]$

d. $\left[\begin{array}{cccc|c} 1 & 2 & 3 & 4 & 5 \\ 0 & 1 & 1 & 3 & 2 \\ 0 & 0 & 1 & 2 & 3 \\ 0 & 0 & 0 & 1 & 4 \end{array}\right]$

20. In each case solve the system of equations if a solution exists.

a. $\begin{bmatrix} 1 & -3 \\ 2 & -1 \end{bmatrix} \begin{bmatrix} x_1 \\ x_2 \end{bmatrix} = \begin{bmatrix} 1 \\ 4 \end{bmatrix}$

b. $\begin{bmatrix} 1 & 3 \\ 2 & 6 \end{bmatrix} \begin{bmatrix} x_1 \\ x_2 \end{bmatrix} = \begin{bmatrix} 2 \\ 3 \end{bmatrix}$

c. $\begin{bmatrix} 1 & 2 & 0 & 1 \\ 5 & 3 & 3 & 3 \\ -2 & 3 & -3 & 0 \end{bmatrix} \begin{bmatrix} x_1 \\ x_2 \\ x_3 \\ x_4 \end{bmatrix} = \begin{bmatrix} 2 \\ 4 \\ 2 \end{bmatrix}$

21. For the system of equations $\mathbf{AX} = \mathbf{B}$, tell whether a solution exists, whether it is unique, and if it is not unique how many unknowns can be assigned arbitrarily.

a. $\mathbf{A}$ is 4×3, rank of $\mathbf{A}$ is 2, rank of $[\mathbf{A}|\mathbf{B}]$ is 2.
b. $\mathbf{A}$ is 4×5, rank of $\mathbf{A}$ is 3, rank of $[\mathbf{A}|\mathbf{B}]$ is 4.
c. $\mathbf{A}$ is 4×5, rank of $\mathbf{A}$ is 4, rank of $[\mathbf{A}|\mathbf{B}]$ is 4.
d. $\mathbf{A}$ is 5×5, rank of $\mathbf{A}$ is 5, rank of $[\mathbf{A}|\mathbf{B}]$ is 5.

22. Find the solution set of each of the following systems of equations.

a.
$$\begin{aligned} x_1 + x_2 + x_3 + x_4 &= 8 \\ -x_1 + 3x_2 - x_3 - 2x_4 &= 0 \\ 2x_1 + 6x_2 - 2x_3 + x_4 &= 16 \end{aligned}$$

b.
$$\begin{aligned} x_1 + x_2 + x_3 + x_4 &= 8 \\ -x_1 + 3x_2 - x_3 - 2x_4 &= 1 \\ 2x_1 + 6x_2 - 2x_3 + x_4 &= 16 \end{aligned}$$

c.
$$\begin{aligned} x_1 + x_2 + x_3 + x_4 &= 8 \\ -x_1 + 3x_2 - x_3 - 2x_4 &= 0 \\ 2x_1 + 6x_2 - 2x_3 + x_4 &= 12 \end{aligned}$$

23. In each case find the solution set if it exists. Find r, r_a, and n, and compare your answer with Theorem 2.

a.
$$\begin{aligned} x_1 + x_2 + x_3 &= 4 \\ 2x_1 + 5x_2 - 2x_3 &= 3 \\ x_1 + 7x_2 - 7x_3 &= 5 \end{aligned}$$

b.
$$\begin{aligned} x_1 + x_2 &= 7 \\ 3x_1 + 5x_2 &= 2 \end{aligned}$$

c.
$$\begin{aligned} x - 2y - z &= 1 \\ x + y + z &= 2 \\ x + 2y + 2z &= 2 \end{aligned}$$

d.
$$\begin{aligned} x + 2y \phantom{{}-z} - w &= 2 \\ x + 3y - z + w &= 1 \\ x + 4y - 2z + 3w &= 0 \\ 2y + z - 2w &= 2 \end{aligned}$$

24. In each case decide whether the system of equations is consistent or inconsistent.

a. $\mathbf{AX} = \mathbf{B}$, where $\mathbf{A}$ is 3×4, the rank of $\mathbf{A}$ is 2, and $[\mathbf{A}|\mathbf{B}]$ has rank 2.

b. $\mathbf{AX} = \mathbf{B}$, where $\mathbf{A}$ is 3×5 and the rank of $\mathbf{A}$ is 3.

c. $\mathbf{AX} = \mathbf{B}$, where $\mathbf{A}$ is 3×3, and the rank of $\mathbf{A}$ is 2, with rank $[\mathbf{A}|\mathbf{B}] = 3$.

d. $\mathbf{AX} = \mathbf{0}$, where $\mathbf{A}$ is 3×3 and the rank of $\mathbf{A}$ is 3.

25. Is any further information needed to decide whether each system of equations is consistent or inconsistent? If so, what is needed? If not, is the system consistent?

a. $\mathbf{AX} = \mathbf{B}$, where $\mathbf{A}$ is 3×4 and the rank of $\mathbf{A}$ is 3.

b. $\mathbf{AX} = \mathbf{B}$, where $\mathbf{A}$ is 3×2 and the rank of $[\mathbf{A}|\mathbf{B}]$ is 3.

c. $\mathbf{AX} = \mathbf{B}$, where $\mathbf{A}$ is 3×2 and the rank of $\mathbf{A}$ is 2.

d. $\mathbf{AX} = \mathbf{B}$, where $\mathbf{A}$ is 3×3 and the rank of $[\mathbf{A}|\mathbf{B}]$ is 3.

e. $\mathbf{AX} = \mathbf{B}$, where $\mathbf{A}$ is 3×2 and the rank of $[\mathbf{A}|\mathbf{B}]$ is 2.

26. Let $\mathbf{A} = \begin{bmatrix} 1 & 2 & 3 \\ 0 & 1 & 3 \\ 1 & 1 & 1 \end{bmatrix}$. The equation $\mathbf{AX} = \mathbf{B}$ is to be solved using four different values of $\mathbf{B}$:

$$\mathbf{B}_1 = \begin{bmatrix} 4 \\ 1 \\ 7 \end{bmatrix}, \quad \mathbf{B}_2 = \begin{bmatrix} -1 \\ -3 \\ 1 \end{bmatrix},$$

$$\mathbf{B}_3 = \begin{bmatrix} 2 \\ 2 \\ 1 \end{bmatrix}, \quad \mathbf{B}_4 = \begin{bmatrix} 0 \\ 1 \\ 0 \end{bmatrix}.$$

This could be done as four separate problems. Devise a way to save yourself work by setting up the problem so that it can be done in a single set of row reductions.

Supplemental Topic

LU Factorization. We have seen that row operations can be performed by multiplication on the left by appropriately chosen matrices. (See Problems 11–14.) For certain matrices this method can be used to write the matrix as a product of a lower-triangular matrix $\mathbf{L}$ and an upper-triangular matrix $\mathbf{U}$. This is called the $\mathbf{LU}$ *factorization* and is illustrated in the following.

27. a. Show that if $\begin{bmatrix} 1 & 0 & 0 \\ 0 & 1 & 0 \\ k & 0 & 1 \end{bmatrix} \mathbf{A} = \mathbf{B}$, then $\begin{bmatrix} 1 & 0 & 0 \\ 0 & 1 & 0 \\ -k & 0 & 1 \end{bmatrix} \mathbf{B} = \mathbf{A}$.

b. What row operation is performed by the product $\begin{bmatrix} 1 & 0 & 0 \\ 0 & 1 & 0 \\ k & 0 & 1 \end{bmatrix} \mathbf{A}$? What row operation is performed by the product $\begin{bmatrix} 1 & 0 & 0 \\ 0 & 1 & 0 \\ -k & 0 & 1 \end{bmatrix} \mathbf{B}$?

28. a. Let $\mathbf{A} = \begin{bmatrix} 1 & 2 & 4 \\ 3 & 1 & 4 \\ -2 & 6 & 2 \end{bmatrix}$. Calculate $\mathbf{A}_1$, $\mathbf{A}_2$, and

U, where $\begin{bmatrix} 1 & 0 & 0 \\ -3 & 1 & 0 \\ 0 & 0 & 1 \end{bmatrix}\mathbf{A} = \mathbf{A}_1$, $\begin{bmatrix} 1 & 0 & 0 \\ 0 & 1 & 0 \\ 2 & 0 & 1 \end{bmatrix}\mathbf{A}_1 = \mathbf{A}_2$,

and $\begin{bmatrix} 1 & 0 & 0 \\ 0 & 1 & 0 \\ 0 & 2 & 1 \end{bmatrix}\mathbf{A}_2 = \mathbf{U}$.

b. Calculate a matrix **C** such that **CA** = **U**.

c. What special type of matrix is **C**? What type of matrix is **U**?

29. a. With **A**, $\mathbf{A}_1$, $\mathbf{A}_2$, **U** as in Problem 28, find matrices $\mathbf{B}_1$, $\mathbf{B}_2$, $\mathbf{B}_3$ such that $\mathbf{B}_3\mathbf{U} = \mathbf{A}_2$, $\mathbf{B}_2\mathbf{A}_2 = \mathbf{A}_1$, and $\mathbf{B}_1\mathbf{A}_1 = \mathbf{A}$.

b. Find a matrix **L** such that **LU** = **A**. Notice that **L** is lower triangular and **U** is upper triangular.

30. a. Write the matrix **L** in Problem 29 as the product of the matrices $\mathbf{B}_i$, $i = 1, 2, 3$. Be careful to write the matrices in the correct order.

b. What special relationship do you observe between the elements of **L** and the elements of $\mathbf{B}_i$, $i = 1, 2, 3$?

c. Does the same simple relation hold in the case of the matrix **C**?

31. a. Find an **LU** factorization of $\begin{bmatrix} 2 & 3 \\ 4 & 5 \end{bmatrix}$.

b. Find an **LU** factorization of $\begin{bmatrix} 3 & 5 & 4 \\ 6 & 7 & -1 \\ -3 & -4 & 4 \end{bmatrix}$.

32. Find an **LU** factorization of

$$\begin{bmatrix} 2 & 1 & 0 & 2 \\ -2 & 3 & 1 & 3 \\ 0 & -12 & -4 & -9 \\ 4 & 6 & 0 & 18 \end{bmatrix}.$$

33. a. Find an **LU** factorization of $\begin{bmatrix} 2 & 1 & 4 \\ 6 & 5 & 2 \\ 4 & 2 & 3 \end{bmatrix}$.

b. What difficulty arises when you try to find an **LU** factorization of $\begin{bmatrix} 2 & 1 & 4 \\ 4 & 2 & 3 \\ 6 & 5 & 2 \end{bmatrix}$?

c. The matrix in (**a**) can be obtained from (**b**) by interchanging rows. This can be performed by multiplying on the left by $\begin{bmatrix} 1 & 0 & 0 \\ 0 & 0 & 1 \\ 0 & 1 & 0 \end{bmatrix}$. Why can this multiplication *not* be a part of the **LU** factorization?

34. Let $\mathbf{A} = \begin{bmatrix} 1 & 2 & 4 \\ 3 & 1 & 4 \\ -2 & 6 & 2 \end{bmatrix}$. In Problems 28 and 29, the matrix **A** was found to have the **LU** factorization $\begin{bmatrix} 1 & 0 & 0 \\ 3 & 1 & 0 \\ -2 & -2 & 1 \end{bmatrix}\begin{bmatrix} 1 & 2 & 4 \\ 0 & -5 & -8 \\ 0 & 0 & -6 \end{bmatrix}$.

This factorization can be used to solve the system of equations

$$\begin{bmatrix} 1 & 2 & 4 \\ 3 & 1 & 4 \\ -2 & 6 & 2 \end{bmatrix}\begin{bmatrix} x_1 \\ x_2 \\ x_3 \end{bmatrix} = \begin{bmatrix} 1 \\ -1 \\ 18 \end{bmatrix}.$$

First solve the system $\begin{bmatrix} 1 & 0 & 0 \\ 3 & 1 & 0 \\ -2 & -2 & 1 \end{bmatrix}\begin{bmatrix} d_1 \\ d_2 \\ d_3 \end{bmatrix} = \begin{bmatrix} 1 \\ -1 \\ 18 \end{bmatrix}$ and then solve the system $\begin{bmatrix} 1 & 2 & 4 \\ 0 & -5 & -8 \\ 0 & 0 & -6 \end{bmatrix}\begin{bmatrix} x_1 \\ x_2 \\ x_3 \end{bmatrix} = \begin{bmatrix} d_1 \\ d_2 \\ d_3 \end{bmatrix}$. The first step involves only front substitution, and the second involves only back substitution.

35. Use the method described in Problem 34 to solve the systems **AX** = **C** for $\mathbf{C} = \begin{bmatrix} 5 \\ 7 \\ 0 \end{bmatrix}$, $\mathbf{C} = \begin{bmatrix} 13 \\ 10 \\ 14 \end{bmatrix}$, and $\mathbf{C} = \begin{bmatrix} -4 \\ -1 \\ -2 \end{bmatrix}$, where $\mathbf{A} = \begin{bmatrix} 1 & 2 & 4 \\ 3 & 1 & 4 \\ -2 & 6 & 2 \end{bmatrix}$. Under what conditions might **LU** factorization save work in solving systems of equations?

2.3 Homogeneous Systems

A special case of importance is a system of equations of the form $\mathbf{AX} = \mathbf{0}$. Such a system cannot be inconsistent. Its augmented matrix has the form $[\mathbf{A}|\mathbf{0}]$. Whatever row operations are performed on such a matrix, it is impossible to introduce a nonzero element in the last column. The rank of $\mathbf{A}$ and the rank of $[\mathbf{A}|\mathbf{0}]$ must be equal.

Homogeneous System

Definition 5

A system of equations of the form $\mathbf{AX} = \mathbf{0}$ is called a **homogeneous system**.

Example 14 a. Solve the system

$$\begin{aligned} x_1 + 2x_2 - 6x_3 &= 0 \\ x_1 + 4x_2 + 4x_3 &= 0 \\ 3x_1 + 10x_2 + 2x_3 &= 0 \end{aligned}$$

The augmented matrix is

$$\left[\begin{array}{ccc|c} 1 & 2 & -6 & 0 \\ 1 & 4 & 4 & 0 \\ 3 & 10 & 2 & 0 \end{array}\right]$$

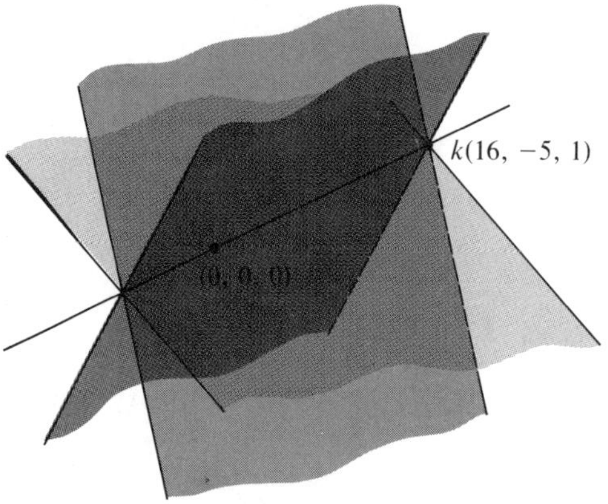

FIGURE 2.3

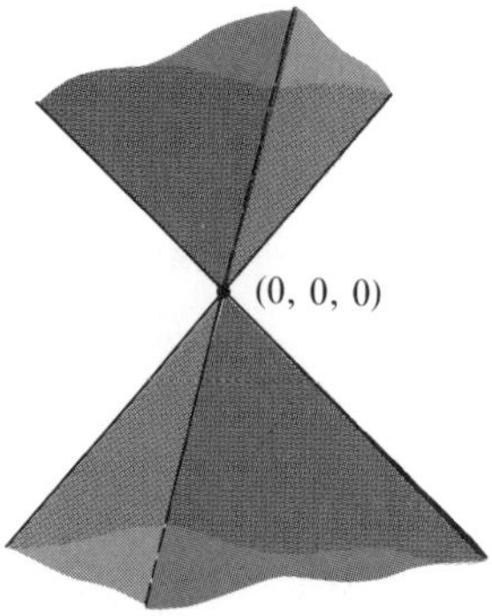

FIGURE 2.4

Put this in row-reduced form:

$$\left[\begin{array}{ccc|c} 1 & 2 & -6 & 0 \\ 0 & 2 & 10 & 0 \\ 0 & 4 & 20 & 0 \end{array}\right] \Leftrightarrow \left[\begin{array}{ccc|c} 1 & 2 & -6 & 0 \\ 0 & 1 & 5 & 0 \\ 0 & 1 & 5 & 0 \end{array}\right] \Leftrightarrow \left[\begin{array}{ccc|c} 1 & 0 & -16 & 0 \\ 0 & 1 & 5 & 0 \\ 0 & 0 & 0 & 0 \end{array}\right]$$

The solution set is the infinite set $\{k(16, -5, 1),\ k \text{ is a real number}\}$.

Each equation in this system represents a plane through the origin, so $(0, 0, 0)$ is a solution. In addition, all three planes contain the same line through the origin, a line parallel to the vector $\mathbf{u} = (16, -5, 1)$.

Note that $\mathbf{u}$ is perpendicular to the normal vectors of the planes: $(16, -5, 1) \cdot (1, 2, -6) = 0$, $(16, -5, 1) \cdot (1, 4, 4) = 0$, and $(16, -5, 1) \cdot (3, 10, 2) = 0$. (See Figure 2.3.)

b. Solve the system

$$\begin{aligned} x_1 + 2x_2 - 6x_3 &= 0 \\ x_1 + 4x_2 + 4x_3 &= 0 \\ 3x_1 + 10x_2 + 6x_3 &= 0 \end{aligned}$$

$$\left[\begin{array}{ccc|c} 1 & 2 & -6 & 0 \\ 1 & 4 & 4 & 0 \\ 3 & 10 & 6 & 0 \end{array}\right] \Leftrightarrow \left[\begin{array}{ccc|c} 1 & 2 & -6 & 0 \\ 0 & 2 & 10 & 0 \\ 0 & 4 & 24 & 0 \end{array}\right] \Leftrightarrow \left[\begin{array}{ccc|c} 1 & 2 & -6 & 0 \\ 0 & 1 & 5 & 0 \\ 0 & 1 & 6 & 0 \end{array}\right]$$

$$\Leftrightarrow \left[\begin{array}{ccc|c} 1 & 2 & -6 & 0 \\ 0 & 1 & 5 & 0 \\ 0 & 0 & 1 & 0 \end{array}\right] \Leftrightarrow \left[\begin{array}{ccc|c} 1 & 2 & 0 & 0 \\ 0 & 1 & 0 & 0 \\ 0 & 0 & 1 & 0 \end{array}\right] \Leftrightarrow \left[\begin{array}{ccc|c} 1 & 0 & 0 & 0 \\ 0 & 1 & 0 & 0 \\ 0 & 0 & 1 & 0 \end{array}\right]$$

The solution set consists of the single 3-tuple $\{(0, 0, 0)\}$.

The three planes in this system of equations intersect in a single point, the origin. (See Figure 2.4.) Since each of the planes passes through the origin, their intersection must contain at least this point.

c. Each system of equations in (a) and (b) has the form $\mathbf{AX} = \mathbf{0}$. As we have seen, the equation $\mathbf{AX} = \mathbf{0}$ asks for a vector orthogonal to each of the rows of $\mathbf{A}$. The case in which $\mathbf{A}$ is 2×3 is of special importance. The system

$$\begin{aligned} a_1x_1 + a_2x_2 + a_3x_3 &= 0 \\ b_1x_1 + b_2x_2 + b_3x_3 &= 0 \end{aligned}$$

asks for a vector orthogonal to the vectors $\mathbf{u} = (a_1, a_2, a_3)$ and $\mathbf{v} = (b_1, b_2, b_3)$. If these vectors are not parallel the solution set of the system of equations is

$$k(a_2b_3 - a_3b_2, a_3b_1 - a_1b_3, a_1b_2 - a_2b_1).$$

(See Exercises 2.3, Problem 17.) This is a family of parallel vectors, each of which is orthogonal to both the vectors $\mathbf{u}$ and $\mathbf{v}$. The cross product of $\mathbf{u}$ and $\mathbf{v}$, written $\mathbf{u} \times \mathbf{v}$, is defined to be

$$\mathbf{u} \times \mathbf{v} = (a_2b_3 - a_3b_2, a_3b_1 - a_1b_3, a_1b_2 - a_2b_1).$$

■

As we have seen, a homogeneous system $\mathbf{AX} = \mathbf{0}$ cannot be inconsistent. Every homogeneous system of equations must have at least one solution $\mathbf{X} = \mathbf{0}$. There are homogeneous systems that have nonzero solutions as well. In Example 14(a), the solution set is the set $\{k(16, -5, 1), k \text{ a real number}\}$—that is, all vectors lying on a line through $(0, 0, 0)$, in the direction of $(16, -5, 1)$. The existence of nonzero solutions is important, for example, in the study of eigenvalues. We consider this in Chapter 3.

Trivial Solution

Definition 6

The zero n-tuple $\mathbf{X} = \mathbf{0}$ is called the **trivial solution** of $\mathbf{AX} = \mathbf{0}$. A nonzero n-tuple such that $\mathbf{AX} = \mathbf{0}$ is called a **nontrivial solution**.

Theorem 3 The homogeneous system $\mathbf{AX} = \mathbf{0}$, where $\mathbf{X}$ is $n \times 1$, has nontrivial solutions if and only if the rank of $\mathbf{A}$ is less than n.

Proof Since the equations are homogeneous, $r = r_a$ and they are consistent. If $r < n$, then there is an infinite solution set, hence nontrivial solutions. Conversely, if nontrivial solutions exist, there must be solutions other than $\mathbf{X} = \mathbf{0}$; hence an infinite set. This implies $r < n$ (Theorem 2, Fundamental Theorem of Linear Systems). □

There is a close relationship between the solution set of the nonhomogeneous system $\mathbf{AX} = \mathbf{B}$ and that of the homogeneous system $\mathbf{AX} = \mathbf{0}$.

Example 15 Consider the nonhomogeneous system

$$\begin{aligned} x_1 + 2x_2 - 6x_3 &= 11 \\ x_1 + 4x_2 + 4x_3 &= 5 \\ 3x_1 + 10x_2 + 2x_3 &= 21 \end{aligned}$$

When we put the augmented matrix in row-reduced form, we get

$$\left[\begin{array}{ccc|c} 1 & 2 & -6 & 11 \\ 1 & 4 & 4 & 5 \\ 3 & 10 & 2 & 21 \end{array}\right] \Leftrightarrow \left[\begin{array}{ccc|c} 1 & 2 & -6 & 11 \\ 0 & 2 & 10 & -6 \\ 0 & 4 & 20 & -12 \end{array}\right] \Leftrightarrow \left[\begin{array}{ccc|c} 1 & 2 & -6 & 11 \\ 0 & 1 & 5 & -3 \\ 0 & 1 & 5 & -3 \end{array}\right]$$

$$\Leftrightarrow \left[\begin{array}{ccc|c} 1 & 0 & -16 & 17 \\ 0 & 1 & 5 & -3 \\ 0 & 0 & 0 & 0 \end{array}\right]$$

The solution set of this system of equations is $\mathbf{X} = \begin{bmatrix} 17 \\ -3 \\ 0 \end{bmatrix} + k \begin{bmatrix} 16 \\ -5 \\ 1 \end{bmatrix}$, k a real number, or $\{x = (17, -3, 0) + k(16, -5, 1), k \text{ a real number}\}$. ■

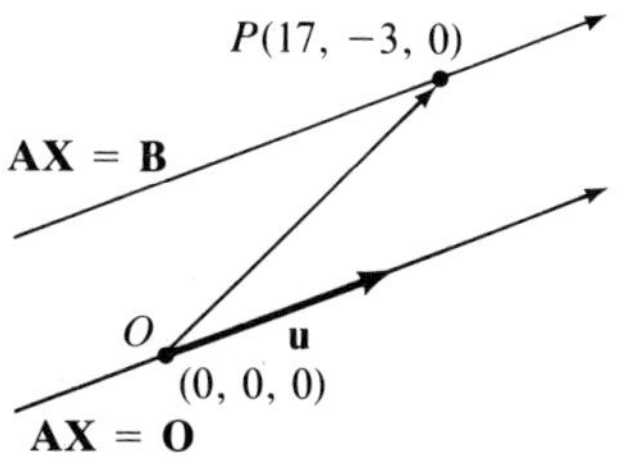

FIGURE 2.5

The system in Example 15 has the form **AX** = **B**, where **A** is the coefficient matrix in Example 14(a). Notice that the solution set in Example 15 is the sum of the triple $(17, -3, 0)$ and the solution set of Example 14(a):

$$\{k(16, -5, 1),\ k \text{ a real number}\}.$$

Geometrically, this means that the solution set in Example 15 represents a line through the fixed point $P(17, -3, 0)$ and in the direction $\mathbf{u} = (16, -5, 1)$. This line is parallel to the line through $(0, 0, 0)$ in the direction of **u**. (See Figure 2.5.) We can think of the solution of the nonhomogeneous system as a translation of the solution set of the homogeneous system by the vector $(17, -3, 0)$.

In general a similar relationship exists between the solution set of **AX** = **B** and the solution set of **AX** = **0**. The following example is set in R^4.

Example 16 Consider two systems of equations with the same coefficient matrix

$$\begin{aligned} x_1 + x_2 - x_3 - x_4 &= 1 \\ 2x_1 + 2x_2 + 2x_3 - 2x_4 &= 6 \\ 3x_1 + 3x_2 + x_3 - 3x_4 &= 7 \\ x_1 + x_2 + 3x_3 - x_4 &= 5 \end{aligned} \quad \text{and} \quad \begin{aligned} x_1 + x_2 - x_3 - x_4 &= 0 \\ 2x_1 + 2x_2 + 2x_3 - 2x_4 &= 0 \\ 3x_1 + 3x_2 + x_3 - 3x_4 &= 0 \\ x_1 + x_2 + 3x_3 - x_4 &= 0 \end{aligned}$$

The augmented matrices are

$$\left[\begin{array}{rrrr|r} 1 & 1 & -1 & -1 & 1 \\ 2 & 2 & 2 & -2 & 6 \\ 3 & 3 & 1 & -3 & 7 \\ 1 & 1 & 3 & -1 & 5 \end{array}\right] \quad \text{and} \quad \left[\begin{array}{rrrr|r} 1 & 1 & -1 & -1 & 0 \\ 2 & 2 & 2 & -2 & 0 \\ 3 & 3 & 1 & -3 & 0 \\ 1 & 1 & 3 & -1 & 0 \end{array}\right]$$

Their row-reduced forms are

$$\left[\begin{array}{rrrr|r} 1 & 1 & 0 & -1 & 2 \\ 0 & 0 & 1 & 0 & 1 \\ 0 & 0 & 0 & 0 & 0 \\ 0 & 0 & 0 & 0 & 0 \end{array}\right] \quad \text{and} \quad \left[\begin{array}{rrrr|r} 1 & 1 & 0 & -1 & 0 \\ 0 & 0 & 1 & 0 & 0 \\ 0 & 0 & 0 & 0 & 0 \\ 0 & 0 & 0 & 0 & 0 \end{array}\right]$$

The solution set of $\mathbf{AX} = \mathbf{B}$ is

$$\mathbf{X} = \begin{bmatrix} 2 \\ 0 \\ 1 \\ 0 \end{bmatrix} + k_1 \begin{bmatrix} -1 \\ 1 \\ 0 \\ 0 \end{bmatrix} + k_2 \begin{bmatrix} 1 \\ 0 \\ 0 \\ 1 \end{bmatrix}, \quad k_1 \text{ and } k_2 \text{ arbitrary scalars}$$

The solution set of $\mathbf{AX} = \mathbf{0}$ is

$$\mathbf{X} = k_1 \begin{bmatrix} -1 \\ 1 \\ 0 \\ 0 \end{bmatrix} + k_2 \begin{bmatrix} 1 \\ 0 \\ 0 \\ 1 \end{bmatrix}, \quad k_1 \text{ and } k_2 \text{ arbitrary scalars}$$

$$\text{Let } \mathbf{X}_0 = \begin{bmatrix} 2 \\ 0 \\ 1 \\ 0 \end{bmatrix} \text{ and } \{\mathbf{X}_h\} = \left\{ k_1 \begin{bmatrix} -1 \\ 1 \\ 0 \\ 0 \end{bmatrix} + k_2 \begin{bmatrix} 1 \\ 0 \\ 0 \\ 1 \end{bmatrix}, \ k_1 \text{ and } k_2 \text{ arbitrary scalars} \right\}.$$

■

Example 16 illustrates the fact that the solution set of a nonhomogeneous system $\mathbf{AX} = \mathbf{B}$ can be described as $\{\mathbf{X}_0 + \mathbf{X}_h\}$, where $\mathbf{X}_0$ is a particular solution of $\mathbf{AX} = \mathbf{B}$ and $\{\mathbf{X}_h\}$ is the solution set of the associated homogeneous equation, $\mathbf{AX} = \mathbf{0}$. This is a consequence of the linearity of the system. If you have already studied differential equations, you will recall a similar situation in the solution set of linear differential equations.

Although we cannot form a geometric picture, when n is greater than 3, the situation in R^n for any n is quite comparable. We shall see this after we look more closely at the structure of the solution set of a homogeneous system in Section 2.4.

This section concludes with two examples of special interest to students of engineering or the physical sciences. In Example 17 the situation gives rise to a homogeneous system. Example 18 involves a nonhomogeneous system.

Example 17 In any equation expressing a physical relationship between quantities, absolute numerical and dimensional equality must exist. Physical relationships in general can be reduced to the fundamental quantities: force F, length L, and time T. The rather simple linear equations that result from the requirement of dimensional equality can be used to help develop equations involving physical relationships. For example, the Reynolds number, R_e, is a dimensionless quantity related to the density, viscosity, and velocity of a fluid, and a characteristic length. This relationship is a function of the form $R_e = K\rho^a \mu^b V^c L^d$. Each of these physical quantities can be reduced to force, length, and time, which determine their dimensions:

Density ρ is expressed in FT^2/L^4.
Viscosity μ is expressed in FT/L^2.
Velocity V is expressed in F/T.
Length L is expressed in L.

The exponents a, b, c, d in the expression for R_e must be chosen to make the dimensions correct. Dimensionally we have

$$F^0 L^0 T^0 = (F^a T^{2a} L^{-4a})(F^b T^b L^{-2b})(L^c T^{-c})L^d$$

Equate exponents:

$$\begin{aligned} a + b \qquad\qquad &= 0 \\ -4a - 2b + c + d &= 0 \\ 2a + b - c \qquad &= 0 \end{aligned}$$

This is a homogeneous system of three equations in four unknowns. We cannot expect a unique solution. Row reduction proceeds as follows:

$$\left[\begin{array}{rrrr|r} 1 & 1 & 0 & 0 & 0 \\ -4 & -2 & 1 & 1 & 0 \\ 2 & 1 & -1 & 0 & 0 \end{array}\right] \Leftrightarrow \left[\begin{array}{rrrr|r} 1 & 1 & 0 & 0 & 0 \\ 0 & 2 & 1 & 1 & 0 \\ 0 & -1 & -1 & 0 & 0 \end{array}\right]$$

$$\Leftrightarrow \left[\begin{array}{rrrr|r} 1 & 1 & 0 & 0 & 0 \\ 0 & 1 & 1 & 0 & 0 \\ 0 & 0 & -1 & 1 & 0 \end{array}\right]$$

from which $c = d$, $b = -d$, and $a = d$. Therefore, $R_e = K(VL\rho/\mu)^d$. The values of K and d must still be determined by physical analysis and experiment. ■

Systems of linear equations arise also in analyzing simple electric circuits. The algebraic equations that express equilibrium conditions in electric circuits come from two important principles called Kirchhoff's Laws:

1. Kirchhoff's Current Law states that the algebraic sum of the currents directed toward a junction is equal to zero. (Currents away from a junction are interpreted as negative currents toward it.)
2. Kirchhoff's Voltage Law states that the algebraic sum of the voltage drops (or rises) around any closed loop of a network is equal to zero.

In the case of steady current flow voltage drop is related to current by Ohm's Law, which states $RI = V$, where R is called the resistance. Its unit is volts/ampere, or ohm. The unit of current is ampere.

Example 18 We wish to find the branch currents I_1, I_2, I_3, in the circuit shown in Figure 2.6. By Ohm's Law, the voltage drop associated with I_1 is $(3 + 10)I_1$. The drop associated with I_3 is $2I_3$. Applying Kirchhoff's Voltage Law to the loop involving

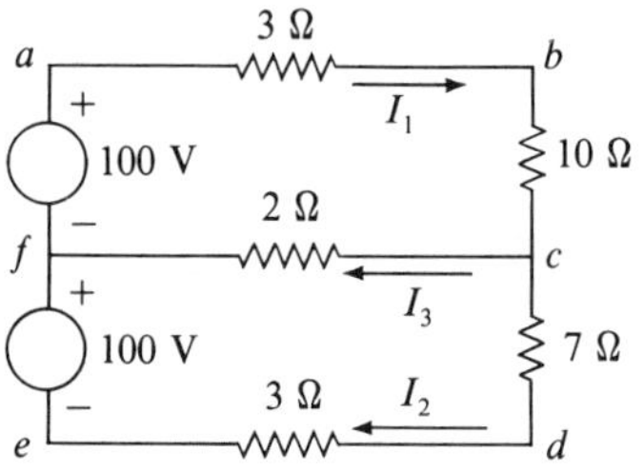

FIGURE 2.6

I_1 and I_3, we obtain $13I_1 + 2I_3 = 100$. In the second loop a similar analysis gives $(3 + 7)I_2 - 2I_3 = 100$. Direction of flow from $-$ to $+$ is assumed positive. Thus the positive direction around the bottom loop is clockwise. The negative sign results from I_3 being positive in the opposite direction.

Kirchhoff's Current Law, applied at the junction f, provides the equation $I_1 = I_2 + I_3$. Thus we have three equations from which to determine I_1, I_2, I_3:

$$\begin{aligned} I_1 - I_2 - I_3 &= 0 \\ 13I_1 \qquad + 2I_3 &= 100 \\ 10I_2 - 2I_3 &= 100 \end{aligned}$$

These can be solved by row reduction as follows:

$$\left[\begin{array}{rrr|r} 1 & -1 & -1 & 0 \\ 13 & 0 & 2 & 100 \\ 0 & 10 & -2 & 100 \end{array}\right] \Leftrightarrow \left[\begin{array}{rrr|r} 1 & -1 & -1 & 0 \\ 0 & 13 & 15 & 100 \\ 0 & 10 & -2 & 100 \end{array}\right] \Leftrightarrow \left[\begin{array}{rrr|r} 1 & -1 & -1 & 0 \\ 0 & 1 & \frac{15}{13} & \frac{100}{13} \\ 0 & 0 & 1 & -\frac{75}{44} \end{array}\right]$$

from which we obtain the solution

$$\begin{aligned} I_1 &= 7.9546 \text{ amp} \\ I_2 &= 9.6591 \text{ amp} \\ I_3 &= -1.7045 \text{ amp} \end{aligned}$$

There is also a junction at c. If the current law is applied there as well, we obtain the equation $I_1 = I_2 + I_3$. This is identical to the equation obtained at f. If it were included, it would produce a row of zeros as the last row of the row-reduced matrix. ■

SUMMARY A homogeneous system of linear equations is always consistent. If the rank of **A** equals the number of unknowns, the unique solution of $\mathbf{AX} = \mathbf{0}$ is $\mathbf{X} = \mathbf{0}$. This is called the trivial solution. If the rank of **A** is less than the number of unknowns, an infinite set of nonzero solutions exists.

The solution set of a nonhomogeneous system $\mathbf{AX} = \mathbf{B}$ can be described as $\{\mathbf{X}_0 + \mathbf{X}_h\}$, where $\mathbf{X}_0$ is a particular solution of $\mathbf{AX} = \mathbf{B}$ and $\{\mathbf{X}_h\}$ is the solution set of the associated homogeneous system $\mathbf{AX} = \mathbf{0}$.

EXERCISES 2.3

1. Find the solution set of each system of equations. State whether or not nontrivial solutions exist.

   a. $\begin{aligned} 2x_1 + 5x_2 + 6x_3 &= 0 \\ x_1 - 2x_2 + x_3 &= 0 \end{aligned}$

   b. $\begin{aligned} x_1 + 2x_2 + x_3 &= 0 \\ 2x_1 + x_2 + 3x_3 &= 0 \\ 3x_1 + 2x_2 - x_3 &= 0 \end{aligned}$

   c. $\begin{aligned} -x_1 + 2x_2 + 3x_3 &= 0 \\ 2x_1 + 3x_2 + x_3 &= 0 \\ -4x_1 + x_2 + 5x_3 &= 0 \end{aligned}$

   d. $x_1 + 2x_2 - x_3 = 0$

2. **a.** The row-reduced form of the augmented matrix of the system

$$\begin{bmatrix} 1 & 4 & 2 \\ 2 & 5 & 1 \\ 1 & 1 & -1 \end{bmatrix} \begin{bmatrix} x_1 \\ x_2 \\ x_3 \end{bmatrix} = \begin{bmatrix} 1 \\ 5 \\ 4 \end{bmatrix}$$

is

$$\left[\begin{array}{ccc|c} 1 & 0 & -2 & 5 \\ 0 & 1 & 1 & -1 \\ 0 & 0 & 0 & 0 \end{array}\right]$$

Write the solution set of this system as a linear combination of triples.

   b. Without doing any further calculation, find the row-reduced form of the augmented matrix of the system

$$\begin{bmatrix} 1 & 4 & 2 \\ 2 & 5 & 1 \\ 1 & 1 & -1 \end{bmatrix} \begin{bmatrix} x_1 \\ x_2 \\ x_3 \end{bmatrix} = \begin{bmatrix} 0 \\ 0 \\ 0 \end{bmatrix}$$

and write the solution set of this system.

3. **a.** Is the following system of three equations in four unknowns consistent?

$$\begin{aligned} x_1 + 2x_2 - x_3 + 5x_4 &= 0 \\ 2x_1 - x_2 + x_3 - 2x_4 &= 0 \\ 4x_1 + 3x_2 - x_3 + 8x_4 &= 0 \end{aligned}$$

Is the solution of this system unique?

   b. Is the following system of three equations in four unknowns consistent?

$$\begin{aligned} x_1 + 2x_2 - x_3 + 5x_4 &= 7 \\ 2x_1 - x_2 + x_3 - 2x_4 &= 3 \\ 4x_1 + 3x_2 - x_3 + 8x_4 &= 5 \end{aligned}$$

   c. Students frequently say that a system of equations can be solved if there are more unknowns than there are equations. Is this statement correct? What determines whether or not a system of equations is consistent?

4. Assume that each of the following matrices is the matrix of coefficients of a homogeneous system of equations. Decide whether the system has any solution other than the trivial solution. If so, write the solution set of $\mathbf{AX} = \mathbf{0}$.

   a. $\begin{bmatrix} 1 & 0 & 0 \\ 0 & 1 & 1 \\ 0 & 0 & 1 \end{bmatrix}$ **b.** $\begin{bmatrix} 1 & 2 & 1 \\ 0 & 1 & 1 \\ 0 & 0 & 0 \end{bmatrix}$

   c. $\begin{bmatrix} 1 & 2 & 0 & 0 \\ 0 & 0 & 1 & 1 \\ 0 & 0 & 0 & 0 \end{bmatrix}$ **d.** $\begin{bmatrix} 0 & 1 & 1 \\ 0 & 0 & 2 \\ 0 & 0 & 0 \end{bmatrix}$

5. For each of the matrices in Problem 4, what is the rank of the matrix? How many unknowns are there in the system $\mathbf{AX} = \mathbf{0}$? How many of the unknowns can be assigned arbitrarily in the solution set?

6. If $\mathbf{AX} = \mathbf{B}$ has a unique solution, what is the solution set of $\mathbf{AX} = \mathbf{0}$? (Think about the rank of $\mathbf{A}$ and the conditions discussed in Theorems 2 and 3.)

7. Find the solution set of each set of equations. Give a geometric interpretation and a sketch in each case.

   a. $\begin{aligned} 2x + 3y + 4z &= 0 \\ 4x + 6y + 8z &= 0 \end{aligned}$

   b. $\begin{aligned} 2x + 3y + 4z &= 2 \\ 4x + 6y + 8z &= 4 \end{aligned}$

   c. $\begin{aligned} 2x + 3y + 4z &= 2 \\ 4x + 6y + 8z &= 3 \end{aligned}$

8. Find the solution set and give a geometric interpretation of the solution.

   a. $\begin{aligned} 2x + 3y + 4z &= 2 \\ 4x + 5y + z &= 3 \end{aligned}$

   b. $\begin{aligned} 2x + 3y + 4z &= 0 \\ 4x + 5y + z &= 0 \end{aligned}$

9. Draw a graph of each equation in the system and give a geometric reason for the system being consistent or inconsistent.

a. $x + 2y = 0$
$2x + 4y = 0$

b. $x + 2y = 3$
$2x + 4y = 2$

c. $x + 2y = 0$
$2x - y = 0$
$3x + y = 0$

d. $x + 2y = 3$
$2x - y = 1$
$3x + y = 4$

e. $x + 2y = 3$
$x - y = 6$
$2x + y = -3$

10. Consider the system of equations $\mathbf{AX} = \mathbf{B}$, where

$$\mathbf{A} = \begin{bmatrix} 1 & 1 & 2 \\ 1 & 0 & 1 \\ 0 & 1 & 1 \end{bmatrix} \quad \text{and} \quad \mathbf{B} = \begin{bmatrix} 4 \\ 2 \\ 2 \end{bmatrix}$$

a. Show that $\mathbf{U}_0 = \begin{bmatrix} 3 \\ 3 \\ -1 \end{bmatrix}$ is a solution of this system.

b. Show that $\mathbf{V}_0 = \begin{bmatrix} -1 \\ -1 \\ 3 \end{bmatrix}$ is a solution of the system.

c. Show that $\mathbf{U}_0 - \mathbf{V}_0$ is a solution of the system $\mathbf{AX} = \mathbf{0}$.

11. Consider the system of equations $\mathbf{AX} = \mathbf{B}$, where $\mathbf{A}$ is $m \times n$, $\mathbf{X}$ is $n \times 1$, and $\mathbf{B}$ is $m \times 1$. Show that if $\mathbf{X}_1$ and $\mathbf{X}_2$ are solutions of $\mathbf{AX} = \mathbf{B}$, then $\mathbf{X}_3 = \mathbf{X}_1 - \mathbf{X}_2$ is a solution of $\mathbf{AX} = \mathbf{0}$.

12. If $\mathbf{X}_1, \mathbf{X}_2, \ldots, \mathbf{X}_k$ are solutions of $\mathbf{AX} = \mathbf{0}$, show that every linear combination of $\mathbf{X}_1, \mathbf{X}_2, \ldots, \mathbf{X}_k$ is also a solution of $\mathbf{AX} = \mathbf{0}$.

13. (Refer to Example 17.) Assume the power delivered to a pump obeys the law $P = KW^aQ^bH^c$, where P is power in LF/T, W is specific weight in F/L^3, Q is rate of flow in L^3/T and H is head in L. Use dimension analysis to establish an equation for power.

14. Determine an expression for dynamic pressure exerted by an incompressible fluid on an immersed object if $P = K\rho^a V^b$, where P is dynamic pressure in F/L^2, ρ is density in FT^2/L^4, and V is velocity in L/T.

15. Assume the drag force exerted by a flowing fluid on a body is $K\mu^a \rho^b V^c L^d$, where μ is viscosity in FT/L^2, ρ is density in FT^2/L^4, V is velocity in L/T, and L is a characteristic length of the body in the unit length of L. Develop an equation for the drag force.

16. (Refer to Example 18.) Find the three branch currents I_1, I_2, I_3 in the circuit shown.

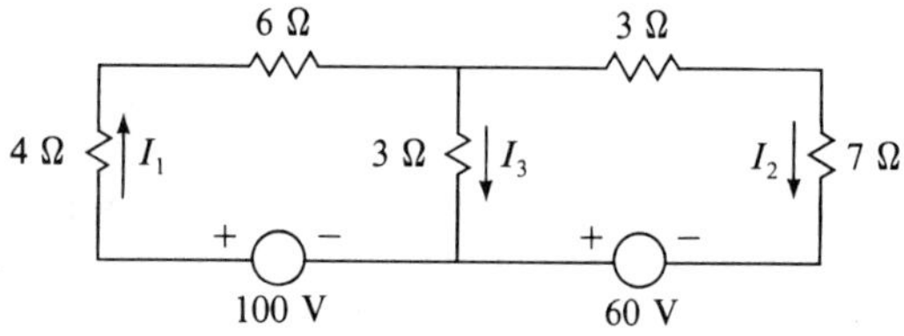

17. Show that the system of equations

$$a_1x_1 + a_2x_2 + a_3x_3 = 0$$
$$b_1x_1 + b_2x_2 + b_3x_3 = 0$$

has the solution set

$$\mathbf{x} = k(a_2b_3 - a_3b_2, a_3b_1 - a_1b_3, a_1b_2 - a_2b_1)$$

and that this represents a set of vectors orthogonal to (a_1, a_2, a_3) and (b_1, b_2, b_3) provided

$$(a_1, a_2, a_3) \neq k(b_1, b_2, b_3).$$

2.4 Linear Independence, Basis, Dimension

In this section our main purpose is to study the structure of the solution set of a homogeneous system of equations. Recall that, in Example 16, the solution set of the homogeneous system of equations $\mathbf{AX} = \mathbf{0}$ was found to be an infinite set of the form

$$\left\{ k_1 \begin{bmatrix} -1 \\ 1 \\ 0 \\ 0 \end{bmatrix} + k_2 \begin{bmatrix} 1 \\ 0 \\ 0 \\ 1 \end{bmatrix}, \quad k_1 \text{ and } k_2 \text{ arbitrary scalars} \right\}$$

Written as n-tuples, this is the set of all possible linear combinations of the two n-tuples $\mathbf{u}_1 = (-1, 1, 0, 0)$ and $\mathbf{u}_2 = (1, 0, 0, 1)$.

The n-tuples $\mathbf{u}_1$ and $\mathbf{u}_2$ have the special property that neither is a multiple of the other. This implies that $c_1\mathbf{u}_1 + c_2\mathbf{u}_2 = \mathbf{0}$ only in case $c_1 = 0$ and $c_2 = 0$. For this reason the set $\{\mathbf{u}_1, \mathbf{u}_2\}$ is called a linearly independent set.

Because the set $\{\mathbf{u}_1, \mathbf{u}_2\}$ is linearly independent and also describes the solution set of $\mathbf{AX} = \mathbf{0}$, $\{\mathbf{u}_1, \mathbf{u}_2\}$ is called a basis for the solution of $\mathbf{AX} = \mathbf{0}$.

If a set has only two vectors, it is easy to see whether or not it is linearly independent. The set will be linearly independent as long as one n-tuple is not a multiple of the other. In order to extend the idea of linear independence to sets of n-tuples with more than two n-tuples, we begin with a formal definition.

Definition 7

Linearly Independent

The set of n-tuples $\{\mathbf{u}_1, \mathbf{u}_2, \ldots, \mathbf{u}_k\}$ is **linearly independent** if

$$c_1\mathbf{u}_1 + c_2\mathbf{u}_2 + \cdots + c_k\mathbf{u}_k = \mathbf{0}$$

only in the case $c_1 = 0, c_2 = 0, \ldots, c_k = 0$.

Linearly Dependent

The set of n-tuples $\{\mathbf{u}_1, \mathbf{u}_2, \ldots, \mathbf{u}_k\}$ is **linearly dependent** if there exist scalars $c_1, c_2, \ldots, c_k$ not all zero such that

$$c_1\mathbf{u}_1 + c_2\mathbf{u}_2 + \cdots + c_k\mathbf{u}_k = \mathbf{0}.$$

Example 19

The simplest example of a linearly independent set of n-tuples is the set $\{\mathbf{e}_1 = (1, 0),\ \mathbf{e}_2 = (0, 1)\}$, the standard 2-tuples in R^2. We can see by inspection that $c_1(1, 0) + c_2(0, 1) = (0, 0)$ implies $c_1 = 0$ and $c_2 = 0$.

Consider the set $\{\mathbf{u}_1, \mathbf{u}_2, \mathbf{u}_3\}$, where $\mathbf{u}_1 = (1, 1)$, $\mathbf{u}_2 = (3, -1)$, and $\mathbf{u}_3 = (-1, 7)$. To decide whether this set is linearly dependent or linearly independent, we must consider the solution of $c_1\mathbf{u}_1 + c_2\mathbf{u}_2 + c_3\mathbf{u}_3 = \mathbf{0}$. This gives the system of equations:

$$\begin{aligned} c_1 + 3c_2 - c_3 &= 0 \\ c_1 - c_2 + 7c_3 &= 0 \end{aligned} \quad \text{or} \quad \begin{bmatrix} 1 & 3 & -1 \\ 1 & -1 & 7 \end{bmatrix} \begin{bmatrix} c_1 \\ c_2 \\ c_3 \end{bmatrix} = \begin{bmatrix} 0 \\ 0 \\ 0 \end{bmatrix}.$$

Theorem 3 tells us that this system of equations has a nontrivial solution, since the rank of the coefficient matrix is 2 and the number of unknowns is 3. Of course, we could easily solve this system and discover that $5\mathbf{u}_1 - 2\mathbf{u}_2 - \mathbf{u}_3 = \mathbf{0}$. According to Definition 7 then, $\{\mathbf{u}_1, \mathbf{u}_2, \mathbf{u}_3\}$ is a linearly dependent set. ■

In the following example, the answer is not so obvious.

Example 20 Let $\mathbf{u}_1 = (1, 1, -1, -1)$, $\mathbf{u}_2 = (2, 2, 2, -2)$, $\mathbf{u}_3 = (3, 3, 1, -3)$, $\mathbf{u}_4 = (1, 1, 3, -1)$. Is the set $\{\mathbf{u}_1, \mathbf{u}_2, \mathbf{u}_3, \mathbf{u}_4\}$ linearly independent? We cannot answer this question by inspection unless we make some good guesses. (Can you find a linear combination of $\mathbf{u}_1$, $\mathbf{u}_2$, $\mathbf{u}_3$, $\mathbf{u}_4$ that gives $\mathbf{0}$?) However, we can always answer the question by examining the nature of the solutions of the equation

$$c_1\mathbf{u}_1 + c_2\mathbf{u}_2 + c_3\mathbf{u}_3 + c_4\mathbf{u}_4 = \mathbf{0}.$$

In matrix form, this equation is

$$\begin{bmatrix} 1 & 2 & 3 & 1 \\ 1 & 2 & 3 & 1 \\ -1 & 2 & 1 & 3 \\ -1 & -2 & -3 & -1 \end{bmatrix} \begin{bmatrix} c_1 \\ c_2 \\ c_3 \\ c_4 \end{bmatrix} = \begin{bmatrix} 0 \\ 0 \\ 0 \\ 0 \end{bmatrix}$$

This is a homogeneous system of equations of the form $\mathbf{MC} = \mathbf{0}$. The coefficient matrix has as its columns the 4-tuples $\{\mathbf{u}_1, \mathbf{u}_2, \mathbf{u}_3, \mathbf{u}_4\}$. The column $\mathbf{C}$ consists of the 4-tuple of unknowns, (c_1, c_2, c_3, c_4). Theorem 3 tells us that this homogeneous system has a nontrivial solution if and only if the rank of $\mathbf{M}$ is less than the number of unknowns. Row reduction of the coefficient matrix shows that

$$\begin{bmatrix} 1 & 2 & 3 & 1 \\ 1 & 2 & 3 & 1 \\ -1 & 2 & 1 & 3 \\ -1 & -2 & -3 & -1 \end{bmatrix} \Leftrightarrow \begin{bmatrix} 1 & 0 & 1 & -1 \\ 0 & 1 & 1 & 1 \\ 0 & 0 & 0 & 0 \\ 0 & 0 & 0 & 0 \end{bmatrix}$$

The rank of $\mathbf{M}$ is 2; the number of unknowns is 4. The equation has nontrivial solutions. In fact, one possible solution is $c_1 = 0$, $c_2 = -2$, $c_3 = 1$, $c_4 = 1$. Thus $-2\mathbf{u}_2 + \mathbf{u}_3 + \mathbf{u}_4 = \mathbf{0}$. The set $\{\mathbf{u}_1, \mathbf{u}_2, \mathbf{u}_3, \mathbf{u}_4\}$ is linearly dependent. Note that the n-tuples $\mathbf{u}_1$, $\mathbf{u}_2$, $\mathbf{u}_3$, $\mathbf{u}_4$ are the columns of the matrix $\mathbf{M}$.

On the other hand, let $\mathbf{v}_1 = (1, 1, -1, 1)$, $\mathbf{v}_2 = (1, 2, 2, -2)$, $\mathbf{v}_3 = (3, 3, -2, -3)$, and $\mathbf{v}_4 = (1, 1, 1, -1)$. Again examine the equation

$$c_1\mathbf{v}_1 + c_2\mathbf{v}_2 + c_3\mathbf{v}_3 + c_4\mathbf{v}_4 = \mathbf{0}$$

Here the coefficient matrix $\mathbf{M}$ is given by

$$\mathbf{M} = \begin{bmatrix} 1 & 1 & 3 & 1 \\ 1 & 2 & 3 & 1 \\ -1 & 2 & -2 & 1 \\ 1 & -2 & -3 & -1 \end{bmatrix} \Leftrightarrow \begin{bmatrix} 1 & 0 & 0 & 0 \\ 0 & 1 & 0 & 0 \\ 0 & 0 & 1 & 0 \\ 0 & 0 & 0 & 1 \end{bmatrix}$$

The equation $\mathbf{MC} = \mathbf{0}$ has only the trivial solution $c_1 = 0$, $c_2 = 0$, $c_3 = 0$, $c_4 = 0$, and the set $\{\mathbf{v}_1, \mathbf{v}_2, \mathbf{v}_3, \mathbf{v}_4\}$ is linearly independent. ∎

Example 20 illustrates the close relationship between the idea of linear independence of the columns of a matrix $\mathbf{A}$ and the existence of nontrivial solutions of a homogeneous system of equations, $\mathbf{AX} = \mathbf{0}$. Theorem 4 states this precisely.

Theorem 4 Let $\mathbf{A}$ be an $n \times n$ matrix. The system of equations $\mathbf{AX} = \mathbf{0}$ has only the trivial solution if and only if the columns of $\mathbf{A}$ form a linearly independent set.

Proof Let $\{\mathbf{u}_1, \mathbf{u}_2, \ldots, \mathbf{u}_n\}$ be the columns of $\mathbf{A}$. Then $\mathbf{AX} = \mathbf{0}$ is equivalent to

$$x_1\mathbf{u}_1 + x_2\mathbf{u}_2 + \cdots + x_n\mathbf{u}_n = \mathbf{0}.$$

If $\{\mathbf{u}_1, \mathbf{u}_2, \ldots, \mathbf{u}_n\}$ is a linearly independent set, then (Definition 7) $x_1 = 0$, $x_2 = 0, \ldots, x_n = 0$, and the system $\mathbf{AX} = \mathbf{0}$ has only the trivial solution.

Suppose the columns of $\mathbf{A}$ do not form a linearly independent set. Then $\{\mathbf{u}_1, \mathbf{u}_2, \ldots, \mathbf{u}_n\}$ is a linearly dependent set and, by Definition 7, there exist scalars $x_1, x_2, \ldots, x_n$, not all zero, such that

$$x_1\mathbf{u}_1 + x_2\mathbf{u}_2 + \cdots + x_n\mathbf{u}_n = \mathbf{0}.$$

This implies that the system $\mathbf{AX} = \mathbf{0}$ has a nontrivial solution. □

Corollary The $n \times n$ matrix $\mathbf{A}$ has rank n if and only if the columns of $\mathbf{A}$ form a linearly independent set. □

Proof This follows from Theorems 3 and 4. □

Theorem 5 gives an alternate characterization of linear independence and linear dependence.

Theorem 5 The set of n-tuples $\{\mathbf{u}_1, \mathbf{u}_2, \ldots, \mathbf{u}_k\}$ is linearly dependent if and only if one of the n-tuples can be written as a linear combination of the remaining $k - 1$ n-tuples.

Proof Suppose

$$\mathbf{u}_i = d_1\mathbf{u}_1 + \cdots + d_{i-1}\mathbf{u}_{i-1} + d_{i+1}\mathbf{u}_{i+1} + \cdots + d_k\mathbf{u}_k$$

This equation can be written

$$d_1\mathbf{u}_1 + \cdots + d_{i-1}\mathbf{u}_{i-1} - \mathbf{u}_i + d_{i+1}\mathbf{u}_{i+1} + \cdots + d_k\mathbf{u}_k = \mathbf{0}$$

This shows that there is a linear combination of vectors that gives the zero vector, in which the coefficients are not all zero, since $\mathbf{u}_i$ has coefficient -1. By Definition 7, the set $\{\mathbf{u}_1, \mathbf{u}_2, \ldots, \mathbf{u}_k\}$ is linearly dependent.

Now suppose $\{\mathbf{u}_1, \mathbf{u}_2, \ldots, \mathbf{u}_k\}$ is a linearly dependent set. By Definition 7, there exist scalars $c_1, c_2, \ldots, c_k$ not all zero such that

$$c_1\mathbf{u}_1 + c_2\mathbf{u}_2 + \cdots + c_k\mathbf{u}_k = \mathbf{0}$$

Suppose c_i is nonzero. Write $c_i\mathbf{u}_i = -c_1\mathbf{u}_1 - \cdots - c_{i-1}\mathbf{u}_{i-1} - c_{i+1}\mathbf{u}_{i+1} - \cdots - c_k\mathbf{u}_k$. Since $c_i \neq 0$, we can multiply both sides of this equation by $1/c_i$ and obtain $\mathbf{u}_i$ as a linear combination of $\{\mathbf{u}_1, \mathbf{u}_2, \ldots, \mathbf{u}_{i-1}, \mathbf{u}_{i+1}, \ldots, \mathbf{u}_k\}$. □

Theorem 5 gives an alternate form of Definition 7 that is often useful: The set of n-tuples $\{\mathbf{u}_1, \mathbf{u}_2, \ldots, \mathbf{u}_k\}$ is linearly dependent if one of the n-tuples can be written as a linear combination of the remaining n-tuples.

The set of n-tuples $\{\mathbf{u}_1, \mathbf{u}_2, \ldots, \mathbf{u}_k\}$ is linearly independent if no one of the n-tuples is a linear combination of the remaining n-tuples.

Many sets are described as all possible linear combinations of a finite set of n-tuples. Any such set would have to contain the zero n-tuple. One of the simplest examples is the set R^n itself.

Example 21 Let $n = 3$. The standard 3-tuples are $\mathbf{e}_1 = (1,0,0)$, $\mathbf{e}_2 = (0,1,0)$, $\mathbf{e}_3 = (0,0,1)$. Since $a_1\mathbf{e}_1 + a_2\mathbf{e}_2 + a_3\mathbf{e}_3 = (a_1, a_2, a_3)$, it follows that every linear combination of the standard 3-tuples is an element of R^3 and every element of R^3 is a linear combination of the standard 3-tuples. Moreover, $a_1\mathbf{e}_1 + a_2\mathbf{e}_2 + a_3\mathbf{e}_3 = \mathbf{0}$ implies $(a_1, a_2, a_3) = \mathbf{0}$—that is, $a_1 = 0$, $a_2 = 0$, $a_3 = 0$, so that $\{\mathbf{e}_1, \mathbf{e}_2, \mathbf{e}_3\}$ is a linearly independent set. For these reasons, $\{\mathbf{e}_1, \mathbf{e}_2, \mathbf{e}_3\}$ is called a basis for R^3. The geometric vectors representing $\mathbf{e}_1$, $\mathbf{e}_2$, and $\mathbf{e}_3$ lie along the coordinate axes. (See Figure 2.7.) We are accustomed to thinking of R^3 as a three-dimensional space. It is natural to extend this to any set with a basis containing three vectors and call it a three-dimensional set.

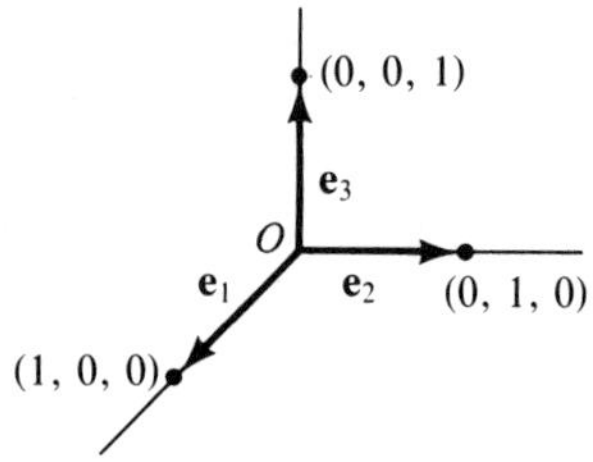

FIGURE 2.7

The set of elements in R^3 that lie in the xy plane have the form $a_1\mathbf{e}_1 + a_2\mathbf{e}_2$. These elements form a two-dimensional subset of R^3 with basis $\{\mathbf{e}_1, \mathbf{e}_2\}$.

In the same way, since $c_1\mathbf{e}_1 + c_2\mathbf{e}_2 + \cdots + c_n\mathbf{e}_n = (c_1, c_2, \ldots, c_n)$, it follows that the standard n-tuples $\{\mathbf{e}_1, \mathbf{e}_2, \ldots, \mathbf{e}_n\}$ form a basis for R^n. Because there are n elements in this basis, R^n is said to have dimension n. ■

The ideas of linear independence, basis, and dimension are studied in greater detail in Chapter 4, in the more general context of a vector space. It is shown there that although a set may have more than one basis, the number of elements in the basis is unique. This fact justifies the definition of dimension.

Definition 8

Let S be the set consisting of all possible linear combinations of the n-tuples $\{\mathbf{u}_1, \mathbf{u}_2, \ldots, \mathbf{u}_k\}$. If the set $\{\mathbf{u}_1, \mathbf{u}_2, \ldots, \mathbf{u}_k\}$ is linearly independent, then this set is called a **basis** for S, and the **dimension** of S is defined to be k. If S consists of only the zero n-tuple, S has dimension zero.

Basis
Dimension

Example 22 Consider the homogeneous system of equations

$$\begin{aligned} x_1 - x_2 - x_3 + x_4 \qquad &= 0 \\ x_1 + x_2 + x_3 - 3x_4 + 2x_5 &= 0 \\ x_1 + 4x_2 + 4x_3 - 9x_4 + 5x_5 &= 0 \end{aligned}$$

The solution of this system by row reduction gives

$$\left[\begin{array}{rrrrr|r} 1 & -1 & -1 & 1 & 0 & 0 \\ 1 & 1 & 1 & -3 & 2 & 0 \\ 1 & 4 & 4 & -9 & 5 & 0 \end{array}\right] \Leftrightarrow \left[\begin{array}{rrrrr|r} 1 & 0 & 0 & -1 & 1 & 0 \\ 0 & 1 & 1 & -2 & 1 & 0 \\ 0 & 0 & 0 & 0 & 0 & 0 \end{array}\right].$$

The solution set of this system in array form is

$$\begin{bmatrix} x_1 \\ x_2 \\ x_3 \\ x_4 \\ x_5 \end{bmatrix} = k_1 \begin{bmatrix} 0 \\ -1 \\ 1 \\ 0 \\ 0 \end{bmatrix} + k_2 \begin{bmatrix} 1 \\ 2 \\ 0 \\ 1 \\ 0 \end{bmatrix} + k_3 \begin{bmatrix} -1 \\ -1 \\ 0 \\ 0 \\ 1 \end{bmatrix}.$$

In terms of 5-tuples, the solution set is

$$\{k_1\mathbf{u}_1 + k_2\mathbf{u}_2 + k_3\mathbf{u}_3, \text{ where } k_1, k_2, k_3 \text{ are real numbers and}$$
$$\mathbf{u}_1 = (0, -1, 1, 0, 0), \quad \mathbf{u}_2 = (1, 2, 0, 1, 0), \quad \mathbf{u}_3 = (-1, -1, 0, 0, 1)\}.$$

Is the set $\{\mathbf{u}_1, \mathbf{u}_2, \mathbf{u}_3\}$ linearly independent? To answer this we consider the equation $c_1\mathbf{u}_1 + c_2\mathbf{u}_2 + c_3\mathbf{u}_3 = \mathbf{0}$. In matrix form this is

$$\begin{bmatrix} 0 & 1 & -1 \\ -1 & 2 & -1 \\ 1 & 0 & 0 \\ 0 & 1 & 0 \\ 0 & 0 & 1 \end{bmatrix} \begin{bmatrix} c_1 \\ c_2 \\ c_3 \end{bmatrix} = \begin{bmatrix} 0 \\ 0 \\ 0 \\ 0 \\ 0 \end{bmatrix}.$$

The coefficient matrix of this equation can be row-reduced by first exchanging rows. It is seen to have rank 3, equal to the number of unknowns, so that the only solution is $c_1 = 0$, $c_2 = 0$, $c_3 = 0$. The set of 5-tuples $\{\mathbf{u}_1, \mathbf{u}_2, \mathbf{u}_3\}$ is linearly independent. It is a basis for the solution set of the homogeneous system of equations, and this solution set has dimension 3. ■

As Example 22 illustrates, Definition 8 provides a way to characterize the solution set of the homogeneous system $\mathbf{AX} = \mathbf{0}$.

Theorem 6 Let $\mathbf{A}$ be an $m \times n$ matrix of rank r. The solution set of $\mathbf{AX} = \mathbf{0}$ is a set of n-tuples of dimension $n - r$.

Proof The proof of this theorem is developed in Exercises 2.4, Problems 15–17. □

To close this section we return to Example 16 and look at the relation between the solution set of the homogeneous equations $\mathbf{AX} = \mathbf{0}$ and the nonhomogeneous equations $\mathbf{AX} = \mathbf{B}$.

Example 23 In Example 16 the solution set of $\mathbf{AX} = \mathbf{B}$ was found to have the form $\{\mathbf{X}_0 + \mathbf{X}_h\}$, where

$$\mathbf{X}_0 \doteq \begin{bmatrix} 2 \\ 0 \\ 1 \\ 0 \end{bmatrix} \quad \text{and} \quad \mathbf{X}_h = k_1 \begin{bmatrix} -1 \\ 1 \\ 0 \\ 0 \end{bmatrix} + k_2 \begin{bmatrix} 1 \\ 0 \\ 0 \\ 1 \end{bmatrix}, \; k_1, k_2 \text{ scalars.}$$

Written as 4-tuples, this set is $\{\mathbf{x}_0 + \mathbf{x}_h\}$, where $\mathbf{x}_0 = (2, 0, 1, 0)$ and $\mathbf{x}_h = k_1(-1, 1, 0, 0) + k_2(1, 0, 0, 1)$. Let $\mathbf{u}_1 = (-1, 1, 0, 0)$ and $\mathbf{u}_2 = (1, 0, 0, 1)$. The set $\{\mathbf{u}_1, \mathbf{u}_2\}$ is linearly independent. (See Exercise 2.4, Problem 1.) Every 4-tuple in $\{\mathbf{x}_h\}$ is a linear combination of $\{\mathbf{u}_1, \mathbf{u}_2\}$. The set $\{\mathbf{x}_h\}$ is a two-dimensional subset of R^4 with basis $\{\mathbf{u}_1, \mathbf{u}_2\}$. The relationship between the solution set of the nonhomogeneous system $\mathbf{AX} = \mathbf{B}$ and the solution set of the homogeneous system $\mathbf{AX} = \mathbf{0}$ can be thought of in a way analogous to that of Example 15. The set $\{\mathbf{x}_h\}$ is a two-dimensional collection of vectors containing the vector $(0, 0, 0, 0)$. The set $\{\mathbf{x}_0 + \mathbf{x}_h\}$ is a translation of this collection by the vector $\mathbf{x}_0$. The set $\{\mathbf{x}_0 + \mathbf{x}_h\}$ does not contain the vector $(0, 0, 0, 0)$. (See Figure 2.8.)

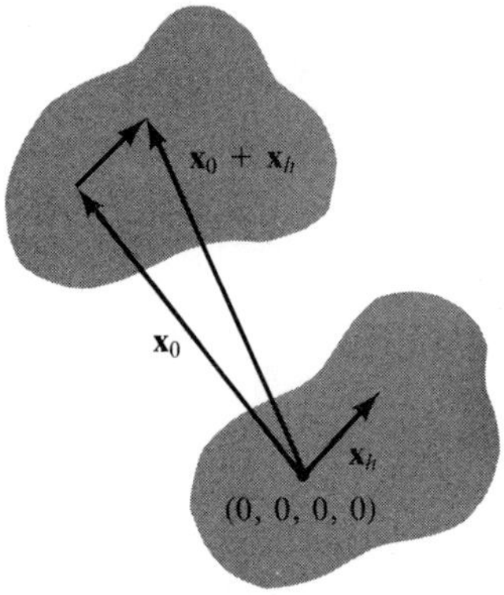

FIGURE 2.8

■

SUMMARY A set of n-tuples $\{\mathbf{u}_1, \mathbf{u}_2, \ldots, \mathbf{u}_k\}$ is linearly independent if $c_1\mathbf{u}_1 + c_2\mathbf{u}_2 + \cdots + c_k\mathbf{u}_k = \mathbf{0}$ only in the case $c_1 = 0, c_2 = 0, \ldots, c_k = 0$. It is linearly dependent if there exist scalars $c_1, c_2, \ldots, c_k$, not all zero, such that $c_1\mathbf{u}_1 + c_2\mathbf{u}_2 + \cdots + c_k\mathbf{u}_k \doteq \mathbf{0}$. In this case one of the n-tuples is a linear combination of the remaining n-tuples.

Let S be the set consisting of all possible linear combinations of the n-tuples $\mathbf{u}_1, \mathbf{u}_2, \ldots, \mathbf{u}_k$. If the set $\{\mathbf{u}_1, \mathbf{u}_2, \ldots, \mathbf{u}_k\}$ is linearly independent, then this set is a basis for S. The dimension of S is k. A set consisting of only the zero n-tuple has dimension 0.

The homogeneous system of equations $\mathbf{AX} = \mathbf{0}$ has nontrivial solutions if the rank of $\mathbf{A}$, r, is less than the number of unknowns, n. The solution set of $\mathbf{AX} = \mathbf{0}$ has dimension $n - r$.

EXERCISES 2.4

1. Decide by inspection whether each set is linearly independent or linearly dependent:
a. $(1,1)$, $(2,1)$, $(3,2)$
b. $(2,0)$, $(0,4)$
c. $(1,0,0)$, $(1,1,0)$, $(1,1,1)$
d. $(-1,1,0,0)$, $(1,0,0,1)$

2. In the set of triples

$$(1,1,0),\ (0,1,1),\ (1,0,1),\ (1,1,1)$$

show that the fourth triple is a linear combination of the first three. Is the set linearly dependent or linearly independent?

3. Let $\mathbf{u}_1 = (1,1,-1,2)$, $\mathbf{u}_2 = (0,1,0,1)$, $\mathbf{u}_3 = (4,2,-1,3)$, $\mathbf{u}_4 = (1,-1,3,1)$. To decide whether the set $\{\mathbf{u}_1, \mathbf{u}_2, \mathbf{u}_3, \mathbf{u}_4\}$ is linearly independent, we need to decide the nature of the solutions of the equations $\mathbf{MX} = \mathbf{0}$, where $\mathbf{M}$ has columns the n-tuples $\mathbf{u}_1, \mathbf{u}_2, \mathbf{u}_3, \mathbf{u}_4$. What is the earliest step in the following calculation at which the question can be answered?

$$\mathbf{M} = \begin{bmatrix} 1 & 0 & 4 & 1 \\ 1 & 1 & 2 & -1 \\ -1 & 0 & -1 & 3 \\ 2 & 1 & 3 & 1 \end{bmatrix} \Leftrightarrow \begin{bmatrix} 1 & 0 & 4 & 1 \\ 0 & 1 & -2 & -2 \\ 0 & 0 & 3 & 4 \\ 0 & 1 & -5 & -1 \end{bmatrix}$$

$$\Leftrightarrow \begin{bmatrix} 1 & 0 & 4 & 1 \\ 0 & 1 & -2 & -2 \\ 0 & 0 & 3 & 4 \\ 0 & 0 & -3 & 1 \end{bmatrix} \Leftrightarrow \begin{bmatrix} 1 & 0 & 4 & 1 \\ 0 & 1 & -2 & -2 \\ 0 & 0 & 3 & 4 \\ 0 & 0 & 0 & 5 \end{bmatrix}$$

$$\Leftrightarrow \begin{bmatrix} 1 & 0 & 4 & 0 \\ 0 & 1 & -2 & 0 \\ 0 & 0 & 1 & 0 \\ 0 & 0 & 0 & 1 \end{bmatrix} \Leftrightarrow \begin{bmatrix} 1 & 0 & 0 & 0 \\ 0 & 1 & 0 & 0 \\ 0 & 0 & 1 & 0 \\ 0 & 0 & 0 & 1 \end{bmatrix}$$

4. Let $\mathbf{u}_1, \mathbf{u}_2, \mathbf{u}_3, \mathbf{u}_4$ be the 4-tuples in Problem 3 and let $\mathbf{u}_5 = (1,-1,3,3)$. Is the set $\{\mathbf{u}_1, \mathbf{u}_2, \mathbf{u}_3, \mathbf{u}_5\}$ a linearly independent set? Is the set $\{\mathbf{u}_1, \mathbf{u}_2, \mathbf{u}_3, \mathbf{u}_4, \mathbf{u}_5\}$ a linearly independent set?

5. Show that any set of five 4-tuples must be linearly dependent. What about a set of three pairs? Can you state a similar result about a set of n-tuples?

6. Decide by inspection whether each set is linearly independent or dependent. Give a reason for your decision.
a. $(1,1,2)$, $(1,4,5)$, $(1,2,7)$, $(-1,8,3)$
b. $(1,1,0,0)$, $(0,0,1,1)$
c. $(1,0,0,0)$, $(1,1,0,0)$, $(1,1,1,0)$
d. The columns of the matrix $\begin{bmatrix} 1 & 5 & 4 \\ 2 & 8 & -3 \end{bmatrix}$
e. $(0,0,0)$, $(1,1,5)$, $(2,8,7)$

7. Let $\mathbf{u}_1 = (1,2,1,3)$, $\mathbf{u}_2 = (1,-1,2,0)$, and $\mathbf{u}_3 = (1,a,2,b)$. Choose a and b so that the set $\{\mathbf{u}_1, \mathbf{u}_2, \mathbf{u}_3\}$ is linearly dependent.

8. a. Show that the set $\{\mathbf{u}_1, \mathbf{u}_2, \mathbf{0}\}$ is a linearly dependent set.
b. Show that any set that contains $\mathbf{0}$ must be linearly dependent.

9. If the vectors $\{\mathbf{u}_1, \mathbf{u}_2, \mathbf{u}_3, \mathbf{u}_4\}$ all belong to R^3, show that the set must be linearly dependent.

10. Show that if the set $\{\mathbf{u}_1, \mathbf{u}_2, \ldots, \mathbf{u}_k\}$ is linearly independent, then any subset of this set is linearly independent.

11. Show that if the set $\{\mathbf{u}_1, \mathbf{u}_2, \ldots, \mathbf{u}_k\}$ is a linearly dependent set, any set containing these as a subset is linearly dependent.

12. If $\mathbf{A}$ is a 4×6 matrix of rank 2, for what n is the solution set of $\mathbf{AX} = \mathbf{0}$ a subset of R^n? What is the dimension of the solution set?

13. a. Let $\mathbf{A}$ be the matrix $[1 \ \ -1 \ \ 1]$. Give a geometric description of the solution set of $\mathbf{AX} = \mathbf{0}$. Find a basis for this set.
b. Let $\mathbf{A} = \begin{bmatrix} 1 & 2 & -1 \\ 1 & -1 & 1 \end{bmatrix}$. Describe the solution set of $\mathbf{AX} = \mathbf{0}$. What planes intersect in this line?

14. Let $\mathbf{A} = \begin{bmatrix} 1 & 1 & 0 & 0 \\ 0 & 1 & 2 & 3 \end{bmatrix}$ and $\mathbf{B} = \begin{bmatrix} 1 & 1 & 0 & 0 \\ 0 & 1 & 2 & 3 \\ 0 & 0 & 1 & 2 \end{bmatrix}$.

a. What is the dimension of the solution set of $\mathbf{AX} = \mathbf{0}$?

b. What is the dimension of the solution set of $\mathbf{BX} = \mathbf{0}$?

c. Show that the solution set of $\mathbf{BX} = \mathbf{0}$ is contained in the solution set of $\mathbf{AX} = \mathbf{0}$.

The following problems concern the solution set of a system of equations of the form $\mathbf{AX} = \mathbf{0}$.

15. Let $\mathbf{A}$ be an $m \times n$ matrix of rank r, where $r = n$. What is the dimension of the solution set of $\mathbf{AX} = \mathbf{0}$?

16. Suppose $\mathbf{A}$ is a 5×7 matrix, and the row-reduced form of $\mathbf{A}$ is

$$\begin{bmatrix} 1 & 2 & 0 & 3 & 0 & 5 & 8 \\ 0 & 0 & 1 & 4 & 0 & 6 & 9 \\ 0 & 0 & 0 & 0 & 1 & 7 & 10 \\ 0 & 0 & 0 & 0 & 0 & 0 & 0 \\ 0 & 0 & 0 & 0 & 0 & 0 & 0 \end{bmatrix}$$

Here $m = 5$, $n = 7$, and $r = 3$.

a. Call the leading columns i_1, i_2, i_3. In this example, what are the columns designated by i_1, i_2, i_3?

b. What elements can be assigned arbitrary values in the n-tuple $(x_1, x_2, x_3, x_4, x_5, x_6, x_7)$? Set $x_2 = k_1$, $x_4 = k_2, \ldots$.

c. Write the three equations resulting from $\mathbf{AX} = \mathbf{0}$. Write the four equations resulting from assigning arbitrary values. Combine these equations into seven equations of the form

$$\begin{aligned} x_1 &= -2x_2 - 3x_4 - 5x_6 - 8x_7 \\ x_2 &= k_1 \\ x_3 &= \cdots \\ x_4 &= \cdots \\ x_5 &= \cdots \\ x_6 &= \cdots \\ x_7 &= \cdots \end{aligned}$$

d. Write the solution set of the system in (**c**) in the form

$$\mathbf{X} = k_1\mathbf{U}_1 + k_2\mathbf{U}_2 + k_3\mathbf{U}_3 + k_4\mathbf{U}_4.$$

e. Write the system of equations that determines whether $\mathbf{U}_1, \mathbf{U}_2, \mathbf{U}_3, \mathbf{U}_4$ is a linearly independent set.

f. Find the rank of the matrix with columns $\mathbf{U}_1, \mathbf{U}_2, \mathbf{U}_3, \mathbf{U}_4$. Is the set of columns in (**e**) linearly independent?

g. What is the dimension of the solution set of $\mathbf{AX} = \mathbf{0}$?

17. Extend the analysis in Problem 16 to the general case:

a. Call the leading columns $i_1, i_2, \ldots, i_r$ and the nonleading columns $j_1, j_2, \ldots, j_{n-r}$. How many nonzero rows are there in the row-reduced form of $\mathbf{A}$?

b. What special property do the leading columns have? When the product $\mathbf{AX}$ is written which of the elements of $\mathbf{X}$ have coefficient 1? When the r elements with coefficient 1 are written in terms of the remaining elements, which can be assigned arbitrary values?

c. Write the r equations resulting from $\mathbf{AX} = \mathbf{0}$ and the $n - r$ equations resulting from assigning arbitrary values in the form suggested in part (**c**) of the preceding problem,

$$\begin{aligned} x_{i_1} &= cx_{j_1} + cx_{j_2} + \cdots + cx_{j_{n-r}}, \quad c \text{ any number,} \\ &\vdots \\ x_{j_1} &= k_1 \\ &\vdots \end{aligned}$$

so that we obtain $\mathbf{X} = k_1\mathbf{U}_1 + k_2\mathbf{U}_2 + \cdots + k_{n-r}\mathbf{U}_{n-r}$. Describe the rows and columns of the matrix with columns $\mathbf{U}_1, \mathbf{U}_2, \ldots, \mathbf{U}_{n-r}$. Which have all zero elements except for exactly one 1?

d. What is the rank of the matrix in part (**c**)?

e. What does this prove about the dimension of the solution set of $\mathbf{AX} = \mathbf{0}$?

2.5 Applications: Heat Diffusion, Balancing a Chemical Reaction, Solution of Equations by Iteration

In this section we will study practical problems whose solutions will be the result of solving a system of linear equations. Often such systems will be difficult to solve by hand. As in the previous chapter, we assume that you have access to computer systems and software that will allow you to perform row operations on matrices and thus solve systems of linear equations. Command-driven programs such as MAX have key words (for example, *rank*, *augment*, and *solve*) to help find solutions to systems of equations. In the event that you do not have such software available to you, we have included a program in the appendix of this book to aid you in solving systems of equations. It is called GAUSS (in honor of the great German mathematician Karl F. Gauss, 1777–1855). However, no computer program can carefully analyze a problem and obtain a system of equations from it. Your task is to understand a given problem thoroughly, set up the resulting linear system, and intelligently use the computer as a tool to find its solutions.

Example 24 Plunge a spoon into a hot liquid. How is the temperature of points inside the spoon changed by heat transfer from the liquid? Because the spoon is made of uniform material (we assume), the heat transfer should be smooth—gradually decreasing from the hot end of the spoon to the cold end. What else seems clear? Certainly, the temperature at any point inside the spoon depends on the temperature of the points surrounding it. One way to make this more precise is to make this assumption: the temperature at any point is the average of the temperatures surrounding that point. This *averaging* assumption is an underlying principle that can be modified for other similar problems.

For simplicity, we replace the spoon by an idealized model—just a square, uniform block of negligible thickness. Now consider a specific problem: this block is being heated in such a way that three of its edges are brought to a constant temperature of 150°F, while the lower, cool edge is at 50°F. Assume that the temperature of points A and B (where the boundaries join) is 50°F. (See Figure 2.9.)

Introduce a 5-by-5 grid into Figure 2.9, thereby assuming that the block is a collection of 25 point masses, as shown in Figure 2.10. Let x_j denote the temperature at the point labeled x_j. We know the values of $x_{10}, x_{11}, x_{12}, \ldots, x_{20}$: they are 150°F. The problem also specifies the values of x_{21}, x_{22}, x_{23}, x_{24}, x_{25} at 50°F. The values of x_1 through x_9 are the unknowns to be determined.

Let's concentrate on x_1. Its surrounding points are $x_{11}, x_{12}, x_{13}, x_{14}, x_{15}, x_2, x_5$, and x_4. The averaging assumption tells us that x_1 is the average of these values, so we have the equation

$$x_1 = \left(\tfrac{1}{8}\right)(x_{11} + x_{12} + x_{13} + x_{14} + x_{15} + x_2 + x_5 + x_4)$$

which simplifies to $8x_1 - x_2 - x_4 - x_5 = 750$.

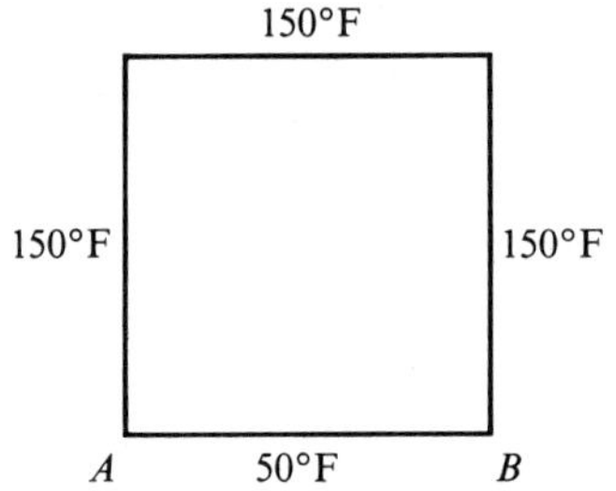

FIGURE 2.9

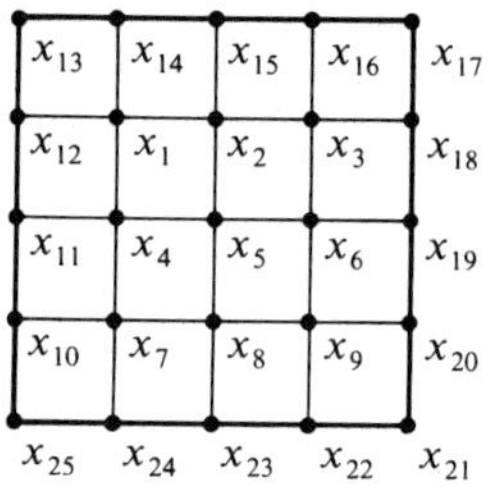

FIGURE 2.10

Now we do the same for $x_2, x_3, \ldots, x_9$. The following 9×9 system of equations results:

$$
\begin{aligned}
8x_1 \quad - x_2 \quad - x_4 - x_5 &= 750\\
8x_2 - x_1 - x_3 - x_4 - x_5 - x_6 &= 450\\
8x_3 \quad - x_2 \quad - x_5 - x_6 &= 750\\
8x_4 - x_1 - x_2 \quad - x_5 \quad - x_7 - x_8 &= 450\\
8x_5 - x_1 - x_2 - x_3 - x_4 \quad - x_6 - x_7 - x_8 - x_9 &= 0\\
8x_6 \quad - x_2 - x_3 \quad - x_5 \quad - x_8 - x_9 &= 450\\
8x_7 \quad - x_4 - x_5 \quad - x_8 &= 450\\
8x_8 \quad - x_4 - x_5 - x_6 - x_7 \quad - x_9 &= 150\\
8x_9 \quad - x_5 - x_6 \quad - x_8 &= 450
\end{aligned}
$$

The augmented matrix for this system is:

$$
\left[\begin{array}{rrrrrrrrr|r}
8 & -1 & 0 & -1 & -1 & 0 & 0 & 0 & 0 & 750\\
-1 & 8 & -1 & -1 & -1 & -1 & 0 & 0 & 0 & 450\\
0 & -1 & 8 & 0 & -1 & -1 & 0 & 0 & 0 & 750\\
-1 & -1 & 0 & 8 & -1 & 0 & -1 & -1 & 0 & 450\\
-1 & -1 & -1 & -1 & 8 & -1 & -1 & -1 & -1 & 0\\
0 & -1 & -1 & 0 & -1 & 8 & 0 & -1 & -1 & 450\\
0 & 0 & 0 & -1 & -1 & 0 & 8 & -1 & 0 & 450\\
0 & 0 & 0 & -1 & -1 & -1 & -1 & 8 & -1 & 150\\
0 & 0 & 0 & 0 & -1 & -1 & 0 & -1 & 8 & 450
\end{array}\right]
$$

Did you notice that the coefficient matrix is symmetric? When this system is solved, the following unique solution is obtained:

$$
\begin{array}{lll}
x_1 = 142.85 & x_2 = 139.91 & x_3 = 142.85\\
x_4 = 130.71 & x_5 = 122.14 & x_6 = 130.71\\
x_7 = 99.30 & x_8 = 91.52 & x_9 = 99.30
\end{array}
$$

■

Example 25 Just what kind of problems will give rise to a system of linear equations? They turn up in many applications. For example, trying to balance a chemical reaction can involve solving a linear system. Consider the chemical reaction

$$Pb(N_3)_2 + Cr(MnO_4)_2 \rightarrow Cr_2O_3 + MnO_2 + Pb_3O_4 + NO.$$

We must find positive *integers* a, b, c, d, e, and f, with no common divisors other than 1, so that

$$(a)\,Pb(N_3)_2 + (b)\,Cr(MnO_4)_2 \rightarrow (c)\,Cr_2O_3 + (d)\,MnO_2 + (e)\,Pb_3O_4 + (f)\,NO.$$

The reaction is *balanced* when the number of atoms on the left and right sides are the same. This will lead to a system of linear equations in the unknowns a, b, c, d, e, and f:

$$\begin{aligned} a &= 3e && \text{Atoms of lead, Pb} \\ 6a &= f && \text{Atoms of nitrogen, N} \\ b &= 2c && \text{Atoms of chromium, Cr} \\ 2b &= d && \text{Atoms of manganese, Mn} \\ 8b &= 3c + 2d + 4e + f && \text{Atoms of oxygen, O} \end{aligned}$$

From this we can form the augmented matrix of the system:

$$\left[\begin{array}{cccccc|c} 1 & 0 & 0 & 0 & -3 & 0 & 0 \\ 6 & 0 & 0 & 0 & 0 & -1 & 0 \\ 0 & 1 & -2 & 0 & 0 & 0 & 0 \\ 0 & 2 & 0 & -1 & 0 & 0 & 0 \\ 0 & 8 & -3 & -2 & -4 & -1 & 0 \end{array}\right]$$

This system is a homogeneous system. This property is imposed by the fact that we are balancing a chemical equation. The constant terms are all zero. We can use row operations on this system to bring it to the equivalent form

$$\left[\begin{array}{cccccc|c} 1 & 0 & 0 & 0 & 0 & -\frac{1}{6} & 0 \\ 0 & 1 & 0 & 0 & 0 & -\frac{22}{45} & 0 \\ 0 & 0 & 1 & 0 & 0 & -\frac{11}{45} & 0 \\ 0 & 0 & 0 & 1 & 0 & -\frac{44}{45} & 0 \\ 0 & 0 & 0 & 0 & 1 & -\frac{1}{18} & 0 \end{array}\right]$$

Thus there are infinitely many solutions, and we may write:

$$\begin{aligned} a &= (\tfrac{1}{6})f & d &= (\tfrac{44}{45})f \\ b &= (\tfrac{22}{45})f & e &= (\tfrac{1}{18})f \\ c &= (\tfrac{11}{45})f & f &= f. \end{aligned}$$

Written this way, we can see that in order to get positive integer solutions, f must be chosen to be a positive integer exactly divisible by 6, 18, and 45. Because we wish the coefficients to have no common divisors other than 1, f must be the smallest such integer. Using the prime factorizations $2 \cdot 3$, $2 \cdot 3 \cdot 3$, and $3 \cdot 3 \cdot 5$, we choose $f = 2 \cdot 3 \cdot 3 \cdot 5 = 90$. Then $a = 15$, $b = 44$, $c = 22$, $d = 88$, and $e = 5$. Incidentally, systems arising from this particular application are a great test of the accuracy of the computer-generated solutions, since the answers must be integers. ■

Example 26 An important computational method for solving $n \times n$ systems of equations for which a unique solution exists is *iterative* in nature. For example, suppose we have the system

$$\begin{aligned} 4x_1 - x_2 + x_3 &= 1 \\ x_1 - 3x_2 + x_3 &= -1 \\ x_1 + x_2 - 3x_3 &= 0 \end{aligned} \tag{1}$$

which has the unique solution $x_1 = 0.3125$, $x_2 = 0.53125$, and $x_3 = 0.28125$. If we solve (1) for each of the unknowns in terms of the remaining ones, we have

$$\begin{aligned} x_1 &= \frac{1 + x_2 - x_3}{4} \\ x_2 &= \frac{1 + x_1 + x_3}{3} \\ x_3 &= \frac{x_1 + x_2}{3}. \end{aligned} \tag{2}$$

This can be written as a matrix product:

$$\begin{bmatrix} x_1 \\ x_2 \\ x_3 \end{bmatrix}' = \begin{bmatrix} 0 & \frac{1}{4} & -\frac{1}{4} \\ \frac{1}{3} & 0 & \frac{1}{3} \\ \frac{1}{3} & \frac{1}{3} & 0 \end{bmatrix} \begin{bmatrix} x_1 \\ x_2 \\ x_3 \end{bmatrix} + \begin{bmatrix} \frac{1}{4} \\ \frac{1}{3} \\ 0 \end{bmatrix} \tag{3}$$

where the unknown column vector represents an initial guess (or estimated solution) on the right side and the resulting new guess (or updated estimate) on the left. Thus if we use $\begin{bmatrix} 1 \\ 1 \\ 1 \end{bmatrix}$ as our initial guess, we get $\begin{bmatrix} x_1 \\ x_2 \\ x_3 \end{bmatrix}' = \begin{bmatrix} \frac{1}{4} \\ 1 \\ \frac{2}{3} \end{bmatrix}$ for our new estimated solution. We then introduce this estimate into the right side of (3) to obtain our next estimate of the solution $\begin{bmatrix} x_1 \\ x_2 \\ x_3 \end{bmatrix}' = \begin{bmatrix} 0.33333 \\ 0.63888 \\ 0.41666 \end{bmatrix}$. If we compare this result with the actual solution, we see we are making progress, but we are not finished. However, after the tenth repetition, the estimated solution is $x_1 = 0.3125032$, $x_2 = 0.5312664$, and $x_3 = 0.2812706$. The efficiency of the method depends heavily on the rapidity of convergence and perhaps even on how the equations are written in terms of each other [the system (2)]. You will have a chance to explore this topic (with the help of a computer) in the exercises. ■

Before we become too complacent about the power of a computer to help us to solve systems of equations, we should realize that no digital computer can give us perfect results all the time. When they do their work in finite decimal arithmetic, strange answers sometimes result.

For example, suppose we have a "modest" computer, which does its work using only four significant digits. Then $\frac{1}{3}$ is represented as 0.3333, and the machine would compute $3(\frac{1}{3})$ to be 0.9999 instead of 1. Such errors have a way of building up during the solution of a problem. For example, suppose we settle for 0.0002 in a column as a choice for use in further row operations. Should we divide each entry in this row by 0.0002, any errors there from previous computations would be magnified by this multiplication by 5000.

To make matters worse, some matrices are extremely sensitive to minor changes. For example, consider the system

$$\begin{aligned} x + y &= 6 \\ x + 1.01y &= 6 \end{aligned}$$

The solution is obviously $x = 6$, $y = 0$. But if we change the constant term in the second equation to 6.01, we have

$$\begin{aligned} x + y &= 6 \\ x + 1.01y &= 6.01 \end{aligned}$$

Just as clearly, the solution now is $x = 5$, $y = 1$. Thus a small change in the hundredths digit of one of the constants has produced a change in the units digit of the answer. For this reason, the coefficient matrix

$$\begin{bmatrix} 1.00 & 1.00 \\ 1.00 & 1.01 \end{bmatrix}$$

is said to be *ill-conditioned.* You may wish to experiment with your software package to see how it reacts to systems with ill-conditioned coefficient matrices.

SUMMARY The process of solving a system of m equations in n unknowns by row reduction can be committed to a set of instructions that can be carried out by a digital computer. The nature of the solution set is related to the relative sizes of m and n and the rank of the coefficient matrix. Solutions computed by machine must, however, be considered inexact. In many cases, great care must be exercised to prevent round-off or truncation errors from building up so that they distort the result.

EXERCISES 2.5

Find the solutions for the following systems of linear equations. Use a computer to help you. (If you have no convenient software available to solve systems of linear equations, use the programs provided in the appendix. An easy-to-use system called MAX is available from Brooks/Cole.)

1.
$$\begin{aligned} x + 2y + z + w &= 10 \\ 2x + 4y + 2z + w &= 15 \\ -x + y + z &= 0 \\ 4x + 3y + w &= 24 \end{aligned}$$

2.
$$\begin{aligned} x_1 + x_2 + 0x_3 + 0x_4 &= 2 \\ -3x_1 - 2x_2 + 0x_3 + 0x_4 &= -1 \end{aligned}$$

3.
$$\begin{aligned} x_1 - x_3 + 3x_4 &= 2 \\ 2x_1 - x_3 + 2x_4 &= 10 \end{aligned}$$

4.
$$\begin{aligned} x_1 + x_2 - x_3 &= -4 \\ 2x_1 + x_2 + x_3 &= 11 \\ x_1 - x_2 - x_3 &= -2 \\ - x_2 + x_3 &= 7 \\ x_1 + 2x_2 - 3x_3 &= -17 \end{aligned}$$

5.
$$\begin{aligned} x_1 - 5x_3 + x_4 &= -1 \\ x_1 - x_3 + 2x_5 &= -2 \\ x_1 - x_3 - x_5 &= -2 \end{aligned}$$

6.
$$\begin{aligned} 4x_1 + 8x_2 - 20x_4 + 4x_5 &= 12 \\ -3x_1 - 6x_2 - 3x_3 + 15x_4 - 3x_5 - 3x_6 &= -15 \\ 2x_1 + 4x_2 + 3x_3 - 10x_4 + 2x_5 + 3x_6 &= 11 \end{aligned}$$

7.
$$\begin{aligned} x_2 + x_3 &= 5 \\ 3x_1 + x_2 + 3x_4 &= -5 \\ x_1 + x_2 - x_3 + x_4 &= 5 \\ 2x_1 + x_2 - 2x_3 + 2x_4 &= 2 \end{aligned}$$

8.
$$\begin{aligned} 3x_1 - x_2 + 2x_3 &= 16 \\ 3x_1 - x_2 + 5x_3 &= 22 \\ 3x_2 - 3x_3 &= 6 \end{aligned}$$

9.
$$\begin{aligned} x_2 + x_3 &= -1 \\ 3x_1 + x_2 - 2x_3 &= -1 \\ 3x_1 + 4x_2 + x_3 &= -4 \\ x_1 + x_2 &= -1 \end{aligned}$$

10.
$$\begin{aligned} 3x_1 - 3x_3 &= 0 \\ 2x_2 + 2x_3 &= -2 \\ 3x_1 + 2x_2 - x_3 &= -2 \\ 3x_1 + 4x_2 + x_3 &= -4 \end{aligned}$$

11.
$$\begin{aligned} x_1 - x_2 - x_3 &= -1 \\ x_1 + 2x_2 + x_3 &= -2 \\ x_1 + x_3 &= -2 \\ x_1 + x_2 + x_3 &= -2 \\ - x_2 - x_3 &= 1 \end{aligned}$$

12.
$$\begin{aligned} 4.5x_1 - 7.8x_2 - 3.4x_3 + 2.1x_4 &= 9.7 \\ 6.7x_1 - 4.5x_2 + 1.2x_3 - 5.3x_4 &= 2.1 \\ -3.9x_1 + 6.5x_2 - 11.9x_3 + 5.0x_4 &= 8.7 \\ -9.3x_1 + 10.9x_2 - 3.2x_3 + 3.1x_4 &= -2.8 \end{aligned}$$

13.
$$\begin{aligned} 5643x_1 - 1120x_2 + 9823x_3 \\ + 6511x_4 + 2098x_5 &= 6621 \\ -3276x_1 + 1109x_2 + 7294x_3 \\ - 1045x_4 + 1093x_5 &= -1074 \\ 7012x_1 - 3276x_2 + 1920x_3 \\ - 3098x_4 + 2075x_5 &= 5811 \\ -2091x_1 + 3209x_2 - 1023x_3 \\ + 9338x_4 + 1202x_5 &= 2320 \\ -6521x_1 + 9844x_2 - 2305x_3 \\ + 2022x_4 - 3031x_5 &= 292 \end{aligned}$$

14. Balance the following chemical reactions:

a. $H_2SO_4 + MnS + As_2(Cr_2O_7)_5 \rightarrow HMnO_4 + AsH_3 + Cr_2(SO_4)_3 + H_2O$

b. $H_2O_2 + NaMnO_4 + HCl \rightarrow MnCl_2 + H_2O + O_2 + NaCl$

15. Balance the following chemical reactions:

a. $KClO_3 + C_{12}H_{22}O_{11} \rightarrow CO_2 + H_2O + KCl$

b. $CH_2O + Ag(NH_3)_2NO_3 + NaOH \rightarrow NaNCO_3 + Ag + NH_3 + NaNO_3 + H_2O$

Problems 16 and 17 refer to Example 24.

16. Refine the given grid by introducing 25 interior points. Set up the resulting system of equations, introducing any appropriate simplifications to reduce the size of the system. Compare your results to those previously obtained.

17. Return to Figure 2.10 and assume that each point has four neighbors instead of eight. For example, the points surrounding x_2 are considered to be x_1, x_3, x_5, and x_{15}. Set up the appropriate system of equations, solve, and compare the results.

18. Given the system of equations with solution $(\frac{1}{2}, \frac{1}{2})$:

$$\begin{aligned} x + y &= 1 \\ x - y &= 0 \end{aligned}$$

a. Write the system as

$$\begin{aligned} x &= 1 - y \\ y &= x \end{aligned}$$

and find matrices $\begin{bmatrix} a & b \\ c & d \end{bmatrix}$ and $\begin{bmatrix} e \\ f \end{bmatrix}$ so that

$$\begin{bmatrix} x \\ y \end{bmatrix}' = \begin{bmatrix} a & b \\ c & d \end{bmatrix} \begin{bmatrix} x \\ y \end{bmatrix} + \begin{bmatrix} e \\ f \end{bmatrix}.$$

b. Use the initial guess $\begin{bmatrix} x \\ y \end{bmatrix} = \begin{bmatrix} 0 \\ 0 \end{bmatrix}$ and find five new vectors $\begin{bmatrix} x \\ y \end{bmatrix}'$ given by (**a**). Does this sequence of column vectors converge to $\begin{bmatrix} \frac{1}{2} \\ \frac{1}{2} \end{bmatrix}$?

c. Plot the points (x, y) obtained in (**b**). Is there an obvious pattern?

d. Redo (**b**) and (**c**) with an initial guess of $\begin{bmatrix} x \\ y \end{bmatrix} = \begin{bmatrix} 1 \\ 2 \end{bmatrix}$. Does this seem to help?

19. Given the system of equations with solution $(\frac{1}{2}, \frac{1}{2})$:

$$\begin{aligned} x + y &= 1 \\ 2x - y &= \tfrac{1}{2} \end{aligned}$$

a. Write the system as

$$\begin{aligned} x &= -y + 1 \\ y &= 2x - \tfrac{1}{2} \end{aligned}$$

and find matrices $\begin{bmatrix} a & b \\ c & d \end{bmatrix}$ and $\begin{bmatrix} e \\ f \end{bmatrix}$ so that

$$\begin{bmatrix} x \\ y \end{bmatrix}' = \begin{bmatrix} a & b \\ c & d \end{bmatrix} \begin{bmatrix} x \\ y \end{bmatrix} + \begin{bmatrix} e \\ f \end{bmatrix}.$$

b. Use the initial guess $\begin{bmatrix} x \\ y \end{bmatrix} = \begin{bmatrix} 0 \\ 0 \end{bmatrix}$, and find five new vectors $\begin{bmatrix} x \\ y \end{bmatrix}'$ given by (**a**). Does this sequence of column vectors converge to $\begin{bmatrix} \frac{1}{2} \\ \frac{1}{2} \end{bmatrix}$?

c. Plot the points (x, y) obtained in (**b**). Is there an obvious pattern?

d. Redo (**b**) and (**c**) with an initial guess of $\begin{bmatrix} x \\ y \end{bmatrix} = \begin{bmatrix} 1 \\ 2 \end{bmatrix}$. Does this seem to help.

20. Repeat Problem 19, except write the equations in part (**a**) as

$$\begin{aligned} x &= \tfrac{1}{2}y + \tfrac{1}{4} \\ y &= -x + 1 \end{aligned}$$

21. Solve the system of equations

$$\begin{aligned} 3x_1 - x_2 + 2x_3 &= 22 \\ x_2 - x_3 &= 2 \\ x_1 - 2x_2 - 4x_3 &= -32 \end{aligned}$$

a. Using row-reduction techniques.

b. Iteratively.

Compare and contrast the two methods.

3 Square Matrices, Inverses, Determinants, Eigenvalues

3.1 The Multiplicative Inverse of a Square Matrix

A system of m linear equations in n unknowns can be written as a single matrix equation $\mathbf{AX} = \mathbf{B}$. This has the same form as the algebraic equation $ax = b$. When $a \neq 0$, this is solved by multiplying both sides of the equation by the multiplicative inverse of a. If we write a^{-1} for this inverse, we obtain

$$ax = b \quad \text{implies} \quad a^{-1}(ax) = a^{-1}b, \quad \text{or} \quad x = a^{-1}b$$

Of course, we would have to know that a^{-1} exists. For real numbers this is the case provided $a \neq 0$. For example, to solve $3x = 7$ we write $\frac{1}{3} \cdot (3x) = \frac{1}{3} \cdot 7$, so $x = \frac{7}{3}$. Can a similar calculation be performed for the matrix equation $\mathbf{AX} = \mathbf{B}$? First, we would need a multiplicative inverse of $\mathbf{A}$, that is, a matrix $\mathbf{C}$ such that $\mathbf{CA} = \mathbf{I}$. In this section we show that for $n \times n$ matrices of rank n there is a unique matrix $\mathbf{C}$ such that $\mathbf{CA} = \mathbf{I}$ and $\mathbf{AC} = \mathbf{I}$.

Example 1

Let $\mathbf{A} = \begin{bmatrix} 1 & 1 & 1 \\ -1 & 3 & 2 \\ 2 & 1 & 1 \end{bmatrix}$. If $\mathbf{AC} = \mathbf{I}_3$, $\mathbf{C}$ must be a 3×3 matrix. Call its columns $\mathbf{C}_1$, $\mathbf{C}_2$, and $\mathbf{C}_3$. The columns of $\mathbf{I}_3$ are the standard arrays $\mathbf{E}_1$, $\mathbf{E}_2$, and $\mathbf{E}_3$. To find $\mathbf{C}_1$ we must solve $\mathbf{AX} = \mathbf{E}_1$. Row reduction yields

$$\left[\begin{array}{rrr|r} 1 & 1 & 1 & 1 \\ -1 & 3 & 2 & 0 \\ 2 & 1 & 1 & 0 \end{array}\right] \Leftrightarrow \left[\begin{array}{rrr|r} 1 & 1 & 1 & 1 \\ 0 & 4 & 3 & 1 \\ 0 & -1 & -1 & -2 \end{array}\right] \Leftrightarrow \left[\begin{array}{rrr|r} 1 & 1 & 1 & 1 \\ 0 & 1 & 1 & 2 \\ 0 & 0 & -1 & -7 \end{array}\right]$$

$$\Leftrightarrow \left[\begin{array}{rrr|r} 1 & 0 & 0 & -1 \\ 0 & 1 & 0 & -5 \\ 0 & 0 & 1 & 7 \end{array}\right]$$

The unique solution is $\mathbf{X} = \begin{bmatrix} -1 \\ -5 \\ 7 \end{bmatrix}$. To find $\mathbf{C}_2$ solve $\mathbf{AX} = \mathbf{E}_2$. Row reduction yields

$$\left[\begin{array}{rrr|r} 1 & 1 & 1 & 0 \\ -1 & 3 & 2 & 1 \\ 2 & 1 & 1 & 0 \end{array}\right] \Leftrightarrow \left[\begin{array}{rrr|r} 1 & 1 & 1 & 0 \\ 0 & 4 & 3 & 1 \\ 0 & -1 & -1 & 0 \end{array}\right] \Leftrightarrow \left[\begin{array}{rrr|r} 1 & 1 & 1 & 0 \\ 0 & 1 & 1 & 0 \\ 0 & 0 & -1 & 1 \end{array}\right]$$

$$\Leftrightarrow \left[\begin{array}{rrr|r} 1 & 0 & 0 & 0 \\ 0 & 1 & 0 & 1 \\ 0 & 0 & 1 & -1 \end{array}\right]$$

The unique solution is $\mathbf{X} = \begin{bmatrix} 0 \\ 1 \\ -1 \end{bmatrix}$. To find $\mathbf{C}_3$ solve $\mathbf{AX} = \mathbf{E}_3$. Row reduction yields

$$\left[\begin{array}{rrr|r} 1 & 1 & 1 & 0 \\ -1 & 3 & 2 & 0 \\ 2 & 1 & 1 & 1 \end{array}\right] \Leftrightarrow \left[\begin{array}{rrr|r} 1 & 1 & 1 & 0 \\ 0 & 4 & 3 & 0 \\ 0 & -1 & -1 & 1 \end{array}\right] \Leftrightarrow \left[\begin{array}{rrr|r} 1 & 1 & 1 & 0 \\ 0 & 1 & 1 & -1 \\ 0 & 0 & -1 & 4 \end{array}\right]$$

$$\Leftrightarrow \left[\begin{array}{rrr|r} 1 & 0 & 0 & 1 \\ 0 & 1 & 0 & 3 \\ 0 & 0 & 1 & -4 \end{array}\right]$$

The unique solution is $\mathbf{X} = \begin{bmatrix} 1 \\ 3 \\ -4 \end{bmatrix}$.

The calculations just completed are very inefficient, since the same steps of the row reduction have been repeated three times. We can organize and simplify the work by setting up the problem in a single matrix.

Start with a six-column matrix $[\mathbf{A}|\mathbf{I}]$ and by row operations transform this into the six-column matrix $[\mathbf{I}|\mathbf{C}]$, as shown below.

$$\left[\begin{array}{rrr|rrr} 1 & 1 & 1 & 1 & 0 & 0 \\ -1 & 3 & 2 & 0 & 1 & 0 \\ 2 & 1 & 1 & 0 & 0 & 1 \end{array}\right] \Leftrightarrow \left[\begin{array}{rrr|rrr} 1 & 1 & 1 & 1 & 0 & 0 \\ 0 & 4 & 3 & 1 & 1 & 0 \\ 0 & -1 & -1 & -2 & 0 & 1 \end{array}\right]$$

$$\Leftrightarrow \left[\begin{array}{rrr|rrr} 1 & 1 & 1 & 1 & 0 & 0 \\ 0 & 1 & 1 & 2 & 0 & -1 \\ 0 & 0 & -1 & -7 & 1 & 4 \end{array}\right] \Leftrightarrow \left[\begin{array}{rrr|rrr} 1 & 0 & 0 & -1 & 0 & 1 \\ 0 & 1 & 0 & -5 & 1 & 3 \\ 0 & 0 & 1 & 7 & -1 & -4 \end{array}\right]$$

Notice that the existence and uniqueness of the solution is assured by the fact that $\mathbf{A}$ has rank 3. By either method we arrive at exactly one matrix $\mathbf{C}$ such that

$\mathbf{AC} = \mathbf{I}_3$—namely,

$$\mathbf{C} = \begin{bmatrix} -1 & 0 & 1 \\ -5 & 1 & 3 \\ 7 & -1 & -4 \end{bmatrix}$$

■

Let $\mathbf{A}$ be an $n \times m$ matrix. The ijth element of the product $\mathbf{AC}$ is the product of the ith row of $\mathbf{A}$ and the jth column of $\mathbf{C}$. Let $\mathbf{C}_1, \mathbf{C}_2, \ldots, \mathbf{C}_n$ represent the columns of $\mathbf{C}$. The columns of $\mathbf{AC}$ are then $\mathbf{AC}_1, \mathbf{AC}_2, \ldots, \mathbf{AC}_n$. The matrix $\mathbf{AC} = \mathbf{I}$ if and only if corresponding columns are equal; that is,

$$\mathbf{AC}_1 = \mathbf{E}_1, \mathbf{AC}_2 = \mathbf{E}_2, \ldots, \mathbf{AC}_n = \mathbf{E}_n$$

where $\mathbf{E}_1, \mathbf{E}_2, \ldots, \mathbf{E}_n$ are the columns of $\mathbf{I}$.

In general, matrix multiplication is not commutative. However, for an $n \times n$ matrix $\mathbf{A}$ of rank n, in the special case of the matrix $\mathbf{C}$ with the property $\mathbf{AC} = \mathbf{I}$, it is also true that $\mathbf{CA} = \mathbf{I}$. The reason for this is illustrated in Example 2.

Example 2 Again let

$$\mathbf{A} = \begin{bmatrix} 1 & 1 & 1 \\ -1 & 3 & 2 \\ 2 & 1 & 1 \end{bmatrix} \quad \text{so that} \quad \mathbf{C} = \begin{bmatrix} -1 & 0 & 1 \\ -5 & 1 & 3 \\ 7 & -1 & -4 \end{bmatrix}.$$

A quick check shows that indeed $\mathbf{CA} = \mathbf{I}$. To see why this must be so, consider the following problem: Find a matrix $\mathbf{F}$ such that $\mathbf{CF} = \mathbf{I}$. As in Example 1 we write the 3×6 matrix $[\mathbf{C}|\mathbf{I}]$,

$$[\mathbf{C}|\mathbf{I}] = \left[\begin{array}{rrr|rrr} -1 & 0 & 1 & 1 & 0 & 0 \\ -5 & 1 & 3 & 0 & 1 & 0 \\ 7 & -1 & -4 & 0 & 0 & 1 \end{array}\right]$$

and use row operations to reduce this to the form $[\mathbf{I}|\mathbf{F}]$. This can be done by performing the row operations of Example 1 in reverse order:

$$\left[\begin{array}{rrr|rrr} -1 & 0 & 1 & 1 & 0 & 0 \\ -5 & 1 & 3 & 0 & 1 & 0 \\ 7 & -1 & -4 & 0 & 0 & 1 \end{array}\right] \Leftrightarrow \left[\begin{array}{rrr|rrr} -6 & 1 & 4 & 1 & 1 & 0 \\ -5 & 1 & 3 & 0 & 1 & 0 \\ -7 & 1 & 4 & 0 & 0 & -1 \end{array}\right]$$

$$\Leftrightarrow \left[\begin{array}{rrr|rrr} 1 & 0 & 0 & 1 & 1 & 1 \\ 2 & 0 & -1 & 0 & 1 & 1 \\ -7 & 1 & 4 & 0 & 0 & -1 \end{array}\right] \Leftrightarrow \left[\begin{array}{rrr|rrr} 1 & 0 & 0 & 1 & 1 & 1 \\ 2 & 0 & -1 & 0 & 1 & 1 \\ 1 & 1 & 0 & 0 & 4 & 3 \end{array}\right]$$

$$\Leftrightarrow \left[\begin{array}{rrr|rrr} 1 & 0 & 0 & 1 & 1 & 1 \\ 1 & 1 & 0 & 0 & 4 & 3 \\ -2 & 0 & 1 & 0 & -1 & -1 \end{array}\right] \Leftrightarrow \left[\begin{array}{rrr|rrr} 1 & 0 & 0 & 1 & 1 & 1 \\ 0 & 1 & 0 & -1 & 3 & 2 \\ 0 & 0 & 1 & 2 & 1 & 1 \end{array}\right]$$

This is exactly $[\mathbf{I}|\mathbf{A}]$, which shows that $\mathbf{A}$ is the unique matrix such that $\mathbf{CA} = \mathbf{I}$. Thus, $\mathbf{AC} = \mathbf{CA} = \mathbf{I}$. ■

Theorem 1 If **A** is an $n \times n$ matrix with rank n, there exists a unique matrix **C** such that $\mathbf{AC} = \mathbf{CA} = \mathbf{I}$.

Proof First we must show that we can calculate a matrix **C** such that $\mathbf{AC} = \mathbf{I}$. The equation $\mathbf{AX} = \mathbf{B}$ has a unique solution for any **B**, since $r = r_a = n$. (See Theorem 2, Chapter 2.) We find the columns of **C** by solving the equations $\mathbf{AX} = \mathbf{E}_i$, $i = 1, 2, \ldots, n$. A convenient technique for calculating **C** is to set up the $n \times 2n$ matrix $[\mathbf{A}|\mathbf{I}]$, and by row reduction generate $[\mathbf{I}|\mathbf{C}]$.

Since $[\mathbf{A}|\mathbf{I}]$ and $[\mathbf{I}|\mathbf{C}]$ are row-equivalent, we can change $[\mathbf{I}|\mathbf{C}]$ to $[\mathbf{A}|\mathbf{I}]$ by a succession of row operations. If we alter the order of columns in the same way in two row-equivalent matrices they remain row-equivalent. (See Problem 16, Section 2.2.) Thus $[\mathbf{C}|\mathbf{I}]$ is row-equivalent to $[\mathbf{I}|\mathbf{A}]$. This implies that the columns of **A** are the solutions of the equations $\mathbf{CX} = \mathbf{E}_i$, $i = 1, 2, \ldots, n$, so that $\mathbf{CA} = \mathbf{I}$.

There can be only one matrix **C** with the property $\mathbf{CA} = \mathbf{AC} = \mathbf{I}$. To see this, suppose $\mathbf{CA} = \mathbf{AC} = \mathbf{I}$ and $\mathbf{DA} = \mathbf{AD} = \mathbf{I}$. Then $\mathbf{CA} = \mathbf{I}$ implies $\mathbf{CAD} = \mathbf{D}$. Since $\mathbf{AD} = \mathbf{I}$, this implies $\mathbf{C} = \mathbf{D}$. □

Inverse
$\mathbf{A}^{-1}$

Definition 1

Let **A** be an $n \times n$ matrix with rank n. The unique matrix **C** with the property that $\mathbf{CA} = \mathbf{AC} = \mathbf{I}$ is called the **inverse** of **A** and is written $\mathbf{A}^{-1}$.

Notice that the word *dividing* has not been used because, in general, multiplying by an inverse is not commutative. In particular, $\mathbf{A}^{-1}\mathbf{B}$ is usually *not* the same as $\mathbf{BA}^{-1}$. The following example illustrates the care that is needed in dealing with matrix equations. When multiplying both sides by a matrix, the multiplication must be done either on the right on both sides or on the left on both sides.

Example 3 Find **A**, given that $\mathbf{AC} = \mathbf{CB}$ and $\mathbf{C}^{-1}$ exists. Multiply on the right by $\mathbf{C}^{-1}$. $\mathbf{ACC}^{-1} = \mathbf{CBC}^{-1}$; that is, $\mathbf{A} = \mathbf{CBC}^{-1}$. We can do nothing more with $\mathbf{CBC}^{-1}$.

Solve for **X**, given that $\mathbf{A}^{-1}$ exists, $\mathbf{B}^{-1}$ exists, and $\mathbf{A}(\mathbf{X} + \mathbf{A})\mathbf{B}^{-1} = \mathbf{C}$. Multiply on the left by $\mathbf{A}^{-1}$: $\mathbf{A}^{-1}\mathbf{A}(\mathbf{X} + \mathbf{A})\mathbf{B}^{-1} = \mathbf{A}^{-1}\mathbf{C}$, or $(\mathbf{X} + \mathbf{A})\mathbf{B}^{-1} = \mathbf{A}^{-1}\mathbf{C}$. Now multiply on the right by **B**: $(\mathbf{X} + \mathbf{A})\mathbf{B}^{-1}\mathbf{B} = \mathbf{A}^{-1}\mathbf{CB}$, or $\mathbf{X} + \mathbf{A} = \mathbf{A}^{-1}\mathbf{CB}$. Finally, add $-\mathbf{A}$ to both sides: $\mathbf{X} = \mathbf{A}^{-1}\mathbf{CB} - \mathbf{A}$. ■

In many cases the answers to questions in linear algebra depend on whether or not a particular matrix has an inverse. For this reason square matrices are classified as singular or nonsingular as described in Definition 2.

Nonsingular
Singular

Definition 2

A square matrix **A** is **nonsingular** if $\mathbf{A}^{-1}$ exists. A square matrix is **singular** if $\mathbf{A}^{-1}$ does not exist.

Thus, Theorem 1 states that an $n \times n$ matrix **A** of rank n is nonsingular, and that $\mathbf{A}^{-1}$ is unique. Theorem 2 lists some important consequences of Theorem 1.

Theorem 2 Let **A** and **B** be nonsingular $n \times n$ matrices and let k be a nonzero scalar. Then:

1. $(\mathbf{AB})^{-1} = \mathbf{B}^{-1}\mathbf{A}^{-1}$
2. $(\mathbf{A}^{-1})^{-1} = \mathbf{A}$
3. $(k\mathbf{A})^{-1} = (1/k)\mathbf{A}^{-1}$
4. $(\mathbf{A}^2)^{-1} = (\mathbf{A}^{-1})^2$ and, in general, $(\mathbf{A}^m)^{-1} = (\mathbf{A}^{-1})^m$, for nonnegative integers m.

Proof This theorem is a direct consequence of the uniqueness of the inverse. For example, to prove statement 1, we argue as follows:

$$\begin{aligned}(\mathbf{AB})(\mathbf{B}^{-1}\mathbf{A}^{-1}) &= \mathbf{A}(\mathbf{BB}^{-1})\mathbf{A}^{-1} && \text{By the associative law}\\ &= \mathbf{AIA}^{-1}\\ &= \mathbf{AA}^{-1}\\ &= \mathbf{I}\end{aligned}$$

Since $(\mathbf{AB})^{-1}$ is unique, it must equal $\mathbf{B}^{-1}\mathbf{A}^{-1}$. □

In Chapter 1 exponential notation was introduced for square matrices **A** so that $\mathbf{A}^n$ is defined for nonnegative integers n. If **A** is nonsingular, we adopt the convention that $(\mathbf{A}^{-1})^k = \mathbf{A}^{-k}$ for positive integers k, and that $\mathbf{A}^0 = \mathbf{I}$. Thus $\mathbf{A}^n$ is defined for any integral power n. The ordinary laws of exponents hold, that is, $\mathbf{A}^m\mathbf{A}^n = \mathbf{A}^{m+n}$, and $(\mathbf{A}^m)^k = \mathbf{A}^{mk}$ for all integers n, m, and k, provided $\mathbf{A}^{-1}$ exists. Example 4 illustrates why this is true.

Example 4 Let $m = 1$ and $n = -1$; then $\mathbf{A}^m\mathbf{A}^n = \mathbf{A}^{m+n}$, in this case, becomes $\mathbf{AA}^{-1} = \mathbf{A}^0 = \mathbf{I}$. If $m = -3$ and $n = 5$, then

$$\begin{aligned}\mathbf{A}^{-3}\mathbf{A}^5 &= (\mathbf{A}^{-1}\mathbf{A}^{-1}\mathbf{A}^{-1})(\mathbf{AAAAA})\\ &= \mathbf{A}^{-1}\mathbf{A}^{-1}(\mathbf{A}^{-1}\mathbf{A})\mathbf{AAAA}\\ &= \mathbf{A}^{-1}(\mathbf{A}^{-1}\mathbf{A})\mathbf{AAA}\\ &= (\mathbf{A}^{-1}\mathbf{A})\mathbf{AA}\\ &= \mathbf{A}^2\end{aligned}$$

If $m = 3$ and $k = -2$, then

$$\begin{aligned}(\mathbf{A}^3)^{-2} &= ((\mathbf{A}^3)^{-1})^2 = (\mathbf{A}^3)^{-1}(\mathbf{A}^3)^{-1}\\ &= (\mathbf{A}^{-3})(\mathbf{A}^{-3})\\ &= \mathbf{A}^{-1}\mathbf{A}^{-1}\mathbf{A}^{-1}\mathbf{A}^{-1}\mathbf{A}^{-1}\mathbf{A}^{-1} = \mathbf{A}^{-6}\end{aligned}$$

Note however that $(\mathbf{AB})^n \neq \mathbf{A}^n\mathbf{B}^n$. (See Exercises 3.1, Problem 29.) ■

A multiplicative inverse of the matrix **A** was suggested in order to use algebraic techniques in solving the matrix equation $\mathbf{AX} = \mathbf{B}$. We now return to this question.

Example 5 Solve the system of equations

$$\begin{aligned} x_1 + x_2 + x_3 &= 5 \\ -x_1 + 3x_2 + 2x_3 &= 2 \\ 2x_1 + x_2 + x_3 &= 1 \end{aligned}$$

In matrix form this is $\mathbf{AX} = \mathbf{B}$, where

$$\mathbf{A} = \begin{bmatrix} 1 & 1 & 1 \\ -1 & 3 & 2 \\ 2 & 1 & 1 \end{bmatrix} \quad \text{and} \quad \mathbf{B} = \begin{bmatrix} 5 \\ 2 \\ 1 \end{bmatrix}$$

The matrix $\mathbf{A}$ is the matrix of Example 1. We found there that $\mathbf{A}$ has rank 3 and that

$$\mathbf{A}^{-1} = \begin{bmatrix} -1 & 0 & 1 \\ -5 & 1 & 3 \\ 7 & -1 & -4 \end{bmatrix}$$

Since we know that $\mathbf{A}^{-1}$ exists, we can multiply the equation $\mathbf{AX} = \mathbf{B}$ on the left by the matrix $\mathbf{A}^{-1}$. This gives $\mathbf{A}^{-1}\mathbf{AX} = \mathbf{A}^{-1}\mathbf{B}$; that is, $\mathbf{X} = \mathbf{A}^{-1}\mathbf{B}$. In this case,

$$\mathbf{X} = \begin{bmatrix} -1 & 0 & 1 \\ -5 & 1 & 3 \\ 7 & -1 & -4 \end{bmatrix} \begin{bmatrix} 5 \\ 2 \\ 1 \end{bmatrix} = \begin{bmatrix} -4 \\ -20 \\ 29 \end{bmatrix}$$ ■

The method of Example 5 can be applied to any system of n equations in n unknowns, provided the coefficient matrix is nonsingular.

Theorem 3 If $\mathbf{A}$ is a nonsingular matrix, the equation $\mathbf{AX} = \mathbf{B}$ has a unique solution. This solution is $\mathbf{X} = \mathbf{A}^{-1}\mathbf{B}$.

Proof The matrix $\mathbf{A}^{-1}\mathbf{B}$ is a solution, since $\mathbf{A}(\mathbf{A}^{-1}\mathbf{B}) = (\mathbf{AA}^{-1})\mathbf{B} = \mathbf{IB} = \mathbf{B}$. This is the only solution, since $\mathbf{AX} = \mathbf{B}$ implies $\mathbf{A}^{-1}\mathbf{AX} = \mathbf{A}^{-1}\mathbf{B}$, so that $\mathbf{X} = \mathbf{A}^{-1}\mathbf{B}$. □

We might be tempted to think that Theorem 3 makes the solution of any system of linear equations simple, but this is not the case. The equations in Example 5 could be solved easily only because we already knew the matrix $\mathbf{A}^{-1}$. The work of calculating $\mathbf{A}^{-1}$ (see Example 1) is just about the same as the work required to solve the system of equations by the method of row reduction. The formula $\mathbf{X} = \mathbf{A}^{-1}\mathbf{B}$ is a useful, practical method of solving equations only if very many different systems of the form $\mathbf{AX} = \mathbf{B}$ have to be solved for the same coefficient matrix $\mathbf{A}$ and for varying values of $\mathbf{B}$.

The existence of $\mathbf{A}^{-1}$ is important in many situations. It will be needed, for example, in defining similar matrices, and in the study of matrix functions. In Section 3.2 we define a number called the determinant of $\mathbf{A}$ and investigate its relation to $\mathbf{A}^{-1}$.

SUMMARY If $\mathbf{A}$ is $n \times n$ and has rank n, a unique matrix $\mathbf{A}^{-1}$ exists such that $\mathbf{A}^{-1}\mathbf{A} = \mathbf{A}\mathbf{A}^{-1} = \mathbf{I}$. To calculate $\mathbf{A}^{-1}$ use row operations on the $n \times 2n$ matrix $[\mathbf{A}|\mathbf{I}]$ to reduce it to $[\mathbf{I}|\mathbf{B}]$; then $\mathbf{B} = \mathbf{A}^{-1}$. This method combines into a single algorithm the solution of n sets of equations.

If $\mathbf{A}^{-1}$ exists and if we adopt the notation $(\mathbf{A}^{-1})^k = \mathbf{A}^{-k}$ and $\mathbf{A}^0 = \mathbf{I}$, then $\mathbf{A}^m\mathbf{A}^n = \mathbf{A}^{m+n}$, and $(\mathbf{A}^m)^k = \mathbf{A}^{mk}$ for any integers m, n, and k.

If $\mathbf{A}$ and $\mathbf{B}$ are both $n \times n$ and of rank n, $(\mathbf{AB})^{-1} = \mathbf{B}^{-1}\mathbf{A}^{-1}$.

If $\mathbf{A}^{-1}$ exists, the system of equations $\mathbf{AX} = \mathbf{B}$ has the unique solution $\mathbf{X} = \mathbf{A}^{-1}\mathbf{B}$.

EXERCISES 3.1

1. For each of the following, state whether $\mathbf{A}^{-1}$ exists and why or why not. You should be able to tell by inspection.

a. $\mathbf{A} = \begin{bmatrix} 2 & 0 \\ 3 & 4 \\ 5 & 6 \end{bmatrix}$ **b.** $\mathbf{A} = \begin{bmatrix} 2 & 0 & 0 \\ 3 & 4 & 0 \\ 5 & 6 & 7 \end{bmatrix}$

c. $\mathbf{A} = \begin{bmatrix} 1 & 2 & 1 \\ 1 & 2 & 1 \\ 2 & 1 & 3 \end{bmatrix}$

2. State whether or not $\mathbf{A}^{-1}$ exists. Give a reason for your answer.

a. $\mathbf{A} = \begin{bmatrix} 1 & 2 & 1 \\ 2 & 1 & 3 \end{bmatrix}$ **b.** $\mathbf{A} = \begin{bmatrix} 1 & 2 \\ 2 & 4 \end{bmatrix}$

c. $\mathbf{A} = \begin{bmatrix} 1 & 0 & 0 \\ 1 & 2 & 1 \\ 2 & 1 & 3 \end{bmatrix}$

3.

$$\mathbf{A} = \begin{bmatrix} 1 & 1 & 1 \\ -1 & 0 & 2 \\ -1 & -1 & 3 \end{bmatrix}$$

Which of the following matrices is the inverse of $\mathbf{A}$?

$$\mathbf{B} = \begin{bmatrix} 1 & -2 & 1 \\ 1 & 1 & -3 \\ 1 & 0 & 1 \end{bmatrix} \qquad \mathbf{C} = \begin{bmatrix} \frac{1}{2} & -1 & \frac{1}{2} \\ \frac{1}{4} & 1 & -\frac{3}{4} \\ \frac{1}{4} & 0 & \frac{1}{4} \end{bmatrix}$$

4.

$$\mathbf{A}^{-1} = \begin{bmatrix} -\frac{1}{3} & \frac{1}{3} & 1 & -\frac{1}{3} \\ -\frac{1}{6} & \frac{1}{6} & 0 & \frac{1}{3} \\ \frac{5}{6} & -\frac{5}{6} & -1 & \frac{1}{3} \\ -\frac{1}{6} & \frac{7}{6} & 1 & -\frac{2}{3} \end{bmatrix}$$

Which of the following matrices is $\mathbf{A}$?

$$\begin{bmatrix} 1 & 2 \\ -1 & 3 \end{bmatrix}, \quad \begin{bmatrix} 1 & 1 & 2 & 1 \\ -1 & 1 & 0 & 1 \\ 2 & 1 & 1 & 0 \\ 1 & 3 & 1 & 0 \end{bmatrix},$$

$$\begin{bmatrix} 1 & 2 & 3 & 1 \\ 1 & 3 & 3 & 2 \\ 2 & 4 & 3 & 3 \\ 1 & 1 & 1 & 1 \end{bmatrix}$$

5. For each of the following calculate $\mathbf{A}^{-1}$ if it exists

a. $\mathbf{A} = \begin{bmatrix} 1 & 1 \\ 1 & 2 \end{bmatrix}$ **b.** $\mathbf{A} = \begin{bmatrix} 1 & 1 & 1 \\ 1 & 2 & 3 \\ 1 & 2 & 4 \end{bmatrix}$

c. $\mathbf{A} = \begin{bmatrix} 1 & 1 & 1 \\ 1 & 2 & 1 \\ 1 & 0 & 1 \end{bmatrix}$ **d.** $\mathbf{A} = \begin{bmatrix} 1 & 2 & 3 \\ 0 & 4 & 5 \\ 0 & 0 & -1 \end{bmatrix}$

6. a. Calculate $\mathbf{A}^{-1}$ for each of the 2×2 matrices:

i. $\mathbf{A} = \begin{bmatrix} 1 & 4 \\ 2 & 7 \end{bmatrix}$ **ii.** $\mathbf{A} = \begin{bmatrix} 2 & 5 \\ 1 & 2 \end{bmatrix}$

iii. $\mathbf{A} = \begin{bmatrix} 3 & 4 \\ 2 & 3 \end{bmatrix}$ **iv.** $\mathbf{A} = \begin{bmatrix} 2 & 5 \\ 2 & 4 \end{bmatrix}$

v. $\mathbf{A} = \begin{bmatrix} 1 & -2 \\ -1 & -3 \end{bmatrix}$ **vi.** $\mathbf{A} = \begin{bmatrix} 2 & 1 \\ 1 & 2 \end{bmatrix}$

b. Verify that in each case in part **a**.

$\mathbf{A} = \begin{bmatrix} a & b \\ c & d \end{bmatrix}$ implies that

$$\mathbf{A}^{-1} = \frac{1}{ad - bc}\begin{bmatrix} d & -b \\ -c & a \end{bmatrix}$$

***c.** Show that, if $ad - bc \neq 0$, the inverse of $\begin{bmatrix} a & b \\ c & d \end{bmatrix}$ is

$$\frac{1}{ad - bc}\begin{bmatrix} d & -b \\ -c & a \end{bmatrix}$$

7. Let $\mathbf{A} = \begin{bmatrix} 1 & 2 \\ 1 & 3 \end{bmatrix}$. Find solutions of each of the following equations. Use $\mathbf{A}^{-1}$.

a. $\mathbf{AX} = \begin{bmatrix} 1 \\ 5 \end{bmatrix}$ **b.** $\mathbf{AX} = \begin{bmatrix} 1 \\ 1 \end{bmatrix}$

c. $\mathbf{AX} = \begin{bmatrix} 1 \\ 4 \end{bmatrix}$ **d.** $\mathbf{AX} = \begin{bmatrix} 2 \\ 3 \end{bmatrix}$

8. Solve the system

$$\begin{aligned} x + 2y &= a \\ 2x + y &= b \end{aligned}$$

for $a = 1, b = 3$; for $a = 5, b = 2$; for $a = 3, b = 1$; and for $a = 0, b = 0$.

9. For what values of k does $\mathbf{A}^{-1}$ fail to exist if

$$\mathbf{A} = \begin{bmatrix} 1-k & 2 \\ 2 & 1-k \end{bmatrix}$$

10. Calculate $\mathbf{A}^{-1}$ for each of the triangular matrices below. What can you predict about the relationship between the diagonal elements of **A** and the diagonal elements of $\mathbf{A}^{-1}$?

a. $\mathbf{A} = \begin{bmatrix} 1 & 2 & 3 \\ 0 & 1 & 5 \\ 0 & 0 & 1 \end{bmatrix}$ **b.** $\mathbf{A} = \begin{bmatrix} 1 & 3 & 2 \\ 0 & 4 & 8 \\ 0 & 0 & 3 \end{bmatrix}$

c. $\mathbf{A} = \begin{bmatrix} 2 & 1 & 7 \\ 0 & 3 & 6 \\ 0 & 0 & 5 \end{bmatrix}$ **d.** $\mathbf{A} = \begin{bmatrix} -4 & 1 & 3 \\ 0 & 3 & 2 \\ 0 & 0 & 5 \end{bmatrix}$

e. $\mathbf{A} = \begin{bmatrix} 1 & 0 & 0 \\ 1 & 2 & 0 \\ 4 & 3 & 1 \end{bmatrix}$ **f.** $\mathbf{A} = \begin{bmatrix} 2 & 0 & 0 \\ 3 & 3 & 0 \\ 5 & 4 & 1 \end{bmatrix}$

***11.** Show that a triangular matrix has an inverse if and only if each of its diagonal elements is not zero.

12. In each case tell what operation is performed when a matrix is multiplied on the left by **A**. Write the matrix $\mathbf{A}^{-1}$ by inspection.

a. $\mathbf{A} = \begin{bmatrix} 1 & 0 \\ 1 & 1 \end{bmatrix}$ **b.** $\mathbf{A} = \begin{bmatrix} 1 & 0 \\ k & 1 \end{bmatrix}$

c. $\mathbf{A} = \begin{bmatrix} 1 & 0 & 0 \\ 0 & 1 & 0 \\ 1 & 0 & 1 \end{bmatrix}$ **d.** $\mathbf{A} = \begin{bmatrix} 1 & 0 & 0 \\ 0 & 1 & 0 \\ k & 0 & 1 \end{bmatrix}$

13. Find a matrix **B** such that

$$\begin{bmatrix} 1 & 2 \\ 1 & 3 \end{bmatrix}\mathbf{B} = \begin{bmatrix} 4 & 1 \\ 2 & 3 \end{bmatrix}$$

Find a matrix **B′** such that

$$\begin{bmatrix} 3 & -2 \\ -1 & 1 \end{bmatrix}\mathbf{B}' = \begin{bmatrix} 4 & 1 \\ 2 & 3 \end{bmatrix}$$

14. In each case, what can you say about $\mathbf{A}^{-1}$?

a. $\mathbf{A}(\mathbf{A} + 3\mathbf{I}) = \mathbf{I}$

b. $\mathbf{A}^2 - \mathbf{A} = \mathbf{I}$

c. $\mathbf{A}^3 - 3\mathbf{A}^2 + 4\mathbf{A} - 6\mathbf{I} = \mathbf{0}$

15. Suppose **A**, **B**, and **C** are $n \times n$ and $\mathbf{ABC} = \mathbf{I}$.

a. Express $\mathbf{A}^{-1}$ in terms of **B** and **C**.

b. What can you say about $\mathbf{C}^{-1}$? Can you express $\mathbf{B}^{-1}$ in terms of **A** and **C**? Remember that for any matrix **A**, if $\mathbf{A}^{-1}$ exists, $\mathbf{AA}^{-1} = \mathbf{A}^{-1}\mathbf{A}$.

16. Let $\mathbf{CA} = \mathbf{BC}$ and assume $\mathbf{C}^{-1}$ exists. What can you conclude about the value of **A**? What can you conclude about **B**?

17. Simplify as much as possible:

a. $\mathbf{A}(\mathbf{B} + \mathbf{A}^{-1})(\mathbf{B}^{-1}\mathbf{A}^{-1})$

b. $(\mathbf{A} + \mathbf{B})(\mathbf{A}^{-1} - \mathbf{B}^{-1})$

c. $[(\mathbf{A}^3)^{-1}\mathbf{A}^2]^{-1}$

18. Let **D** be a diagonal matrix with diagonal elements d_{ii}, $i = 1, 2, \ldots, n$. Show that $\mathbf{D}^{-1}$, if it exists, is a diagonal matrix with diagonal elements $1/d_{ii}$.

19. Find the inverse of the following matrices using the partition shown:

a. $\left[\begin{array}{cc|cc} 1 & 2 & 0 & 0 \\ 3 & 4 & 0 & 0 \\ \hline 0 & 0 & 1 & 0 \\ 0 & 0 & 2 & 1 \end{array}\right]$ **b.** $\left[\begin{array}{cc|ccc} 1 & 1 & 0 & 0 & 0 \\ 0 & 1 & 0 & 0 & 0 \\ \hline 0 & 0 & 1 & 2 & 3 \\ 0 & 0 & 0 & -1 & 2 \\ 0 & 0 & 0 & 0 & 4 \end{array}\right]$

20. Choose a suitable partition and find the inverse of the matrices.

a. $\begin{bmatrix} 1 & 2 & 0 & 0 & 0 \\ -1 & 1 & 0 & 0 & 0 \\ 0 & 0 & 1 & 2 & 0 \\ 0 & 0 & 3 & 1 & 0 \\ 0 & 0 & 0 & 0 & 4 \end{bmatrix}$

b. $\begin{bmatrix} 1 & 0 & 0 & 0 & 0 \\ 0 & 2 & 0 & 0 & 0 \\ 0 & 0 & 0 & 1 & 1 \\ 0 & 0 & 0 & -1 & 1 \\ 0 & 0 & 1 & 0 & 2 \end{bmatrix}$

21. Given $\mathbf{A} = \begin{bmatrix} 1 & 2 \\ 2 & 3 \end{bmatrix}$ and $\mathbf{B} = \begin{bmatrix} 1 & 1 \\ -1 & 2 \end{bmatrix}$.

a. Calculate $\mathbf{A}^{-1}$ and $\mathbf{B}^{-1}$.

b. Calculate $\mathbf{AB}$, $(\mathbf{AB})^{-1}$, $\mathbf{B}^{-1}\mathbf{A}^{-1}$, and $\mathbf{A}^{-1}\mathbf{B}^{-1}$. Note that $(\mathbf{AB})^{-1} = \mathbf{B}^{-1}\mathbf{A}^{-1}$, but $(\mathbf{AB})^{-1} \neq \mathbf{A}^{-1}\mathbf{B}^{-1}$.

c. Calculate $\mathbf{A} + \mathbf{B}$, $(\mathbf{A} + \mathbf{B})^{-1}$, and $\mathbf{A}^{-1} + \mathbf{B}^{-1}$. Note that $(\mathbf{A} + \mathbf{B})^{-1} \neq \mathbf{A}^{-1} + \mathbf{B}^{-1}$.

22. a. Give an example of matrices $\mathbf{A}$ and $\mathbf{B}$ such that $\mathbf{A}^{-1}$ exists, $\mathbf{B}^{-1}$ exists, but $(\mathbf{A} + \mathbf{B})^{-1}$ does not exist.

b. Give an example of matrices $\mathbf{A}$ and $\mathbf{B}$ such that $\mathbf{A}^{-1}$ and $\mathbf{B}^{-1}$ do not exist, but $(\mathbf{A} + \mathbf{B})^{-1}$ does exist.

23. a. Let $\mathbf{A} = \begin{bmatrix} 1 & -2 \\ -1 & 3 \end{bmatrix}$. What is $\mathbf{A}^T$? Calculate $\mathbf{A}^{-1}$, $(\mathbf{A}^T)^{-1}$. How do $\mathbf{A}^{-1}$ and $(\mathbf{A}^T)^{-1}$ appear to be related?

b. Set up an argument to justify the statement $(\mathbf{A}^T)^{-1} = (\mathbf{A}^{-1})^T$ using the fact that $(\mathbf{AB})^T = \mathbf{B}^T\mathbf{A}^T$.

24. a. Show that the set $\{\mathbf{u}_1, \mathbf{u}_2, \mathbf{u}_3\}$ is an orthonormal set, where $\mathbf{u}_1 = (\frac{2}{3}, -\frac{2}{3}, \frac{1}{3})$, $\mathbf{u}_2 = (\frac{1}{3}, \frac{2}{3}, \frac{2}{3})$, $\mathbf{u}_3 = (\frac{2}{3}, \frac{1}{3}, -\frac{2}{3})$.

b. Let $\mathbf{A}$ be the matrix with rows the triples $\mathbf{u}_1, \mathbf{u}_2, \mathbf{u}_3$. Show that $\mathbf{AA}^T = \mathbf{I}$.

c. What is $\mathbf{A}^{-1}$ in this case?

***25.** Let $\mathbf{A}$ be a 3×3 matrix with rows $\mathbf{A}_1, \mathbf{A}_2, \mathbf{A}_3$. Then $\mathbf{A}^T$ is a 3×3 matrix with columns $\mathbf{A}_1, \mathbf{A}_2, \mathbf{A}_3$. Show that the product $\mathbf{AA}^T$ has the form

$$\mathbf{AA}^T = \begin{bmatrix} \mathbf{A}_1 \cdot \mathbf{A}_1 & \mathbf{A}_1 \cdot \mathbf{A}_2 & \mathbf{A}_1 \cdot \mathbf{A}_3 \\ \mathbf{A}_2 \cdot \mathbf{A}_1 & \mathbf{A}_2 \cdot \mathbf{A}_2 & \mathbf{A}_2 \cdot \mathbf{A}_3 \\ \mathbf{A}_3 \cdot \mathbf{A}_1 & \mathbf{A}_3 \cdot \mathbf{A}_2 & \mathbf{A}_3 \cdot \mathbf{A}_3 \end{bmatrix}$$

and hence show that $\mathbf{AA}^T = \mathbf{I}$ if and only if the rows $\{\mathbf{A}_1, \mathbf{A}_2, \mathbf{A}_3\}$ form an orthonormal set.

26. Suppose $\mathbf{A}$, $\mathbf{B}$, and $\mathbf{C}$ are $n \times n$ matrices and that $\mathbf{A}^{-1}$, $\mathbf{B}^{-1}$, $\mathbf{C}^{-1}$ exist. Find $(\mathbf{ABC})^{-1}$ in terms of $\mathbf{A}^{-1}$, $\mathbf{B}^{-1}$, and $\mathbf{C}^{-1}$.

27. Let $\mathbf{A}$, $\mathbf{X}$, $\mathbf{B}$, and $\mathbf{C}$ be $n \times n$ matrices, and suppose $\mathbf{A}^{-1}$ exists. Solve the equation $\mathbf{A}(\mathbf{X} + \mathbf{B})\mathbf{A}^{-1} = \mathbf{C}$ for $\mathbf{X}$.

28. Prove parts 2, 3, and 4 of Theorem 2.

29. a. Let $\mathbf{A} = \begin{bmatrix} 1 & 3 \\ 2 & -1 \end{bmatrix}$ and $\mathbf{B} = \begin{bmatrix} 1 & 1 \\ 3 & 2 \end{bmatrix}$.

Calculate $\mathbf{A}^2$, $\mathbf{B}^2$, $\mathbf{A}^2\mathbf{B}^2$, $\mathbf{AB}$, and $(\mathbf{AB})^2$. Show that $\mathbf{A}^2\mathbf{B}^2 \neq (\mathbf{AB})^2$.

b. Why does the property of real numbers $(ab)^2 = a^2b^2$ fail to hold in general for matrices?

3.2 The Determinant of A

In this section we define a number associated with a square matrix. This number is called the determinant of the matrix. We will see that an $n \times n$ matrix $\mathbf{A}$ has rank n if and only if the determinant of $\mathbf{A}$ is not zero.

Example 6 Let $\mathbf{A} = \begin{bmatrix} a & b \\ c & d \end{bmatrix}$. In Exercise 3.1, Problem 6, you were asked to show that

$$\mathbf{A}^{-1} = \frac{1}{ad - bc}\begin{bmatrix} d & -b \\ -c & a \end{bmatrix}$$

For this formula to be meaningful we must have $ad - bc \neq 0$. The number $ad - bc$ is the determinant of the 2×2 matrix $\mathbf{A}$. Subscript notation generalizes more readily:

$$\text{if } \mathbf{A} = \begin{bmatrix} a_{11} & a_{12} \\ a_{21} & a_{22} \end{bmatrix}, \text{ the determinant of } \mathbf{A} = a_{11}a_{22} - a_{12}a_{21}$$

■

The basic definition of the determinant of an $n \times n$ matrix **A** involves the calculation of a sum formed by the following process:

General Case	*4 × 4 Case*
Step 1. Form products.	
Choose one element from each row of **A**, no two elements from the same column. Write the row subscripts in their natural order (you can see that no columns are repeated).	Sample products $a_{13}a_{22}a_{34}a_{41}$, $a_{12}a_{23}a_{34}a_{41}$, $\vdots$
Form the product $a_{1j_1}a_{2j_2}\cdots a_{nj_n}$	
How many such products are there? $n(n-1)(n-2)\cdots(3)(2)(1) = n!$	4 choices for first element; 3 for the second (one column has already been used); 2 for the third; 1 for the fourth; 4! products altogether
The column subscripts are $1, 2, \ldots, n$ in some order.	The column subscripts are $1, 2, 3, 4$ in some order.
Step 2. Attach a sign to each product.	
Look at the column subscripts. Count the number of inversions. An **inversion** occurs when an integer is to the left of a smaller integer.	In $a_{13}a_{22}a_{34}a_{41}$ column subscripts are $3, 2, 4, 1$. Since $3 > 2$, $3 > 1$, $2 > 1$, $4 > 1$, there are four inversions, so $(-1)^4 a_{13}a_{22}a_{34}a_{41}$
$j_1, j_2, \ldots, j_n$, k inversions. Multiply the product by $(-1)^k$: $(-1)^k a_{1j_1}a_{2j_2}\cdots a_{nj_n}$	In $a_{12}a_{23}a_{34}a_{41}$, $2 > 1$, $3 > 1$, and $4 > 1$, so there are three inversions. $(-1)^3 a_{12}a_{23}a_{34}a_{41}$
Step 3. Add all the signed products.	
$\sum (-1)^k a_{1j_1}a_{2j_2}\cdots a_{nj_n}$	$\sum (-1)^k a_{1j_1}a_{2j_2}a_{3j_3}a_{4j_4}$
$n!$ terms in the sum.	24 terms in the sum.

The formal statement of this process is given in Definition 3. Example 7 discusses the 2×2 and 3×3 cases in detail.

det A

Definition 3

With each $n \times n$ matrix **A** there is associated a unique number called the **determinant** of **A** and written det **A**. It is defined as follows:

$$\det \mathbf{A} = \sum (-1)^k a_{1j_1}a_{2j_2}a_{3j_3}\cdots a_{nj_n}$$

where the sum includes all possible terms of the given form in which no two column subscripts are the same and k is the number of inversions in the column subscripts $j_1, j_2, j_3, \ldots, j_n$.

Example 7 A single scalar a_{11} can be thought of as a 1×1 array. In this case we define $\det[a_{11}] = a_{11}$. Let $\mathbf{A} = \begin{bmatrix} a_{11} & a_{12} \\ a_{21} & a_{22} \end{bmatrix}$. There are two possible arrangements of the column subscripts; therefore, there are two terms in the sum. These terms are $a_{11}a_{22}$ in which $k = 0$ (since 1, 2 has no inversions) and $a_{12}a_{21}$ for which $k = 1$ (since 2, 1 has one inversion). In this case, then, $\det \mathbf{A} = a_{11}a_{22} - a_{12}a_{21}$. Compare this with Example 6.

Now let

$$\mathbf{A} = \begin{bmatrix} a_{11} & a_{12} & a_{13} \\ a_{21} & a_{22} & a_{23} \\ a_{31} & a_{32} & a_{33} \end{bmatrix}$$

Since there are six arrangements of the numbers 1, 2, 3, there are six terms in the sum. These are listed below:

Term	*Column Subscripts*	*k*	*Sign*
$a_{11}a_{22}a_{33}$	1, 2, 3	0	+
$a_{11}a_{23}a_{32}$	1, 3, 2	1	−
$a_{12}a_{23}a_{31}$	2, 3, 1	2	+
$a_{12}a_{21}a_{33}$	2, 1, 3	1	−
$a_{13}a_{21}a_{32}$	3, 1, 2	2	+
$a_{13}a_{22}a_{31}$	3, 2, 1	3	−

In the 2×2 case and in the 3×3 case simple patterns can be followed to write the appropriate sum.

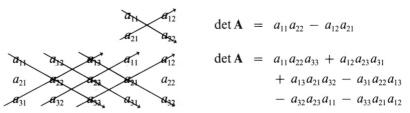

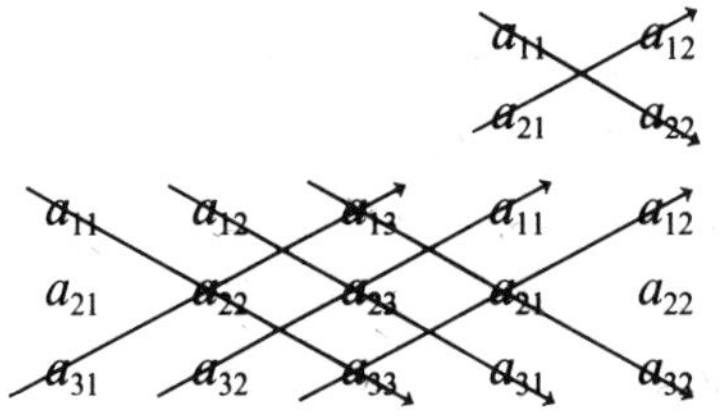

$$\det \mathbf{A} = a_{11}a_{22} - a_{12}a_{21}$$

$$\det \mathbf{A} = a_{11}a_{22}a_{33} + a_{12}a_{23}a_{31} + a_{13}a_{21}a_{32} - a_{31}a_{22}a_{13} - a_{32}a_{23}a_{11} - a_{33}a_{21}a_{12}$$

The positive terms in the sum are the products designated by the descending arrows and the negative terms are the products designated by the ascending arrows. ■

Caution For $n > 3$ there is no simple device for calculating $\det \mathbf{A}$ from its definition as a sum.

When n is large, Definition 3 is quite cumbersome. For a 4×4 matrix the sum consists of 24 terms, for a 6×6 matrix there are 720 terms, and for a 10×10 matrix there are over 3.5 million! An efficient method of calculating $\det \mathbf{A}$ uses row operations.

The three types of row operations on matrices are defined in Chapter 2: (1) interchange rows; (2) multiply a row by a nonzero scalar; (3) add a multiple of one row to another. The following theorem describes the effect of these row operations on the determinant of a matrix and evaluates the determinant in an important special case.

Theorem 4 Let **A** be an $n \times n$ matrix.

1. If **B** is obtained from **A** by interchanging two rows, $\det \mathbf{B} = -\det \mathbf{A}$.
2. If row i of $\mathbf{B} = c$ (row i of **A**), $\det \mathbf{B} = c \det \mathbf{A}$.
3. If **B** is obtained from **A** by adding k times row i to row j, where $i \neq j$, $\det \mathbf{B} = \det \mathbf{A}$.
4. If **A** is triangular, $\det \mathbf{A} = a_{11}a_{22}a_{33} \cdots a_{nn}$, the product of the diagonal elements.

Rationale A formal proof of this theorem would use Definition 3 to write $\det \mathbf{B}$ and $\det \mathbf{A}$ as sums. Comparison of the sums then leads to the stated relations. This is illustrated in each case for 3×3 matrices.

1. **B** is obtained from **A** by interchanging rows 1 and 2.

$$\mathbf{A} = \begin{bmatrix} a_{11} & a_{12} & a_{13} \\ a_{21} & a_{22} & a_{23} \\ a_{31} & a_{32} & a_{33} \end{bmatrix} \qquad \mathbf{B} = \begin{bmatrix} a_{21} & a_{22} & a_{23} \\ a_{11} & a_{12} & a_{13} \\ a_{31} & a_{32} & a_{33} \end{bmatrix}$$

$$\det \mathbf{A} = a_{11}a_{22}a_{33} + a_{12}a_{23}a_{31} + a_{13}a_{21}a_{32} - a_{31}a_{22}a_{13} - a_{11}a_{32}a_{23} - a_{21}a_{12}a_{33}$$
$$\det \mathbf{B} = a_{21}a_{12}a_{33} + a_{22}a_{13}a_{31} + a_{23}a_{11}a_{32} - a_{31}a_{12}a_{23} - a_{32}a_{13}a_{21} - a_{33}a_{11}a_{22}$$

Each term in the sum for $\det \mathbf{A}$ occurs in the sum for $\det \mathbf{B}$ with the opposite sign, so $\det \mathbf{B} = -\det \mathbf{A}$.

2. Row 2 of **B** is c times row 2 of **A**.

$$\mathbf{A} = \begin{bmatrix} a_{11} & a_{12} & a_{13} \\ a_{21} & a_{22} & a_{23} \\ a_{31} & a_{32} & a_{33} \end{bmatrix} \qquad \mathbf{B} = \begin{bmatrix} a_{11} & a_{12} & a_{13} \\ ca_{21} & ca_{22} & ca_{23} \\ a_{31} & a_{32} & a_{33} \end{bmatrix}$$

$$\begin{aligned} \det \mathbf{B} &= a_{11}ca_{22}a_{33} + a_{12}ca_{23}a_{31} + a_{13}ca_{21}a_{32} - a_{31}ca_{22}a_{13} \\ &\quad - a_{32}ca_{23}a_{11} - a_{33}ca_{21}a_{12} \\ &= c \det \mathbf{A} \end{aligned}$$

3. Add k times row 2 of **A** to row 1.

$$\mathbf{A} = \begin{bmatrix} a_{11} & a_{12} & a_{13} \\ a_{21} & a_{22} & a_{23} \\ a_{31} & a_{32} & a_{33} \end{bmatrix} \qquad \mathbf{B} = \begin{bmatrix} a_{11} + ka_{21} & a_{12} + ka_{22} & a_{13} + ka_{23} \\ a_{21} & a_{22} & a_{23} \\ a_{31} & a_{32} & a_{33} \end{bmatrix}$$

$$\begin{aligned} \det \mathbf{B} &= (a_{11} + ka_{21})a_{22}a_{33} + (a_{12} + ka_{22})a_{23}a_{31} + (a_{13} + ka_{23})a_{21}a_{32} \\ &\quad - a_{31}a_{22}(a_{13} + ka_{23}) - a_{32}a_{23}(a_{11} + ka_{21}) - a_{33}a_{21}(a_{12} + ka_{22}) \\ &= \det \mathbf{A} + k(a_{21}a_{22}a_{33} + a_{22}a_{23}a_{31} + a_{23}a_{21}a_{32} \\ &\quad - a_{31}a_{22}a_{23} - a_{32}a_{23}a_{21} - a_{33}a_{21}a_{22}) \\ &= \det \mathbf{A} \end{aligned}$$

4. Let

$$\mathbf{A} = \begin{bmatrix} a_{11} & a_{12} & a_{13} \\ 0 & a_{22} & a_{23} \\ 0 & 0 & a_{33} \end{bmatrix}$$

Each term in the sum in Definition 3 has a factor of 0 except the term $a_{11}a_{22}a_{33}$, so $\det \mathbf{A} = a_{11}a_{22}a_{33}$. □

To evaluate $\det \mathbf{A}$ using row operations, first use parts 1, 2, and 3 of Theorem 4 to express $\det \mathbf{A}$ in terms of the determinant of a triangular matrix and then use part 4. Example 8 illustrates the method.

Example 8 Evaluate using Theorem 4. Notice how *det* is used before each matrix; we are comparing *numbers* in this example, not matrices.

a.

$$\det \begin{bmatrix} -1 & 1 & 2 \\ 0 & 6 & 3 \\ 4 & 7 & 5 \end{bmatrix} \underset{\text{(part 3)}}{=} \det \begin{bmatrix} -1 & 1 & 2 \\ 0 & 6 & 3 \\ 0 & 11 & 13 \end{bmatrix}$$

$$\underset{\text{(part 2)}}{=} 3\det \begin{bmatrix} -1 & 1 & 2 \\ 0 & 2 & 1 \\ 0 & 11 & 13 \end{bmatrix} \underset{\text{(part 3)}}{=} 3\det \begin{bmatrix} -1 & 1 & 2 \\ 0 & 2 & 1 \\ 0 & 0 & \frac{15}{2} \end{bmatrix}$$

$$\underset{\text{(part 4)}}{=} 3(-1)(2)(\tfrac{15}{2}) = -45$$

b.

$$\det \begin{bmatrix} 2 & 1 & 3 & 4 \\ 0 & 1 & 1 & 0 \\ 1 & 0 & 1 & 1 \\ 4 & 2 & 1 & -1 \end{bmatrix} \underset{\text{(part 1)}}{=} -\det \begin{bmatrix} 1 & 0 & 1 & 1 \\ 0 & 1 & 1 & 0 \\ 2 & 1 & 3 & 4 \\ 4 & 2 & 1 & -1 \end{bmatrix}$$

$$\underset{\text{(part 3)}}{=} -\det \begin{bmatrix} 1 & 0 & 1 & 1 \\ 0 & 1 & 1 & 0 \\ 0 & 1 & 1 & 2 \\ 0 & 2 & -3 & -5 \end{bmatrix} \underset{\text{(part 3)}}{=} -\det \begin{bmatrix} 1 & 0 & 1 & 1 \\ 0 & 1 & 1 & 0 \\ 0 & 0 & 0 & 2 \\ 0 & 0 & -5 & -5 \end{bmatrix}$$

$$\underset{\text{(part 1)}}{=} \det \begin{bmatrix} 1 & 0 & 1 & 1 \\ 0 & 1 & 1 & 0 \\ 0 & 0 & -5 & -5 \\ 0 & 0 & 0 & 2 \end{bmatrix} \underset{\text{(part 4)}}{=} -10$$

■

Since row reduction of $\mathbf{A}$ to triangular form helps us to find $\det \mathbf{A}$, it is not surprising that there is a relation between $\det \mathbf{A}$ and the rank of $\mathbf{A}$, which in turn is related to the existence of $\mathbf{A}^{-1}$. Theorem 5 describes these interrelations.

Theorem 5 For an $n \times n$ matrix $\mathbf{A}$, the following statements are equivalent:

1. $\operatorname{Det} \mathbf{A} \neq 0$
2. $\mathbf{A}$ has rank n.
3. $\mathbf{A}^{-1}$ exists.

Proof We are required to show that if we assume any one of the three statements is true, the other two statements follow. This could be a lengthy process but we can shorten it by setting up a chain of logic that leads from any assertion to any of the other assertions. In this case we show $1 \Rightarrow 2 \Rightarrow 3 \Rightarrow 2 \Rightarrow 1$.

1 ⇒ 2. Assume $\det \mathbf{A} \neq 0$. The triangular matrix row-equivalent to $\mathbf{A}$ has no zeros on the diagonal. The row-reduced form of $\mathbf{A}$ is $\mathbf{I}$, and the rank of $\mathbf{A}$ is n.

2 ⇒ 3. If the rank of $\mathbf{A}$ is n, $\mathbf{A}^{-1}$ exists (Theorem 1).

3 ⇒ 2. If $\mathbf{A}^{-1}$ exists, $\mathbf{AX} = \mathbf{B}$ has a unique solution for every $\mathbf{B}$ (Theorem 3), so the rank of $\mathbf{A}$ is n (Chapter 2, Theorem 2, Corollary).

2 ⇒ 1. If the rank of $\mathbf{A}$ is n, $\mathbf{A}$ is a row equivalent to $\mathbf{I}$ and $\det \mathbf{A} \neq 0$ (Theorem 4). □

The nature of the definition of $\det \mathbf{A}$ motivates the following theorem.

Theorem 6 $\operatorname{Det}(\mathbf{A}^T) = \det \mathbf{A}$.

Proof Close observation of the sum in Definition 3 shows that exactly the same terms will be obtained if the sum is written with the column subscripts in their natural order and no two of the row subscripts repeated. Thus, for an $n \times n$ matrix $\mathbf{A}$,

$$\det \mathbf{A} = \sum (-1)^k a_{i_1 1} a_{i_2 2} a_{i_3 3} \cdots a_{i_n n}$$

where the sum includes all possible terms of the given form in which no two row subscripts are the same, and k is the number of inversions in the arrangement of the row subscripts.

This is exactly the sum that Definition 3 gives for $\det \mathbf{A}^T$. □

This theorem has a very useful corollary that allows us to calculate $\det \mathbf{A}$ by operating with columns rather than rows.

Corollary

1. If $\mathbf{B}$ is obtained from $\mathbf{A}$ by interchanging two columns, $\det \mathbf{B} = -\det \mathbf{A}$.
2. If column i of $\mathbf{B}$ is c (column i of $\mathbf{A}$), $\det \mathbf{B} = c \det \mathbf{A}$.
3. If $\mathbf{B}$ is obtained from $\mathbf{A}$ by adding k times column i to column j, where $i \neq j$, then $\det \mathbf{B} = \det \mathbf{A}$. □

Example 9

$$\det \begin{bmatrix} 2 & 1 & 3 & 4 \\ 0 & 1 & 1 & 0 \\ 1 & 0 & 1 & 1 \\ 4 & 2 & 1 & -1 \end{bmatrix} \underset{C_1 \leftrightarrow C_2}{=} -\det \begin{bmatrix} 1 & 2 & 3 & 4 \\ 1 & 0 & 1 & 0 \\ 0 & 1 & 1 & 1 \\ 2 & 4 & 1 & -1 \end{bmatrix}$$

$$\underset{\substack{C_2-2C_1\to C_2\\ C_3-3C_1\to C_3\\ C_4-4C_1\to C_4}}{=} -\det\begin{bmatrix}1&0&0&0\\1&-2&-2&-4\\0&1&1&1\\2&0&-5&-9\end{bmatrix} \underset{\substack{C_3-\ C_2\to C_3\\ C_4-2C_2\to C_4}}{=} -\det\begin{bmatrix}1&0&0&0\\1&-2&0&0\\0&1&0&-1\\2&0&-5&-9\end{bmatrix}$$

$$\underset{C_3\leftrightarrow C_4}{=} \det\begin{bmatrix}1&0&0&0\\1&-2&0&0\\0&1&-1&0\\2&0&-9&-5\end{bmatrix} = -10$$

It is perfectly legal and sometimes quite useful to use both column and row operations together. For example,

$$\det\begin{bmatrix}2&1&3&4\\0&1&1&0\\1&0&1&1\\4&2&1&-1\end{bmatrix} \underset{C_1\leftrightarrow C_2}{=} -\det\begin{bmatrix}1&2&3&4\\1&0&1&0\\0&1&1&1\\2&4&1&-1\end{bmatrix}$$

$$\underset{R_1\leftrightarrow R_2}{=} \det\begin{bmatrix}1&0&1&0\\1&2&3&4\\0&1&1&1\\2&4&1&-1\end{bmatrix} \underset{C_3-C_1\to C_3}{=} \det\begin{bmatrix}1&0&0&0\\1&2&2&4\\0&1&1&1\\2&4&-1&-1\end{bmatrix}$$

$$\underset{R_2\leftrightarrow R_3}{=} -\det\begin{bmatrix}1&0&0&0\\0&1&1&1\\1&2&2&4\\2&4&-1&-1\end{bmatrix} \underset{\substack{C_3-C_2\to C_3\\ C_4-C_2\to C_4}}{=} -\det\begin{bmatrix}1&0&0&0\\0&1&0&0\\1&2&0&2\\2&4&-5&-5\end{bmatrix}$$

$$\underset{C_3\leftrightarrow C_4}{=} \det\begin{bmatrix}1&0&0&0\\0&1&0&0\\1&2&2&0\\2&4&-5&-5\end{bmatrix} = -10$$

■

Other useful facts about determinants are developed in the starred problems in Exercises 3.2.

Theorem 7 If $\mathbf{A}$ is an $n \times n$ matrix and the ith row can be written as a sum of n-tuples $\mathbf{u}_i + \mathbf{v}_i$, then $\det \mathbf{A} = \det \mathbf{B} + \det \mathbf{C}$, where the ith row of $\mathbf{B}$ is $\mathbf{u}_i$ and all other rows of $\mathbf{B}$ are identical to those of $\mathbf{A}$, and the ith row of $\mathbf{C}$ is $\mathbf{v}_i$ while all other rows of $\mathbf{C}$ are identical to those of $\mathbf{A}$. □

A similar statement is true for columns.

Theorem 8 If $\mathbf{A}$ is an $n \times n$ matrix, and k is a scalar, then

$$\det(k\mathbf{A}) = k^n \det \mathbf{A}$$ □

SUMMARY Associated with each $n \times n$ matrix $\mathbf{A}$ is a scalar called the determinant of $\mathbf{A}$, written $\det \mathbf{A}$. The determinant of a triangular matrix is the product of its diagonal elements. To calculate $\det \mathbf{A}$, use row operations to reduce $\mathbf{A}$ to a triangular matrix. The following statements are used in this reduction:

If $\mathbf{B}$ is obtained from $\mathbf{A}$ by interchanging two rows, $\det \mathbf{B} = -\det \mathbf{A}$.
If $\mathbf{B}$ is obtained from $\mathbf{A}$ by multiplying one row by c, $\det \mathbf{B} = c \det \mathbf{A}$.
If $\mathbf{B}$ is obtained from $\mathbf{A}$ by replacing the jth row by itself plus k times the ith row where $i \neq j$, then $\det \mathbf{B} = \det \mathbf{A}$.

The previous three statements remain true when *row* is replaced by *column*.

An $n \times n$ matrix $\mathbf{A}$ has rank n if and only if $\det \mathbf{A} \neq 0$.
The inverse of an $n \times n$ matrix $\mathbf{A}$ exists if and only if $\det \mathbf{A} \neq 0$.

EXERCISES 3.2

1. Calculate $\det \mathbf{A}$ by two methods, using row reduction and using Definition 2.

a. $\mathbf{A} = \begin{bmatrix} -1 & 4 \\ 1 & 3 \end{bmatrix}$ **b.** $\mathbf{A} = \begin{bmatrix} 4 & 1 & -1 \\ 0 & 2 & 1 \\ 0 & 3 & -1 \end{bmatrix}$

c. $\mathbf{A} = \begin{bmatrix} 3 & 8 & 0 \\ -1 & 0 & 1 \\ 1 & 2 & 3 \end{bmatrix}$

2. a. Let

$$\mathbf{A} = \begin{bmatrix} -1 & 1 & 2 \\ 0 & 6 & 3 \\ 4 & 7 & 5 \end{bmatrix}$$

Calculate $\det \mathbf{A}$ by the method suggested in Example 7.

b. If a similar method were tried in the case of a 4×4 matrix, how many terms would there be in the sum? How many terms would you need?

3. a.

$$\mathbf{A} = \begin{bmatrix} 1 & 1 & 2 & 4 \\ 1 & 0 & 4 & 2 \\ 1 & -1 & 0 & 0 \\ 2 & 2 & 2 & 6 \end{bmatrix}$$

Use row operations to calculate $\det \mathbf{A}$.

b. Use column operations to calculate $\det \mathbf{A}$.

c. What is the rank of $\mathbf{A}$?

4. Calculate $\det \mathbf{A}$ using any combination of row and column operations you wish, where

$$\mathbf{A} = \begin{bmatrix} 1 & 1 & -1 & 2 & 1 \\ 2 & -1 & 4 & 3 & 1 \\ 1 & 3 & 1 & 0 & 1 \\ 0 & 2 & 4 & 2 & 1 \\ 1 & 0 & -1 & 0 & 1 \end{bmatrix}$$

5. Calculate $\det \mathbf{A}$ using any method you wish.

a. $\mathbf{A} = \begin{bmatrix} 1 & -1 & 2 & -4 \\ 1 & 0 & -4 & 2 \\ 1 & -1 & 0 & 0 \\ 2 & 2 & -2 & 6 \end{bmatrix}$

b. $\mathbf{A} = \begin{bmatrix} 3 & 0 & 0 & 0 & 0 \\ 1 & 1 & -1 & 2 & -4 \\ 2 & 1 & 0 & -4 & 2 \\ 3 & 1 & -1 & 0 & 0 \\ 4 & 2 & 2 & -2 & 6 \end{bmatrix}$

6. Let

$$\mathbf{A} = \begin{bmatrix} 1 & -1 & 1 \\ -1 & x & 1 \\ -1 & -1 & 1 \end{bmatrix}$$

Find $\det \mathbf{A}$ as a polynomial in x. For what value of x is $\det \mathbf{A} = 0$?

7. Let

$$\mathbf{A} = \begin{bmatrix} 1 & 1 & 2 & 1 \\ 1 & 0 & 1 & 1 \\ 2 & 1 & 3 & 5 \\ 1 & 1 & -1 & x \end{bmatrix}$$

Find det **A**. For what value of x, if any, is det **A** = 0?

***8.** **a.** Calculate det **A** in each case.

$$\mathbf{A} = \begin{bmatrix} 1 & 2 \\ 0 & 0 \end{bmatrix} \qquad \mathbf{A} = \begin{bmatrix} 3 & 1 & 4 \\ 0 & 0 & 0 \\ 1 & 5 & 7 \end{bmatrix}$$

$$\mathbf{A} = \begin{bmatrix} 1 & 1 & 0 \\ 2 & 1 & 0 \\ -1 & 4 & 0 \end{bmatrix}$$

b. What is the value of det **A** if **A** has a row or column of zeros? Justify your answer.

***9.** **a.** Calculate det **A** in each case.

$$\mathbf{A} = \begin{bmatrix} 1 & 2 \\ 2 & 4 \end{bmatrix} \qquad \mathbf{A} = \begin{bmatrix} 3 & 1 & 4 \\ 3 & 1 & 4 \\ 1 & 5 & 7 \end{bmatrix}$$

$$\mathbf{A} = \begin{bmatrix} 1 & -2 & 2 \\ 1 & -2 & 3 \\ 2 & -4 & 5 \end{bmatrix}$$

b. What is the value of det **A** if two rows or two columns of **A** are proportional? Justify your answer. Theorem 4, part 1 can help with this.

10. If **A** = **0**, is it necessarily true that det **A** = 0? If det **A** = 0, is it necessarily true that **A** = **0**? Justify your answers.

11. If **A** and **B** are matrices and **A** = **B**, is it necessarily true that det **A** = det **B**? If **A** and **B** are matrices and det **A** = det **B**, is it necessarily true that **A** = **B**? Justify your answers.

12. **a.** Let

$$\mathbf{A} = \begin{bmatrix} 1 & 5 \\ 2 & 4 \end{bmatrix}$$

Write 2**A**. Calculate det **A** and det (2**A**).

b. Let

$$\mathbf{A} = \begin{bmatrix} a & b \\ c & d \end{bmatrix}$$

Write k**A**. Compare det **A** and det (k**A**).

***13.** Let **A** be an $n \times n$ matrix with rows $\mathbf{u}_1, \mathbf{u}_2, \ldots, \mathbf{u}_n$.

a. What are the rows of k**A**?

b. In calculating det (k**A**), how many times should Theorem 4 be used to remove the factors of k from the rows?

c. State the relationship between det (k**A**) and det **A**.

***14.** Use Theorem 4 to show that

$$\det \begin{bmatrix} a_{11} & a_{12} & a_{13} & a_{14} \\ 0 & a_{22} & a_{23} & a_{24} \\ 0 & 0 & a_{33} & a_{34} \\ 0 & 0 & a_{43} & a_{44} \end{bmatrix} = a_{11}a_{22} \det \begin{bmatrix} a_{33} & a_{34} \\ a_{43} & a_{44} \end{bmatrix}$$

15. Find det **A** when the matrix **A** is partitioned as shown.

$$\mathbf{A} = \left[\begin{array}{cc|cc|cc} 1 & 4 & 0 & 0 & 5 & 7 \\ 1 & 3 & 0 & 0 & 1 & 1 \\ \hline 0 & 0 & 2 & -1 & 0 & 0 \\ 0 & 0 & 2 & 2 & 0 & 0 \\ \hline 0 & 0 & 0 & 0 & -1 & 2 \\ 0 & 0 & 0 & 0 & -2 & 1 \end{array}\right]$$

16. Introduce a suitable partition and calculate det **A**.

$$\mathbf{A} = \begin{bmatrix} 3 & 5 & 0 & 0 & 0 \\ 1 & 1 & 0 & 0 & 0 \\ 3 & 6 & 7 & 2 & 0 \\ 2 & 5 & 2 & 1 & 0 \\ 9 & 8 & 7 & 6 & 3 \end{bmatrix}$$

17. Let

$$\mathbf{A} = \begin{bmatrix} a + b & c + d \\ e & f \end{bmatrix}$$

Show that

$$\det \mathbf{A} = \det \begin{bmatrix} a & c \\ e & f \end{bmatrix} + \det \begin{bmatrix} b & d \\ e & f \end{bmatrix}$$

***18.** Let

$$\mathbf{A} = \begin{bmatrix} a_{11} + b_{11} & a_{12} + b_{12} & a_{13} + b_{13} \\ a_{21} & a_{22} & a_{23} \\ a_{31} & a_{32} & a_{33} \end{bmatrix}$$

Show that

$$\det \mathbf{A} = \det\begin{bmatrix} a_{11} & a_{12} & a_{13} \\ a_{21} & a_{22} & a_{23} \\ a_{31} & a_{32} & a_{33} \end{bmatrix} + \det\begin{bmatrix} b_{11} & b_{12} & b_{13} \\ a_{21} & a_{22} & a_{23} \\ a_{31} & a_{32} & a_{33} \end{bmatrix}$$

***19.** Use Definition 3 to establish the following: if in the square matrix **A** the ith row can be expressed as a sum $\mathbf{u}_i + \mathbf{v}_i$, then $\det \mathbf{A} = \det \mathbf{B} + \det \mathbf{C}$, where the ith row of **B** is $\mathbf{u}_i$ and all other rows of **B** are identical with the rows of **A**, and the ith row of **C** is $\mathbf{v}_i$ while all other rows of **C** are identical with those of **A**.

20. Write as a sum of two determinants and compute (use Problem 19).

a. $\det\begin{bmatrix} 1-k & 2+0 & 3+0 \\ 4 & 1 & 7 \\ 2 & 8 & 9 \end{bmatrix}$

b. $\det\begin{bmatrix} 1-k & 4-2 & 1+2 \\ 4 & 1 & 7 \\ 2 & 8 & 9 \end{bmatrix}$

21. a. Write as a sum of two determinants.

$$\det\begin{bmatrix} a+b & c+d \\ e & g \end{bmatrix}$$

b. Write as a sum of four determinants.

$$\det\begin{bmatrix} a+b & c+d \\ e+f & g+h \end{bmatrix}$$

22. Write as a sum of four determinants.

$$\det\begin{bmatrix} x-1 & 2 \\ 3 & x-6 \end{bmatrix}$$

23. Write as a polynomial in λ in which the coefficients are determinants or sums of determinants:

$$\det\begin{bmatrix} a_{11}-\lambda & a_{12} & a_{13} \\ a_{21} & a_{22}-\lambda & a_{23} \\ a_{31} & a_{32} & a_{33}-\lambda \end{bmatrix}$$

24. If

$$\mathbf{A} = \begin{bmatrix} 5 & 4 & 1 \\ 3 & 2 & 0 \\ 6 & 7 & 8 \end{bmatrix}$$

$\det \mathbf{A} = -7$. Use this fact to answer the following questions:

a. Does $\mathbf{A}^{-1}$ exist?

b. Is the following system of equations consistent:

$$\begin{aligned} 5x_1 + 4x_2 + x_3 &= 3 \\ 3x_1 + 2x_2 \quad &= 0 \\ 6x_1 + 7x_2 + 8x_3 &= 7 \end{aligned}$$

c. Do there exist numbers c_1, c_2, c_3 such that

$$c_1(5,3,6) + c_2(4,2,7) + c_3(1,0,8) = (1,2,-3)$$

d. Does the system of equations

$$\begin{bmatrix} 5 & 4 & 1 \\ 3 & 2 & 0 \\ 6 & 7 & 8 \end{bmatrix}\begin{bmatrix} x_1 \\ x_2 \\ x_3 \end{bmatrix} = \begin{bmatrix} 0 \\ 0 \\ 0 \end{bmatrix}$$

have nontrivial solutions?

e. What is the rank of $\mathbf{A}^T$?

25. Let

$$\mathbf{A} = \begin{bmatrix} 1 & 2 & 3 \\ 4 & 5 & 6 \\ 7 & 8 & 9 \end{bmatrix}$$

Calculate $\det \mathbf{A}$. Use the value of $\det \mathbf{A}$ to answer the following questions:

a. Is the rank of **A** equal to 3?

b. Is the system of equations $\mathbf{AX} = \mathbf{B}$ consistent for every **B**?

c. Does $\mathbf{A}^{-1}$ exist?

d. Does the system of equations $\mathbf{AX} = \mathbf{0}$ have nontrivial solutions?

26. **B** is an $r \times s$ **submatrix** of the $m \times n$ matrix **A** if $m - r$ of the rows of **A** are eliminated and $n - s$ of the columns of **A** are eliminated and the remaining elements are kept in the same order. Let

$$\mathbf{A} = \begin{bmatrix} 1 & 2 & 4 & 5 & 7 \\ -1 & 3 & 1 & 2 & 5 \\ 0 & 4 & 0 & 2 & 7 \end{bmatrix}.$$

Then

$$\mathbf{B} = \begin{bmatrix} 1 & 2 & 4 \\ -1 & 3 & 1 \\ 0 & 4 & 0 \end{bmatrix}$$

is a 3×3 submatrix of **A**. Find det **B**; find the rank of **A**.

***27.** Show that if **A** is an $m \times n$ matrix, $m < n$, it has rank m if some $m \times m$ submatrix of **A** has determinant not zero.

28. Show that

$$\det \begin{bmatrix} 1 & x_1 & x_1^2 \\ 1 & x_2 & x_2^2 \\ 1 & x_3 & x_3^2 \end{bmatrix} = (x_1 - x_2)(x_2 - x_3)(x_3 - x_1),$$

if x_1, x_2, x_3 are distinct.

29. Show that

$$\begin{bmatrix} 1 & x_1 & x_1^2 & x_1^3 \\ 1 & x_2 & x_2^2 & x_2^3 \\ 1 & x_3 & x_3^2 & x_3^3 \end{bmatrix}$$

has rank 3 if x_1, x_2, and x_3 are distinct.

30. Show that

$$\begin{bmatrix} 1 & x_1 & x_1^2 & \cdots & x_1^n \\ 1 & x_2 & x_2^2 & \cdots & x_2^n \\ \vdots & \vdots & \vdots & & \vdots \\ 1 & x_m & x_m^2 & \cdots & x_m^n \end{bmatrix}$$

has rank m if $x_1, x_2, \ldots, x_m$ are distinct and $n \geqslant m - 1$.

3.3 Determinants, Cofactors, Inverses

Another useful method of computing the number det **A** is based on cofactors. This method shows how to express $\mathbf{A}^{-1}$ in terms of det **A** and a matrix related to **A**.

For any matrix a **submatrix** can be formed by eliminating some rows and/or columns of **A**. We are especially interested in the square submatrices that result from a square matrix **A** when one row and one column of **A** are omitted. The symbol $\mathbf{A}_{ij}$ represents the $(n-1) \times (n-1)$ submatrix obtained from the $n \times n$ matrix **A** by eliminating the ith row and jth column of **A**.

Example 10 Let

$$\mathbf{A} = \begin{bmatrix} -1 & 1 & 2 \\ 0 & 6 & 3 \\ 4 & 7 & 5 \end{bmatrix}$$

There are nine 2×2 submatrices of **A**:

$$\mathbf{A}_{11} = \begin{bmatrix} 6 & 3 \\ 7 & 5 \end{bmatrix}, \quad \mathbf{A}_{12} = \begin{bmatrix} 0 & 3 \\ 4 & 5 \end{bmatrix}, \quad \mathbf{A}_{13} = \begin{bmatrix} 0 & 6 \\ 4 & 7 \end{bmatrix}$$

$$\mathbf{A}_{21} = \begin{bmatrix} 1 & 2 \\ 7 & 5 \end{bmatrix}, \quad \mathbf{A}_{22} = \begin{bmatrix} -1 & 2 \\ 4 & 5 \end{bmatrix}, \quad \mathbf{A}_{23} = \begin{bmatrix} -1 & 1 \\ 4 & 7 \end{bmatrix}$$

$$\mathbf{A}_{31} = \begin{bmatrix} 1 & 2 \\ 6 & 3 \end{bmatrix}, \quad \mathbf{A}_{32} = \begin{bmatrix} -1 & 2 \\ 0 & 3 \end{bmatrix}, \quad \mathbf{A}_{33} = \begin{bmatrix} -1 & 1 \\ 0 & 6 \end{bmatrix}$$

Definition 4

Cofactor γ_{ij}

Let $\gamma_{ij} = (-1)^{i+j} \det \mathbf{A}_{ij}$. The scalar γ_{ij} is called the **cofactor** of a_{ij} in **A**.

Example 11 Let $\mathbf{A}$ be the matrix in Example 10.

$$\begin{aligned}
\det \mathbf{A}_{11} &= 9, & \gamma_{11} &= (-1)^2 9 = 9\\
\det \mathbf{A}_{12} &= -12, & \gamma_{12} &= (-1)^3(-12) = 12\\
\det \mathbf{A}_{13} &= -24, & \gamma_{13} &= (-1)^4(-24) = -24\\
\det \mathbf{A}_{21} &= -9, & \gamma_{21} &= 9\\
\det \mathbf{A}_{22} &= -13, & \gamma_{22} &= -13\\
\det \mathbf{A}_{23} &= -11, & \gamma_{23} &= 11\\
\det \mathbf{A}_{31} &= -9, & \gamma_{31} &= -9\\
\det \mathbf{A}_{32} &= -3, & \gamma_{32} &= 3\\
\det \mathbf{A}_{33} &= -6, & \gamma_{33} &= -6
\end{aligned}$$

■

Example 12 illustrates the relationship between $\det \mathbf{A}$ and the cofactors of the elements in the rows of $\mathbf{A}$.

Example 12 Let $\mathbf{A}$ be the matrix of Example 10,

$$\mathbf{A} = \begin{bmatrix} -1 & 1 & 2 \\ 0 & 6 & 3 \\ 4 & 7 & 5 \end{bmatrix}$$

Calculate the scalar product of each row of the matrix and the corresponding row of cofactors:

$$\begin{aligned}
a_{11}\gamma_{11} + a_{12}\gamma_{12} + a_{13}\gamma_{13} &= -1(9) + 1(12) + 2(-24) = -45\\
a_{21}\gamma_{21} + a_{22}\gamma_{22} + a_{23}\gamma_{23} &= 0(9) + 6(-13) + 3(11) = -45\\
a_{31}\gamma_{31} + a_{32}\gamma_{32} + a_{33}\gamma_{33} &= 4(-9) + 7(3) + 5(-6) = -45
\end{aligned}$$

The value of the sum in each case is -45, which is $\det \mathbf{A}$ (see Example 8a).

Now consider the scalar product of the first row of $\mathbf{A}$ and the cofactors of a different row.

$$\begin{aligned}
(-1)(-9) + (1)(3) + (2)(-6) &= 9 + 3 - 12 = 0\\
(-1)(9) + (1)(-13) + (2)(11) &= -9 - 13 + 22 = 0
\end{aligned}$$

■

The results of Example 12 are not accidental as the following theorem asserts.

Theorem 9 Let $\mathbf{A}$ be an $n \times n$ matrix and γ_{ij} be the cofactor of a_{ij} in $\mathbf{A}$. For each i, $i = 1, 2, \ldots, n$,

1. $a_{i1}\gamma_{i1} + a_{i2}\gamma_{i2} + \cdots + a_{in}\gamma_{in} = \det \mathbf{A}$
2. $a_{i1}\gamma_{j1} + a_{i2}\gamma_{j2} + \cdots + a_{in}\gamma_{jn} = 0 \qquad$ for $j \neq i$, $\; j = 1, 2, \ldots, n$.

Proof These facts are consequences of the definition of $\det \mathbf{A}$ since the sums represent appropriate grouping of terms. The proof is illustrated in the 3×3 case.

Let

$$\mathbf{A} = \begin{bmatrix} a_{11} & a_{12} & a_{13} \\ a_{21} & a_{22} & a_{23} \\ a_{31} & a_{32} & a_{33} \end{bmatrix}$$

and consider $i = 2$. Then

$$\begin{aligned} a_{21}\gamma_{21} + a_{22}\gamma_{22} + a_{23}\gamma_{23} &= a_{21}\left(-\det\begin{bmatrix} a_{12} & a_{13} \\ a_{32} & a_{33} \end{bmatrix}\right) \\ &\quad + a_{22}\left(\det\begin{bmatrix} a_{11} & a_{13} \\ a_{31} & a_{33} \end{bmatrix}\right) + a_{23}\left(-\det\begin{bmatrix} a_{11} & a_{12} \\ a_{31} & a_{32} \end{bmatrix}\right) \\ &= a_{21}a_{13}a_{32} - a_{21}a_{12}a_{33} + a_{22}a_{11}a_{33} - a_{22}a_{13}a_{31} \\ &\quad + a_{23}a_{12}a_{31} - a_{23}a_{11}a_{32} \\ &= \det \mathbf{A}. \end{aligned}$$

Statement 2 can be derived directly or it can be obtained from statement 1. For example,

$$a_{21}\gamma_{11} + a_{22}\gamma_{12} + a_{23}\gamma_{13} = \det\begin{bmatrix} a_{21} & a_{22} & a_{23} \\ a_{21} & a_{22} & a_{23} \\ a_{31} & a_{32} & a_{33} \end{bmatrix}$$

which is zero since two rows are identical. (See Problem 9, Section 3.2.) □

As is to be expected, the statements about rows have their counterparts using columns.

Corollary $a_{1j}\gamma_{1j} + a_{2j}\gamma_{2j} + \cdots + a_{nj}\gamma_{nj} = \det \mathbf{A}, \quad j = 1, 2, \ldots, n$

$$a_{1i}\gamma_{1j} + a_{2i}\gamma_{2j} + \cdots + a_{ni}\gamma_{nj} = 0, \quad i \neq j,\ i = 1, 2, \ldots, n; \quad j = 1, 2, \ldots, n$$

These statements follow from Theorem 9 using the fact that $\det \mathbf{A}^T = \det \mathbf{A}$. □

If we let $\mathbf{A}_i$ represent the ith row of $\mathbf{A}$, and $\mathbf{C}_i$ be the corresponding row of cofactors, Theorem 9 can be stated in the form

$$\mathbf{A}_i\mathbf{C}_i^T = \det \mathbf{A} \quad i = 1, 2, \ldots, n; \qquad \mathbf{A}_i\mathbf{C}_j^T = 0, \quad i, j = 1, 2, \ldots, n,\ i \neq j$$

When $\det \mathbf{A}$ is written in the form $\det \mathbf{A} = a_{i1}\gamma_{i1} + a_{i2}\gamma_{i2} + \cdots + a_{in}\gamma_{in}$, it is said to be **expanded by the ith row.** When written as

$$\det \mathbf{A} = a_{1j}\gamma_{1j} + a_{2j}\gamma_{2j} + \cdots + a_{nj}\gamma_{nj}$$

it is said to be **expanded by the jth column.**

We should note that we have now two quite distinct methods of calculating $\det \mathbf{A}$. One is by row reduction, column reduction, or a combination of these. The other is by expanding by a row or column. The most efficient way of calculating $\det \mathbf{A}$ may well be a combination of both these approaches. Example 13 illustrates this.

Example 13

a. Let

$$\mathbf{A} = \begin{bmatrix} 1 & 1 & 2 & 0 \\ 2 & 1 & 1 & 0 \\ 1 & 3 & 0 & 1 \\ 1 & 1 & 4 & 2 \end{bmatrix}$$

Use row or column operations to obtain a row or column in which only one nonzero element remains:

$$\det \mathbf{A} = \det \begin{bmatrix} 1 & 1 & 2 & 0 \\ 2 & 1 & 1 & 0 \\ 1 & 3 & 0 & 1 \\ -1 & -5 & 4 & 0 \end{bmatrix}$$

Expand by column 4:

$$\det \mathbf{A} = (-1)^7 \det \begin{bmatrix} 1 & 1 & 2 \\ 2 & 1 & 1 \\ -1 & -5 & 4 \end{bmatrix}$$

Again work for a row or column with one nonzero element:

$$\det \mathbf{A} = -\det \begin{bmatrix} 1 & 1 & 2 \\ 2 & 1 & 1 \\ -1 & -5 & 4 \end{bmatrix} = -\det \begin{bmatrix} 1 & 0 & 0 \\ 2 & -1 & -3 \\ -1 & -4 & 6 \end{bmatrix}$$

Now expand by the first row:

$$\det \mathbf{A} = -\det \begin{vmatrix} -1 & -3 \\ -4 & 6 \end{vmatrix} = -(-6 - 12) = 18$$

b. An alternate method for the same matrix **A** is:

$$\det \mathbf{A} = \det \begin{bmatrix} 1 & 1 & 2 & 0 \\ 2 & 1 & 1 & 0 \\ 1 & 3 & 0 & 1 \\ 1 & 1 & 4 & 2 \end{bmatrix} = \det \begin{bmatrix} 1 & 1 & 2 & 0 \\ 0 & -1 & -3 & 0 \\ 0 & 2 & -2 & 1 \\ 0 & 0 & 2 & 2 \end{bmatrix}$$

$$= \det \begin{bmatrix} -1 & -3 & 0 \\ 2 & -2 & 1 \\ 0 & 2 & 2 \end{bmatrix} = 2\det \begin{bmatrix} -1 & -3 & 0 \\ 2 & -2 & 1 \\ 0 & 1 & 1 \end{bmatrix}$$

$$= 2\det \begin{bmatrix} -1 & -3 & 0 \\ 2 & -3 & 0 \\ 0 & 1 & 1 \end{bmatrix} = 2\det \begin{bmatrix} -1 & -3 \\ 2 & -3 \end{bmatrix} = 2(9) = 18 \quad \blacksquare$$

One of the rewards of mastering the ideas of matrix multiplication is that the somewhat messy statements of Theorem 9 can be summarized with beautiful clarity in a simple matrix product:

$$\begin{bmatrix} a_{11} & a_{12} & a_{13} & \cdots & a_{1n} \\ a_{21} & a_{22} & a_{23} & \cdots & a_{2n} \\ \vdots & \vdots & \vdots & & \vdots \\ a_{n1} & a_{n2} & a_{n3} & \cdots & a_{nn} \end{bmatrix} \begin{bmatrix} \gamma_{11} & \gamma_{21} & \gamma_{31} & \cdots & \gamma_{n1} \\ \gamma_{12} & \gamma_{22} & \gamma_{32} & \cdots & \gamma_{n2} \\ \vdots & \vdots & \vdots & & \vdots \\ \gamma_{1n} & \gamma_{2n} & \gamma_{3n} & \cdots & \gamma_{nn} \end{bmatrix}$$

$$= \begin{bmatrix} \det \mathbf{A} & 0 & 0 & \cdots & 0 \\ 0 & \det \mathbf{A} & 0 & \cdots & 0 \\ 0 & 0 & \det \mathbf{A} & \cdots & 0 \\ \vdots & \vdots & \vdots & & \vdots \\ 0 & 0 & 0 & \cdots & \det \mathbf{A} \end{bmatrix} = (\det \mathbf{A})\mathbf{I}$$

The matrix on the right in the original product is called the *adjoint* of **A**.

Adj A

Definition 5

Let **A** be an $n \times n$ matrix and let γ_{ij} be the cofactor of a_{ij} in **A**. The transpose of the matrix with elements γ_{ij} is called the **adjoint** of **A**, written Adj **A**.

Let $\mathbf{A}_i$ represent the ith row of **A** and $\mathbf{C}_i$ the corresponding row of cofactors. We can write the product **A** Adj **A** in the form

$$\mathbf{A}(\text{Adj}\,\mathbf{A}) = \begin{bmatrix} \mathbf{A}_1 \\ \mathbf{A}_2 \\ \vdots \\ \mathbf{A}_n \end{bmatrix} \begin{bmatrix} \mathbf{C}_1 \\ \mathbf{C}_2 \\ \vdots \\ \mathbf{C}_n \end{bmatrix}^T = (\det \mathbf{A})\mathbf{I}.$$

Example 14 Let

$$\mathbf{A} = \begin{bmatrix} -1 & 1 & 2 \\ 0 & 6 & 3 \\ 4 & 7 & 5 \end{bmatrix}$$ See Example 10.

$$\text{Adj}\,\mathbf{A} = \begin{bmatrix} 9 & 9 & -9 \\ 12 & -13 & 3 \\ -24 & 11 & -6 \end{bmatrix}$$ Use results in Example 11.

$$\mathbf{A}(\text{Adj}\,\mathbf{A}) = \begin{bmatrix} -1 & 1 & 2 \\ 0 & 6 & 3 \\ 4 & 7 & 5 \end{bmatrix} \begin{bmatrix} 9 & 9 & -9 \\ 12 & -13 & 3 \\ -24 & 11 & -6 \end{bmatrix} = \begin{bmatrix} -45 & 0 & 0 \\ 0 & -45 & 0 \\ 0 & 0 & -45 \end{bmatrix}$$

Also

$$(\operatorname{Adj}\mathbf{A})\mathbf{A} = \begin{bmatrix} 9 & 9 & -9 \\ 12 & -13 & 3 \\ -24 & 11 & -6 \end{bmatrix} \begin{bmatrix} -1 & 1 & 2 \\ 0 & 6 & 3 \\ 4 & 7 & 5 \end{bmatrix} = \begin{bmatrix} -45 & 0 & 0 \\ 0 & -45 & 0 \\ 0 & 0 & -45 \end{bmatrix}$$

Now write $\mathbf{B} = \dfrac{1}{\det \mathbf{A}} \operatorname{Adj}\mathbf{A} = -\frac{1}{45}\operatorname{Adj}\mathbf{A} = \begin{bmatrix} -\frac{1}{5} & -\frac{1}{5} & \frac{1}{5} \\ -\frac{4}{15} & \frac{13}{45} & -\frac{1}{15} \\ \frac{8}{15} & -\frac{11}{45} & \frac{2}{15} \end{bmatrix}$. The calculation $\mathbf{AB} = \mathbf{BA} = \mathbf{I}$ verifies that $\mathbf{B}$ is the inverse of $\mathbf{A}$. ■

Theorem 10 Let $\mathbf{A}$ be an $n \times n$ matrix. Then $\mathbf{A}(\operatorname{Adj}\mathbf{A}) = (\det \mathbf{A})\mathbf{I}$, and $(\operatorname{Adj}\mathbf{A})\mathbf{A} = (\det \mathbf{A})\mathbf{I}$. If $\det \mathbf{A} \neq 0$, $\mathbf{A}^{-1} = \dfrac{1}{\det \mathbf{A}} \operatorname{Adj}\mathbf{A}$.

Proof The definition of adjoint of $\mathbf{A}$ and Theorem 9 imply that $\mathbf{A}(\operatorname{Adj}\mathbf{A}) = (\det \mathbf{A})\mathbf{I}$. The statement $(\operatorname{Adj}\mathbf{A})\mathbf{A} = (\det \mathbf{A})\mathbf{I}$ follows from the corollary to Theorem 9. If $\det \mathbf{A} \neq 0$, we can divide these equations by $\det \mathbf{A}$ and obtain

$$\left(\frac{1}{\det \mathbf{A}} \operatorname{Adj}\mathbf{A}\right)\mathbf{A} = \mathbf{A}\left(\frac{1}{\det \mathbf{A}} \operatorname{Adj}\mathbf{A}\right) = \mathbf{I}$$

Since the inverse of $\mathbf{A}$ is unique, we can conclude that

$$\mathbf{A}^{-1} = \frac{1}{\det \mathbf{A}} \operatorname{Adj}\mathbf{A}$$ □

For purposes of calculation, the formula for $\mathbf{A}^{-1}$ is useful in the 2×2 and possibly in the 3×3 cases. For larger matrices, row reduction or other related numerical techniques are more efficient. However, the formula has both practical and theoretical importance in the more advanced study of matrices. Also, it is the basis of Cramer's Rule, a technique of solving certain systems of linear equations.

If $\det \mathbf{A} \neq 0$, the system of equations $\mathbf{AX} = \mathbf{B}$ has a unique solution $\mathbf{X} = \mathbf{A}^{-1}\mathbf{B}$. Cramer's Rule makes use of the formula $\mathbf{A}^{-1} = (1/\det \mathbf{A})(\operatorname{Adj}\mathbf{A})$ to write $\mathbf{X}$ as a ratio of determinants. The following discussion develops Cramer's Rule in the 3×3 case. The product $(\operatorname{Adj}\mathbf{A})\mathbf{B}$ is

$$\begin{bmatrix} \gamma_{11} & \gamma_{21} & \gamma_{31} \\ \gamma_{12} & \gamma_{22} & \gamma_{32} \\ \gamma_{13} & \gamma_{23} & \gamma_{33} \end{bmatrix} \begin{bmatrix} b_1 \\ b_2 \\ b_3 \end{bmatrix} = \begin{bmatrix} \gamma_{11}b_1 + \gamma_{21}b_2 + \gamma_{31}b_3 \\ \gamma_{12}b_1 + \gamma_{22}b_2 + \gamma_{32}b_3 \\ \gamma_{13}b_1 + \gamma_{23}b_2 + \gamma_{33}b_3 \end{bmatrix}$$

From Theorem 9,

$$\det \begin{bmatrix} a_{11} & a_{12} & a_{13} \\ a_{21} & a_{22} & a_{23} \\ a_{31} & a_{32} & a_{33} \end{bmatrix} = a_{11}\gamma_{11} + a_{21}\gamma_{21} + a_{31}\gamma_{31}$$

Compare this sum with $\gamma_{11}b_1 + \gamma_{21}b_2 + \gamma_{31}b_3$. The only difference is that b_1, b_2, b_3

are replaced by a_{11}, a_{21}, a_{31}. Thus we see that

$$\det\begin{bmatrix} b_1 & a_{12} & a_{13} \\ b_2 & a_{22} & a_{23} \\ b_3 & a_{32} & a_{33} \end{bmatrix} = \gamma_{11}b_1 + \gamma_{21}b_2 + \gamma_{31}b_3$$

Introduce the notation

$$\mathbf{M}_1 = \begin{bmatrix} b_1 & a_{12} & a_{13} \\ b_2 & a_{22} & a_{23} \\ b_3 & a_{32} & a_{33} \end{bmatrix}, \quad \mathbf{M}_2 = \begin{bmatrix} a_{11} & b_1 & a_{13} \\ a_{21} & b_2 & a_{23} \\ a_{31} & b_3 & a_{33} \end{bmatrix}, \quad \mathbf{M}_3 = \begin{bmatrix} a_{11} & a_{12} & b_1 \\ a_{21} & a_{22} & b_2 \\ a_{31} & a_{32} & b_3 \end{bmatrix}$$

Then

$$\begin{aligned} \gamma_{11}b_1 + \gamma_{21}b_2 + \gamma_{31}b_3 &= \det\mathbf{M}_1 \\ \gamma_{12}b_1 + \gamma_{22}b_2 + \gamma_{32}b_3 &= \det\mathbf{M}_2 \\ \gamma_{13}b_1 + \gamma_{23}b_2 + \gamma_{33}b_3 &= \det\mathbf{M}_3 \end{aligned}$$

With this notation,

$$(\text{Adj}\,\mathbf{A})\mathbf{B} = \begin{bmatrix} \det\mathbf{M}_1 \\ \det\mathbf{M}_2 \\ \det\mathbf{M}_3 \end{bmatrix}$$

Since $\mathbf{A}^{-1} = \dfrac{\text{Adj}\,\mathbf{A}}{\det\mathbf{A}}$, the solution of the system of equations $\mathbf{AX} = \mathbf{B}$ can now be written

$$x_1 = \frac{\det\mathbf{M}_1}{\det\mathbf{A}}, \qquad x_2 = \frac{\det\mathbf{M}_2}{\det\mathbf{A}}, \qquad x_3 = \frac{\det\mathbf{M}_3}{\det\mathbf{A}}$$

This formula is called **Cramer's Rule**. It is illustrated in a numerical case in Example 15.

Example 15 For the system of equations

$$\begin{aligned} x_1 + x_2 + x_3 &= 5 \\ -x_1 + 3x_2 + 2x_3 &= 2 \\ 2x_1 + x_2 + x_3 &= 1 \end{aligned} \quad \text{(See Example 5)}, \quad \det\mathbf{A} = \det\begin{bmatrix} 1 & 1 & 1 \\ -1 & 3 & 2 \\ 2 & 1 & 1 \end{bmatrix} = -1$$

Cramer's Rule gives

$$x_1 = -\det\begin{bmatrix} 5 & 1 & 1 \\ 2 & 3 & 2 \\ 1 & 1 & 1 \end{bmatrix} = -4, \qquad x_2 = -\det\begin{bmatrix} 1 & 5 & 1 \\ -1 & 2 & 2 \\ 2 & 1 & 1 \end{bmatrix} = -20,$$

$$x_3 = -\det\begin{bmatrix} 1 & 1 & 5 \\ -1 & 3 & 2 \\ 2 & 1 & 1 \end{bmatrix} = 29$$

■

Cramer's Rule is applicable only if $\mathbf{A}^{-1}$ exists. Even then it involves a great deal of calculation and for $n > 3$ it is not an efficient method for solving equations. However, it provides a concise form for the solutions of a system of equations that is useful in theoretical arguments.

Circuit analysis like that illustrated in Example 18, Chapter 2, can be frequently done more easily using loop-current equations rather than branch-current equations. A loop current is continuous around a closed network. When only one loop current is present in a branch, the loop current and the branch current are equal. When more than one loop current is present in a branch, the actual current in the branch is the algebraic sum of the loop currents in that branch.

Kirchhoff's Laws can be written in terms of loop currents rather than branch currents. The requirement is that the entire resistance of loop 1 be multiplied by loop current 1; that portion of the resistance of loop 1 through which loop current 2 flows must also be multiplied by loop current 2, and similarly for all currents affecting the first loop. All must be included in calculating the voltage drop associated with loop 1.

Example 16 The circuit of Example 18 of Chapter 2 is represented in Figure 3.1.

Two loop currents I_{L1} and I_{L2} are drawn as shown. The branch currents calculated in the previous example are designated I_{B1}, I_{B2}, I_{B3}. In the first branch only the loop current I_{L1} is present so that $I_{B1} = I_{L1}$. In the branch fc, both I_{L1} and I_{L2} are present; I_{L1} is in the same direction as I_{B3} and I_{L2} is in the opposite direction, so that we have $I_{B3} = I_{L1} - I_{L2}$. Finally, $I_{B2} = I_{L2}$.

The entire resistance of loop 1 is $3 + 10 + 2 = 15$. The resistance of loop 1 through which loop current 2 flows is 2. Kirchhoff's Law yields $15I_{L1} - 2I_{L2} = 100$. For loop 2, the resistance of loop 2 through which loop current 1 flows is 2, and the entire resistance of loop 2 is $2 + 7 + 3 = 12$. Thus we have $-2I_{L1} + 12I_{L2} = 100$. The negative signs are used because I_{L1} and I_{L2} are opposite in direction on the common portion fc. The pair of equations

$$\begin{aligned} 15I_{L1} - 2I_{L2} &= 100 \\ -2I_{L1} + 12I_{L2} &= 100 \end{aligned}$$

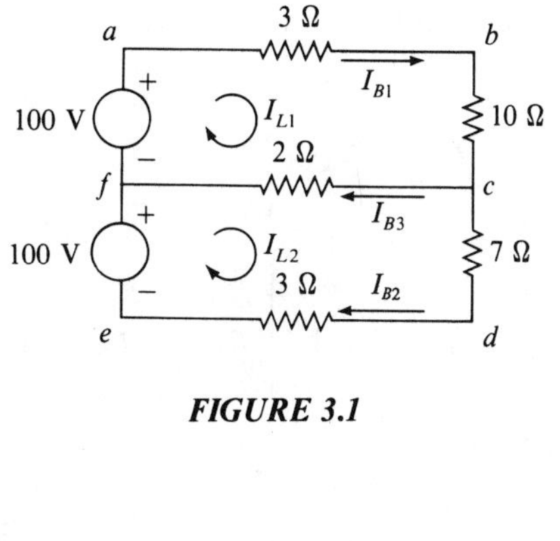

FIGURE 3.1

can be solved by Cramer's Rule:

$$I_{L1} = \frac{\det\begin{bmatrix} 100 & -2 \\ 100 & 12 \end{bmatrix}}{\det\begin{bmatrix} 15 & -2 \\ -2 & 12 \end{bmatrix}} = \frac{1400}{176} = 7.9545$$

$$I_{L2} = \frac{\det\begin{bmatrix} 15 & 100 \\ -2 & 100 \end{bmatrix}}{\det\begin{bmatrix} 15 & -2 \\ -2 & 12 \end{bmatrix}} = \frac{1700}{176} = 9.6591$$

This gives for the branch currents the values $I_{B1} = 7.9545$ amp, $I_{B2} = 9.6591$ amp, and $I_{B3} = -1.7046$ amp. (See Example 18, Chapter 2.) ■

The great advantage of the loop-current method is that engineers are able to write down the solution by Cramer's Rule from an inspection of the circuit arrangement. For a three-loop network like Figure 3.2, the system of equations resulting from application of Kirchhoff's Laws is

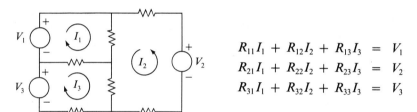

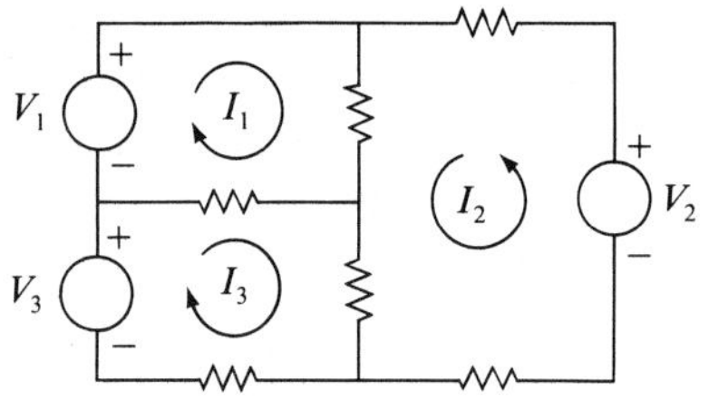

FIGURE 3.2

$$\begin{aligned} R_{11}I_1 + R_{12}I_2 + R_{13}I_3 &= V_1 \\ R_{21}I_1 + R_{22}I_2 + R_{23}I_3 &= V_2 \\ R_{31}I_1 + R_{32}I_2 + R_{33}I_3 &= V_3 \end{aligned}$$

where I_1, I_2, I_3 are loop currents, R_{11} is the total resistance of loop 1 to current I_1, R_{22} the total resistance of loop 2 to I_2, R_{33} the total resistance of loop 3 to I_3, $R_{12} = R_{21}$ is the resistance common to loops 1 and 2, $R_{13} = R_{31}$ is the resistance common to loops 1 and 3, and $R_{23} = R_{32}$ is the resistance common to loops 2 and 3. The driving voltages V_1, V_2, V_3 of loops 1, 2, and 3 are considered positive when the arrow directions assigned to the loop currents are from $-$ to $+$.

The solution can be written by Cramer's Rule:

$$I_1 = \frac{1}{\Delta}\det\begin{bmatrix} V_1 & R_{12} & R_{13} \\ V_2 & R_{22} & R_{23} \\ V_3 & R_{32} & R_{33} \end{bmatrix}, \qquad I_2 = \frac{1}{\Delta}\det\begin{bmatrix} R_{11} & V_1 & R_{13} \\ R_{21} & V_2 & R_{23} \\ R_{31} & V_2 & R_{33} \end{bmatrix},$$

$$I_3 = \frac{1}{\Delta}\det\begin{bmatrix} R_{11} & R_{12} & V_1 \\ R_{21} & R_{22} & V_2 \\ R_{31} & R_{32} & V_3 \end{bmatrix}$$

where

$$\Delta = \det \begin{bmatrix} R_{11} & R_{12} & R_{13} \\ R_{21} & R_{22} & R_{23} \\ R_{31} & R_{32} & R_{33} \end{bmatrix}$$

Notice that Δ depends only on the values of R in the electrical system. It is called the resistance system determinant. The method requires obviously that the denominator Δ be different from zero. This will be guaranteed provided the correct number of loop currents is employed and that these loop currents are independent. In simple cases it is not difficult to see how this can be done, but in more complicated circuits making sure that these conditions are satisfied is part of the "art" of the electrical engineer.

SUMMARY For an $n \times n$ matrix $\mathbf{A}$, the cofactor of a_{ij} in $\mathbf{A}$ is the scalar $\gamma_{ij} = (-1)^{i+j} \det \mathbf{A}_{ij}$, where $\mathbf{A}_{ij}$ is the $(n-1) \times (n-1)$ matrix obtained from $\mathbf{A}$ by eliminating the ith row and the jth column. These cofactors have the properties:

$$\begin{aligned} \det \mathbf{A} &= (a_{i1}, a_{i2}, \ldots, a_{in}) \cdot (\gamma_{i1}, \gamma_{i2}, \ldots, \gamma_{in}), && i = 1, 2, \ldots, n \\ 0 &= (a_{i1}, a_{i2}, \ldots, a_{in}) \cdot (\gamma_{j1}, \gamma_{j2}, \ldots, \gamma_{jn}), && i \neq j \\ \det \mathbf{A} &= (a_{1i}, a_{2i}, \ldots, a_{ni}) \cdot (\gamma_{1i}, \gamma_{2i}, \ldots, \gamma_{ni}), && i = 1, 2, \ldots, n \\ 0 &= (a_{1j}, a_{2j}, \ldots, a_{nj}) \cdot (\gamma_{1i}, \gamma_{2i}, \ldots, \gamma_{ni}), && i \neq j \end{aligned}$$

The matrix $[\gamma_{ij}]^T$ is called the adjoint of $\mathbf{A}$, written Adj $\mathbf{A}$. For any square matrix $\mathbf{A}$, $\mathbf{A}(\text{Adj}\,\mathbf{A}) = (\det \mathbf{A})\mathbf{I}$. If $\det \mathbf{A} \neq 0$, $\mathbf{A}^{-1}$ exists and

$$\mathbf{A}^{-1} = \frac{1}{\det \mathbf{A}} \text{Adj}\,\mathbf{A}$$

EXERCISES 3.3

1. Let

$$\mathbf{A} = \begin{bmatrix} 1 & 2 & 3 \\ 0 & 1 & 5 \\ 1 & 1 & 3 \end{bmatrix}$$

a. Write the submatrices $\mathbf{A}_{11}, \mathbf{A}_{12}$, and $\mathbf{A}_{13}$. Calculate $\gamma_{11}, \gamma_{12}, \gamma_{13}$. Calculate $\det \mathbf{A}$ using these values.

b. Calculate $\det \mathbf{A}$ by expanding by the second row.

2. Let

$$\mathbf{A} = \begin{bmatrix} 1 & 2 & 1 & 0 \\ 0 & 1 & 1 & 2 \\ 1 & 0 & 0 & 0 \\ 2 & 1 & 0 & 1 \end{bmatrix}.$$

a. Find the value of $\det \mathbf{A}$ by expanding by the first row.

b. Find the value of $\det \mathbf{A}$ by expanding by the third row.

c. Which method was easier?

3. The cofactor of $a_{ij} = (-1)^{i+j} \det \mathbf{A}_{ij}$.

a. Show that for a 2×2 matrix, the values of $(-1)^{i+j}$ follow the pattern $\begin{bmatrix} + & - \\ - & + \end{bmatrix}$.

b. Show that for a 3×3 matrix, the values of $(-1)^{i+j}$ follow the pattern $\begin{bmatrix} + & - & + \\ - & + & - \\ + & - & + \end{bmatrix}$.

c. Write the pattern of the values of $(-1)^{i+j}$ in a 4×4 matrix; in a 5×5 matrix.

4. Show that in an $n \times n$ matrix, the sign used in calculating cofactors alternates along a row and down a column.

5. Calculate $\det \mathbf{A}$ using cofactors.

a. $\mathbf{A} = \begin{bmatrix} 2 & 1 & 5 \\ 1 & 3 & 1 \\ 2 & -1 & 0 \end{bmatrix}$

b. $\mathbf{A} = \begin{bmatrix} 1 & 0 & -1 & 1 \\ 1 & 1 & 0 & 1 \\ 0 & 1 & -1 & 0 \\ 1 & 1 & -1 & 1 \end{bmatrix}$

c. $\mathbf{A} = \begin{bmatrix} 3 & 1 & -1 & 2 \\ 0 & 2 & 0 & 0 \\ 4 & 1 & 0 & 2 \\ -2 & 1 & 3 & 4 \end{bmatrix}$

6. Calculate $\det \mathbf{A}$ using cofactors.

a. $\mathbf{A} = \begin{bmatrix} 2 & 3 & 4 \\ 0 & 1 & 0 \\ 1 & 1 & 2 \end{bmatrix}$ **b.** $\mathbf{A} = \begin{bmatrix} 1 & 0 & 3 & 1 \\ 2 & 1 & 5 & 2 \\ 3 & 0 & 0 & 1 \\ 4 & 0 & 0 & 1 \end{bmatrix}$

c. $\mathbf{A} = \begin{bmatrix} 1 & 0 & 2 & 0 \\ 3 & 1 & 4 & 2 \\ 0 & 5 & 0 & 7 \\ 1 & -1 & 1 & -1 \end{bmatrix}$

7. Combine the method of row reduction and cofactors to calculate $\det \mathbf{A}$.

a. $\mathbf{A} = \begin{bmatrix} 1 & 1 & 3 & 1 \\ 2 & 1 & 4 & 2 \\ 1 & -1 & 5 & 7 \\ -2 & 1 & 1 & 3 \end{bmatrix}$

b. $\mathbf{A} = \begin{bmatrix} 1 & 2 & -1 & 5 \\ 2 & 1 & 0 & 1 \\ 1 & 4 & -1 & 5 \\ 3 & 1 & 1 & 2 \end{bmatrix}$

8. In Chapter 2, the cross product of two vectors was defined. Show that a convenient way of remembering the formula for the vector $(a_1, a_2, a_3) \times (b_1, b_2, b_3)$ is to expand formally the determinant

$$\det \begin{bmatrix} \mathbf{e}_1 & \mathbf{e}_2 & \mathbf{e}_3 \\ a_1 & a_2 & a_3 \\ b_1 & b_2 & b_3 \end{bmatrix}$$

by the first row.

9. In each case write $\operatorname{Adj} \mathbf{A}$.

a. $\mathbf{A} = \begin{bmatrix} 2 & 4 \\ 5 & 1 \end{bmatrix}$ **b.** $\mathbf{A} = \begin{bmatrix} 1 & -1 & 1 \\ 2 & 1 & 0 \\ 1 & 1 & 1 \end{bmatrix}$

c. $\mathbf{A} = \begin{bmatrix} 1 & 1 & -1 & 1 \\ 1 & 1 & 0 & 1 \\ 1 & 1 & -1 & 0 \\ 1 & 1 & -1 & 1 \end{bmatrix}$

Find $\mathbf{A}(\operatorname{Adj} \mathbf{A})$.

10. Show that $\operatorname{Adj} \mathbf{A}^T = (\operatorname{Adj} \mathbf{A})^T$.

11. In each case, write $\operatorname{Adj} \mathbf{A}$ and calculate $\mathbf{A}(\operatorname{Adj} \mathbf{A})$.

a. $\mathbf{A} = \begin{bmatrix} 1 & 2 \\ -1 & 3 \end{bmatrix}$ **b.** $\mathbf{A} = \begin{bmatrix} 2 & 1 & 5 \\ 1 & 3 & 1 \\ 2 & -1 & 0 \end{bmatrix}$

c. $\mathbf{A} = \begin{bmatrix} 1 & 2 & 3 \\ 0 & 1 & 2 \\ 0 & 0 & 1 \end{bmatrix}$

12. Show that for a 2×2 matrix, $\operatorname{Adj}(\operatorname{Adj} \mathbf{A}) = \mathbf{A}$.

13. Let

$$\mathbf{A} = \begin{bmatrix} 1 & 2 & 3 \\ 0 & 1 & 5 \\ 1 & 1 & 3 \end{bmatrix}$$

Write $\operatorname{Adj} \mathbf{A}$. Also write $\operatorname{Adj}(\operatorname{Adj} \mathbf{A})$. Compare your answer with $\mathbf{A}$.

14. Show that for a 3×3 matrix $\mathbf{A}$, $\gamma_{22}\gamma_{33} - \gamma_{23}\gamma_{32} = a_{11} \det \mathbf{A}$.

15. For the matrices in Problem 9, use $\operatorname{Adj} \mathbf{A}$ to find $\mathbf{A}^{-1}$ if it exists.

16. For the matrices in Problem 11, use $\operatorname{Adj} \mathbf{A}$ to determine whether or not $\mathbf{A}^{-1}$ exists.

17. Show that if $\det \mathbf{A} = 0$, then $\mathbf{A}(\operatorname{Adj} \mathbf{A}) = \mathbf{0}$. Show that if $\det \mathbf{A} \neq 0$, then $\det(\operatorname{Adj} \mathbf{A}) \neq 0$.

18. For the matrix in Problem 13, find $\mathbf{A}^{-1}$. Use it to solve the system of equations

$$\begin{aligned} x_1 + 2x_2 + 3x_3 &= 5 \\ x_2 + 5x_3 &= 2 \\ x_1 + x_2 + 3x_3 &= -1 \end{aligned}$$

19. Use Cramer's Rule to solve the system of equations in Problem 18. Compare your answer with that obtained in Problem 18.

20. Use Cramer's Rule to solve the following system:

$$\begin{aligned} 2x + 3y + z &= 9 \\ x + 2y + 3z &= 6 \\ 3x + y + 2z &= 8 \end{aligned}$$

21. Can Cramer's Rule be used to solve the following system?

$$\begin{aligned} 2x + 3y + z &= 9 \\ x + 2y + 3z &= 6 \\ x + y - 2z &= 3 \end{aligned}$$

Does the system of equations have a solution?

22. Show that $\operatorname{Adj}(k\mathbf{A}) = k^{n-1} \operatorname{Adj} \mathbf{A}$, where k is a scalar, and $\mathbf{A}$ is an $n \times n$ matrix.

23. Without expanding the determinant, find the value of

$$\det \begin{bmatrix} 1 & a & b + c \\ 1 & b & c + a \\ 1 & c & a + b \end{bmatrix}$$

24. Verify that

$$\det \begin{bmatrix} 1 & 1 & 1 \\ a & b & c \\ a^2 & b^2 & c^2 \end{bmatrix} = (c - a)(b - a)(c - b)$$

25. Find the value of

$$\det \begin{bmatrix} t & 1 & 1 & 1 \\ 1 & t & 0 & 0 \\ 1 & 0 & t & 0 \\ 1 & 0 & 0 & t \end{bmatrix}$$

26. With as little direct evaluation as possible, show that

$$\det \begin{bmatrix} -4 & 1 & 1 & 1 & 1 \\ 1 & -4 & 1 & 1 & 1 \\ 1 & 1 & -4 & 1 & 1 \\ 1 & 1 & 1 & -4 & 1 \\ 1 & 1 & 1 & 1 & -4 \end{bmatrix} = 0$$

27. Show that $\det \mathbf{A} = 0$, where $\mathbf{A}$ is the $(n + 1) \times (n + 1)$ matrix

$$\begin{bmatrix} -n & 1 & 1 & \cdots & 1 \\ 1 & -n & 1 & \cdots & 1 \\ 1 & 1 & -n & \cdots & 1 \\ \vdots & \vdots & \vdots & & \vdots \\ 1 & 1 & 1 & \cdots & -n \end{bmatrix}$$

28. Consider the current in Example 16. Choose loop currents I_1 and I_2 as shown. Write the branch currents in terms of these loop currents. Calculate the loop currents and show that although the loop currents are different they lead to the same branch currents.

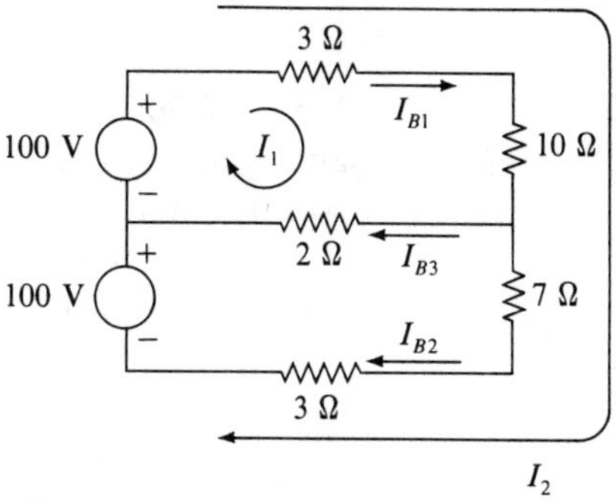

29. Use the method of loop currents on the circuit of Problem 16, Section 2.3.

3.4 The Determinant of a Product, Nonsingular Matrices

In this section we discuss the determinant of the product of two square matrices, and show $\det(\mathbf{AB}) = (\det \mathbf{A})(\det \mathbf{B})$. This multiplicative property of determinants is one of the most valuable consequences of the definition of the determinant.

Example 17 Let $\mathbf{A} = \begin{bmatrix} 1 & 5 \\ -1 & 2 \end{bmatrix}$ and $\mathbf{B} = \begin{bmatrix} 2 & -1 \\ 2 & 3 \end{bmatrix}$. Then $\mathbf{AB} = \begin{bmatrix} 12 & 14 \\ 2 & 7 \end{bmatrix}$. Also, $\det \mathbf{A} = 7$, $\det \mathbf{B} = 8$, and $\det(\mathbf{AB}) = 56$. This verifies that in this case $\det(\mathbf{AB}) = (\det \mathbf{A})(\det \mathbf{B})$.

This numerical example, however, gives very little insight into the reason for this result. ■

Theorem 11 If **A** and **B** are $n \times n$ matrices, $\det(\mathbf{AB}) = (\det \mathbf{A})(\det \mathbf{B})$.

Rationale A proof of this theorem is given in the 3×3 case. It uses Theorem 7 and the fact that multiplication treats the columns of a matrix as a single entity.

Let $\mathbf{A} = [\mathbf{A}_1 \quad \mathbf{A}_2 \quad \mathbf{A}_3]$, where $\mathbf{A}_i$ is a 3×1 array representing the ith column of **A**. Then

$$\mathbf{AB} = [\mathbf{A}_1 \quad \mathbf{A}_2 \quad \mathbf{A}_3] \begin{bmatrix} b_{11} & b_{12} & b_{13} \\ b_{21} & b_{22} & b_{23} \\ b_{31} & b_{32} & b_{33} \end{bmatrix}$$

$$= [b_{11}\mathbf{A}_1 + b_{21}\mathbf{A}_2 + b_{31}\mathbf{A}_3 \quad b_{12}\mathbf{A}_1 + b_{22}\mathbf{A}_2 + b_{32}\mathbf{A}_3 \quad b_{13}\mathbf{A}_1 + b_{23}\mathbf{A}_2 + b_{33}\mathbf{A}_3]$$

Now because each row of **AB** is expressed as a sum of three elements, $\det(\mathbf{AB})$ can be written as a sum of determinants (Theorem 7). The sum in the 3×3 case will have 27 terms:

$$\det(\mathbf{AB}) = \sum \det[b_{i_1 1}\mathbf{A}_{i_1} \quad b_{i_2 2}\mathbf{A}_{i_2} \quad b_{i_3 3}\mathbf{A}_{i_3}], \qquad i_1, i_2, i_3 = 1, 2, 3$$

Since each column of the determinant has a common factor, Theorem 4 can be used to write the sum in the form

$$\det(\mathbf{AB}) = \sum b_{i_1 1} b_{i_2 2} b_{i_3 3} \det[\mathbf{A}_{i_1} \quad \mathbf{A}_{i_2} \quad \mathbf{A}_{i_3}]$$

Many of the determinants in this sum will be zero. For example, suppose both i_1 and i_2 are 1 and $i_3 = 3$. We have $\det[\mathbf{A}_1 \quad \mathbf{A}_1 \quad \mathbf{A}_3]$, which has two identical columns and is therefore zero (Problem 9, Section 3.2). The only nonzero terms in the sum are those for which i_1, i_2, i_3 are distinct. There are six possible arrangements of the numbers 1, 2, 3 when duplications are not allowed. Thus

$$\begin{aligned} \det(\mathbf{AB}) = {} & b_{11}b_{22}b_{33}\det[\mathbf{A}_1 \quad \mathbf{A}_2 \quad \mathbf{A}_3] + b_{11}b_{32}b_{23}\det[\mathbf{A}_1 \quad \mathbf{A}_3 \quad \mathbf{A}_2] \\ & + b_{21}b_{12}b_{33}\det[\mathbf{A}_2 \quad \mathbf{A}_1 \quad \mathbf{A}_3] + b_{21}b_{32}b_{13}\det[\mathbf{A}_2 \quad \mathbf{A}_3 \quad \mathbf{A}_1] \\ & + b_{31}b_{12}b_{23}\det[\mathbf{A}_3 \quad \mathbf{A}_1 \quad \mathbf{A}_2] + b_{31}b_{22}b_{13}\det[\mathbf{A}_3 \quad \mathbf{A}_2 \quad \mathbf{A}_1] \end{aligned}$$

Each of the determinants in this sum is $(-1)^k \det[\mathbf{A}_1 \quad \mathbf{A}_2 \quad \mathbf{A}_3]$, where k is the number of interchanges required to put the subscripts into their natural order. Now factor $\det[\mathbf{A}_1 \quad \mathbf{A}_2 \quad \mathbf{A}_3]$ out of the sum. The remaining factor is precisely the sum defining $\det \mathbf{B}$ since each product $b_{i_1 1} b_{i_2 2} b_{i_3 3}$ is multiplied by $(-1)^k$. □

Corollary The product **AB** has rank n if and only if **A** and **B** each have rank n. (See Exercises 3.4, Problems 9 and 10, and Theorem 5, Section 3.2.) □

Theorem 11 leads directly to the following two theorems, 12 and 13.

Theorem 12 If $\mathbf{A}^{-1}$ exists, $\det(\mathbf{A}^{-1}) = 1/(\det \mathbf{A})$.

Proof Since $\mathbf{AA}^{-1} = \mathbf{I}$, $(\det \mathbf{A})(\det \mathbf{A}^{-1}) = 1$. Because $\mathbf{A}^{-1}$ exists, $\det \mathbf{A} \neq 0$, so $\det \mathbf{A}^{-1} = 1/(\det \mathbf{A})$. □

Many different matrices have the same determinant. An important class of such matrices is defined in Definition 6.

Similar

Definition 6

Let **A** and **B** be $n \times n$ matrices. **A** is **similar** to **B** if there exists a nonsingular $n \times n$ matrix **C** such that

$$\mathbf{A} = \mathbf{C}^{-1}\mathbf{B}\mathbf{C}$$

Theorem 13 If **A** is similar to **B**, then $\det \mathbf{A} = \det \mathbf{B}$.

Proof If **A** is similar to **B**, there exists a nonsingular matrix **C** such that $\mathbf{A} = \mathbf{C}^{-1}\mathbf{B}\mathbf{C}$.

$$\begin{aligned}\det \mathbf{A} &= \det(\mathbf{C}^{-1}\mathbf{B}\mathbf{C}) = (\det \mathbf{C}^{-1})(\det \mathbf{B})(\det \mathbf{C}) = \frac{1}{\det \mathbf{C}}(\det \mathbf{B})(\det \mathbf{C}) \\ &= \det \mathbf{B}\end{aligned}$$ □

Similarity in the set of $n \times n$ matrices has some interesting properties that are stated in the following theorem. You are asked to prove these in Problem 19.

Theorem 14 If **A**, **B**, and **C** are $n \times n$ matrices:

a. **A** is similar to **A** (reflexive property).
b. If **A** is similar to **B** then **B** is similar to **A** (symmetric property).
c. If **A** is similar to **B** and **B** is similar to **C**, then **A** is similar to **C** (transitive property). □

Given a matrix **A**, it is easy to generate many matrices similar to **A**. One has only to choose a nonsingular matrix **C** and calculate $\mathbf{C}^{-1}\mathbf{A}\mathbf{C}$. However, given two matrices **A** and **B**, it is not always easy to decide whether or not they are indeed similar. Certainly they must be square, of the same size, and $\det \mathbf{A} = \det \mathbf{B}$. But this is not sufficient to guarantee that they are similar.

Similar matrices have many common properties. Section 3.5 is devoted to a study of eigenvalues. Similar matrices have the same eigenvalues.

Notice that if **A** and **B** are similar $n \times n$ matrices and **A** has rank n, then **B** also has rank n.

The property of being nonsingular is of importance in many situations already discussed, as well as in material yet to be considered. Definition 2 says a matrix **A** is nonsingular if $\mathbf{A}^{-1}$ exists. It is well worth the time to stop here and tie together our ideas by listing the "if and only if" statements that characterize a nonsingular matrix. Any one of these could be used as a definition. The facts have already been proved in Theorem 5 and in Theorems 2 and 4, Chapter 2.

Theorem 15 Let **A** be an $n \times n$ matrix. The following statements are equivalent:

1. The matrix **A** is nonsingular.
2. The row-reduced form of **A** is the identity matrix.
3. The rank of **A** is n.
4. $\det \mathbf{A} \neq 0$.
5. The inverse of **A** exists.
6. The matrix equation $\mathbf{AX} = \mathbf{C}$ has a unique solution, $\mathbf{X} = \mathbf{A}^{-1}\mathbf{C}$.
7. The equation $\mathbf{AX} = \mathbf{0}$ has a unique solution, $\mathbf{X} = \mathbf{0}$; that is, the only solution of $\mathbf{AX} = \mathbf{0}$ is the trivial solution.
8. The columns of **A** form a linearly independent set. □

The most important circumstances in which we look for a singular matrix are related to homogeneous systems of equations.

To emphasize the importance of parts 4 and 7 of Theorem 15, they are restated in a different form.

Corollary If **A** is $n \times n$, the homogeneous system $\mathbf{AX} = \mathbf{0}$ has a nontrivial solution if and only if $\det \mathbf{A} = 0$. □

Example 18 illustrates a geometric application of this corollary.

Example 18 The equation of a line in the plane has the form $ax + by + c = 0$. Two distinct points determine a line. We wish to find the equation of the line determined by the points $(1, 2)$ and $(5, 7)$. Since $(1, 2)$ lies on the line, we know $a + 2b + c = 0$. Since $(5, 7)$ lies on the line, $5a + 7b + c = 0$ also. A point (x, y) will lie on the line if and only if we can find a, b, and c not all zero so that the following equations hold:

$$\begin{aligned} ax + by + c &= 0 \\ a + 2b + c &= 0 \\ 5a + 7b + c &= 0 \end{aligned}$$

that is, if and only if the matrix equation

$$\begin{bmatrix} x & y & 1 \\ 1 & 2 & 1 \\ 5 & 7 & 1 \end{bmatrix} \begin{bmatrix} a \\ b \\ c \end{bmatrix} = \begin{bmatrix} 0 \\ 0 \\ 0 \end{bmatrix}$$

has a nontrivial solution. This will be the case if and only if

$$\det \begin{bmatrix} x & y & 1 \\ 1 & 2 & 1 \\ 5 & 7 & 1 \end{bmatrix} = 0$$

When this determinant is expanded by the first row, the equation takes the more familiar form $-5x + 4y - 3 = 0$, the equation of the line through $(1, 2)$ and $(5, 7)$. ■

Example 19 Recall that a straight line divides the plane into two half-planes. Let L be the line of Example 18 with equation $-5x + 4y - 3 = 0$. A point (x_0, y_0) not on the line is on the same side of the line L as the origin if and only if the sign of $-5x_0 + 4y_0 - 3$ is the same as the sign of $0 + 0 - 3$. Thus $(1, 1)$ is on the same side as the origin, since $-5 + 4 - 3 = -4$, but $(1, 4)$ is on the other side, since $-5 + (4)(4) - 3 = 8$ and is positive. This can be checked in determinant form:

$$\det\begin{bmatrix} 1 & 1 & 1 \\ 1 & 2 & 1 \\ 5 & 7 & 1 \end{bmatrix} = -4 \quad \text{and} \quad \det\begin{bmatrix} 1 & 4 & 1 \\ 1 & 2 & 1 \\ 5 & 7 & 1 \end{bmatrix} = 8$$

So the points $(1, 1)$ and $(1, 4)$ are on opposite sides of the line.

This reasoning can be used in considering the allowable heights of buildings or other structures in the neighborhood of an airport. Think of the problem as being two-dimensional, so that the landing pattern of a plane can be represented by a succession of line segments. If a structure is not to interfere with the landing of planes, it must lie below the height represented by the line segments. Consider the buildings lying in a fixed direction from the airport, and represent their distance from the airport by x and their height by y. Suppose the line

$$\det\begin{bmatrix} x & y & 1 \\ 1 & 2 & 1 \\ 5 & 7 & 1 \end{bmatrix} = 0$$

represents the minimum glide path to clear existing obstacles. A projected building is six units from the airport and ten units high. Will this building be above the allowable height? We have only to calculate two determinants:

$$\det\begin{bmatrix} 6 & 10 & 1 \\ 1 & 2 & 1 \\ 5 & 7 & 1 \end{bmatrix} = 7 \quad \text{and} \quad \det\begin{bmatrix} 6 & 0 & 1 \\ 1 & 2 & 1 \\ 5 & 7 & 1 \end{bmatrix} = -33$$

The fact that the determinants have opposite signs shows that the top of the building, $(6, 10)$, is on the other side of the line from the base of the building, $(6, 0)$. (See Figure 3.3.) It is, therefore, too tall. This technique can easily be implemented by computer and many such judgments made quickly.

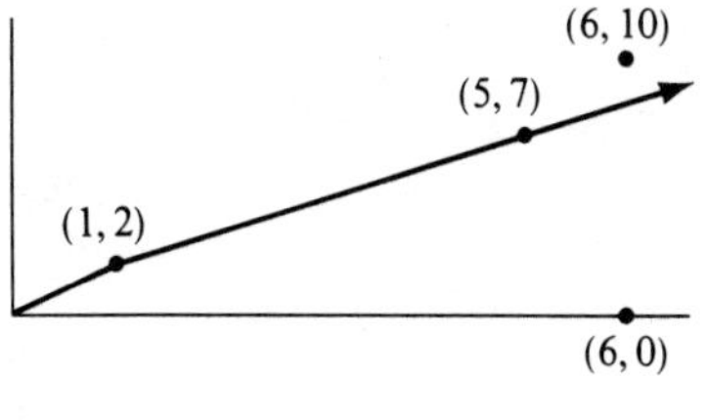

FIGURE 3.3

■

SUMMARY If $\mathbf{A}$ and $\mathbf{B}$ are square, $\det \mathbf{AB} = (\det \mathbf{A})(\det \mathbf{B})$. As a consequence of this, if $\mathbf{A}^{-1}$ exists, $\det \mathbf{A}^{-1} = 1/\det \mathbf{A}$. Also $\det(\mathbf{C}^{-1}\mathbf{AC}) = \det \mathbf{A}$. If $\mathbf{A}$ is $n \times n$ and $\det \mathbf{A} \neq 0$, $\mathbf{A}$ is nonsingular. The product of nonsingular matrices is a nonsingular matrix. The inverse of a nonsingular matrix is nonsingular.

The homogeneous system of equations $\mathbf{AX} = \mathbf{0}$ has a nontrivial solution if and only if $\det \mathbf{A} = 0$.

Let $\mathbf{A}$ and $\mathbf{B}$ be $n \times n$ matrices. $\mathbf{A}$ is similar to $\mathbf{B}$ if there exists a nonsingular $n \times n$ matrix $\mathbf{C}$ such that $\mathbf{A} = \mathbf{C}^{-1}\mathbf{BC}$. If $\mathbf{A}$ is similar to $\mathbf{B}$, $\det \mathbf{A} = \det \mathbf{B}$.

EXERCISES 3.4

1. Check Theorem 11 by calculating $\det \mathbf{A}$, $\det \mathbf{B}$, and $\det \mathbf{AB}$ in each case.

a. $\mathbf{A} = \begin{bmatrix} 1 & 4 \\ -1 & 2 \end{bmatrix}, \quad \mathbf{B} = \begin{bmatrix} 3 & 2 \\ 1 & 0 \end{bmatrix}$

b. $\mathbf{A} = \begin{bmatrix} -1 & 1 \\ 3 & -3 \end{bmatrix}, \quad \mathbf{B} = \begin{bmatrix} 2 & 3 \\ 4 & 5 \end{bmatrix}$

c. $\mathbf{A} = \begin{bmatrix} 1 & 1 & 2 \\ -1 & 1 & 3 \\ 0 & 2 & 4 \end{bmatrix}, \quad \mathbf{B} = \begin{bmatrix} 3 & 0 & 7 \\ 3 & 1 & 0 \\ 0 & 1 & 1 \end{bmatrix}$

2. Calculate $\det \mathbf{A}$, $\det \mathbf{B}$, and $\det \mathbf{AB}$, if

$$\mathbf{A} = \begin{bmatrix} 1 & 0 & 1 & 5 \\ 2 & 0 & -1 & 3 \\ 1 & 2 & 0 & 2 \\ -1 & 1 & 0 & -1 \end{bmatrix},$$

$$\mathbf{B} = \begin{bmatrix} 1 & 2 & 1 & 2 \\ 0 & 1 & 1 & 2 \\ 1 & 4 & 0 & 1 \\ 0 & 1 & 1 & 0 \end{bmatrix}$$

3. Characterize each of the following matrices as either singular or nonsingular. Justify your answer.

a. $\begin{bmatrix} 2 & 3 \\ 4 & 6 \end{bmatrix}$ **b.** $\begin{bmatrix} 1 & 2 & 1 \\ -3 & 0 & 6 \\ -2 & 2 & 7 \end{bmatrix}$

c. $\begin{bmatrix} 1 & 2 & 4 & 1 \\ 7 & 0 & 0 & 0 \\ 6 & -1 & 1 & 0 \\ 11 & 0 & 0 & 4 \end{bmatrix}$

d. $\begin{bmatrix} 1 & 0 & 0 & 0 & 0 \\ 0 & 1 & 0 & 0 & 0 \\ 0 & 0 & 2 & 0 & 0 \\ 0 & 0 & 0 & 1 & 0 \\ 0 & 3 & 6 & 7 & 1 \end{bmatrix}$

4. Which of the following matrices is singular?

a. $\begin{bmatrix} 1 & 3 & 4 \\ 0 & 2 & 5 \\ 0 & 0 & 3 \end{bmatrix}$ **b.** $\begin{bmatrix} 1 & 0 & 1 \\ 0 & 2 & 0 \\ 3 & 0 & 3 \end{bmatrix}$

c. $\begin{bmatrix} 1 & -1 & 1 \\ 2 & 1 & 0 \\ 1 & 1 & 1 \end{bmatrix}$ **d.** $\begin{bmatrix} 1 & -1 & 1 \\ 2 & 1 & 0 \\ 3 & 0 & 1 \end{bmatrix}$

5. Given that $\mathbf{A}$ is 6×6 and $\det \mathbf{A} = 5$, what is the rank of $\mathbf{A}$?

6. The system of equations $\mathbf{AX} = \mathbf{B}$ is a system of five equations in five unknowns. It has a unique solution. What is the rank of $\mathbf{A}$?

7. Show that the system of equations

$$\begin{bmatrix} 1 & -1 & -4 \\ -2 & 5 & 14 \\ 3 & -1 & -8 \end{bmatrix} \begin{bmatrix} x_1 \\ x_2 \\ x_3 \end{bmatrix} = \begin{bmatrix} 0 \\ 0 \\ 0 \end{bmatrix}$$

has an infinite number of solutions, and find their general form.

8. $\mathbf{A}$ is the matrix

$$\begin{bmatrix} 1 & a & 0 & 0 \\ a & 1 & 0 & 0 \\ 1 & a & 1 & a \\ 1 & -1 & a & 1 \end{bmatrix}$$

Show that if the system of equations $\mathbf{AX} = \mathbf{0}$ has more than one solution, then we must have $a = 1$ or $a = -1$.

***9. a.** Show that if $\mathbf{A}$ and $\mathbf{B}$ are both nonsingular matrices, then $\mathbf{AB}$ and $\mathbf{BA}$ are nonsingular matrices.

b. If $\mathbf{A}$ and $\mathbf{B}$ are nonzero $n \times n$ matrices and $\mathbf{AB} = \mathbf{0}$, show that both $\mathbf{A}$ and $\mathbf{B}$ must be singular.

*10. **a.** If **A** and **B** are $n \times n$ with rank n, show that **AB** has rank n.
b. If **A** and **B** are $n \times n$ and **A** has rank $< n$, show that **AB** has rank $< n$.

11. **a.** Let $\mathbf{A} = \begin{bmatrix} 1 & 2 \\ 1 & 3 \end{bmatrix}$ and $\mathbf{B} = \begin{bmatrix} 4 & 1 \\ 6 & 2 \end{bmatrix}$. Calculate **AB**, Adj (**AB**), Adj **A**, Adj **B**. Verify that Adj (**AB**) = (Adj **B**)(Adj **A**).
b. If **A** and **B** are nonsingular, show that Adj (**AB**) = (Adj **B**)(Adj **A**).

12. **a.** Prove that $\det(\text{Adj}\,\mathbf{A}) = (\det \mathbf{A})^{n-1}$ for all $n \times n$ matrices **A**.
b. If $\det \mathbf{A} \neq 0$, show that $\text{Adj}(\text{Adj}\,\mathbf{A}) = (\det \mathbf{A})^{n-2}\mathbf{A}$.

13. The general equation for a parabola with principal axis parallel to the y-axis is $y = ax^2 + bx + c$. Show that there is a unique parabola passing through (1, 1), (0, 0), and (2, 4).

14. The general equation of a plane in 3-space is $ax + by + cz + d = 0$. Three noncollinear points determine a plane. Use a method similar to Example 18 to find the equation of the plane through (0, −1, −1), (3, 1, 0), (2, 5, 1).

15. Use the method of Problem 14 to find the equation of the plane through (1, 2, 3), (2, 4, 6), and (3, 6, 9). Why do you not get a solution in this case?

16. For what a is there a nonzero vector (x_1, x_2, x_3) such that the following is true?

$$\begin{bmatrix} 1-a & 0 & -4 \\ 0 & 5-a & 4 \\ -4 & 4 & 3-a \end{bmatrix}\begin{bmatrix} x_1 \\ x_2 \\ x_3 \end{bmatrix} = \begin{bmatrix} 0 \\ 0 \\ 0 \end{bmatrix}$$

17. Which pairs of matrices are similar? Justify your answers.

a. $\mathbf{A} = \begin{bmatrix} 1 & -1 \\ 2 & 1 \end{bmatrix}$, $\quad \mathbf{B} = \begin{bmatrix} 1 & 3 & 0 \\ 0 & -1 & 1 \end{bmatrix}$

b. $\mathbf{A} = \begin{bmatrix} 0 & 0 \\ 0 & 0 \end{bmatrix}$, $\quad \mathbf{B} = \begin{bmatrix} 1 & 0 \\ 0 & 1 \end{bmatrix}$

c. $\mathbf{A} = \begin{bmatrix} 1 & 4 \\ -1 & 2 \end{bmatrix}$, $\quad \mathbf{B} = \begin{bmatrix} 3 & -1 \\ 1 & 2 \end{bmatrix}$

18. **a.** Show that the only matrix similar to a zero matrix is the zero matrix.
b. Show that the only matrix similar to an identity matrix is the identity matrix.

*19. Verify the following properties of similarity between matrices:
a. If **A** is similar to **B**, then **B** is similar to **A**.
b. Matrix **A** is similar to itself.
c. If **A** is similar to **B** and **B** is similar to **C**, then **A** is similar to **C**.

20. Show that $(\mathbf{C}^{-1}\mathbf{AC})(\mathbf{C}^{-1}\mathbf{AC}) = \mathbf{C}^{-1}\mathbf{A}^2\mathbf{C}$. Show that if **B** is similar to **A**, then $\mathbf{B}^2$ is similar to $\mathbf{A}^2$.

21. If **B** is similar to **A**, show that $\mathbf{B}^n$ is similar to $\mathbf{A}^n$ for any positive integer n.

22. If **B** is similar to **A**, show that **B** + **I** is similar to **A** + **I**. (*Hint:* Recall that $\mathbf{I} = \mathbf{C}^{-1}\mathbf{IC}$.)

23. If **B** is similar to **A** and $p(x)$ is a polynomial, show that $p(\mathbf{B})$ is similar to $p(\mathbf{A})$.

24. Show that if the nonsingular matrices **A** and **B** are similar, then $\mathbf{A}^{-1}$ and $\mathbf{B}^{-1}$ are also similar.

3.5 Eigenvalues and Eigenvectors

Let **A** be a square matrix. This section concerns some special numbers related to **A**, called its characteristic values or eigenvalues (the German word Eigen means special, or characteristic). These numbers arise from a system of equations of the form $\mathbf{AX} = \lambda\mathbf{X}$, where λ represents a scalar. This is a homogeneous system as we see when we write it in the form $\mathbf{AX} - \lambda\mathbf{X} = \mathbf{0}$, or $(\mathbf{A} - \lambda\mathbf{I})\mathbf{X} = \mathbf{0}$. The coefficient matrix is $\mathbf{A} - \lambda\mathbf{I}$ rather than **A** itself.

Example 20 describes a simple situation in which an equation of the form $\mathbf{AX} = \lambda\mathbf{X}$ might arise.

Example 20 Two grocery stores serve a small community. Although some of the clientele are very loyal, others get tired of one store and change to the other. Let x_1 be the number of customers trading at Top Value Grocery at the beginning of the year and x_2 the number of customers trading at Best Bargains Grocery. During the year $\frac{4}{5}$ of Top Value's customers remain loyal but $\frac{1}{5}$ change to Best Bargains. At the same time, $\frac{3}{5}$ of Best Bargain's customers remain loyal but $\frac{2}{5}$ change to Top Value.

By the first of the following year the number of customers using Top Value is

$$x_1^{(1)} = 0.8x_1 + 0.4x_2$$

and the number using Best Bargains is

$$x_2^{(1)} = 0.2x_1 + 0.6x_2$$

In matrix form, these equations are

$$\begin{bmatrix} 0.8 & 0.4 \\ 0.2 & 0.6 \end{bmatrix} \begin{bmatrix} x_1 \\ x_2 \end{bmatrix} = \begin{bmatrix} x_1^{(1)} \\ x_2^{(1)} \end{bmatrix}$$

Suppose the initial values are $x_1 = 3000$ and $x_2 = 7000$. By the first of the following year we have $x_1^{(1)} = 5200$ and $x_2^{(1)} = 4800$. If the customer behavior continues in the same manner, after 2 years we have

$$\begin{bmatrix} x_1^{(2)} \\ x_2^{(2)} \end{bmatrix} = \begin{bmatrix} 0.8 & 0.4 \\ 0.2 & 0.6 \end{bmatrix} \begin{bmatrix} 5200 \\ 4800 \end{bmatrix} = \begin{bmatrix} 6080 \\ 3920 \end{bmatrix}$$

The question arises: Is there a set of values (x_1, x_2) that is stable in the sense that although the customers using the stores may change, the distribution of trade remains the same? Mathematically, we are asking: Is there a nonzero pair (x_1, x_2) such that

$$\begin{bmatrix} 0.8 & 0.4 \\ 0.2 & 0.6 \end{bmatrix} \begin{bmatrix} x_1 \\ x_2 \end{bmatrix} = \lambda \begin{bmatrix} x_1 \\ x_2 \end{bmatrix}$$

for some real number λ?

A little algebra shows that this is really a homogeneous system of the form $\begin{bmatrix} 0.8 - \lambda & 0.4 \\ 0.2 & 0.6 - \lambda \end{bmatrix} \begin{bmatrix} x_1 \\ x_2 \end{bmatrix} = \begin{bmatrix} 0 \\ 0 \end{bmatrix}$. It will have a nonzero solution provided the coefficient matrix is singular (Corollary, Theorem 15). We must have, then,

$$\det \begin{bmatrix} 0.8 - \lambda & 0.4 \\ 0.2 & 0.6 - \lambda \end{bmatrix} = 0, \qquad \text{that is,} \qquad 0.4 - 1.4\lambda + \lambda^2 = 0$$

This polynomial factors: $(\lambda - 1)(\lambda - 0.4) = 0$. The numbers 1 and 0.4, which are the roots of this equation, are called the eigenvalues of the matrix $\begin{bmatrix} 0.8 & 0.4 \\ 0.2 & 0.6 \end{bmatrix}$.

If $\lambda = 1$, the system of equations is

$$\begin{aligned} (0.8 - 1)x_1 + \quad 0.4x_2 &= 0 \\ 0.2x_1 + (0.6 - 1)x_2 &= 0 \end{aligned} \qquad \text{or} \qquad \begin{aligned} -0.2x_1 + 0.4x_2 &= 0 \\ 0.2x_1 - 0.4x_2 &= 0 \end{aligned}$$

In this case the solution is $x_1 = 2k$, $x_2 = k$, which is nontrivial for $k \neq 0$. The distribution of trade will be stable provided Top Value has twice as many customers as Best Bargains.

The second value of λ that yields a nontrivial solution is 0.4. In this case we have

$$\begin{aligned} 0.4x_1 + 0.4x_2 &= 0 \\ 0.2x_1 + 0.2x_2 &= 0 \end{aligned}$$

which has the nontrivial solutions: $x_1 = -k$, $x_2 = k$, $k \neq 0$. In the context of this problem negative values of x_1 or x_2 do not make sense. When a mathematical model is made of a real-world problem, only part of the mathematical solution may be applicable. ■

Definition 7 lists the vocabulary connected with eigenvalue problems.

Definition 7

Let $\mathbf{A}$ be a square matrix and λ a scalar.

Characteristic Matrix Polynomial Equation

1. The matrix $\mathbf{A} - \lambda\mathbf{I}$ is called the **characteristic matrix** of $\mathbf{A}$. The polynomial in λ, $\det(\mathbf{A} - \lambda\mathbf{I})$, is called the **characteristic polynomial** of $\mathbf{A}$. The equation $\det(\mathbf{A} - \lambda\mathbf{I}) = 0$ is called the **characteristic equation** of $\mathbf{A}$.

Eigenvalue

2. The roots of the equation $\det(\mathbf{A} - \lambda\mathbf{I}) = 0$ are called the characteristic values of $\mathbf{A}$, or the **eigenvalues** of $\mathbf{A}$.

Eigenvector

3. If λ is an eigenvalue of $\mathbf{A}$, the nontrivial solutions of the equation $(\mathbf{A} - \lambda\mathbf{I})\mathbf{X} = \mathbf{0}$ are called characteristic vectors or **eigenvectors** of $\mathbf{A}$ corresponding to λ. A nonzero vector $\mathbf{X}$ is an eigenvector of $\mathbf{A}$ if and only if $\mathbf{AX} = \lambda\mathbf{X}$ for some real number λ.

Parts 2 and 3 of Definition 7 tell how to calculate the eigenvalues of $\mathbf{A}$ and the eigenvectors corresponding to a particular eigenvalue. They also tell how to recognize these special numbers and vectors if they arise. Example 21 illustrates this.

Example 21

a. Let $\mathbf{A} = \begin{bmatrix} 1 & 2 \\ 2 & 1 \end{bmatrix}$. The characteristic matrix is $\begin{bmatrix} 1 - \lambda & 2 \\ 2 & 1 - \lambda \end{bmatrix}$. The characteristic polynomial is $(1 - \lambda)(1 - \lambda) - 4$, that is, $-3 - 2\lambda + \lambda^2$. The characteristic equation is $-3 - 2\lambda + \lambda^2 = 0$. The factored form of this equation is $(\lambda - 3)(\lambda + 1) = 0$. The eigenvalues are $\lambda = 3$ and $\lambda = -1$. The eigenvectors corresponding to 3 are nontrivial solutions of

$$\begin{bmatrix} -2 & 2 \\ 2 & -2 \end{bmatrix} \begin{bmatrix} x_1 \\ x_2 \end{bmatrix} = \begin{bmatrix} 0 \\ 0 \end{bmatrix},$$ that is, any nonzero multiple of (1, 1).

The eigenvectors corresponding to -1 are nontrivial solutions of

$$\begin{bmatrix} 2 & 2 \\ 2 & 2 \end{bmatrix} \begin{bmatrix} x_1 \\ x_2 \end{bmatrix} = \begin{bmatrix} 0 \\ 0 \end{bmatrix}$$

that is, any nonzero multiple of $(1, -1)$.

b. Let $\mathbf{A} = \begin{bmatrix} 2 & 2 & 1 \\ 1 & 3 & 1 \\ 1 & 2 & 2 \end{bmatrix}$. Is the vector $\mathbf{X}_1 = \begin{bmatrix} -1 \\ 1 \\ 3 \end{bmatrix}$ an eigenvector of **A**? We can short-cut the process of finding all the eigenvalues and eigenvectors by simply checking whether $\mathbf{AX}_1 = \lambda \mathbf{X}_1$ for some λ:

$$\begin{bmatrix} 2 & 2 & 1 \\ 1 & 3 & 1 \\ 1 & 2 & 2 \end{bmatrix} \begin{bmatrix} -1 \\ 1 \\ 3 \end{bmatrix} = \begin{bmatrix} 3 \\ 5 \\ 7 \end{bmatrix}$$

Since $\begin{bmatrix} 3 \\ 5 \\ 7 \end{bmatrix}$ is not a multiple of $\begin{bmatrix} -1 \\ 1 \\ 3 \end{bmatrix}$, $\begin{bmatrix} -1 \\ 1 \\ 3 \end{bmatrix}$ is **not** an eigenvector.

Is $\mathbf{X}_2 = \begin{bmatrix} 1 \\ 1 \\ 1 \end{bmatrix}$ an eigenvector of **A**? Check $\begin{bmatrix} 2 & 2 & 1 \\ 1 & 3 & 1 \\ 1 & 2 & 2 \end{bmatrix} \begin{bmatrix} 1 \\ 1 \\ 1 \end{bmatrix} = \begin{bmatrix} 5 \\ 5 \\ 5 \end{bmatrix}$. Yes, $\begin{bmatrix} 1 \\ 1 \\ 1 \end{bmatrix}$ **is** an eigenvector. We also know that 5 is an eigenvalue since $\mathbf{AX}_2 = 5\mathbf{X}_2$ and $\mathbf{X}_2 \neq \mathbf{0}$. ∎

The study of eigenvalues uses many skills we have learned in earlier sections. The following theorem proves that eigenvectors exist.

Theorem 16 Let **A** be an $n \times n$ marix and let k be an eigenvalue of **A**. Then there is an eigenvector corresponding to k.

Proof The fact that k is an eigenvalue means that it is a root of the equation $\det(\mathbf{A} - \lambda\mathbf{I}) = 0$; that is, $\det(\mathbf{A} - k\mathbf{I}) = 0$. To find an eigenvector corresponding to k, we must find a nontrivial solution of the homogeneous equations $(\mathbf{A} - k\mathbf{I})\mathbf{X} = \mathbf{0}$. Because $\det(\mathbf{A} - k\mathbf{I}) = 0$, this homogeneous system has a nontrivial solution (Corollary, Theorem 15); in fact, it has an infinite set of nontrivial solutions. □

Finding eigenvalues and eigenvectors appears deceptively simple in Examples 20 and 21. It is easy to calculate the determinant of a 2×2 matrix. For the particular numbers chosen the eigenvalues turned out to be integers. In a realistic situation, even in the 2×2 case, the eigenvalues may be irrational numbers or complex numbers. In the case of 3×3 matrices or larger matrices, the work of calculating $\det(\mathbf{A} - \lambda\mathbf{I})$ may be considerable; even factoring the characteristic polynomial may be nearly impossible. In the case of 3×3 or larger matrices, much of this computation in realistic situations may need to be done by a computer. Even that is not without its problems, as is discussed in Chapter 6. •

There is much to be gained by working through these simple examples by hand if at the same time you observe the important principles and theorems that are sometimes obscured by technical difficulties or hidden in a computer program.

Example 22 Let

$$\mathbf{A} = \begin{bmatrix} 5 & 4 & 4 \\ -7 & -3 & -1 \\ 7 & 4 & 2 \end{bmatrix}$$

The characteristic polynomial of **A** is

$$\det \begin{bmatrix} 5-\lambda & 4 & 4 \\ -7 & -3-\lambda & -1 \\ 7 & 4 & 2-\lambda \end{bmatrix}$$

This determinant can be evaluated by any of the ways discussed in Sections 3.2 and 3.3. In this case row reduction can be used to advantage:

$$\det(\mathbf{A} - \lambda\mathbf{I}) = \det \begin{bmatrix} 5-\lambda & 4 & 4 \\ 0 & 1-\lambda & 1-\lambda \\ 7 & 4 & 2-\lambda \end{bmatrix} \quad \text{Add row 3 to row 2.}$$

$$= (1-\lambda)\det \begin{bmatrix} 5-\lambda & 4 & 4 \\ 0 & 1 & 1 \\ 7 & 4 & 2-\lambda \end{bmatrix} \quad \text{Factor } 1-\lambda \text{ from row 2.}$$

$$= (1-\lambda)\left\{(5-\lambda)\det \begin{bmatrix} 1 & 1 \\ 4 & 2-\lambda \end{bmatrix} + 7\det \begin{bmatrix} 4 & 4 \\ 1 & 1 \end{bmatrix}\right\} \quad \text{Expand by column 1.}$$

$$= (1-\lambda)(5-\lambda)(-2-\lambda)$$

The eigenvalues of **A** are $1, 5, -2$. Not only did row operations make finding the determinant easy, but the polynomial came out in factored form. We are not always so lucky! ■

In Example 23 we look at the same characteristic polynomial in a different way in order to illustrate two important facts about eigenvalues that are proved in Theorem 17.

Example 23

$$\mathbf{A} = \begin{bmatrix} 5 & 4 & 4 \\ -7 & -3 & -1 \\ 7 & 4 & 2 \end{bmatrix};$$

its characteristic polynomial is $\det \begin{bmatrix} 5-\lambda & 4 & 4 \\ -7 & -3-\lambda & -1 \\ 7 & 4 & 2-\lambda \end{bmatrix}$. Write this as the sum of eight determinants. (It is easier if you add some zeros.)

$$\det\begin{bmatrix} 5-\lambda & 4+0 & 4+0 \\ -7+0 & -3-\lambda & -1+0 \\ 7+0 & 4+0 & 2-\lambda \end{bmatrix}$$

$$= \det\begin{bmatrix} 5 & 4 & 4 \\ -7 & -3 & -1 \\ 7 & 4 & 2 \end{bmatrix} + \det\begin{bmatrix} 5 & 4 & 0 \\ -7 & -3 & 0 \\ 7 & 4 & -\lambda \end{bmatrix} + \det\begin{bmatrix} 5 & 0 & 4 \\ -7 & -\lambda & -1 \\ 7 & 0 & 2 \end{bmatrix}$$

$$+ \det\begin{bmatrix} -\lambda & 4 & 4 \\ 0 & -3 & -1 \\ 0 & 4 & 2 \end{bmatrix} + \det\begin{bmatrix} -\lambda & 0 & 4 \\ 0 & -\lambda & -1 \\ 0 & 0 & 2 \end{bmatrix} + \det\begin{bmatrix} -\lambda & 4 & 0 \\ 0 & -3 & 0 \\ 0 & 4 & -\lambda \end{bmatrix}$$

$$+ \det\begin{bmatrix} 5 & 0 & 0 \\ -7 & -\lambda & 0 \\ 7 & 0 & -\lambda \end{bmatrix} + \det\begin{bmatrix} -\lambda & 0 & 0 \\ 0 & -\lambda & 0 \\ 0 & 0 & -\lambda \end{bmatrix}$$

$$= \det \mathbf{A} - \lambda\left\{\det\begin{bmatrix} 5 & 4 \\ -7 & -3 \end{bmatrix} + \det\begin{bmatrix} 5 & 4 \\ 7 & 2 \end{bmatrix} + \det\begin{bmatrix} -3 & -1 \\ 4 & 2 \end{bmatrix}\right\}$$

$$+ \lambda^2(2 - 3 + 5) - \lambda^3 \det \mathbf{I}$$

$$= -10 + 7\lambda + 4\lambda^2 - \lambda^3$$

$$= (-2-\lambda)(5-\lambda)(1-\lambda)$$

Notice that the term not involving λ is $\det \mathbf{A}$, and the highest power of λ is 3. The coefficient of λ^3 is $(-1)^3$. The coefficient of λ^2 is $(-1)^2$ times the sum of the elements on the main diagonal. Since -10 is also the product of the roots of the polynomial, it follows that the product of the eigenvalues is $\det \mathbf{A}$. Moreover, the coefficient of λ^2 is $(-1)^2$ (the sum of the roots of the polynomial). Thus, the sum of the diagonal elements of **A** is also the sum of the eigenvalues. ■

The sum $a_{11} + a_{22} + \cdots + a_{nn}$ is called the **trace** of **A**.

Theorem 17 Let **A** be an $n \times n$ matrix, and let $\lambda_1, \lambda_2, \ldots, \lambda_n$ be the eigenvalues of **A**. Then $\lambda_1 \lambda_2 \ldots \lambda_n = \det \mathbf{A}$, and $\lambda_1 + \lambda_2 + \cdots + \lambda_n = \text{trace } \mathbf{A}$.

Proof Let **A** be an $n \times n$ matrix. The characteristic matrix $\mathbf{A} - \lambda\mathbf{I}$ is also $n \times n$. If the method of Example 23 is used in this case, the expansion will have one determinant in which every column contains $-\lambda$ and the rest of the elements are zero. This determinant has the value $(-1)^n\lambda^n$. There will be one determinant, which is $\det \mathbf{A}$. There will be n determinants $a_{ii}(-1)^{n-1}\lambda^{n-1}$. The sum of these is $(-1)^{n-1}(a_{11} + a_{22} + \cdots + a_{nn})\lambda^{n-1}$.

Since the sum of the roots is $-a_1$ and the product of the roots is $(-1)^n a_n$ in the polynomial equation $x^n + a_1x^{n-1} + \cdots + a_n = 0$, it follows that the sum of the eigenvalues is $a_{11} + a_{22} + \cdots + a_{nn} = \text{trace } \mathbf{A}$, and the product of the eigenvalues is $\det \mathbf{A}$. □

For some matrices it is especially easy to find the eigenvalues. These are the triangular matrices. If $\mathbf{A}$ is triangular, so is $\mathbf{A} - \lambda\mathbf{I}$. The determinant of a triangular matrix is the product of the diagonal elements. So

$$\det(\mathbf{A} - \lambda\mathbf{I}) = (a_{11} - \lambda)(a_{22} - \lambda)\cdots(a_{nn} - \lambda)$$

This implies that the eigenvalues of a triangular matrix are the diagonal elements. In particular this is true of a diagonal matrix.

Example 24 Let

$$\mathbf{A} = \begin{bmatrix} 3 & 0 & 0 \\ 0 & 4 & 0 \\ 0 & 0 & -1 \end{bmatrix}$$

The characteristic matrix of $\mathbf{A}$ is $\begin{bmatrix} 3-\lambda & 0 & 0 \\ 0 & 4-\lambda & 0 \\ 0 & 0 & -1-\lambda \end{bmatrix}$ with determinant $(3 - \lambda)(4 - \lambda)(-1 - \lambda)$; the characteristic polynomial of $\mathbf{A}$ is $(3 - \lambda)(4 - \lambda)(-1 - \lambda)$ and the eigenvalues of $\mathbf{A}$ are its diagonal elements.

■

Since many triangular matrices can have the same diagonal elements, there are many matrices with the same eigenvalues. In fact, as the following theorem shows, similar matrices have the same eigenvalues.

Theorem 18 If $\mathbf{A}$ is an $n \times n$ matrix and $\mathbf{A}$ is similar to $\mathbf{B}$, then $\mathbf{A}$ and $\mathbf{B}$ have the same characteristic polynomial and consequently the same eigenvalues.

Proof Suppose $\mathbf{B} = \mathbf{C}^{-1}\mathbf{A}\mathbf{C}$ for some nonsingular matrix $\mathbf{C}$.

$$\begin{aligned} \det(\mathbf{B} - \lambda\mathbf{I}) &= \det(\mathbf{C}^{-1}\mathbf{A}\mathbf{C} - \lambda\mathbf{I}) = \det(\mathbf{C}^{-1}\mathbf{A}\mathbf{C} - \lambda\mathbf{C}^{-1}\mathbf{I}\mathbf{C}) \\ &= \det(\mathbf{C}^{-1}(\mathbf{A} - \lambda\mathbf{I})\mathbf{C}) \\ &= (\det\mathbf{C}^{-1})(\det(\mathbf{A} - \lambda\mathbf{I}))(\det\mathbf{C}) \\ &= (\det\mathbf{C})^{-1}\det(\mathbf{A} - \lambda\mathbf{I})\det\mathbf{C} = \det(\mathbf{A} - \lambda\mathbf{I}) \end{aligned}$$

The sequence of equalities follows from the properties of determinants and leads to the conclusion that $\det(\mathbf{B} - \lambda\mathbf{I}) = \det(\mathbf{A} - \lambda\mathbf{I})$. Thus if $\mathbf{B}$ is similar to $\mathbf{A}$, they have the same characteristic polynomial. This of course implies that $\mathbf{B}$ and $\mathbf{A}$ have the same eigenvalues. □

We now explore the following question: Given a square matrix $\mathbf{A}$, is it possible to find a diagonal matrix similar to $\mathbf{A}$?

If we can find a diagonal matrix similar to $\mathbf{A}$, then that diagonal matrix must have the eigenvalues of $\mathbf{A}$ on its diagonal. In Example 25 we look for and find a matrix $\mathbf{P}$ such that $\mathbf{P}^{-1}\mathbf{A}\mathbf{P} = \mathbf{D}$, where $\mathbf{D}$ is diagonal, with the eigenvalues of $\mathbf{A}$ as diagonal elements.

Example 25 Let

$$\mathbf{A} = \begin{bmatrix} 5 & 4 & 4 \\ -7 & -3 & -1 \\ 7 & 4 & 2 \end{bmatrix}$$

The eigenvalues of **A** are $-2, 5, 1$ (Example 22). To find the eigenvectors corresponding to -2 we must solve the system of equations $(\mathbf{A} + 2\mathbf{I})\mathbf{X} = \mathbf{0}$, that is,

$$\begin{bmatrix} 7 & 4 & 4 \\ -7 & -1 & -1 \\ 7 & 4 & 4 \end{bmatrix} \begin{bmatrix} x_1 \\ x_2 \\ x_3 \end{bmatrix} = \begin{bmatrix} 0 \\ 0 \\ 0 \end{bmatrix}$$

Row reduction yields

$$\left[\begin{array}{rrr|r} 7 & 4 & 4 & 0 \\ -7 & -1 & -1 & 0 \\ 7 & 4 & 4 & 0 \end{array}\right] \Leftrightarrow \left[\begin{array}{rrr|r} 7 & 4 & 4 & 0 \\ 0 & 3 & 3 & 0 \\ 0 & 0 & 0 & 0 \end{array}\right] \Leftrightarrow \left[\begin{array}{rrr|r} 1 & 0 & 0 & 0 \\ 0 & 1 & 1 & 0 \\ 0 & 0 & 0 & 0 \end{array}\right]$$

from which the solution set is $k(0, -1, 1)$.

To find the eigenvectors corresponding to 5, we solve $(\mathbf{A} - 5\mathbf{I})\mathbf{X} = \mathbf{0}$, or

$$\begin{bmatrix} 0 & 4 & 4 \\ -7 & -8 & -1 \\ 7 & 4 & -3 \end{bmatrix} \begin{bmatrix} x_1 \\ x_2 \\ x_3 \end{bmatrix} = \begin{bmatrix} 0 \\ 0 \\ 0 \end{bmatrix}$$

The solution set is $k(1, -1, 1)$. Similarly, to find the eigenvectors corresponding to 1, we solve $(\mathbf{A} - \mathbf{I})\mathbf{X} = \mathbf{0}$, or

$$\begin{bmatrix} 4 & 4 & 4 \\ -7 & -4 & -1 \\ 7 & 4 & 1 \end{bmatrix} \begin{bmatrix} x_1 \\ x_2 \\ x_3 \end{bmatrix} = \begin{bmatrix} 0 \\ 0 \\ 0 \end{bmatrix}$$

The solution set is $k(1, -2, 1)$.

Now form a matrix **C** by choosing for its columns one eigenvector from each of the three solution sets:

$$\mathbf{C} = \begin{bmatrix} 0 & 1 & 1 \\ -1 & -1 & -2 \\ 1 & 1 & 1 \end{bmatrix}$$

Form the product **AC**:

$$\begin{bmatrix} 5 & 4 & 4 \\ -7 & -3 & -1 \\ 7 & 4 & 2 \end{bmatrix} \begin{bmatrix} 0 & 1 & 1 \\ -1 & -1 & -2 \\ 1 & 1 & 1 \end{bmatrix} = \begin{bmatrix} 0 & 5 & 1 \\ 2 & -5 & -2 \\ -2 & 5 & 1 \end{bmatrix}$$

The form of the product should not be surprising when we recall that the columns of **C** are eigenvectors, which means that

$$\mathbf{A}\begin{bmatrix}0\\-1\\1\end{bmatrix} = 2\begin{bmatrix}0\\-1\\1\end{bmatrix}, \qquad \mathbf{A}\begin{bmatrix}1\\-1\\1\end{bmatrix} = 5\begin{bmatrix}1\\-1\\1\end{bmatrix}, \qquad \mathbf{A}\begin{bmatrix}1\\-2\\1\end{bmatrix} = 1\begin{bmatrix}1\\-2\\1\end{bmatrix}$$

The matrix on the right can also be written as a product:

$$\begin{bmatrix}0 & 5 & 1\\2 & -5 & -2\\-2 & 5 & 1\end{bmatrix} = \begin{bmatrix}0 & 1 & 1\\-1 & -1 & -2\\1 & 1 & 1\end{bmatrix}\begin{bmatrix}-2 & 0 & 0\\0 & 5 & 0\\0 & 0 & 1\end{bmatrix}$$

Thus we have $\mathbf{AC} = \mathbf{CD}$, where **D** is a diagonal matrix with diagonal elements the eigenvalues of **A**.

Now

$$\det \mathbf{C} = \det\begin{bmatrix}0 & 1 & 1\\-1 & -1 & -2\\1 & 1 & 1\end{bmatrix} = \det\begin{bmatrix}0 & 1 & 1\\0 & 0 & -1\\1 & 1 & 1\end{bmatrix} = -1$$

Thus $\mathbf{C}^{-1}$ exists. In fact,

$$\mathbf{C}^{-1} = \begin{bmatrix}-1 & 0 & 1\\1 & 1 & 1\\0 & -1 & -1\end{bmatrix}$$

and

$$\mathbf{C}^{-1}\mathbf{AC} = \begin{bmatrix}-2 & 0 & 0\\0 & 5 & 0\\0 & 0 & 1\end{bmatrix}$$

Thus the matrix **A** in this example is similar to the diagonal matrix, which has as its diagonal elements the eigenvalues of **A**. ■

Example 25 illustrates the statements in Theorem 19.

Theorem 19 Let **A** be an $n \times n$ matrix and let **D** be a diagonal matrix with diagonal elements $d_1, d_2, \ldots, d_n$. Then:

1. If there exists a nonsingular matrix **C** such that $\mathbf{C}^{-1}\mathbf{AC} = \mathbf{D}$, the numbers $d_1, d_2, \ldots, d_n$ are eigenvalues of **A** and the columns of **C** are corresponding eigenvectors.
2. If **A** has n real eigenvalues $d_1, d_2, \ldots, d_n$ with corresponding eigenvectors $\mathbf{v}_1, \mathbf{v}_2, \ldots, \mathbf{v}_n$, and if the matrix **C** with these eigenvectors as columns is nonsingular, then $\mathbf{C}^{-1}\mathbf{AC} = \mathbf{D}$.

Proof Let the columns of **C** be $\mathbf{V}_1, \mathbf{V}_2, \ldots, \mathbf{V}_n$. Then the columns of **AC** are $\mathbf{AV}_1, \mathbf{AV}_2, \ldots, \mathbf{AV}_n$ and the columns of **CD** are $d_1\mathbf{V}_1, d_2\mathbf{V}_2, \ldots, d_n\mathbf{V}_n$.

1. Suppose $\mathbf{C}^{-1}\mathbf{AC} = \mathbf{D}$. Then $\mathbf{AC} = \mathbf{CD}$, and $\mathbf{AV}_1 = d_1\mathbf{V}_1$, $\mathbf{AV}_2 = d_2\mathbf{V}_2, \ldots,$ $\mathbf{AV}_n = \mathrm{d}_n\mathbf{V}_n$. This implies that $d_1, d_2, \ldots, d_n$ are eigenvalues of **A** and $\mathbf{v}_1, \mathbf{v}_2, \ldots, \mathbf{v}_n$ are corresponding eigenvectors.

2. On the other hand, if $d_1, d_2, \ldots, d_n$ are eigenvalues and $\mathbf{v}_1, \mathbf{v}_2, \ldots, \mathbf{v}_n$ are corresponding eigenvectors, then $\mathbf{AV}_1 = d_1\mathbf{V}_1$, $\mathbf{AV}_2 = d_2\mathbf{V}_2, \ldots, \mathbf{AV}_n = d_n\mathbf{V}_n$, so that $\mathbf{AC} = \mathbf{CD}$. Since $\mathbf{C}$ is assumed to be nonsingular, this implies that $\mathbf{C}^{-1}\mathbf{AC} = \mathbf{D}$. □

In Theorem 19 we have assumed that **C** is nonsingular. This will be the case as long as the eigenvalues of **A** are distinct. Recall that a matrix **C** is nonsingular if its columns form a linearly independent set (Theorem 4, Chapter 2). Theorem 20 shows that eigenvectors corresponding to distinct eigenvalues form a linearly independent set.

Theorem 20 Let **A** be an $n \times n$ matrix, $\lambda_1, \lambda_2, \ldots, \lambda_k$ distinct eigenvalues of **A**, and $\mathbf{u}_1, \mathbf{u}_2, \ldots, \mathbf{u}_k$ eigenvectors of **A** corresponding to $\lambda_1, \lambda_2, \ldots, \lambda_k$. The set $\{\mathbf{u}_1, \mathbf{u}_2, \ldots, \mathbf{u}_k\}$ is linearly independent.

Rationale The argument is given in detail for the case $k = 3$. From the definition of eigenvectors we have $(\mathbf{A} - \lambda_1\mathbf{I})\mathbf{U}_1 = \mathbf{0}$, $(\mathbf{A} - \lambda_2\mathbf{I})\mathbf{U}_2 = \mathbf{0}$, and $(\mathbf{A} - \lambda_3\mathbf{I})\mathbf{U}_3 = \mathbf{0}$. It is useful also to calculate $(\mathbf{A} - \lambda_1\mathbf{I})\mathbf{U}_2$. We have $(\mathbf{A} - \lambda_1\mathbf{I})\mathbf{U}_2 = \mathbf{AU}_2 - \lambda_1\mathbf{IU}_2 = \lambda_2\mathbf{U}_2 - \lambda_1\mathbf{U}_2 = (\lambda_2 - \lambda_1)\mathbf{U}_2$. By a similar calculation we obtain: $(\mathbf{A} - \lambda_1\mathbf{I})\mathbf{U}_3 = (\lambda_3 - \lambda_1)\mathbf{U}_3$ and $(\mathbf{A} - \lambda_2\mathbf{I})\mathbf{U}_3 = (\lambda_3 - \lambda_2)\mathbf{U}_3$. To show that the columns $\mathbf{U}_1, \mathbf{U}_2, \mathbf{U}_3$ form a linearly independent set, we show that the equation $c_1\mathbf{U}_1 + c_2\mathbf{U}_2 + c_3\mathbf{U}_3 = \mathbf{0}$ is true only if $c_1 = 0$, $c_2 = 0$, and $c_3 = 0$. Let $c_1\mathbf{U}_1 + c_2\mathbf{U}_2 + c_3\mathbf{U}_3 = \mathbf{0}$. Multiply this equation on the left by $\mathbf{A} - \lambda_1\mathbf{I}$:

$$c_1(\mathbf{A} - \lambda_1\mathbf{I})\mathbf{U}_1 + c_2(\mathbf{A} - \lambda_1\mathbf{I})\mathbf{U}_2 + c_3(\mathbf{A} - \lambda_1\mathbf{I})\mathbf{U}_3 = \mathbf{0}$$

or

$$\mathbf{0} + c_2(\lambda_2 - \lambda_1)\mathbf{U}_2 + c_3(\lambda_3 - \lambda_1)\mathbf{U}_3 = \mathbf{0}$$

Now multiply on the left by $\mathbf{A} - \lambda_2\mathbf{I}$:

$$c_2(\lambda_2 - \lambda_1)(\mathbf{A} - \lambda_2\mathbf{I})\mathbf{U}_2 + c_3(\lambda_3 - \lambda_1)(\mathbf{A} - \lambda_2\mathbf{I})\mathbf{U}_3 = \mathbf{0}$$

or

$$\mathbf{0} + c_3(\lambda_3 - \lambda_1)(\lambda_3 - \lambda_2)\mathbf{U}_3 = \mathbf{0}$$

But $\mathbf{U}_3$ is not a zero column, $\lambda_3 - \lambda_1 \neq 0$, and $\lambda_3 - \lambda_2 \neq 0$; thus $c_3 = 0$. This implies that $c_2(\lambda_2 - \lambda_1)\mathbf{U}_2 = \mathbf{0}$. Again, $\mathbf{U}_2 \neq \mathbf{0}$, and $\lambda_1 - \lambda_2 \neq 0$, so $c_2 = 0$. From the original equation we now have $c_1\mathbf{U}_1 = \mathbf{0}$. But $\mathbf{U}_1 \neq \mathbf{0}$, so $c_1 = 0$.

This argument can easily be extended to the general case. □

If the eigenvalues of **A** are not distinct, it may or may not be possible to find a nonsingular matrix **C** such that $\mathbf{C}^{-1}\mathbf{AC}$ is a diagonal matrix. The following example illustrates both possibilities.

Example 26 Let

$$\mathbf{A} = \begin{bmatrix} 2 & -1 & 0 \\ 2 & 1 & 1 \\ -2 & 2 & 1 \end{bmatrix}$$

Then

$$\det(\mathbf{A} - \lambda\mathbf{I}) = \det\begin{bmatrix} 2-\lambda & -1 & 0 \\ 2 & 1-\lambda & 1 \\ -2 & 2 & 1-\lambda \end{bmatrix}$$
$$= 2 - 5\lambda + 4\lambda^2 - \lambda^3$$

The characteristic equation is $(\lambda - 2)(\lambda - 1)^2 = 0$. The eigenvalues are 2 and 1, which is a repeated value.

The eigenvectors corresponding to 2 are solutions of $(\mathbf{A} - 2\mathbf{I})\mathbf{X} = \mathbf{0}$, or

$$\begin{bmatrix} 0 & -1 & 0 \\ 2 & -1 & 1 \\ -2 & 2 & -1 \end{bmatrix}\begin{bmatrix} x_1 \\ x_2 \\ x_3 \end{bmatrix} = \begin{bmatrix} 0 \\ 0 \\ 0 \end{bmatrix}$$

The solution set of this system is $k(-1, 0, 2)$.

The eigenvectors corresponding to 1 are solutions of $(\mathbf{A} - \mathbf{I})\mathbf{X} = \mathbf{0}$, or

$$\begin{bmatrix} 1 & -1 & 0 \\ 2 & 0 & 1 \\ -2 & 2 & 0 \end{bmatrix}\begin{bmatrix} x_1 \\ x_2 \\ x_3 \end{bmatrix} = \begin{bmatrix} 0 \\ 0 \\ 0 \end{bmatrix}$$

The solution set of this system is $k(-1, -1, 2)$.

If we proceed as in Example 25, we can write

$$\begin{bmatrix} 2 & -1 & 0 \\ 2 & 1 & 1 \\ -2 & 2 & 1 \end{bmatrix}\begin{bmatrix} -1 & -1 & -2 \\ 0 & -1 & -2 \\ 2 & 2 & 4 \end{bmatrix} = \begin{bmatrix} -2 & -1 & -2 \\ 0 & -1 & -2 \\ 4 & 2 & 4 \end{bmatrix}$$
$$= \begin{bmatrix} -1 & -1 & -2 \\ 0 & -1 & -2 \\ 2 & 2 & 4 \end{bmatrix}\begin{bmatrix} 2 & 0 & 0 \\ 0 & 1 & 0 \\ 0 & 0 & 1 \end{bmatrix}$$

Again, we have $\mathbf{AC} = \mathbf{CD}$. The matrix $\mathbf{C}$ has two proportional columns, so $\det\mathbf{C} = 0$. In this case there is no possible way to choose $\mathbf{C}$ without using two proportional columns since all the eigenvectors corresponding to 1 are proportional. Thus the matrix $\mathbf{C}$ is a singular matrix and $\mathbf{C}^{-1}$ does not exist.

Now let $\mathbf{A} = \begin{bmatrix} 6 & 7 & 7 \\ -7 & -8 & -7 \\ 7 & 7 & 6 \end{bmatrix}$.

$$\det[\mathbf{A} - \lambda\mathbf{I}] = \det\begin{bmatrix} 6-\lambda & 7 & 7 \\ -7 & -8-\lambda & -7 \\ 7 & 7 & 6-\lambda \end{bmatrix} = -(1+\lambda)^2(6-\lambda)$$

The eigenvectors corresponding to $\lambda = -1$ are the solutions of the system

$$\begin{bmatrix} 7 & 7 & 7 \\ -7 & -7 & -7 \\ 7 & 7 & 7 \end{bmatrix}\mathbf{X} = \mathbf{0}$$

Here the coefficient matrix has rank 1 and the solution set has dimension 2. The eigenvectors have the form $\{k_1(-1,1,0) + k_2(-1,0,1),\ k_1, k_2 \text{ not both } 0\}$. The eigenvectors corresponding to $\lambda = 6$ are the solutions of the system

$$\begin{bmatrix} 0 & 7 & 7 \\ -7 & -14 & -7 \\ 7 & 7 & 0 \end{bmatrix} \mathbf{X} = \mathbf{0}$$

The solution set has dimension 1, and the eigenvectors are $\{k(1,-1,1),\ k \neq 0\}$.

The matrix $\mathbf{C} = \begin{bmatrix} -1 & -1 & 1 \\ 1 & 0 & -1 \\ 0 & 1 & 1 \end{bmatrix}$ is nonsingular, $\mathbf{C}^{-1} = \begin{bmatrix} 1 & 2 & 1 \\ -1 & -1 & 0 \\ 1 & 1 & 1 \end{bmatrix}$, and

$$\begin{aligned} \mathbf{C}^{-1}\mathbf{AC} &= \begin{bmatrix} 1 & 2 & 1 \\ -1 & -1 & 0 \\ 1 & 1 & 1 \end{bmatrix} \begin{bmatrix} 6 & 7 & 7 \\ -7 & -8 & -7 \\ 7 & 7 & 6 \end{bmatrix} \begin{bmatrix} -1 & -1 & 1 \\ 1 & 0 & -1 \\ 0 & 1 & 1 \end{bmatrix} \\ &= \begin{bmatrix} 1 & 2 & 1 \\ -1 & -1 & 0 \\ 1 & 1 & 1 \end{bmatrix} \begin{bmatrix} 1 & 1 & 6 \\ -1 & 0 & -6 \\ 0 & -1 & 6 \end{bmatrix} \\ &= \begin{bmatrix} -1 & 0 & 0 \\ 0 & -1 & 0 \\ 0 & 0 & 6 \end{bmatrix} \end{aligned}$$

(Notice that in forming the product $\mathbf{C}^{-1}\mathbf{AC}$, the product $\mathbf{AC}$ yields a matrix, the columns of which are the columns of $\mathbf{C}$ multiplied by the appropriate eigenvalue. It is a good check of your work to perform this multiplication first.) ■

In this discussion we have touched briefly on some very important topics and ideas that lie at the heart of linear algebra. Some of these are discussed more fully in the next chapter. The topic of eigenvalues, eigenvectors, and their uses are considered again in Chapter 6.

To illustrate how one might use a diagonal matrix similar to $\mathbf{A}$, we return to the situation described in Example 20 at the beginning of this section. Further illustrations are in the exercises.

Example 27 Top Value Grocery and Best Bargains Grocery divide the trade in their community. The pattern of community behavior remains relatively undisturbed from year to year so that if at the end of year i Top Value has $x_1^{(i)}$ customers and Best Bargains has $x_2^{(i)}$ customers, the distribution at the end of year $i + 1$ is

$$\begin{bmatrix} x_1^{(i+1)} \\ x_2^{(i+1)} \end{bmatrix} = \begin{bmatrix} 0.8 & 0.4 \\ 0.2 & 0.6 \end{bmatrix} \begin{bmatrix} x_1^{(i)} \\ x_2^{(i)} \end{bmatrix} \quad \text{or} \quad \mathbf{X}^{(i+1)} = \mathbf{AX}^{(i)}$$

$$\mathbf{X}^{(2)} = \mathbf{AX}^{(1)} = \mathbf{A}^2\mathbf{X}^{(0)}, \qquad \mathbf{X}^{(3)} = \mathbf{AX}^{(2)} = \mathbf{A}(\mathbf{A}^2\mathbf{X}^{(0)}) = \mathbf{A}^3\mathbf{X}^{(0)}$$

In general, if the community situation is not radically changed in the meantime,

$\mathbf{X}^{(n)} = \mathbf{A}^n\mathbf{X}^{(0)}$. After 10 years, then,

$$\begin{bmatrix} x_1^{(10)} \\ x_2^{(10)} \end{bmatrix} = \begin{bmatrix} 0.8 & 0.4 \\ 0.2 & 0.6 \end{bmatrix}^{10} \begin{bmatrix} 3000 \\ 7000 \end{bmatrix}$$

Direct calculation of $\begin{bmatrix} 0.8 & 0.4 \\ 0.2 & 0.6 \end{bmatrix}^{10}$ is possible but not palatable. There is a better way! Form $\mathbf{C}$ from the eigenvectors of $\mathbf{A}$. Then $\mathbf{C}^{-1}\mathbf{AC} = \mathbf{D}$, provided $\mathbf{C}^{-1}$ exists. Here $\mathbf{C} = \begin{bmatrix} 2 & -1 \\ 1 & 1 \end{bmatrix}$ and $\mathbf{C}^{-1} = (\frac{1}{3})\begin{bmatrix} 1 & 1 \\ -1 & 2 \end{bmatrix}$; then $\mathbf{D} = \begin{bmatrix} 1 & 0 \\ 0 & 0.4 \end{bmatrix}$. Now $(\mathbf{C}^{-1}\mathbf{AC})^2 = \mathbf{C}^{-1}\mathbf{ACC}^{-1}\mathbf{AC} = \mathbf{C}^{-1}\mathbf{A}^2\mathbf{C}$, and in general $(\mathbf{C}^{-1}\mathbf{AC})^n = \mathbf{C}^{-1}\mathbf{A}^n\mathbf{C}$. Thus $\mathbf{C}^{-1}\mathbf{A}^n\mathbf{C} = \mathbf{D}^n$ and $\mathbf{A}^n = \mathbf{CD}^n\mathbf{C}^{-1}$. Since $\mathbf{D}$ is diagonal, $\mathbf{D}^n$ is easy to calculate. In this case we have

$$\begin{bmatrix} 0.8 & 0.4 \\ 0.2 & 0.6 \end{bmatrix}^n = \begin{bmatrix} 2 & -1 \\ 1 & 1 \end{bmatrix} \begin{bmatrix} 1 & 0 \\ 0 & (0.4)^n \end{bmatrix} \begin{bmatrix} \frac{1}{3} & \frac{1}{3} \\ -\frac{1}{3} & \frac{2}{3} \end{bmatrix}$$
$$= \begin{bmatrix} \frac{2}{3} + \frac{1}{3}(0.4)^n & \frac{2}{3} - \frac{1}{3}(0.4)^n \\ \frac{1}{3} - \frac{1}{3}(0.4)^n & \frac{1}{3} + \frac{1}{3}(0.4)^n \end{bmatrix}$$

After 10 years the distribution of customers is

$$x_1^{(10)} = \left(\frac{2}{3} + \frac{(0.4)^{10}}{3}\right)3000 + \left(\frac{2}{3} - \frac{(0.4)^{10}}{3}\right)7000$$
$$= \frac{20000}{3} - \frac{(0.4)^{10}4000}{3}$$
$$x_2^{(10)} = \left(\frac{1}{3} - \frac{(0.4)^{10}}{3}\right)3000 + \left(\frac{1}{3} + \frac{(0.4)^{10}}{3}\right)7000$$
$$= \frac{10000}{3} + \frac{(0.4)^{10}4000}{3}$$

Since 0.4 is less than 1, $(0.4)^{10}$ is a very small number, and, in fact, $(0.4)^n$ approaches 0 as n increases. The distribution after 10 years then is almost in the stable condition, since Top Value has almost twice as many customers as Best Bargains. Unless the community gets a defense contract or Best Bargains gets new management, when n is large enough the stable situation will be reached. ■

SUMMARY Let $\mathbf{A}$ be an $n \times n$ matrix and λ a scalar. The system of equations $\mathbf{AX} = \lambda\mathbf{X}$, or $(\mathbf{A} - \lambda\mathbf{I})\mathbf{X} = \mathbf{0}$, has nontrivial solutions if and only if $\det(\mathbf{A} - \lambda\mathbf{I}) = 0$. The polynomial $\det(\mathbf{A} - \lambda\mathbf{I})$ is a polynomial of degree n in λ and is called the characteristic polynomial of $\mathbf{A}$. The zeros of this polynomial are called the eigenvalues of $\mathbf{A}$. If $\mathbf{A}$ has eigenvalue λ_0, the equations $\mathbf{AX} = \lambda_0\mathbf{X}$ have nontrivial solutions. These nontrivial solutions are called eigenvectors of $\mathbf{A}$ corresponding to λ_0.

Similar matrices have the same eigenvalues. The eigenvalues of a diagonal matrix are the diagonal elements. If it is possible to find a nonsingular matrix $\mathbf{C}$ with columns that are eigenvectors of $\mathbf{A}$, then $\mathbf{C}^{-1}\mathbf{AC}$ is a diagonal matrix with diagonal elements that are eigenvalues of $\mathbf{A}$.

EXERCISES 3.5

1. For what λ does $\mathbf{AX} = \lambda\mathbf{X}$ have a nontrivial solution?

a. $\mathbf{A} = \begin{bmatrix} 2 & 1 \\ 0 & 3 \end{bmatrix}$ **b.** $\mathbf{A} = \begin{bmatrix} 2 & 1 \\ 1 & 2 \end{bmatrix}$

c. $\mathbf{A} = \begin{bmatrix} 2 & 1 \\ 1 & 3 \end{bmatrix}$ **d.** $\mathbf{A} = \begin{bmatrix} 6 & 0 & 2 \\ 0 & 2 & 0 \\ -4 & 0 & 0 \end{bmatrix}$

2. Find the characteristic values of $\mathbf{A}$.

a. $\mathbf{A} = \begin{bmatrix} 3 & 1 \\ 4 & 6 \end{bmatrix}$ **b.** $\mathbf{A} = \begin{bmatrix} 3 & -1 \\ 9 & -4 \end{bmatrix}$

c. $\mathbf{A} = \begin{bmatrix} 7 & 7 & 7 \\ -5 & -7 & -9 \\ 5 & 7 & 9 \end{bmatrix}$

d. $\mathbf{A} = \begin{bmatrix} 3 & -1 & 2 \\ 0 & -1 & 0 \\ -4 & 2 & -3 \end{bmatrix}$

3. For the matrices in Problem 1, find the eigenvectors corresponding to each eigenvalue.

4. For the matrices in Problem 2, find the eigenvectors corresponding to each eigenvalue.

5. a. Find the eigenvalues for each matrix $\mathbf{A}$. How many distinct eigenvalues are there in each case?

i. $\mathbf{A} = \begin{bmatrix} 2 & 4 \\ 3 & 6 \end{bmatrix}$ **ii.** $\mathbf{A} = \begin{bmatrix} 6 & 7 & 7 \\ -7 & -8 & -7 \\ 7 & 7 & 6 \end{bmatrix}$

iii. $\mathbf{A} = \begin{bmatrix} 2 & 1 & 5 \\ -3 & -2 & -8 \\ 3 & 3 & 9 \end{bmatrix}$

iv. $\mathbf{A} = \begin{bmatrix} -1 & -1 & 2 & -10 \\ 4 & 3 & 0 & 14 \\ 0 & 0 & 5 & 9 \\ 0 & 0 & -1 & -1 \end{bmatrix}$

b. Find the eigenvectors corresponding to each eigenvalue. What is the rank of $\mathbf{A} - \lambda\mathbf{I}$ in each case?

6. Find the eigenvalues of $\mathbf{A}$ in each case. How many distinct eigenvalues are there in each case?

a. $\mathbf{A} = \begin{bmatrix} 7 & 4 \\ -2 & -2 \end{bmatrix}$ **b.** $\mathbf{A} = \begin{bmatrix} 6 & 4 & 4 \\ -7 & -2 & -1 \\ 7 & 4 & 3 \end{bmatrix}$

c. $\mathbf{A} = \begin{bmatrix} 2 & -1 & 0 \\ 2 & 1 & 1 \\ -2 & 2 & 1 \end{bmatrix}$

For the matrices in **a.** and **b.**, find a matrix $\mathbf{C}$ with columns eigenvectors such that $\mathbf{C}^{-1}\mathbf{AC} = \mathbf{D}$, where $\mathbf{D}$ is a diagonal matrix having the eigenvalues of $\mathbf{A}$ on the diagonal.

7. a. Consider the matrix

$$\mathbf{A} = \begin{bmatrix} 0 & 0 & 1 \\ -3 & 0 & 0 \\ 1 & 1 & 3 \end{bmatrix}$$

One of the eigenvalues of $\mathbf{A}$ is $\lambda = 1$. Find the eigenvectors corresponding to $\lambda = 1$. What is the rank of $\mathbf{A} - \mathbf{I}$?

b. Consider the matrix

$$\mathbf{A} = \begin{bmatrix} 5 & 0 & 2 \\ 0 & 1 & 0 \\ -4 & 0 & -1 \end{bmatrix}$$

Find the eigenvectors corresponding to $\lambda = 1$. What is the rank of $\mathbf{A} - \mathbf{I}$?

8. a. Let $\mathbf{A} = \begin{bmatrix} 8 & 7 & 7 \\ -7 & -6 & -7 \\ 7 & 7 & 8 \end{bmatrix}$. Find a matrix $\mathbf{C}$ such that

$$\mathbf{C}^{-1}\mathbf{AC} = \begin{bmatrix} 1 & 0 & 0 \\ 0 & 1 & 0 \\ 0 & 0 & 8 \end{bmatrix}$$

b. Let $\mathbf{A} = \begin{bmatrix} 2 & -1 & 0 \\ 2 & 1 & 1 \\ -2 & 2 & 1 \end{bmatrix}$. Explain why it is not possible to find a matrix $\mathbf{C}$ such that $\mathbf{C}^{-1}\mathbf{AC} = \begin{bmatrix} 1 & 0 & 0 \\ 0 & 1 & 0 \\ 0 & 0 & 2 \end{bmatrix}$

9. Find the eigenvalues of $\begin{bmatrix} 2 & 0 & 0 \\ 0 & 2 & 0 \\ 0 & 0 & 3 \end{bmatrix}$. Find the eigenvalues of $\begin{bmatrix} 2 & 1 & 0 \\ 0 & 2 & 0 \\ 0 & 0 & 3 \end{bmatrix}$. Show that the converse of Theorem 18 is not true; that is, two matrices $\mathbf{A}$ and $\mathbf{B}$ may have the same eigenvalues when $\mathbf{A}$ is not similar to $\mathbf{B}$.

10. For the matrices in Problem 1, find a matrix $\mathbf{C}$ such that $\mathbf{C}^{-1}\mathbf{AC}$ is diagonal. (Problem 3 will help here.)

11. The matrix $\mathbf{A}$ is diagonalizable. Its eigenvalues are 1, 2, and -4, and corresponding eigenvectors are $\begin{bmatrix}1\\0\\1\end{bmatrix}$, $\begin{bmatrix}1\\1\\0\end{bmatrix}$, and $\begin{bmatrix}0\\1\\0\end{bmatrix}$. Find the matrix $\mathbf{A}$.

12. Let $\mathbf{A} = \begin{bmatrix}3 & -1 & -1\\ -2 & 3 & 2\\ 4 & -1 & -2\end{bmatrix}$.

a. Given that 2 is an eigenvalue of $\mathbf{A}$, find a corresponding eigenvector.

b. Given that $(1, -1, 1)$ is an eigenvector of $\mathbf{A}$, find the corresponding eigenvalue.

13. If $\mathbf{A}$ is an $n \times n$ matrix and the rank of $\mathbf{A} - 3\mathbf{I}$ is n, is 3 an eigenvalue of $\mathbf{A}$? Give a reason for your answer.

14. Given that

$$\begin{bmatrix}2 & 2 & 1\\ 1 & 3 & 1\\ 1 & 2 & 2\end{bmatrix}\begin{bmatrix}1\\1\\1\end{bmatrix} = \begin{bmatrix}5\\5\\5\end{bmatrix}$$

state one eigenvalue of the matrix $\begin{bmatrix}2 & 2 & 1\\ 1 & 3 & 1\\ 1 & 2 & 2\end{bmatrix}$ and its corresponding eigenvector.

15. Calculation will show that

$$\det\begin{bmatrix}1 & 2 & 1\\ 2 & 4 & 3\\ 1 & 2 & 2\end{bmatrix} = 0$$

What does this information tell you about the eigenvalues of the matrix $\begin{bmatrix}1 & 2 & 1\\ 2 & 4 & 3\\ 1 & 2 & 2\end{bmatrix}$? Write a matrix for which 1 is an eigenvalue.

16. Find the eigenvalues and eigenvectors of the following matrices:

a. $\mathbf{A} = \begin{bmatrix}2 & 5\\ 4 & 3\end{bmatrix}$ **b.** $\mathbf{A} + \mathbf{I} = \begin{bmatrix}3 & 5\\ 4 & 4\end{bmatrix}$

c. $\mathbf{A} - 2\mathbf{I} = \begin{bmatrix}0 & 5\\ 4 & 1\end{bmatrix}$

d. $\mathbf{A} - k\mathbf{I} = \begin{bmatrix}2-k & 5\\ 4 & 3-k\end{bmatrix}$

17. The eigenvalues of $\begin{bmatrix}1 & 2\\ 2 & 1\end{bmatrix}$ are 3 and -1. Write a matrix with 2 and -2 for eigenvalues. (Problem 16 should suggest a method.)

18. Show that if $\mathbf{X}_0$ is an eigenvector of $\mathbf{A}$ corresponding to the eigenvalue λ_0, then $\mathbf{X}_0$ is also an eigenvector of $\mathbf{A} - k\mathbf{I}$ corresponding to the eigenvalue $\lambda_0 - k$.

19. A student is working the following problem: find the eigenvalues of $\mathbf{A}$ and calculate the corresponding eigenvectors. The student finds the number 2 is an eigenvalue and obtains the equations

$$\begin{bmatrix}1 & -2 & -1\\ -1 & 1 & -4\\ -1 & -2 & -5\end{bmatrix}\mathbf{X} = \mathbf{0}$$

from which the eigenvector corresponding to 2 must be found. What is the solution of these equations? Should the student use this for an eigenvector? What conclusion do you draw about this work? Why?

20. **a.** The characteristic equation of $\mathbf{A} = \begin{bmatrix}1 & 2\\ 2 & 1\end{bmatrix}$ is $\lambda^2 - 2\lambda - 3 = 0$. Verify that $\mathbf{A}^2 - 2\mathbf{A} - 3\mathbf{I} = \mathbf{0}$.

b. If

$$\mathbf{B} = \begin{bmatrix}2 & -1 & 0\\ 2 & 1 & 1\\ -2 & 2 & 1\end{bmatrix}$$

its characteristic equation is $\lambda^3 - 4\lambda^2 + 5\lambda - 2 = 0$. Verify that $\mathbf{B}^3 - 4\mathbf{B}^2 + 5\mathbf{B} - 2\mathbf{I} = \mathbf{0}$.

c. Based on the evidence above, what would you conjecture is true about a matrix $\mathbf{A}$ in relation to its characteristic equation?

21. For the matrices in Problem 20, show that:

a. $\mathbf{A}$ is nonsingular and $\mathbf{A}^{-1} = \frac{1}{3}(\mathbf{A} - 2\mathbf{I})$.

b. $\mathbf{B}$ is nonsingular and $\mathbf{B}^{-1} = \frac{1}{2}(\mathbf{B}^2 - 4\mathbf{B} + 5\mathbf{I})$.

22. Show that if $\mathbf{P}^{-1}\mathbf{AP} = \mathbf{D}$, $\mathbf{P}^{-1}\mathbf{A}^2\mathbf{P} = \mathbf{D}^2$, so that $\mathbf{A}^2 = \mathbf{PD}^2\mathbf{P}^{-1}$.

23. Calculate $\begin{bmatrix}6 & 4 & 4\\ -7 & -2 & -1\\ 7 & 4 & 3\end{bmatrix}^2$ by the method of Problem 22, and also by direct multiplication.

24. Show that if $\mathbf{C}^{-1}\mathbf{AC} = \mathbf{D}$, then $\mathbf{C}^{-1}\mathbf{A}^n\mathbf{C} = \mathbf{D}^n$ and $\mathbf{C}^{-1}(k\mathbf{A})\mathbf{C} = k\mathbf{D}$.

25. Let $f(\mathbf{A}) = \mathbf{A}^n + c_1\mathbf{A}^{n-1} + \cdots + c_n\mathbf{I}$. Show that $\mathbf{C}^{-1}f(\mathbf{A})\mathbf{C} = \mathbf{D}^n + c_1\mathbf{D}^{n-1} + \cdots + c_n\mathbf{I}$, where $\mathbf{D} = \mathbf{C}^{-1}\mathbf{A}\mathbf{C}$.

26. Let **A** be an $n \times n$ matrix. Show that **A** is singular if and only if the characteristic polynomial of **A** has a factor λ.

27. Let **A** be an $n \times n$ matrix. Show that 0 is an eigenvalue of **A** if and only if **A** is a singular matrix.

28. Work Example 20 assuming that 40% of Top Value's customers remain with the store and 60% change to Best Bargains, while 70% of Best Bargain's customers remain with the store and 30% change to Top Value.

29. Work Example 20 with the following changes. The distribution of customers is assumed to be the same as in Example 20, but the population of the town grows by 10% a year. The newcomers choose a grocery store in the same proportion as existing customers, so that at the end of 1 year an additional $0.1x_1$ is added to Top Value and $0.1x_2$ is added to Best Bargains.

30. Work Problem 29 assuming that all newcomers go to Top Value so that $x_1^{(1)} = 0.8x_1 + 0.4x_2 + 0.1(x_1 + x_2)$.

3.6 *Applications: Markov Chains, Leontief Input–Output Economic Model, Population Study, and Eigenvectors*

This section is devoted to three important applications: Markov Chains (which use elementary probability and eigenvalues), the Leontief Input–Output Economic Model (which requires the inverse of a matrix), and population dynamics (based on eigenvalues). The computations you will need to carry out to study these applications will certainly be easier if you have access to computer software that finds the determinant of a matrix, the inverse of a matrix, and matrix powers. You may use any of the sample programs provided for you in the appendix or a professionally written package of your choice. In either case, you should understand that most of the computations for the examples and problems in this section are best carried out with the aid of a calculator or computer.

Markov Chains

You will see in this section that multiplication of matrices can be used to predict future events. Since mathematicians are not much better at fortune-telling than anyone else, "prediction" must use the concept of the probability of random events. We need to review just a few facts about probabilities before discussing how they are used in Markov Chains. The probability of a random event is always a real number between 0 and 1, inclusive. In practical situations, we can think of a probability value as a percentage; for example, if a baseball player's batting average is 0.250, then we could expect that he will get 25 hits in the next 100 times at bat. Events with probability 0 are called impossible. Those with probability 1 are called certain. If two or more events completely account for all possibilities in a given situation but no two can occur simultaneously, their probabilities must have a sum of 1.

The probability of events can be found using two useful facts. If two events are independent, the probability of them both occurring is the product of their separate probabilities. For example, the probability that both coins show heads on the toss of two fair coins is $(\frac{1}{2})(\frac{1}{2}) = \frac{1}{4}$. If two events cannot occur simultaneously, then the probability of one or the other is the sum of their separate probabilities. For example, exactly one head on the toss of two coins occurs either as *HT* or *TH*. Thus, the probability of exactly one head is $(\frac{1}{2})(\frac{1}{2}) + (\frac{1}{2})(\frac{1}{2}) = \frac{1}{2}$.

We can now describe Markov Chains. An activity is studied by making repeated observations at regular intervals. The current state of the activity is then recorded (we assume that only a finite number of states is possible). For example, the voting habits of a particular neighborhood have been tabulated over the course of many elections. Four parties are always represented: Democratic (D), Independent (I), Labor (L), and Republican (R). Based on the studies made, we know the voting behavior of each category of voters in the current election. Of the group of persons who voted a certain way in the past election, we know the percentage who vote the same way in the present election and the percentage who change to each of the other categories. An important assumption is that these percentages remain the same from one election to the next. Given a stable population, this may not be an unreasonable assumption. In any event, Figure 3.4 shows these percentages for this neighborhood:

		Current Election			
		D	I	L	R
Last Election	D	0.63	0.17	0.14	0.06
	I	0.23	0.52	0.14	0.11
	L	0.09	0.01	0.89	0.01
	R	0.15	0.12	0.02	0.71

FIGURE 3.4

How would we interpret the first row of the table? Of those who voted Democratic in the last election, 63% will vote Democratic in the current election, 17% will change their vote to Independent, 14% will change to Labor, and 6% will change to Republican. We can also think of these percentages as probabilities. For example, the probability that a person will vote Independent in the current election, knowing that person voted Labor in the last election, is 0.01.

Of course, a matrix efficiently records all these possibilities. Let us code the parties (Democratic = 1, Independent = 2, Labor = 3, Republican = 4). Let $\mathbf{T} = [a_{ij}]_{4\times 4}$, where a_{ij} is the percentage of those who voted party j in the last election who vote party i in the current election. Then $\mathbf{T}$ is the *transpose* of the entries in Figure 3.4.

$$\mathbf{T} = \begin{bmatrix} 0.63 & 0.23 & 0.09 & 0.15 \\ 0.17 & 0.52 & 0.01 & 0.12 \\ 0.14 & 0.14 & 0.89 & 0.02 \\ 0.06 & 0.11 & 0.01 & 0.71 \end{bmatrix}$$

A matrix $\mathbf{S} = [b_{ij}]_{m \times m}$ is called a *change-of-state matrix* when all $b_{ij} \geqslant 0$ and the sum of the entries in each column of **S** is less than or equal to 1. If, in addition, the sum of the entries in each column is exactly 1 in a change-of-state matrix **S**, **S** is called a *transition matrix* (*for a Markov Chain*); transition matrices are also called *Markov matrices*, *probability matrices*, or *stochastic matrices* (see Problem 10, Section 1.6). Since we are assuming there are only four possible parties in any election and we are measuring the total voting population of the neighborhood in our example, the matrix **T** is a transition matrix.

As a hypothetical example, suppose 100% of the voters voted Democratic in the last election. This can be represented as probabilities by the 4-tuple $\mathbf{x} = (1, 0, 0, 0)$. How would we predict voter behavior in the next election? According to Figure 3.4, the result should be the first column of **T**, and this is the result of the matrix product $\mathbf{Y} = \mathbf{TX}$:

$$\mathbf{Y} = \begin{bmatrix} 0.63 & 0.23 & 0.09 & 0.15 \\ 0.17 & 0.52 & 0.01 & 0.12 \\ 0.14 & 0.14 & 0.89 & 0.02 \\ 0.06 & 0.11 & 0.01 & 0.71 \end{bmatrix} \begin{bmatrix} 1 \\ 0 \\ 0 \\ 0 \end{bmatrix} = \begin{bmatrix} 0.63 \\ 0.17 \\ 0.14 \\ 0.06 \end{bmatrix}$$

But what about *two* elections from now? After the first election, we know $\mathbf{x} = (0.63, 0.17, 0.14, 0.06)$, and then $\mathbf{Y} = \mathbf{TX}$ is

$$\mathbf{Y} = \begin{bmatrix} 0.63 & 0.23 & 0.09 & 0.15 \\ 0.17 & 0.52 & 0.01 & 0.12 \\ 0.14 & 0.14 & 0.89 & 0.02 \\ 0.06 & 0.11 & 0.01 & 0.71 \end{bmatrix} \begin{bmatrix} 0.63 \\ 0.17 \\ 0.14 \\ 0.06 \end{bmatrix} = \begin{bmatrix} 0.46 \\ 0.20 \\ 0.24 \\ 0.10 \end{bmatrix}$$

Notice that the 4-tuples **x** and **y** computed so far have the property that all their entries are nonnegative and have a sum of 1. This is easy to understand, since each 4-tuple accounts for the entire voting population. An n-tuple with the property that its entries are nonnegative and have a sum of 1 is called a *probability vector*.

Notice that the probability vector **y** of the last computation can be given by $\mathbf{T}(\mathbf{TX}) = \mathbf{T}^2\mathbf{X}$, where **x** is a probability vector $(1, 0, 0, 0)$. In fact, this leads us to ask what $\mathbf{T}^2$ would represent. A short computation gives (rounding all results to the nearest hundredth)

$$\mathbf{T}^2 = \begin{bmatrix} 0.46 & 0.29 & 0.14 & 0.23 \\ 0.20 & 0.33 & 0.03 & 0.17 \\ 0.24 & 0.23 & 0.81 & 0.07 \\ 0.10 & 0.15 & 0.02 & 0.53 \end{bmatrix}$$

Again, the column sums are all 1 (notice that the first column is our last probability vector, **y**).

What does the entry a_{12} in $\mathbf{T}^2$ mean? From the definition of matrix multiplication, we see that

$$a_{12} = (0.23)(0.63) + (0.52)(0.23) + (0.14)(0.09) + (0.11)(0.15) = 0.29$$

Since party 2 is the Independent party, visualize all the voters who voted Independent in a given election. In the next election, **T** gives the various percentages who vote for any of the parties. The following diagram lists all the possibilities.

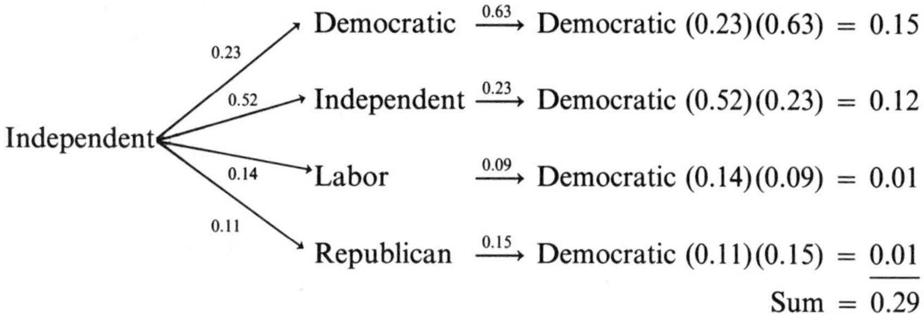

Of all those who voted Independent in the first election, 23% will vote Democratic in the second election; of these, 63% will continue to vote Democratic in the third election. Since we are assuming these events are independent and $(0.23)(0.63) = 0.15$, we see that approximately 15% of those who voted Independent in the first election will vote Democratic in the third election. This explains the significance of the first product in the sum defining a_{12}. But the remaining products account for those who voted other than Democratic in the second election. Since there are only four parties and no one may vote for more than one candidate, all possibilities are taken into account by adding the respective products. Thus a_{12} gives the percentage of those who vote Democratic (Party 1) in the third election based on those who vote Independent (Party 2) in the first election. All entries in $\mathbf{T}^2$ are predictions of the voting patterns of the neighborhood in the third election based on the first election.

Based on these observations, we see that to go from a given election to a later one, we simply multiply the 4-tuple that represents the current voting percentages by a power of **T**. The sequence of results, $\mathbf{X}$, $\mathbf{TX}$, $\mathbf{T}^2\mathbf{X}$, $\mathbf{T}^3\mathbf{X}$, and so on is called a *Markov Chain*. This is summarized in general for an experiment with n possible states.

Markov Chain Process

1. Set up an $n \times n$ matrix, whose entry in the ith row, jth column is the probability of moving from state i to state j in any given time interval.
2. Let **T** be the transpose of this matrix.
3. If $\mathbf{x}$ is an n-tuple that is a probability vector and **T** is a transition matrix for a Markov chain, then $\mathbf{Y} = \mathbf{T}^k\mathbf{X}$ is a probability vector k time periods into the future.

To continue with the current example, suppose we let $\mathbf{x} = (1, 0, 0, 0)$ and compute $\mathbf{X}$, $\mathbf{TX}$, $\mathbf{T}(\mathbf{TX}) = \mathbf{T}^2\mathbf{X}$, $\mathbf{T}(\mathbf{T}(\mathbf{TX})) = \mathbf{T}^3\mathbf{X}$, and so on. The following table gives these results for various values of k (for convenience, each matrix $\mathbf{T}^k\mathbf{X}$ is written in the table as a 4-tuple):

k	$\mathbf{T}^k\mathbf{X}$
1	(0.63, 0.17, 0.14, 0.06)
2	(0.46, 0.20, 0.24, 0.10)
3	(0.37, 0.20, 0.31, 0.12)
4	(0.33, 0.18, 0.36, 0.13)
5	(0.30, 0.17, 0.39, 0.14)
10	(0.26, 0.14, 0.47, 0.13)
15	(0.25, 0.13, 0.50, 0.12)
20	(0.25, 0.13, 0.50, 0.12)

(Check that $\mathbf{T}^k\mathbf{X}$ is a probability vector in each case.)

These results suggest that there is a probability vector **x** for this transition matrix **T** such that $\mathbf{X} = \mathbf{TX}$. Such a tuple is called an *equilibrium*, or *steady-state*, vector associated with **T**. Clearly, an equilibrium vector **X** for **T** is an eigenvector associated with the eigenvalue 1. The following results confirm this suspicion and indicate how to find steady-state vectors for transition matrices.

Theorem 21 Let **T** be the transition matrix for a Markov Chain. Then $\lambda = 1$ is an eigenvalue of **T**. If **x** is an eigenvector corresponding to $\lambda = 1$ and all the components of **x** are nonnegative, then $(1/s)\mathbf{x}$ is an equilibrium vector for **T**, where s is the sum of the components of **x**. □

Theorem 22 Let **T** be the transition matrix for a Markov Chain. If some power of **T** has all positive entries, then there is a unique equilibrium vector **x** for **T**. Also, if **y** is any probability vector, $\mathbf{T}^k\mathbf{Y}$ converges to **X** as k takes on larger and larger positive values. □

Example 28 Let

$$\mathbf{T} = \begin{bmatrix} \frac{1}{2} & 0 & \frac{1}{2} \\ \frac{1}{2} & \frac{1}{2} & 0 \\ 0 & \frac{1}{2} & \frac{1}{2} \end{bmatrix}$$

Then

$$\begin{aligned}
\det(\mathbf{T} - \lambda\mathbf{I}) &= \det \begin{bmatrix} \frac{1}{2} - \lambda & 0 & \frac{1}{2} \\ \frac{1}{2} & \frac{1}{2} - \lambda & 0 \\ 0 & \frac{1}{2} & \frac{1}{2} - \lambda \end{bmatrix} \\
&= (\tfrac{1}{2} - \lambda) \det \begin{bmatrix} \frac{1}{2} - \lambda & 0 \\ \frac{1}{2} & \frac{1}{2} - \lambda \end{bmatrix} + \tfrac{1}{2} \det \begin{bmatrix} \frac{1}{2} & \frac{1}{2} - \lambda \\ 0 & \frac{1}{2} \end{bmatrix} \\
&= (\tfrac{1}{2} - \lambda)(\tfrac{1}{2} - \lambda)^2 + \tfrac{1}{2}(\tfrac{1}{4}) \\
&= (\tfrac{1}{2} - \lambda)^3 + \tfrac{1}{8}
\end{aligned}$$

Thus, $\det(\mathbf{T} - \lambda\mathbf{I}) = 0$ means $\frac{1}{2} - \lambda = -\frac{1}{2}$, or $\lambda = 1$. To find the associated eigenvector, row reduce the matrix

$$\begin{bmatrix} -\frac{1}{2} & 0 & \frac{1}{2} \\ \frac{1}{2} & -\frac{1}{2} & 0 \\ 0 & \frac{1}{2} & -\frac{1}{2} \end{bmatrix} \quad \text{to} \quad \begin{bmatrix} 1 & 0 & -1 \\ 0 & 1 & -1 \\ 0 & 0 & 0 \end{bmatrix},$$

which gives the general solution $k(1, 1, 1)$. A steady-state vector $\mathbf{y}$ can be chosen when $k = 1$; then $s = 1 + 1 + 1 = 3$ and $\mathbf{y} = (\frac{1}{3}, \frac{1}{3}, \frac{1}{3})$. ■

To illustrate Theorem 22, let $\mathbf{x} = (1, 0, 0)$ (a probability vector) and compute $\mathbf{T}^k\mathbf{X}$ for increasing values of k. These are given in the table:

k	$\mathbf{T}^k\mathbf{X}$
1	$(\frac{1}{2}, \frac{1}{2}, 0)$
2	$(\frac{1}{4}, \frac{2}{4}, \frac{1}{4})$
3	$(\frac{2}{8}, \frac{3}{8}, \frac{3}{8})$
4	$(\frac{5}{16}, \frac{5}{16}, \frac{6}{16})$
5	$(\frac{11}{32}, \frac{10}{32}, \frac{11}{32})$
10	$(\frac{341}{1024}, \frac{341}{1024}, \frac{342}{1024})$
15	$(0.333, 0.333, 0.333)$
20	$(0.33333, 0.33333, 0.33333)$

Leontief Input–Output Economic Model

The techniques introduced up to this point can be applied to any problem in which systems of linear equations must be solved. The discussion here relates to the model of exchange referred to as the *Leontief input–output economic model*. Essentially the problem is to investigate the relationships among n interconnected industries (or activities) and the products (or commodities or services) they produce. Assume that it is possible to identify a finite number of industries $W_1, W_2, \ldots, W_n$, each producing exactly one distinct product $C_1, C_2, \ldots, C_n$. It is apparent that each industry uses the products or services of other industries and possibly some of its own products as well. To make the products C_i comparable, their amounts are measured in dollar values. Specifically, let a_{ij} represent the amount of commodity C_i required to produce a dollar's worth of commodity C_j. Immediately, we assume that each a_{ij} is a real number between 0 and 1—otherwise, we have an economic disaster! Also, the first subscript, i, relates to the commodity used (input), while the second subscript, j, refers to the commodity produced (output).

Example 29 Suppose there are four activities in a simple economic model: W_1, coal mining; W_2, transport; W_3, steel manufacture; and W_4, electric utility. The numbers a_{ij} are written in a 4×4 matrix $\mathbf{A}$. Assume that this matrix is

$$\mathbf{A} = \begin{array}{c} \\ C_1 \\ C_2 \\ C_3 \\ C_4 \end{array} \begin{array}{c} \begin{array}{cccc} C_1 & C_2 & C_3 & C_4 \end{array} \\ \begin{bmatrix} 0.05 & 0.17 & 0.35 & 0.55 \\ 0.18 & 0.07 & 0.12 & 0.20 \\ 0.37 & 0.38 & 0.05 & 0.10 \\ 0.32 & 0.20 & 0.37 & 0.03 \end{bmatrix} \end{array}$$

The diagonal elements show how much of its own commodity each activity uses internally. For example, in steel manufacture, 5¢ of every dollar's worth of steel is used in its manufacture (say, for new equipment, buildings, trucks, stockpiles, wastage). Also, 35¢ worth of coal, 12¢ worth of transport, and 37¢ worth of electricity are needed to manufacture a dollar's worth of steel. ■

Several observations can be made. The sum of each column of $\mathbf{A}$ represents the total input from the n activity sectors of the model economy required to produce a unit value of output of each commodity. The entries a_{ij} can reasonably be expected to have the following properties:

1. $0 \leqslant a_{ij} < 1$ for all i, j.
2. $\Sigma_{i=1}^{n} a_{ij} < 1$, for each $j = 1, 2, \ldots, n$; that is, the sum of each column of $\mathbf{A}$ is less than 1.

So far, the model has considered only the demands that the n industries make on themselves and each other. However, the society outside the set of n activities $W_1, W_2, \ldots, W_n$ also enters into the picture in the form of labor costs, profit, dividends, taxes, and so on. To bring these into the analysis, let d_i represent the total amount (in dollars) of activity W_i required to meet the demands of the sector of society outside $W_1, W_2, \ldots, W_n$. Let x_i be the total output (in dollars) of activity W_i. The requirement that x_i dollars of output from the industry W_i must meet the demands of the other industries and of society results in a system of equations. These equations, in the case $n = 4$, are:

$$\begin{aligned} x_1 &= a_{11}x_1 + a_{12}x_2 + a_{13}x_3 + a_{14}x_4 + d_1 \\ x_2 &= a_{21}x_1 + a_{22}x_2 + a_{23}x_3 + a_{24}x_4 + d_2 \\ x_3 &= a_{31}x_1 + a_{32}x_2 + a_{33}x_3 + a_{34}x_4 + d_3 \\ x_4 &= a_{41}x_1 + a_{42}x_2 + a_{43}x_3 + a_{44}x_4 + d_4 \end{aligned}$$

The system of equations can be rewritten in a more natural form if all entries involving x_1, x_2, x_3, and x_4 are put on the left-hand side. The system becomes:

$$\begin{aligned} (1 - a_{11})x_1 - a_{12}x_2 - a_{13}x_3 - a_{14}x_4 &= d_1 \\ -a_{21}x_1 + (1 - a_{22})x_2 - a_{23}x_3 - a_{24}x_4 &= d_2 \\ -a_{31}x_1 - a_{32}x_2 + (1 - a_{33})x_3 - a_{34}x_4 &= d_3 \\ -a_{41}x_1 - a_{42}x_2 - a_{43}x_3 + (1 - a_{44})x_4 &= d_4 \end{aligned}$$

Notice that the coefficient matrix of this system of equations is $\mathbf{I}_4 - \mathbf{A}$, so if the unknown amounts x_i are written to form the 4-tuple **x** of unknowns and the demands are similarly written

$$\mathbf{D} = \begin{bmatrix} d_1 \\ d_2 \\ d_3 \\ d_4 \end{bmatrix}$$

then the preceding system can be written simply as $(\mathbf{I} - \mathbf{A})\mathbf{X} = \mathbf{D}$.

The setting of the model requires that each value of x_i be nonnegative. This may not be possible for certain values of d_i. The nonsingularity of the matrix $\mathbf{I} - \mathbf{A}$ determines whether the system of equations can be solved. Many interesting questions are centered around this point. For example, what conditions on the entries of **A**, compatible within this framework, guarantee the nonsingularity of $\mathbf{I} - \mathbf{A}$? Also, can $(\mathbf{I} - \mathbf{A})^{-1}$ be found in terms of **A**?

Consider the product $(\mathbf{I} - \mathbf{A})(\mathbf{I} + \mathbf{A} + \mathbf{A}^2 + \cdots + \mathbf{A}^m)$, where m is a positive integer. We have

$$\begin{aligned} &(\mathbf{I} - \mathbf{A})(\mathbf{I} + \mathbf{A} + \mathbf{A}^2 + \cdots + \mathbf{A}^m) \\ &\quad = (\mathbf{I} + \mathbf{A} + \mathbf{A}^2 + \cdots + \mathbf{A}^m) - (\mathbf{A} + \mathbf{A}^2 + \mathbf{A}^3 + \cdots + \mathbf{A}^{m+1}) \\ &\quad = \mathbf{I} - \mathbf{A}^{m+1} \end{aligned}$$

If there is a value of m large enough to make $\mathbf{A}^{m+1} = \mathbf{0}$, we will have found the inverse of $\mathbf{I} - \mathbf{A}$, since, in this case $(\mathbf{I} - \mathbf{A})(\mathbf{I} + \mathbf{A} + \mathbf{A}^2 + \cdots + \mathbf{A}^m) = \mathbf{I}$ and $(\mathbf{I} - \mathbf{A})^{-1} = \mathbf{I} + \mathbf{A} + \mathbf{A}^2 + \cdots + \mathbf{A}^m$.

The project of actually making $\mathbf{A}^{m+1}$ equal to $\mathbf{0}$ is doomed to failure unless **A** is a singular matrix, since if $\det \mathbf{A} \neq 0$, $\det \mathbf{A}^{m+1} \neq 0$, and so $\mathbf{A}^{m+1} \neq \mathbf{0}$. But, for practical purposes, it may suffice to make $\mathbf{A}^{m+1}$ close enough to zero that it can be neglected in computations. If, by choosing n large enough, each element of the matrix $\mathbf{A}^n$ is arbitrarily close to zero, we say $\lim_{n\to\infty} \mathbf{A}^n = \mathbf{0}$. If $\lim_{n\to\infty} \mathbf{A}^n = \mathbf{0}$, the matrix $\mathbf{I} + \mathbf{A} + \mathbf{A}^2 + \cdots + \mathbf{A}^m$ will be a good approximation to $(\mathbf{I} - \mathbf{A})^{-1}$ for large enough m.

Population Study and Eigenvectors

Suppose there is a population of living organisms that reproduces and dies off before reaching more than a given number of time cycles. These cycles can be measured in units that are convenient for the organisms being considered—centuries (for trees, perhaps), years, months, days, or even minutes in a very hostile environment. For simplicity, let us assume that the number of time cycles, n, is 4. This means that the oldest living organism has age 4. Whatever is said for this value of n readily generalizes to other values. Being sophisticated demographers, we are interested in plotting the population statistics for the organisms we are studying. There are certain facts we need to know:

1. x_{it} = number of living organisms of age i ($i = 0, 1, 2, 3, 4$) alive at time t.

2. p_i = probability that an organism of age i alive at time t will survive until time $t + 1$ (in this case, $i = 0, 1, 2, 3$).
3. f_i = number of new organisms created per organism of age i.

The column vector

$$\mathbf{X}_t = \begin{bmatrix} x_{0t} \\ x_{1t} \\ x_{2t} \\ x_{3t} \\ x_{4t} \end{bmatrix}$$

describes the population at any time, and this is the vector we want to determine at any value of time t. This is easily done by relating $\mathbf{X}_t$ and $\mathbf{X}_{t+1}$ in a matrix equation.

First, we form the *population matrix* $\mathbf{W}$:

$$\mathbf{W} = \begin{bmatrix} f_0 & f_1 & f_2 & f_3 & f_4 \\ p_0 & 0 & 0 & 0 & 0 \\ 0 & p_1 & 0 & 0 & 0 \\ 0 & 0 & p_2 & 0 & 0 \\ 0 & 0 & 0 & p_3 & 0 \end{bmatrix}$$

Now, examine the matrix $\mathbf{WX}_t$. It is the column vector

$$\mathbf{WX}_t = \begin{bmatrix} f_0x_{0t} + f_1x_{1t} + f_2x_{2t} + f_3x_{3t} + f_4x_{4t} \\ p_0x_{0t} \\ p_1x_{1t} \\ p_2x_{2t} \\ p_3x_{3t} \end{bmatrix}$$

The first entry, $f_0x_{0t} + f_1x_{1t} + \cdots + f_4x_{4t}$ is precisely the number of offspring produced in the population during the current time cycle (from t to $t + 1$), so this entry must equal $x_{0,t+1}$. Similarly, from the way the probabilities are defined, $p_jx_{jt} = x_{j+1,t+1}$ for $j = 0, 1, 2, 3$. Thus, the population change is described by the matrix equation $\mathbf{WX}_t = \mathbf{X}_{t+1}$, for any t, $t = 0, 1, 2, \ldots$.

What, then, does it mean to ask whether there is a value of t so that for some constant λ, $\mathbf{X}_{t+1} = \lambda\mathbf{X}_t$? It means that we want to know the composition of the population should there be some time when $\mathbf{X}_{t+1}$ is a multiple of $\mathbf{X}_t$—that is, a time when the population stabilizes. The word *stabilizes* here implies that the proportion of the population in each category remains constant, although the total population may change. If a time comes when $\mathbf{X}_{t+1} = \lambda\mathbf{X}_t$, we have $\mathbf{X}_{t+2} = \mathbf{W}(\lambda\mathbf{X}_t) = \lambda\mathbf{WX}_t = \lambda\mathbf{X}_{t+1}$, so $\mathbf{X}_{t+2}$ is the same multiple of $\mathbf{X}_{t+1}$.

But the equations $\mathbf{WX}_t = \mathbf{X}_{t+1}$ and $\mathbf{X}_{t+1} = \lambda\mathbf{X}_t$ together imply $\mathbf{WX}_t = \lambda\mathbf{X}_t$. So this is an eigenvalue problem.

Example 30 Suppose $n = 2$ and $\mathbf{W} = \begin{bmatrix} 0.0 & 8 \\ 0.5 & 0 \end{bmatrix}$. Then $\mathbf{WX}_t = \lambda\mathbf{X}_t$ implies

$$\det\begin{bmatrix} \lambda & -8 \\ -0.5 & \lambda \end{bmatrix} = 0$$

Thus, $\lambda^2 - 4 = 0$, so $\lambda = \pm 2$. For $\lambda = 2$, the characteristic vector is $\begin{bmatrix} 4 \\ 1 \end{bmatrix}$. Therefore, a population with population matrix $\mathbf{W}$ and a ratio of 4 to 1 in the ages of its organisms will exhibit stability. ■

EXERCISES 3.6

You will probably find it helpful to use a computer program (for instance, MAX) to aid you in solving several of the following problems. The first few exercises find the determinant or inverse of matrices. Most answers provided are *exact* so that you may judge the accuracy of your system and software.

1. Find the determinants of the following matrices.

a. $\mathbf{A} = \begin{bmatrix} 1 & -3 & 2 \\ 7 & 0 & -1 \\ 6 & -1 & 2 \end{bmatrix}$

b. $\mathbf{B} = \begin{bmatrix} 4.7 & 5.3 & -8.4 \\ -3.3 & 3.1 & -3.8 \\ 4.6 & -2.7 & 7.9 \end{bmatrix}$

c. $\mathbf{C} = \begin{bmatrix} 4.67 & 8.99 & -10.09 \\ -2.00 & 0.01 & 0.04 \\ 59.22 & 9.08 & -26.25 \end{bmatrix}$

2. Find the determinants of the following matrices:

a. $\mathbf{A} = \begin{bmatrix} 1 & 0 & 4 & -5 \\ 0 & 6 & 8 & -2 \\ 1 & -3 & 7 & 5 \\ 2 & 4 & -6 & 3 \end{bmatrix}$

b. $\mathbf{B} = \begin{bmatrix} 1.37 & 0 & 0 & 0 \\ 0 & 0 & -9.78 & 1.75 \\ 0 & 4.69 & 0 & 0 \\ 0 & 0 & 5.39 & 0 \end{bmatrix}$

3. Find the determinants of the following matrices:

a. $\mathbf{A} = \begin{bmatrix} 1 & -1 & 1 & 1 & -1 \\ 1 & 1 & 0 & 0 & 1 \\ 0 & 0 & 1 & 0 & 0 \\ -1 & 1 & 0 & 1 & -1 \\ 1 & 1 & 0 & -1 & 0 \end{bmatrix}$

b. $\mathbf{B} = \begin{bmatrix} 53 & 21 & -19 & 43 & 27 \\ -6 & -17 & -92 & 73 & 54 \\ 36 & 21 & -11 & 42 & -60 \\ -19 & -87 & 47 & 30 & 21 \\ 60 & -55 & 31 & -81 & -12 \end{bmatrix}$

4. Find the inverses of the matrices of Problem 2.

5. Find the inverses of the matrices in Problem 3.

6. Find the change-of-state matrix $\mathbf{T}$ for a linear algebra class that is taught in two sections, if every week $\frac{1}{4}$ of those in Section A and $\frac{1}{3}$ of those in Section B drop the course and $\frac{1}{6}$ of each section transfer to the other section. Is $\mathbf{T}$ a transition matrix for a Markov Chain?

7. At State University, no one is allowed to drop linear algebra. If a student is not doing well, that student is transferred to a remedial linear algebra section. Find the change-of-state matrix $\mathbf{T}$ for a linear algebra class that is taught in three sections, if every week $\frac{1}{4}$ of those in Section A and $\frac{1}{3}$ of those in Section B transfer to Section C (the remedial section), $\frac{1}{6}$ of those in Section A transfer to Section B, $\frac{1}{6}$ of those in Section B transfer to Section A, and finally (it appears the remedial section is doing some good!), $\frac{1}{8}$ of the remedial class moves back to Section A and $\frac{1}{4}$ of the remedial class moves back to Section B. Is **T** a transition matrix for a Markov Chain? If the total linear algebra enrollment was 100 students at the start of the 15-week semester, can you estimate how many students are in each section at the end of the semester?

8. Consider the following three matrices:

$$\mathbf{A} = \begin{bmatrix} 1 & \frac{1}{2} & \frac{1}{3} \\ 0 & \frac{1}{2} & \frac{1}{3} \\ 0 & 0 & \frac{1}{3} \end{bmatrix}, \quad \mathbf{B} = \begin{bmatrix} \frac{1}{6} & \frac{1}{6} & \frac{2}{3} & 0 \\ \frac{1}{2} & \frac{1}{2} & 0 & 0 \\ \frac{1}{3} & \frac{1}{3} & \frac{1}{3} & 0 \\ 0 & 0 & 0 & 1 \end{bmatrix},$$

$$\mathbf{C} = \begin{bmatrix} 0.1 & 0.5 & 0.4 \\ 0.3 & 0.2 & 0.1 \\ 0.6 & 0.3 & 0.5 \end{bmatrix}$$

a. Verify that each of the matrices **A**, **B**, **C** is a transition matrix for a Markov Chain.
b. Verify that 1 is an eigenvalue of **A**, **B**, and **C**.
c. In each case find the set of eigenvectors, **x**, corresponding to the eigenvalue 1.
d. In each case find any steady-state vectors. Is the steady-state vector unique?
e. Which of the matrices **A**, **B**, **C** satisfy the hypotheses of Theorem 22?
f. Use Theorem 22 to calculate the equilibrium vector for **C**.
g. Is the converse of Theorem 22 true? Justify your answer.

9. Let

$$\mathbf{T} = \begin{bmatrix} 0.5 & 0.8 & 0.7 \\ 0.3 & 0.2 & 0.1 \\ 0.2 & 0.0 & 0.2 \end{bmatrix}$$

a. Let $\mathbf{y} = (1, 0, 0)$. Calculate $\mathbf{T}^k\mathbf{Y}$ for $k = 1$ to 10. Show that $\mathbf{T}^k\mathbf{Y}$ is an equilibrium vector for **T**.
b. Find this vector by a different method as follows:
  i. Show that 1 is an eigenvalue for **T**.
  ii. Find an eigenvector corresponding to 1.
  iii. Use this information to find a steady-state vector for **T** using Theorem 21.

10. Fill in the reasons for each of the following statements, thereby proving Theorem 21 (**T** is an $n \times n$ transition matrix for a Markov Chain).
a. The sum of the entries in each column of $\mathbf{T} - \mathbf{I}$ is zero.
b. Adding to the last row all the other rows of $\mathbf{T} - \mathbf{I}$ produces a zero row.
c. The determinant of $\mathbf{T} - \mathbf{I}$ is zero.
d. $\lambda = 1$ is an eigenvalue of **T**.
e. If **x** is an eigenvector of **T** corresponding to $\lambda = 1$, then $\mathbf{TX} = \mathbf{X}$.
f. If **x** is an eigenvector of **T** corresponding to $\lambda = 1$, $\mathbf{x} = (x_1, x_2, \ldots, x_n)$, all $x_i \geqslant 0$, and $s = x_1 + x_2 + \cdots + x_n$, then $s > 0$.
g. $\mathbf{y} = (1/s)\mathbf{x}$ has nonnegative components that have a sum of 1. Thus, **y** is a probability vector.
h. $\mathbf{TY} = \mathbf{Y}$, so **y** is an equilibrium vector for **T**.

11. Let **T** be a 2×2 transition matrix for a Markov Chain. If $\mathbf{TX} = \lambda\mathbf{X}$ and $\lambda \neq 1$, show that the components of **x** must add up to zero.

12. A simplified economy has three interacting sectors: energy, food, and manufactured goods. It takes \$0.20 worth of energy (but no food or goods) to produce \$1 of energy; it takes \$0.10 of energy and \$0.10 of goods to produce \$1 of food; and it takes \$0.30 of energy and \$0.50 of goods to produce \$1 of goods. How many dollars should be produced by each sector in order to meet a demand for \$400 (worth) of energy, \$500 of food, and \$200 of goods?

13. An interacting economy contains five producing sectors: utilities, textiles, chemicals, machinery, and transportation. To produce \$1 of each of these commodities respectively, the input requirements are:

Ut	*Tex*	*Chem*	*Mach*	*Trns*
0.25	0.21	0.12	0.00	0.00
0.00	0.13	0.00	0.00	0.00
0.02	0.09	0.35	0.03	0.00
0.05	0.03	0.01	0.08	0.14
0.07	0.10	0.02	0.04	0.10

How many dollars output should be produced by each commodity to meet the demand of \$100 (worth) each of utilities, textiles, chemicals, machinery, and transportation?

14. a. Let $\mathbf{A} = \begin{bmatrix} 0.5 & 0.5 \\ 0.5 & 0.5 \end{bmatrix}$. Show that $\mathbf{A}^m \neq \mathbf{0}$ for any m and is not close to the zero matrix even for large m.

b. Let $\mathbf{A} = \begin{bmatrix} 0.5 & 0.25 \\ 0 & 0.5 \end{bmatrix}$. Calculate $\mathbf{A}^2$, $\mathbf{A}^3$, and $\mathbf{A}^4$. Find $(\mathbf{I} - \mathbf{A})^{-1}$ exactly. Calculate $\mathbf{I} + \mathbf{A} + \mathbf{A}^2 + \mathbf{A}^3 + \mathbf{A}^4$. Compare the values.

15. (*The following problem is Problem 4 in the Additional Exercises, Teacher Resource Book, TEAM Learning Module, The Statue of Liberty, the Mathematical Association of America.*) When the project to repair the Statue of Liberty was begun in the early 1980s, much time was devoted to analyzing the statue's supporting structure (designed by Gustave Eiffel). Was it still strong enough to allow the statue to survive the horizontal and vertical forces it would encounter in very severe weather, sometimes called a "100-year storm"? In studying the head of the statue, for example, the supporting structure was assumed to consist of nine straight beams connected at 10 points (called *nodes*). The most severe weather conditions in the New York harbor area of the past century were studied. If h_3, h_5, h_8 represent the horizontal deflections and v_3, v_5, v_8 the vertical deflections at nodes number 3, 5, and 8 of the supporting structure of the head, structural analysis finds that the following 6×6 system relates h_3, h_5, h_8, v_3, v_5, and v_8 when node 8 experiences the severe weather forces:

$$\begin{bmatrix} 1.720 & 3.095 & -0.751 & -0.941 & 0.553 & -0.313 \\ 3.095 & 61.430 & -10.107 & -49.771 & 9.179 & -5.195 \\ -0.751 & -10.107 & 11.810 & 10.140 & -8.405 & 15.458 \\ -0.941 & -49.771 & 10.140 & 46.479 & -9.175 & 1.376 \\ 0.553 & 9.179 & -8.405 & -9.175 & 27.316 & 51.886 \\ -0.313 & -5.195 & 15.457 & 1.376 & 51.886 & 227.269 \end{bmatrix} \begin{bmatrix} h_3 \\ h_5 \\ h_8 \\ v_3 \\ v_5 \\ v_8 \end{bmatrix} = \begin{bmatrix} 0.6 \\ -0.6 \\ 0.4 \\ -0.5 \\ 0.2 \\ -1.1 \end{bmatrix}$$

Solve this system to find the deflections.

16. The Eastern Mining Company produces two grades of ore. Grade A contains 20% copper and 50% iron by weight. Grade B contains 30% copper and 25% iron by weight. How many tons of each grade should be sent to the refinery to fill the following orders exactly (without wasting any copper or iron)? You are not allowed to combine the orders!

a. 1000 tons of copper, 1000 tons of iron
b. 750 tons of copper, 1500 tons of iron
c. 2000 tons of copper, 3000 tons of iron
d. 1500 tons of copper, 500 tons of iron

Solve this problem using a single matrix product $\mathbf{A}^{-1}\mathbf{B}$.

17. Three major cities have submitted requests for government urban-renewal grants. The cities intend to allocate their grant monies as follows:

City	*Low-cost Housing*	*Job Programs*	*Other*
A	20%	50%	30%
B	40%	40%	20%
C	50%	10%	40%

The government has decided that no matter how much money is appropriated for renewal grants, 40% is to go toward low-cost housing and 30% toward job programs. How much should each city receive if the following sums are under consideration to be allocated for the grants?

a. \$120 million
b. \$180 million
c. \$75 million

Solve this problem using a single matrix product $\mathbf{A}^{-1}\mathbf{B}$.

18. Suppose we have found a tropical beetle with population matrix

$$\begin{bmatrix} 0 & 0 & 144 \\ 0.25 & 0 & 0 \\ 0 & 0.75 & 0 \end{bmatrix}$$

What age distribution of these beetles will sustain a stable population?

19. Suppose as budding ornithologists our study of the local population of ospreys shows the effects of DDT absorption: mated pairs are producing young less frequently and dying off before reaching 6 years of age. Our research leads to the following population matrix (the time cycle is 1 year);

$$\mathbf{W} = \begin{bmatrix} 0 & 0 & 1 & 1 & 0 \\ 0.60 & 0 & 0 & 0 & 0 \\ 0 & 0.65 & 0 & 0 & 0 \\ 0 & 0 & 0.65 & 0 & 0 \\ 0 & 0 & 0 & 0.50 & 0 \end{bmatrix}$$

a. What is the significance of our finding $p_0 = 0.60$?

b. If $\mathbf{x}_1 = (30, 40, 45, 40, 18)$, find $\mathbf{x}_2$. (One of your previous computer programs may help here.) Find $\mathbf{x}_4$ by finding $\mathbf{W}^3\mathbf{X}_1$.

c. What is your long-term prognosis for the health of the osprey population?

4 Vector Spaces

4.1 Vector Spaces, Subspaces

In Chapter 3, we saw that the answers to some important questions depend on the properties of sets of n-tuples and the operations of addition and scalar multiplication. These properties are shared by a number of mathematical systems called **linear vector spaces**, or **vector spaces**. Our main interest is in R^n, but we can understand R^n better if we look at other vector spaces as well.

A vector space is a set of objects (called vectors) together with two operations that involve these objects and satisfy certain properties. As you read Definition 1, you can think, for example, that the objects in V might be n-tuples of real numbers and the operations might be addition of n-tuples and multiplication of n-tuples by real numbers (scalars). Examples 2, 4, and 5 indicate that the objects in V might also be something quite different.

Vector Space over R

Definition 1

Let V be a nonempty set of objects called **vectors** and let R be the real numbers. (In this definition, capital letters denote elements of V and lowercase letters denote real numbers.) An operation called *addition*, written $A + B$, is defined for any two vectors in V. An operation called *scalar multiplication*, written cA, is defined for any scalar from R and any vector from V. The set V is a **vector space over R** provided that the following statements are true for all A, B, and C in V and all c and d in R.

1. $A + B$ is a vector in V (closure with respect to addition).
2. $A + B = B + A$ (commutative law of addition).
3. $(A + B) + C = A + (B + C)$ (associative law of addition).
4. There is a unique vector O in V such that $A + O = A$, for all A (additive identity).
5. Given A in V, there is a unique vector in V, call it $-A$, such that $A + (-A) = O$ (additive inverse).

6. cA is a vector in V (closure with respect to scalar multiplication).
7. $c(A + B) = cA + cB$ (scalar multiplication is distributive over vector addition).
8. $(c + d)A = cA + dA$ (scalar multiplication is distributive over scalar addition).
9. $c(dA) = (cd)A$ (scalar multiplication is associative).
10. $1A = A$ (identity property of the scalar 1).

For convenience, statements 4 and 5 in Definition 1 include the uniqueness of the additive identity and the additive inverse. This uniqueness can be proved using the other properties. You are asked to do this in Problems 22 and 23.

Example 1

The set of n-tuples, with the operations of addition and scalar multiplication defined in Chapter 1, is a vector space designated by R^n. The additive identity in this space is the vector $(0, 0, 0, \ldots, 0)$. The special case R^2 can be thought of as the xy plane, and the special case R^3 can be pictured as three-dimensional space. ■

Example 2

The set of $m \times n$ matrices with the operations of addition and scalar multiplication defined in Chapter 1 is a vector space designated by $M_{m \times n}$. If $m = 2$ and $n = 3$, the additive identity is $\begin{bmatrix} 0 & 0 & 0 \\ 0 & 0 & 0 \end{bmatrix}$, and the additive inverse of the vector

$$\mathbf{A} = \begin{bmatrix} 1 & 2 & 4 \\ -1 & 3 & 0 \end{bmatrix} \text{ is the vector } -\mathbf{A} = \begin{bmatrix} -1 & -2 & -4 \\ 1 & -3 & 0 \end{bmatrix}.$$

■

Example 3

The set of $m \times n$ matrices with *integer* entries is not a vector space. This set is closed with respect to addition but is not closed with respect to scalar multiplication, since, for example, $\pi\mathbf{A}$ is not a matrix with integer entries. ■

The following examples use polynomial functions rather than arrays of numbers as elements of a vector space. Examples from these spaces will be used from time to time to help clarify ideas.

Example 4

A polynomial is an expression of the form $a_0 + a_1x + a_2x^2 + \cdots + a_nx^n$. We assume that the coefficients $a_0, a_1, a_2, \ldots, a_n$ are real numbers. The exponent of the highest power of x for which the coefficient is not zero is called the degree of the polynomial. If a_0 is the only nonzero coefficient, the polynomial has degree 0. If all the coefficients are zero, the polynomial is called the zero polynomial and is written 0. Its degree is not defined.

Let $p_1 = a_0 + a_1x + a_2x^2 + \cdots + a_nx^n$ and $p_2 = b_0 + b_1x + b_2x^2 + \cdots + b_nx^n$. The polynomials are defined to be equal if and only if they are identical: that is, $p_1 = p_2$ if and only if $a_0 = b_0, a_1 = b_1, \ldots, a_n = b_n$. Polynomials are added by adding like terms:

$$p_1 + p_2 = (a_0 + b_0) + (a_1 + b_1)x + \cdots + (a_n + b_n)x^n$$

Multiplication of a polynomial by a scalar k yields a polynomial in which each coefficient is multiplied by k:

$$kp_1 = ka_0 + (ka_1)x + (ka_2)x^2 + \cdots + (ka_n)x^n$$

The set consisting of the zero polynomial and all polynomials of degree n or lower, with addition and scalar multiplication as defined above, constitutes a vector space. The notation P_n is frequently used to represent this space. ■

Example 4A In particular, consider the vector space P_2. This consists of all expressions of the form $a_0 + a_1x + a_2x^2$, in which a_0, a_1, a_2 are real numbers and any or all of them may have the value 0. Read Definition 1 with this set in mind. It is not hard to see that the statements are all true. For example, if $p_1 = 3 + x$ and $p_2 = 1 + x^2$, then $p_1 + p_2 = 4 + x + x^2$, an element of P_2. The additive identity in P_2 is the zero polynomial. The additive inverse of p_1 is $-3 - x$. ■

Example 4B A more general vector space involving polynomials is the set of *all* possible polynomials with no restriction on the degree of the polynomials included. This vector space is designated by P. ■

The following example describes a vector space in which the elements are functions that belong to a more general class.

Example 5 Let V be the set of continuous real-valued functions defined on some interval $[a, b]$ of the real line. Two functions are equal if and only if they are equal at every point in their domains: $f = g$ if and only if $f(x) = g(x)$ for each x in $[a, b]$. Addition and scalar multiplication are defined point-wise: $(f + g)(x) = f(x) + g(x)$ for each x in $[a, b]$ and $(kf)(x) = kf(x)$ for each x in $[a, b]$. The sum of two continuous functions is a continuous function, so the set is closed with respect to addition. A multiple of a continuous function is a continuous function, so the set is closed with respect to scalar multiplication. The other properties in Definition 1 can be verified using the properties of real numbers. The vector space is frequently designated by $C[a, b]$, or C. ■

The properties listed in Definition 1 imply some very convenient facts that appear obvious but still need to be justified.

Theorem 1 Let V be a vector space over R. If A is an element of V and c is any element of R, then

1. $cO = O$; any scalar times the vector O is the vector O.
2. $0A = O$; the scalar 0 times the vector A is the vector O.
3. $(-1)A = -A$; the scalar -1 times the vector A is the vector $-A$, the additive inverse of A.

Proof

1.

$cA = c(A + O)$	Property 4
$cA = cA + cO$	Property 7
$-cA + cA = -cA + (cA + cO)$	Add the additive inverse of cA to both sides.
$O = (-cA + cA) + cO$	Properties 3 and 5
$O = O + cO$	Property 5
$O = cO$	Property 4

2.

$0A + A = 0A + 1A$	Property 10
$= (0 + 1)A$	Property 8
$= 1A$	
$0A + A = A$	Property 10
$0A = O$	Property 4

3.

$(-1)A + A = (-1)A + 1A$	Property 10
$= (-1 + 1)A$	Property 8
$= 0A$	
$= O$	Part 2

$(-1)A + A = O$ implies $(-1)A = -A$ by Property 5. □

The solution set of a linear system of equations in n unknowns is a set of n-tuples, and hence a subset of R^n. This subset may have some or all of the properties listed in Definition 1. This raises the question: given a subset of a vector space V, will the properties of V listed in Definition 1 still hold for this subset? In Definition 1, statements 2, 3, and 7–10 are properties of addition and scalar multiplication that are true for any choice of vectors in V and therefore are true for any choice of vectors in a subset of V. Statements 1, 4, 5, and 6 are somewhat different. Example 6 discusses these statements for two subsets of R^3.

Example 6

Two subsets of R^3 are defined as follows: S_1 = all triples of the form $(a, b, 0)$, and S_2 = all triples of the form $(a, b, 1)$. We investigate statements 1, 4, 5, and 6 of Definition 1 for each of these:

S_1: *All Triples of the Form* $(a, b, 0)$	S_2: *All Triples of the Form* $(a, b, 1)$
1. *True* since $(a_1, b_1, 0) + (a_2, b_2, 0) = (a_1 + a_2, b_1 + b_2, 0)$ which is an element of S_1.	1. *False* since $(a_1, b_1, 1) + (a_2, b_2, 1) = (a_1 + a_2, b_1 + b_2, 2)$ which is not an element of S_2.
4. *True* since $(0, 0, 0)$ belongs to S_1	4. *False* since $(0, 0, 0)$ does not belong to S_2.
5. *True* since $(a, b, 0)$ and $(-a, -b, 0)$ both belong to S_1.	5. *False*; $(a, b, 1)$ belongs to S_2, but its additive inverse $(-a, -b, -1)$ does not belong to S_2.
6. *True* since $k(a, b, 0) = (ka, kb, 0)$, which belongs to S_1 for all k.	6. *False* since $k(a, b, 1) = (ka, kb, k)$, which does not belong to S_2 if $k \neq 1$.

The subset S_1 is a vector space. That the subset S_2 is not a vector space is shown by any *one* of these false statements. ■

In this example we could have avoided testing 4 and 5, since if 6 is true, 4 follows using $k = 0$ and 5 follows using $k = -1$ (Theorem 1).

Example 6 shows that a subset of a vector space may or may not be itself a vector space. Subsets of vector spaces that are vector spaces are called subspaces. In Example 6, S_1 is a subspace of R^3; S_2 is a subset but not a subspace.

Subspace

Definition 2

Let V be a vector space over the real numbers and let S be a nonempty subset of V. Define the operations in S to be the same as those in V. If S is also a vector space over the real numbers, S is called a **subspace** of V.

In the vector space V, the subset consisting of only the zero vector is a subspace. It is contained in every subspace of V, so it can be thought of as the smallest subspace of V. On the other hand, the space V is a subspace of itself. Since every other subspace is contained in V, it is the largest subspace of V.

Theorem 2 helps identify whether or not a particular subset is also a subspace.

Theorem 2 A nonempty subset S of a vector space is a subspace if and only if it is closed with respect to both addition and scalar multiplication.

Proof Since S is a subset of a vector space, properties 2, 3, and 7–10 are satisfied. If S is closed with respect to addition and scalar multiplication, S also has properties 1 and 6. Theorem 1 then implies that if A is in S, $0A$ is the zero vector, and $(-1)A = -A$. Because of property 6, $0A$ and $-A$ are in S, so that properties 4 and 5 are satisfied.

Conversely, if S is a subspace it is also a vector space and properties 1–10 are satisfied. In particular, properties 1 and 6 are satisfied.

Thus, S is a subspace of a vector space if and only if it is closed with respect to both addition and scalar multiplication. □

Example 7 The set T of polynomials of the form $a_0 + a_2x^2$ is a subspace of P_2. Notice that T is nonempty, since, for example, x^2 is in T. It is a subset of P_2 since every element of T is in P_2. To determine whether or not T is a subspace of P_2, we must investigate whether or not T is closed with respect to addition and scalar multiplication. Let $p_1 = a_0 + a_2x^2$ and $p_2 = b_0 + b_2x^2$. Is $p_1 + p_2$ again a polynomial in P_2 without an x term?

$$\begin{aligned} p_1 + p_2 &= a_0 + a_2x^2 + b_0 + b_2x^2 \\ &= (a_0 + b_0) + (a_2 + b_2)x^2 \end{aligned}$$

Thus, $p_1 + p_2$ also belongs to the subset.

Similarly, for any scalar c, $cp_1 = ca_0 + ca_2x^2$ and this too belongs to T. The set of polynomials of the form $a_0 + a_2x^2$ *is* a subspace of P_2. ■

Since every subspace of a vector space must contain the zero vector, it is sometimes possible to see that a given subset is *not* a subspace by noticing that it does not contain the zero vector.

Example 8 The set of polynomials of the form $1 + ax$ is not a subspace of P_2, since it does not contain the polynomial 0. The set of triples of the form $(a, 1 + a, a)$ is not a subspace of R^3, since no value of a can make both a and $1 + a$ zero, so the set does not include the triple $(0, 0, 0)$. The set of pairs of the form $(0, a)$, where a is an integer, does contain the zero vector, but it is not a subspace of R^2, since it is not closed with respect to scalar multiplication. ■

Example 9 Let $\mathbf{A}$ be an $m \times n$ matrix. The set of solutions of the homogeneous system of equations $\mathbf{AX} = \mathbf{0}$ is a subspace of R^n. To see this, let $\mathbf{X}_1$ and $\mathbf{X}_2$ be any two solutions, that is, $\mathbf{AX}_1 = \mathbf{0}$ and $\mathbf{AX}_2 = \mathbf{0}$. Since $\mathbf{A}(\mathbf{X}_1 + \mathbf{X}_2) = \mathbf{AX}_1 + \mathbf{AX}_2 = \mathbf{0} + \mathbf{0} = \mathbf{0}$, $\mathbf{X}_1 + \mathbf{X}_2$ is also a solution and the set is closed with respect to addition. Similarly, if $\mathbf{X}_0$ is a solution of $\mathbf{AX} = \mathbf{0}$, then $\mathbf{A}(k\mathbf{X}_0) = k\mathbf{AX}_0 = k\mathbf{0} = \mathbf{0}$. The set of solutions is closed with respect to scalar multiplication. By Theorem 2, the set of solutions of the homogeneous system $\mathbf{AX} = \mathbf{0}$ is a subspace of R^n. ■

Example 10 The functions $f(x) = \sin x$ and $g(x) = \cos x$ are continuous real-valued functions and therefore belong to the space C defined in Example 5. Now consider the subset of C made up of all linear combinations of $\sin x$ and $\cos x$. The elements of this subset have the form $c_1 \sin x + c_2 \cos x$, where c_1 and c_2 are real numbers. This set is closed with respect to addition, since $(c_1 \sin x + c_2 \cos x) + (d_1 \sin x + d_2 \cos x) = (c_1 + d_1)\sin x + (c_2 + d_2)\cos x$, an element of the set. Also, since $k(c_1 \sin x + c_2 \cos x) = kc_1 \sin x + kc_2 \cos x$, the set is closed with respect to scalar multiplication. Thus the set of all linear combinations of $\sin x$ and $\cos x$ is a subspace of C. ■

Every subspace of a vector space V must be a subset of V. Notice that P_2 is a subspace of P_n for each $n \geqslant 2$. Also, P_n is a subspace of the space of continuous functions defined on the whole real line. However, R^2 is not a subspace of R^3. The elements of R^2 are pairs and the elements of R^3 are triples. The set of triples of the form $(a, b, 0)$ is a subspace of R^3, and is "very like" R^2. The mathematical expression *isomorphic to* gives an accurate description of this likeness. (See Problem 19.)

The following example describes subspaces of R^3 and how they can be visualized geometrically. Related examples occur in later sections of this chapter.

Example 11

a. The subspace S_0 of R^3 consisting of the triple $(0, 0, 0)$ is the smallest subspace. Geometrically we can think of this as a single point—the origin.
b. Let S_1 be the set of triples of the form $(a, -2a, 3a)$, where a is any real number.

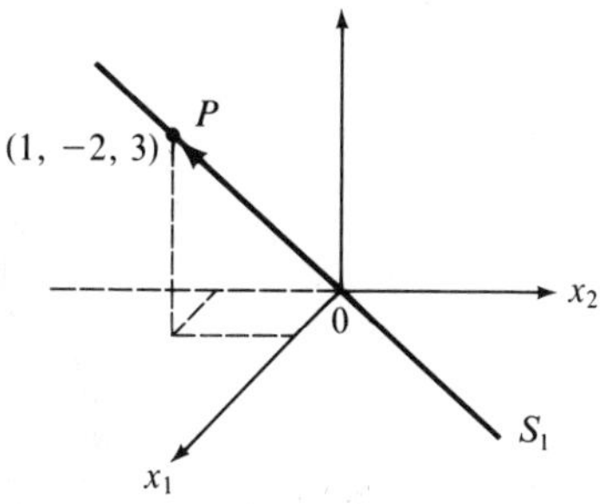

FIGURE 4.1

Use Theorem 2 to see whether S_1 is a subspace:

1. $(a, -2a, 3a) + (b, -2b, 3b) = ((a + b), -2(a + b), 3(a + b))$. This shows that addition of triples of the given form produces a triple of the same form, so the set is closed with respect to addition.
2. $k(a, -2a, 3a) = (ka, -2ka, 3ka)$. Multiplication by a scalar produces a triple of the same form, so the set is closed under scalar multiplication. By Theorem 1, S_1 is a subspace of R^3.

Another way of describing S_1 is: $S_1 = \{a(1, -2, 3), a \text{ a real number}\}$; that is, S_1 is the set of multiples of the triple $\mathbf{u} = (1, -2, 3)$. If we use the geometric vector OP to represent $\mathbf{u}$, S_1 is the set of all vectors on the line containing OP. A representation of the subspace S_1 is then a line through the origin in three-space. (Figure 4.1.)

A similar subspace can be defined using any nonzero triple in place of $\mathbf{u}$. Given any $\mathbf{u}$, a set of the form $\{k\mathbf{u}, k \text{ a real number}\}$ is a subspace of R^3 corresponding to the line through the origin. Conversely, any line through the origin can be described in this way and represents a subspace of R^3. A line not through the origin is not a subspace since it does not contain O and is not closed with respect to addition or scalar multiplication.

c. Now consider the set S_2 consisting of all triples in R^3 that are orthogonal to a fixed triple, for example, $\mathbf{u} = (1, -2, 3)$. Any triple $\mathbf{x} = (x_1, x_2, x_3)$ that belongs to the set can be described by the equation $\mathbf{u} \cdot \mathbf{x} = 0$. To show that S_2 is a subspace, we again use Theorem 1. If $\mathbf{v}$ and $\mathbf{w}$ are any two triples in S_2, we know $\mathbf{u} \cdot \mathbf{v} = 0$ and $\mathbf{u} \cdot \mathbf{w} = 0$. But $\mathbf{u} \cdot (\mathbf{v} + \mathbf{w}) = \mathbf{u} \cdot \mathbf{v} + \mathbf{u} \cdot \mathbf{w} = 0 + 0 = 0$, so $\mathbf{v} + \mathbf{w}$ belongs to S_2, and S_2 is closed with respect to addition. Also if k is any scalar and $\mathbf{v}$ a triple in S_2, then $\mathbf{u} \cdot (k\mathbf{v}) = k(\mathbf{u} \cdot \mathbf{v}) = k(0) = 0$; so $k\mathbf{v}$ belongs to S_2, whence S_2 is closed with respect to scalar multiplication. S_2 is a subspace of R^3. (See Figure 4.2.)

The equation $\mathbf{u} \cdot \mathbf{x} = 0$ can be written as $\mathbf{u} \cdot (\mathbf{x} - \mathbf{0}) = 0$, which is the equation of a plane through the origin perpendicular to the vector $\mathbf{u}$. In this case, $\mathbf{u} = (1, -2, 3)$, but a similar subspace could be defined using any vector $\mathbf{u} = (a, b, c)$. The set of all vectors orthogonal to a vector $\mathbf{u}$ is a subspace of R^3

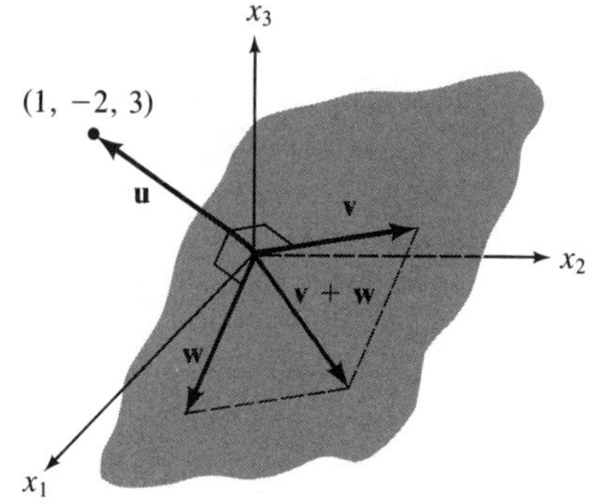

FIGURE 4.2

represented by a plane through the origin. Conversely, any plane through the origin represents a subspace in R^3.

d. The set of all triples—that is, R^3—is a subspace of itself (the "largest" possible subspace). ■

Four types of subspaces of R^3 are described in Example 11. Are these the only possible subspaces? Can they be classified in a way that does not depend on geometric considerations so that the subspaces of R^n can be identified in a similar way?

The sections that follow relate to these questions. Example 12 shows how the same subspace of R^3 can be described in a variety of ways.

Example 12 S_2 is the set of triples $\mathbf{x} = (x_1, x_2, x_3)$ such that $\mathbf{x} \cdot \mathbf{u} = 0$, where $\mathbf{u} = (1, -2, 3)$. This set can be described in several ways.

1. S_2 is the set of triples $\mathbf{x}$ such that $\mathbf{x} \cdot \mathbf{u} = 0$.

Write out $\mathbf{x} \cdot \mathbf{u} = 0$ explicitly.

2. S_2 is the solution set of the equation $x_1 - 2x_2 + 3x_3 = 0$.

In matrix form, this is the equation $\mathbf{AX} = \mathbf{0}$, where $\mathbf{A} = [1 \;\; -2 \;\; 3]$. The solution set of $\mathbf{AX} = \mathbf{0}$ is $\{\mathbf{x} = k_1(2, 1, 0) + k_2(-3, 0, 1),\ k_1, k_2 \text{ real numbers}\}$.

3. S_2 is the set of all linear combinations of the two vectors $(2, 1, 0)$ and $(-3, 0, 1)$.

Now write the linear combination in statement 3 as a single vector.

4. S_2 is the set of all triples of the form $(2k_1 - 3k_2, k_1, k_2)$, where k_1 and k_2 are real numbers. ■

Section 4.2 deals with subspaces defined as linear combinations of given vectors, as in statement 3 of Example 12.

SUMMARY Definition 1 lists the properties of the general mathematical system called a vector space. An important vector space is R^n, in which the vectors are n-tuples of real numbers and addition and scalar multiplication are defined as in Chapter 1.

The vector space P_n is the set of all polynomials of the form $a_0 + a_1x + a_2x^2 + \cdots + a_nx^n$, in which the coefficients are real numbers. Addition and multiplication of a polynomial by a scalar are defined pointwise.

The vector space $M_{m\times n}$ is the set of all $m \times n$ matrices with operations addition and scalar multiplication.

Certain nonempty subsets of a vector space also satisfy the definition of a vector space. Such subsets are called subspaces. A nonempty subset of V is a subspace if it is closed with respect to addition and scalar multiplication.

EXERCISES 4.1

1. Write the zero vector in each of the following vector spaces:
a. R^2 **b.** R^4
c. $M_{2\times 3}$ (defined in Example 2)
d. P_3 (defined in Example 4)

2. In each case, write the additive inverse:
a. $(3, -1)$ in R^2 **b.** $(-1, 0, -1, 0)$ in R^4
c. $\begin{bmatrix} 1 & 3 & -2 \\ 0 & -1 & -3 \end{bmatrix}$ in $M_{2\times 3}$
d. $3 - 4x + 2x^2 - 5x^3$ in P_3

3. a. Show that the set of triples $(a, a, -a)$, where a is a real number, is a subspace of R^3.
b. Show that the set of triples $(a, 1, -a)$ is not a subspace of R^3.
c. Is the set of triples $(a, b, -a)$ a subspace of R^3, where a and b are any real numbers?

4. a. Show that the set of polynomials $a_0 + a_1(x + 1)$ is a subspace of P_2.
b. Show that the set of polynomials $a_0 + x + 1$ is not a subspace of P_2.
c. Is the set of polynomials $a_0 + x$ a subspace of P_2?

5. Let S be the set of 3×3 symmetric matrices. Show that S is a subspace of $M_{3\times 3}$.

6. a. Let S be the set of 3×3 upper triangular matrices. Is S a subspace of $M_{3\times 3}$?
b. Let T be the set of all 3×3 triangular matrices. Is T a subspace of $M_{3\times 3}$?

7. a. Is the vector space P_2 a subspace of the vector P_3? Why or why not?
b. Is the vector space $M_{3\times 2}$ a subspace of the vector space $M_{3\times 3}$? Why or why not?

8. In each case is the given subset of P_2 a subspace? Give a reason for your answer.
a. All polynomials of the form ax^2, where a is a real number.
b. All polynomials of the form $b + x^2$, b a real number.
c. All polynomials of degree $\leqslant 2$ and with integral coefficients.

9. a. Is the set of 4-tuples of the form $(x_1, x_2, 0, 0)$, x_1 and x_2 real numbers, a subspace of R^4?
b. Is the set of 5-tuples of the form $(1, x_2, x_3, x_4, x_5)$ where x_2, x_3, x_4, x_5 are real numbers, a subspace of R^5?

10. Which of the following sets are subspaces of R^3? Give a reason for your answer.
a. The triples (a, b, c), where a, b, and c are real numbers and $c = 2a - b$.
b. The triples (a, b, c), where a, b and c are real numbers and $ab = c^2$.
c. The triples (a, b, c), where a, b, and c are real numbers and $a + b + c = 4$.

11. a. Explain why the following statement is true: If A belongs to a subspace S, then kA belongs to S for every scalar k.
b. Show that if a subspace of V contains a nonzero vector, it must contain an infinite set of vectors. Can there be a subspace with exactly two distinct vectors?

12. Suppose A and B belong to a subspace S. What can be said of all linear combinations of the vectors A and B? Explain your answer.

13. a. Show that the set consisting of a single vector, the n-tuple $\mathbf{0}$, is a subspace of R^n.
    b. Let S and T be subspaces of R^n. What vector must be common to S and T? Can there be more than one vector common to S and T?

14. Let: S_1 be the set of triples $\{(x_1, 0, 0),\ x_1$ a real number$\}$; S_2 be the set of triples $\{(0, x_2, 0),\ x_2$ a real number$\}$; S_3 be the set of triples $\{(0, x_2, x_3),\ x_2, x_3$ real numbers$\}$.
    a. What vectors are common to S_1 and S_2—that is, in $S_1 \cap S_2$?
    b. What vectors are common to S_1 and S_3?
    c. What vectors are common to S_2 and S_3?

15. If S and T are subspaces of R^n, show that $S \cap T$ must also be a subspace of R^n.

16. The set $S \cup T$ consists of all vectors that are in S and all vectors in T. If S and T are subspaces of R^n, show that $S \cup T$ is not necessarily a subspace of R^n.

17. In each case construct subspaces S and T of R^3 with the indicated properties: S and T should each have an infinite set of vectors.
    a. $S \cap T$ contains only the zero vector.
    b. $S \cap T$ is an infinite subspace different from S and from T.
    c. S is a subset of T.

18. a. Let $\mathbf{u} = (1, 2, 1)$ and $\mathbf{x}_0 = (3, 1, 4)$. Show that the line in R^3 given by $\mathbf{x} = k\mathbf{u} + \mathbf{x}_0$ is not a subspace of R^3.
    b. Show that the plane with equation $2x_1 + 3x_2 + x_3 = 7$ is not a subspace of R^3.

19. Two sets A and B are said to be isomorphic if there is a one-to-one pairing of the elements of the sets which has the property that if a_1 is paired with b_1 and a_2 is paired with b_2, then $a_1 * a_2$ is paired with $b_1 * b_2$ for every operation $*$ defined on the sets.
    a. Set up a one-to-one correspondence between the subspace of R^3 consisting of triples of the form $(x_1, x_2, 0)$ and the space R^2, which has the properties of an isomorphism.
    b. Show that with your correspondence if $\mathbf{u}_1$ corresponds to $\mathbf{v}_1$ and $\mathbf{u}_2$ corresponds to $\mathbf{v}_2$, then $\mathbf{u}_1 + \mathbf{u}_2$ corresponds to $\mathbf{v}_1 + \mathbf{v}_2$.
    c. Show that your correspondence is preserved under scalar multiplication.

20. Show that R^2 is isomorphic to the subspace of R^3 consisting of all triples of the form $(5a - 3b, a, b)$.

21. Show that P_2 is isomorphic to R^3.

*22. In part 4 of Definition 1, the zero vector O of a vector space V was assumed to be unique. Show, in fact, that if O and O' are two (perhaps different) vectors in V, each with the property of being a zero vector in V, then $O = O'$.

*23. In part 5 of Definition 1, it was assumed that each vector A in V has a unique additive inverse $-A$. Show, in fact, that if $-A$ and $-A'$ are two (perhaps different) vectors in V, each with the property of being an additive inverse of a vector A, then $-A = -A'$.

4.2 Spanning Set, Linear Independence, Basis

In Section 4.1, there are examples in which a subspace of a vector space V is described as the set of all possible linear combinations of a finite set of vectors from V. (See Examples 10, 11(b), and 12.) In the following theorem we see that, given any vector space V and a set of k vectors from V, the set S of all linear combinations of these vectors is a subspace of V.

Throughout the rest of this book we use the more convenient notation $\mathbf{u}_i$ to represent a vector in a general finite-dimensional vector space, as well as a vector in R^n.

Theorem 3 Let $\{\mathbf{u}_1, \mathbf{u}_2, \ldots, \mathbf{u}_k\}$ be a nonempty set of vectors in the vector space V. The set S of all possible linear combinations of $\{\mathbf{u}_1, \mathbf{u}_2, \ldots, \mathbf{u}_k\}$ is a subspace of V.

Proof Since $\mathbf{u}_1$ belongs to S, S is nonempty. Any two vectors can be written in the form

$$\mathbf{v} = a_1\mathbf{u}_1 + a_2\mathbf{u}_2 + \cdots + a_k\mathbf{u}_k \quad \text{and} \quad \mathbf{w} = b_1\mathbf{u}_1 + b_2\mathbf{u}_2 + \cdots + b_k\mathbf{u}_k$$

From this it follows that

$$\mathbf{v} + \mathbf{w} = (a_1 + b_1)\mathbf{u}_1 + (a_2 + b_2)\mathbf{u}_2 + \cdots + (a_k + b_k)\mathbf{u}_k$$

which is a linear combination of $\{\mathbf{u}_1, \mathbf{u}_2, \ldots, \mathbf{u}_k\}$ and belongs to S. Also $c\mathbf{v} = ca_1\mathbf{u}_1 + ca_2\mathbf{u}_2 + \cdots + ca_k\mathbf{u}_k$, a linear combination of $\{\mathbf{u}_1, \mathbf{u}_2, \ldots, \mathbf{u}_k\}$, belongs to S. Hence S is closed with respect to addition and scalar multiplication and is a subspace of V (Theorem 2). □

Definition 3

Space Spanned by $\{\mathbf{u}_1, \mathbf{u}_2, \ldots, \mathbf{u}_k\}$
Spanning Set
Span

Let $\{\mathbf{u}_1, \mathbf{u}_2, \ldots, \mathbf{u}_k\}$ be vectors from the vector space V. The set of all vectors of the form $c_1\mathbf{u}_1 + c_2\mathbf{u}_2 + \cdots + c_k\mathbf{u}_k$, where $c_1, c_2, \ldots, c_k$ are scalars, is a vector space called the **space spanned by** $\{\mathbf{u}_1, \mathbf{u}_2, \ldots, \mathbf{u}_k\}$. The notation $\operatorname{lin}\{\mathbf{u}_1, \mathbf{u}_2, \ldots, \mathbf{u}_k\}$ is used to represent this space.

A set $\{\mathbf{u}_1, \mathbf{u}_2, \ldots, \mathbf{u}_k\}$ is called a **spanning set** for a vector space V if every $\mathbf{v}$ in V can be written as $\mathbf{v} = c_1\mathbf{u}_1 + c_2\mathbf{u}_2 + \cdots + c_k\mathbf{u}_k$ where $c_1, c_2, \ldots, c_k$ are scalars. We say that the set $\{\mathbf{u}_1, \mathbf{u}_2, \ldots, \mathbf{u}_k\}$ **spans** V.

A spanning set for a vector space S gives us a way of writing any vector in S in terms of a finite set of vectors $\{\mathbf{u}_1, \mathbf{u}_2, \ldots, \mathbf{u}_k\}$. A given vector $\mathbf{v}$ belongs to S if and only if it can be written in the form $c_1\mathbf{u}_1 + c_2\mathbf{u}_2 + c_3\mathbf{u}_3 + \cdots + c_k\mathbf{u}_k$. Note that $\{\mathbf{u}_1, \mathbf{u}_2, \ldots, \mathbf{u}_k\}$ is a spanning set for $\operatorname{lin}\{\mathbf{u}_1, \mathbf{u}_2, \ldots, \mathbf{u}_k\}$.

Example 13 Let $\mathbf{v} = (2, 5, -6, 4)$. Does $\mathbf{v}$ belong to the space spanned by $\{\mathbf{u}_1, \mathbf{u}_2, \mathbf{u}_3\}$, where $\mathbf{u}_1 = (1, 2, -1, 1)$, $\mathbf{u}_2 = (0, 1, -4, 2)$, and $\mathbf{u}_3 = (1, 1, 3, -1)$? This question is the same as: Is $\mathbf{v}$ a linear combination of $\mathbf{u}_1, \mathbf{u}_2, \mathbf{u}_3$? This, in turn, is equivalent to: Can we find c_1, c_2, c_3 so that the following is true?

$$(2, 5, -6, 4) = c_1(1, 2, -1, 1) + c_2(0, 1, -4, 2) + c_3(1, 1, 3, -1)$$

or

$$(2, 5, -6, 4) = (c_1 + 0c_2 + c_3, 2c_1 + c_2 + c_3, -c_1 - 4c_2 + 3c_3, c_1 + 2c_2 - c_3)$$

This single vector equation represents four simultaneous equations (one for each element of the 4-tuples):

$$\begin{aligned} c_1 + 0c_2 + c_3 &= 2 \\ 2c_1 + c_2 + c_3 &= 5 \\ -c_1 - 4c_2 + 3c_3 &= -6 \\ c_1 + 2c_2 - c_3 &= 4 \end{aligned}$$

Thus, answering the question "Does **v** belong to the space spanned by $\{\mathbf{u}_1, \mathbf{u}_2, \mathbf{u}_3\}$?" is equivalent to solving the system of equations $\mathbf{AC} = \mathbf{V}$, where the columns of **A** are the 4-tuples $\mathbf{u}_1, \mathbf{u}_2, \mathbf{u}_3$ and **V** is the particular vector in question.

Row reduction of the augmented matrix gives

$$\left[\begin{array}{ccc|c} 1 & 0 & 1 & 2 \\ 2 & 1 & 1 & 5 \\ -1 & -4 & 3 & -6 \\ 1 & 2 & -1 & 4 \end{array}\right] \Leftrightarrow \left[\begin{array}{ccc|c} 1 & 0 & 1 & 2 \\ 0 & 1 & -1 & 1 \\ 0 & -4 & 4 & -4 \\ 0 & 2 & -2 & 2 \end{array}\right] \Leftrightarrow \left[\begin{array}{ccc|c} 1 & 0 & 1 & 2 \\ 0 & 1 & -1 & 1 \\ 0 & 0 & 0 & 0 \\ 0 & 0 & 0 & 0 \end{array}\right]$$

The equations are consistent and have an infinite solution set. For example, $c_1 = 1$, $c_2 = 2$, and $c_3 = 1$ is a possible solution, so that $\mathbf{v} = \mathbf{u}_1 + 2\mathbf{u}_2 + \mathbf{u}_3$. Because the equations have a solution, the answer to the original question is: Yes, **v** belongs to the space spanned by $\{\mathbf{u}_1, \mathbf{u}_2, \mathbf{u}_3\}$.

Does the set $\{\mathbf{u}_1, \mathbf{u}_2, \mathbf{u}_3\}$ span all of R^4? This is equivalent to the question: Can we find c_1, c_2, c_3 such that the following is true?

$$(a_1, a_2, a_3, a_4) = c_1(1, 2, -1, 1) + c_2(0, 1, -4, 2) + c_3(1, 1, 3, -1)$$

where (a_1, a_2, a_3, a_4) represents *any* vector in R^4.

This is the question: Can we solve $\mathbf{AC} = \mathbf{V}$ for all **V** in R^4? Row reduction gives

$$\left[\begin{array}{ccc|c} 1 & 0 & 1 & a_1 \\ 2 & 1 & 1 & a_2 \\ -1 & -4 & 3 & a_3 \\ 1 & 2 & -1 & a_4 \end{array}\right] \Leftrightarrow \left[\begin{array}{ccc|c} 1 & 0 & 1 & a_1 \\ 0 & 1 & -1 & a_2 - 2a_1 \\ 0 & 0 & 0 & a_3 + 4a_2 - 7a_1 \\ 0 & 0 & 0 & a_4 - 2a_2 + 3a_1 \end{array}\right]$$

These equations are inconsistent unless $a_3 + 4a_2 - 7a_1 = 0$ and $a_4 - 2a_2 + 3a_1 = 0$. The set $\{\mathbf{u}_1, \mathbf{u}_2, \mathbf{u}_3\}$ is not a spanning set for R^4. ■

In general, given a set of vectors $\{\mathbf{u}_1, \mathbf{u}_2, \ldots, \mathbf{u}_k\}$, the question "Does **v** belong to lin $\{\mathbf{u}_1, \mathbf{u}_2, \ldots, \mathbf{u}_k\}$?" is equivalent to the question "Can we find $c_1, c_2, \ldots, c_k$ such that $c_1\mathbf{u}_1 + c_2\mathbf{u}_2 + \cdots + c_k\mathbf{u}_k = \mathbf{v}$?" The technique for answering this question depends on the vector space involved.

Example 14 Let $p_1 = 1 + x$, $p_2 = 1 - x$, $p_3 = 1 + 2x$, and $p = 4 + 3x$. Does p belong to the space spanned by $\{p_1, p_2, p_3\}$? This question is the same as the question: Can we find c_1, c_2, and c_3 so that $c_1p_1 + c_2p_2 + c_3p_3 = p$? This can be written as

$$(c_1 + c_2 + c_3) + (c_1 - c_2 + 2c_3)x = 4 + 3x$$

The definition of equality of polynomials gives the pair of equations

$$\begin{aligned} c_1 + c_2 + c_3 &= 4 \\ c_1 - c_2 + 2c_3 &= 3 \end{aligned}$$

which brings us to the familiar procedures of Chapter 2.

$$\left[\begin{array}{rrr|r} 1 & 1 & 1 & 4 \\ 1 & -1 & 2 & 3 \end{array}\right] \Leftrightarrow \left[\begin{array}{rrr|r} 1 & 0 & \frac{3}{2} & \frac{7}{2} \\ 0 & 1 & -\frac{1}{2} & \frac{1}{2} \end{array}\right]$$

The equation has an infinite set of solutions, so p does lie in the space spanned by $\{p_1, p_2, p_3\}$. ■

A spanning set for a particular space is not unique. Suppose S is spanned by $\{\mathbf{u}_1, \mathbf{u}_2, \ldots, \mathbf{u}_k\}$. Let $\mathbf{v}_1 = \mathbf{u}_1 + \mathbf{u}_2$. Then $\{\mathbf{v}_1, \mathbf{u}_2, \ldots, \mathbf{u}_k\}$ also spans the space since a vector $\mathbf{w}$ is of the form $\mathbf{w} = c_1\mathbf{u}_1 + c_2\mathbf{u}_2 + \cdots + c_k\mathbf{u}_k$ if and only if it is also of the form $\mathbf{w} = c_1(\mathbf{u}_1 + \mathbf{u}_2) + (c_2 - c_1)\mathbf{u}_2 + \cdots + c_k\mathbf{u}_k$; that is, $\mathbf{w} = c_1\mathbf{v}_1 + (c_2 - c_1)\mathbf{u}_2 + \cdots + c_k\mathbf{u}_k$.

We can decrease the number of vectors in the spanning set by removing from the set any vectors not really needed. Suppose, for example, that $\mathbf{u}_k$ is a linear combination of $\{\mathbf{u}_1, \mathbf{u}_2, \ldots, \mathbf{u}_{k-1}\}$. Every vector that is a linear combination of $\{\mathbf{u}_1, \mathbf{u}_2, \ldots, \mathbf{u}_k\}$ is also a linear combination of $\{\mathbf{u}_1, \mathbf{u}_2, \ldots, \mathbf{u}_{k-1}\}$. Example 15 illustrates this idea.

Example 15

In Example 13, the set spanned by $\{\mathbf{u}_1, \mathbf{u}_2, \mathbf{u}_3\}$ was defined, where $\mathbf{u}_1 = (1, 2, -1, 1)$, $\mathbf{u}_2 = (0, 1, -4, 2)$, and $\mathbf{u}_3 = (1, 1, 3, -1)$. Since $\mathbf{u}_3 = \mathbf{u}_1 - \mathbf{u}_2$, $\mathbf{u}_3$ is a linear combination of $\mathbf{u}_1$ and $\mathbf{u}_2$. If $\mathbf{v} = c_1\mathbf{u}_1 + c_2\mathbf{u}_2 + c_3\mathbf{u}_3$, we can also write $\mathbf{v} = (c_1 + c_3)\mathbf{u}_1 + (c_2 - c_3)\mathbf{u}_2$. Thus, the space spanned by $\{\mathbf{u}_1, \mathbf{u}_2, \mathbf{u}_3\}$ is also spanned by $\{\mathbf{u}_1, \mathbf{u}_2\}$, since every vector in the space is a linear combination of $\mathbf{u}_1, \mathbf{u}_2$. Thus $\operatorname{lin}\{\mathbf{u}_1, \mathbf{u}_2, \mathbf{u}_3\} \subseteq \operatorname{lin}\{\mathbf{u}_1, \mathbf{u}_2\}$. Also, if $\mathbf{v} = c_1\mathbf{u}_1 + c_2\mathbf{u}_2$, we can write $\mathbf{v} = c_1\mathbf{u}_1 + c_2\mathbf{u}_2 + 0\mathbf{u}_3$, so that $\operatorname{lin}\{\mathbf{u}_1, \mathbf{u}_2\} \subseteq \operatorname{lin}\{\mathbf{u}_1, \mathbf{u}_2, \mathbf{u}_3\}$. In this example, then, $\operatorname{lin}\{\mathbf{u}_1, \mathbf{u}_2, \mathbf{u}_3\} = \operatorname{lin}\{\mathbf{u}_1, \mathbf{u}_2\}$.

Consider the space spanned by $p_1 = 1 + x + x^2$, $p_2 = 1 + x$, $p_3 = x^2$. Here $p_1 = p_2 + p_3$. A vector in $\operatorname{lin}\{p_1, p_2, p_3\}$ has the form $c_1p_1 + c_2p_2 + c_3p_3$ and can also be written in the form $(c_1 + c_2)p_2 + (c_1 + c_3)p_3$, so that $\operatorname{lin}\{p_1, p_2, p_3\} \subseteq \operatorname{lin}\{p_2, p_3\}$. Since $\operatorname{lin}\{p_2, p_3\} \subseteq \operatorname{lin}\{p_1, p_2, p_3\}$, this implies $\operatorname{lin}\{p_1, p_2, p_3\} = \operatorname{lin}\{p_2, p_3\}$. Some simple algebra also shows that we could write $c_1p_1 + c_2p_2 + c_3p_3 = (c_1 + c_2)p_1 + (c_3 - c_2)p_3$, so that $\operatorname{lin}\{p_1, p_2, p_3\} = \operatorname{lin}\{p_1, p_3\}$. Could we use a single vector in the spanning set? Not in this case, since the space spanned by the vector p_1, for example, would consist only of multiples of p_1. Neither p_2 nor p_3 is a multiple of p_1. Thus, in this case, the minimum number of vectors needed in the spanning set is 2. ■

The simplest and most efficient spanning set for a space would certainly be one that has as few vectors in it as possible. There are more vectors than needed when one is a linear combination of the others. This happens when there is a linear relation of the form $c_1\mathbf{u}_1 + c_2\mathbf{u}_2 + \cdots + c_k\mathbf{u}_k = \mathbf{0}$ in which not all the coefficients $c_1, c_2, \ldots, c_k$ are zero. If $c_1 \neq 0$, for example, we can solve for $\mathbf{u}_1$ and write $\mathbf{u}_1 = -(c_2/c_1)\mathbf{u}_2 - (c_3/c_1)\mathbf{u}_3 - \cdots - (c_k/c_1)\mathbf{u}_k$. A set in which one vector is a linear combination of the others is said to be a linearly dependent set.

Sets with this property were defined in Chapter 2, Definition 7, in the special setting of R^n. The same definition can be applied to any vector space.

Linearly Dependent Set

Linearly Independent Set

Definition 4

The set of vectors $\{\mathbf{u}_1, \mathbf{u}_2, \ldots, \mathbf{u}_k\}$ is a **linearly dependent set** if there exist scalars $c_1, c_2, \ldots, c_k$, not all zero, such that

$$c_1\mathbf{u}_1 + c_2\mathbf{u}_2 + \cdots + c_k\mathbf{u}_k = \mathbf{0}$$

The set of vectors $\{\mathbf{u}_1, \mathbf{u}_2, \ldots, \mathbf{u}_k\}$ is a **linearly independent set** if

$$c_1\mathbf{u}_1 + c_2\mathbf{u}_2 + \cdots + c_k\mathbf{u}_k = \mathbf{0}$$

only in the case $c_1 = 0, c_2 = 0, \ldots, c_k = 0$.

Questions about linear dependence or independence in R^n can often be related to properties of matrices.

Example 16 Let $\mathbf{u}_1 = (1, 2, -1, 1)$, $\mathbf{u}_2 = (0, 1, -4, 2)$, and $\mathbf{u}_3 = (1, 1, 3, -1)$, as in Example 13. The nature of the solution of $c_1\mathbf{u}_1 + c_2\mathbf{u}_2 + c_3\mathbf{u}_3 = \mathbf{0}$ can be found from the matrix representation $\mathbf{MC} = \mathbf{0}$, where the coefficient matrix $\mathbf{M}$ has as its columns the 4-tuples $\mathbf{u}_1, \mathbf{u}_2, \mathbf{u}_3$. In this case

$$\mathbf{M} = \begin{bmatrix} 1 & 0 & 1 \\ 2 & 1 & 1 \\ -1 & -4 & 3 \\ 1 & 2 & -1 \end{bmatrix} \Leftrightarrow \begin{bmatrix} 1 & 0 & 1 \\ 0 & 1 & -1 \\ 0 & 0 & 0 \\ 0 & 0 & 0 \end{bmatrix}$$

The matrix $\mathbf{M}$ has rank 2, and the number of unknowns is 3. The equation has nontrivial solutions (Theorem 3, Chapter 2). The set $\{\mathbf{u}_1, \mathbf{u}_2, \mathbf{u}_3\}$ is linearly dependent. ■

Theorem 4 Let $\{\mathbf{u}_1, \mathbf{u}_2, \ldots, \mathbf{u}_k\}$ be a set of vectors in R^n. Form the $n \times k$ matrix $\mathbf{M}$ with columns the n-tuples $\mathbf{u}_1, \mathbf{u}_2, \ldots, \mathbf{u}_k$. If the rank of $\mathbf{M}$ is equal to k, the set $\{\mathbf{u}_1, \mathbf{u}_2, \ldots, \mathbf{u}_k\}$ is linearly independent. If the rank of $\mathbf{M}$ is less than k, the set $\{\mathbf{u}_1, \mathbf{u}_2, \ldots, \mathbf{u}_k\}$ is linearly dependent.

Proof The equation $c_1\mathbf{u}_1 + c_2\mathbf{u}_2 + \cdots + c_k\mathbf{u}_k = \mathbf{0}$ in matrix form is $\mathbf{MC} = \mathbf{0}$. The nature of the solution set depends on the rank of $\mathbf{M}$ and its relation to the number of unknowns. If the rank of $\mathbf{M}$ is equal to k, the only solution is $\mathbf{C} = \mathbf{0}$, and the set $\{\mathbf{u}_1, \mathbf{u}_2, \ldots, \mathbf{u}_k\}$ is linearly independent. If the rank of $\mathbf{M}$ is less than k, there are nontrivial solutions and the set is linearly dependent. □

Two important consequences of Theorem 4 are stated as corollaries. (You are asked to prove these in the exercises.)

Corollary 1 A set of n vectors in R^n is linearly independent if $\det \mathbf{M} \neq 0$. □

Corollary 2 If a set of vectors in R^n has more than n vectors, it must be a linearly dependent set. □

Example 17

In each case determine whether the set is linearly independent or linearly dependent.

1. $\{\mathbf{u}_1, \mathbf{u}_2, \mathbf{u}_3\}$, where $\mathbf{u}_1 = (1, 0, 0)$, $\mathbf{u}_2 = (0, 1, 0)$, $\mathbf{u}_3 = (1, 1, 0)$.

Solution First, see if you can spot an obvious relation among the vectors. This set is dependent because $\mathbf{u}_1 + \mathbf{u}_2 = \mathbf{u}_3$.

2. $\{\mathbf{u}_1, \mathbf{u}_2, \mathbf{u}_3\}$, where $\mathbf{u}_1 = (1, 2, 3, 4)$, $\mathbf{u}_2 = (-1, 1, 0, 1)$, $\mathbf{u}_3 = (-1, 4, 3, 6)$.

Solution Form the matrix

$$\mathbf{M} = \begin{bmatrix} 1 & -1 & -1 \\ 2 & 1 & 4 \\ 3 & 0 & 3 \\ 4 & 1 & 6 \end{bmatrix} \Leftrightarrow \begin{bmatrix} 1 & -1 & -1 \\ 0 & 1 & 2 \\ 0 & 0 & 0 \\ 0 & 0 & 0 \end{bmatrix}$$

Since $\mathbf{M}$ has rank 2 and $2 < 3$, the set is dependent. In fact, $\mathbf{u}_1 + 2\mathbf{u}_2 = \mathbf{u}_3$.

3. $\{\mathbf{u}_1, \mathbf{u}_2, \mathbf{u}_3\}$, where $\mathbf{u}_1 = (1, 1, -1)$, $\mathbf{u}_2 = (0, 1, 1)$, $\mathbf{u}_3 = (1, 2, 3)$.

Solution

$$\mathbf{M} = \begin{bmatrix} 1 & 0 & 1 \\ 1 & 1 & 2 \\ -1 & 1 & 3 \end{bmatrix} \quad \text{and} \quad \det \mathbf{M} = 3 \neq 0$$

Since $\det \mathbf{M} \neq 0$, the set is linearly independent.

4. $\{\mathbf{u}_1, \mathbf{u}_2, \mathbf{u}_3, \mathbf{u}_4\}$, where $\mathbf{u}_1 = (1, 1, 2)$, $\mathbf{u}_2 = (1, 0, 1)$, $\mathbf{u}_3 = (1, 4, 7)$, $\mathbf{u}_4 = (2, 5, 3)$.

Solution The set is dependent, since a set of four vectors from R^3 is linearly dependent. ■

If a spanning set for a vector space is also a linearly independent set, it is then called a basis for the space.

Basis

> **Definition 5**
>
> The set $U = \{\mathbf{u}_1, \mathbf{u}_2, \ldots, \mathbf{u}_k\}$ is a **basis** for the vector space S if and only if U is a linearly independent set and U spans the vector space S.

Example 18

Let $\mathbf{u}_1 = (1, 1, 1)$, $\mathbf{u}_2 = (1, -1, 1)$, $\mathbf{u}_3 = (1, 2, 3)$. Is $\{\mathbf{u}_1, \mathbf{u}_2, \mathbf{u}_3\}$ a basis for R^3?

Solution First, does $\{\mathbf{u}_1, \mathbf{u}_2, \mathbf{u}_3\}$ span R^3? That is, can we solve the equation

$$c_1\mathbf{u}_1 + c_2\mathbf{u}_2 + c_3\mathbf{u}_3 = \mathbf{v}$$

for any $\mathbf{v}$ in R^3, say $\mathbf{v} = (a_1, a_2, a_3)$? This vector equation is the same as the system

$$\begin{aligned} c_1 + c_2 + c_3 &= a_1 \\ c_1 - c_2 + 2c_3 &= a_2 \\ c_1 + c_2 + 3c_3 &= a_3 \end{aligned}$$

By row reduction we obtain

$$\left[\begin{array}{rrr|c} 1 & 1 & 1 & a_1 \\ 1 & -1 & 2 & a_2 \\ 1 & 1 & 3 & a_3 \end{array}\right] \Leftrightarrow \left[\begin{array}{rrr|c} 1 & 1 & 1 & a_1 \\ 0 & -2 & 1 & a_2 - a_1 \\ 0 & 0 & 2 & a_3 - a_1 \end{array}\right]$$

The coefficient matrix has rank 3 so this system can be solved for any set (a_1, a_2, a_3).

Second, is $\{\mathbf{u}_1, \mathbf{u}_2, \mathbf{u}_3\}$ a linearly independent set?

The coefficient matrix is the matrix $\mathbf{M}$ of Theorem 4. Since it has rank 3, the set is linearly independent.

Yes, $\{\mathbf{u}_1, \mathbf{u}_2, \mathbf{u}_3\}$ is a basis for R^3.

A basis for a given space, however, is not unique. We can see that a very simple basis for R^3 is the set of standard 3-tuples $\mathbf{e}_1 = (1, 0, 0)$, $\mathbf{e}_2 = (0, 1, 0)$, and $\mathbf{e}_3 = (0, 0, 1)$. Another is the set $\{\mathbf{u}_1, \mathbf{u}_2, \mathbf{u}_3\}$ in this example. Yet another is $\{(1, 0, 0), (1, 1, 0), (1, 1, 1)\}$, and there are many more. ■

Example 19 Let $p_1 = x^3 - 3x^2 + 2x$, $p_2 = x^3 + 3x^2 + 3x + 1$, $p_3 = x^2 - 5x - 1$, and $p_4 = 2x^3 + x^2$. Find a basis for $\text{lin}\{p_1, p_2, p_3, p_4\}$.

Solution By definition, the set $\{p_1, p_2, p_3, p_4\}$ spans the space $\text{lin}\{p_1, p_2, p_3, p_4\}$. Is this set linearly independent? The answer lies in the nature of c_1, c_2, c_3, c_4 that satisfy the equation $c_1p_1 + c_2p_2 + c_3p_3 + c_4p_4 = 0$.

The coefficient of x^0 in this equation gives $0c_1 + c_2 - c_3 + 0c_4 = 0$.
The coefficient of x gives $2c_1 + 3c_2 - 5c_3 + 0c_4 = 0$.
The coefficient of x^2 gives $-3c_1 + 3c_2 + c_3 + c_4 = 0$.
The coefficient of x^3 gives $c_1 + c_2 + 0c_3 + 2c_4 = 0$.

Row reduction of the augmented matrix of this system of equations gives

$$\left[\begin{array}{rrrr|r} 0 & 1 & -1 & 0 & 0 \\ 2 & 3 & -5 & 0 & 0 \\ -3 & 3 & 1 & 1 & 0 \\ 1 & 1 & 0 & 2 & 0 \end{array}\right] \Leftrightarrow \left[\begin{array}{rrrr|r} 1 & 0 & 0 & 1 & 0 \\ 0 & 1 & 0 & 1 & 0 \\ 0 & 0 & 1 & 1 & 0 \\ 0 & 0 & 0 & 0 & 0 \end{array}\right]$$

Since the coefficient matrix has rank 3, which is less than 4, the number of unknowns, a set of numbers $\{c_1, c_2, c_3, c_4\}$ not all zero exists such that $c_1p_1 + c_2p_2 + c_3p_3 + c_4p_4 = 0$. Thus the set $\{p_1, p_2, p_3, p_4\}$ is a linearly dependent set. We could have predicted this result had we noticed that $p_1 + p_2 + p_3 = p_4$.

The fact that p_4 is a linear combination of $\{p_1, p_2, p_3\}$ shows that $\{p_1, p_2, p_3\}$ spans $\text{lin}\{p_1, p_2, p_3, p_4\}$. We must now examine the solutions of $c_1p_1 + c_2p_2 +$

$c_3p_3 = 0$. This time the system of equations is

$$\begin{bmatrix} 0 & 1 & -1 \\ 2 & 3 & -5 \\ -3 & 3 & 1 \\ 1 & 1 & 0 \end{bmatrix} \begin{bmatrix} c_1 \\ c_2 \\ c_3 \end{bmatrix} = \begin{bmatrix} 0 \\ 0 \\ 0 \\ 0 \end{bmatrix}$$

The rank of the coefficient matrix is 3 but, since there are only 3 unknowns, this implies that the equations have only the trivial solution. The set $\{p_1, p_2, p_3\}$ is a linearly independent set and spans lin $\{p_1, p_2, p_3, p_4\}$, so it is a basis for this space. ■

Example 20 Let

$$\mathbf{M}_1 = \begin{bmatrix} 1 & 1 & 1 \\ 0 & 0 & 0 \end{bmatrix}, \quad \mathbf{M}_2 = \begin{bmatrix} 0 & 0 & 0 \\ 0 & 1 & 1 \end{bmatrix},$$

$$\mathbf{M}_3 = \begin{bmatrix} 0 & 0 & 0 \\ 0 & 1 & 0 \end{bmatrix}, \quad \mathbf{M}_4 = \begin{bmatrix} 0 & 0 & 0 \\ 0 & 0 & 1 \end{bmatrix}$$

The space lin $\{\mathbf{M}_1, \mathbf{M}_2, \mathbf{M}_3, \mathbf{M}_4\}$ is a subspace of $\mathbf{M}_{2\times 3}$ (Example 2). Is $\{\mathbf{M}_1, \mathbf{M}_2, \mathbf{M}_3, \mathbf{M}_4\}$ a basis for lin $\{\mathbf{M}_1, \mathbf{M}_2, \mathbf{M}_3, \mathbf{M}_4\}$?

Solution Since $c_1\mathbf{M}_1 + c_2\mathbf{M}_2 + c_3\mathbf{M}_3 + c_4\mathbf{M}_4 = \begin{bmatrix} c_1 & c_1 & c_1 \\ 0 & c_2 + c_3 & c_2 + c_4 \end{bmatrix} = \begin{bmatrix} 0 & 0 & 0 \\ 0 & 0 & 0 \end{bmatrix}$ implies $c_1 = 0$, $c_2 + c_3 = 0$, $c_2 + c_4 = 0$, we must solve the equation $\mathbf{MC} = \mathbf{0}$, where

$$\mathbf{M} = \begin{bmatrix} 1 & 0 & 0 & 0 \\ 0 & 1 & 1 & 0 \\ 0 & 1 & 0 & 1 \end{bmatrix}$$

← where from ?

Since $\mathbf{M}$ has rank 3, there exists a nontrivial solution:

$$c_1 = 0, \qquad c_2 = 1, \qquad c_3 = -1, \qquad c_4 = -1$$

Thus, $\{\mathbf{M}_1, \mathbf{M}_2, \mathbf{M}_3, \mathbf{M}_4\}$ is linearly dependent and not a basis.

A similar argument shows that the set $\{\mathbf{M}_1, \mathbf{M}_3, \mathbf{M}_4\}$ is a linearly independent set and also spans lin $\{\mathbf{M}_1, \mathbf{M}_2, \mathbf{M}_3, \mathbf{M}_4\}$. Thus, $\{\mathbf{M}_1, \mathbf{M}_3, \mathbf{M}_4\}$ is a basis for this space. ■

In order to illustrate the use of the theorems, we have worked Example 20 in detail. In many simple cases, a basis can be found by inspection. (See Exercises 4.2.)

Example 21 Let $u_1 = \sin x$, $u_2 = \cos x$, $u_3 = x\sin x$, and $u_4 = x\cos x$. Is the set $\{u_1, u_2, u_3, u_4\}$ a linearly independent set? Definition 4 requires us to consider the solution of the vector equation $c_1u_1 + c_2u_2 + c_3u_3 + c_4u_4 = 0$.

We cannot write this vector equation immediately in matrix form as we could in Example 18. We can, however, find a way of using matrices to give at least a partial answer to this question by creating a system of vector equations as follows.

If a function is the zero function, then all of its derivatives must be the zero function. It follows that c_1, c_2, c_3, c_4 must satisfy the system of equations, provided the derivatives exist.

$$\begin{aligned} c_1u_1 + c_2u_2 + c_3u_3 + c_4u_4 &= 0 \\ c_1u_1' + c_2u_2' + c_3u_3' + c_4u_4' &= 0 \\ c_1u_1'' + c_2u_2'' + c_3u_3'' + c_4u_4'' &= 0 \\ c_1u_1''' + c_2u_2''' + c_3u_3''' + c_4u_4''' &= 0 \end{aligned}$$

Notice that each equation is the derivative of the one above it. We could continue indefinitely in this way, but as our system now stands we have four equations in four unknowns. We can write this system in the form $\mathbf{MC} = \mathbf{0}$. The coefficient matrix is a matrix of functions:

$$\mathbf{M} = \begin{bmatrix} u_1 & u_2 & u_3 & u_4 \\ u_1' & u_2' & u_3' & u_4' \\ u_1'' & u_2'' & u_3'' & u_4'' \\ u_1''' & u_2''' & u_3''' & u_4''' \end{bmatrix}$$

The determinant of $\mathbf{M}$ is called the Wronskian of the set of functions $\{u_1, u_2, u_3, u_4\}$.

In general, the use of the Wronskian to determine whether or not a set of functions is linearly independent is not simple. It does have an important role in the solution set of linear differential equations. It can be shown that if $y_1, y_2, \ldots, y_n$ are solutions of a linear homogeneous differential equation

$$y^{(n)} + p_1(x)y^{(n-1)} + \cdots + p_n(x)y = 0$$

in which $p_i(x)$, $i = 1, 2, \ldots, n$, are continuous on the open interval $a < x < b$, then:

a. If the Wronskian $W(y_1, y_2, \ldots, y_n)$ is not identically zero on $a < x < b$, the set $\{y_1, y_2, \ldots, y_n\}$ is linearly independent.
b. If the set $\{y_1, y_2, \ldots, y_n\}$ is linearly independent, then $W(y_1, y_2, \ldots, y_n)$ is nowhere zero on $a < x < b$.

The Wronskian of the functions u_1, u_2, u_3, u_4 in our example is $\det \mathbf{M}$, where

$$\mathbf{M} = \begin{bmatrix} \sin x & \cos x & x\sin x & x\cos x \\ \cos x & -\sin x & \sin x + x\cos x & \cos x - x\sin x \\ -\sin x & -\cos x & 2\cos x - x\sin x & -2\sin x - x\cos x \\ -\cos x & \sin x & -3\sin x - x\cos x & -3\cos x + x\sin x \end{bmatrix}$$

We can evaluate this determinant by the methods of Chapter 3. We obtain

$$\begin{aligned}
\det \mathbf{M} &= \det\begin{bmatrix} \sin x & \cos x & x\sin x & x\cos x \\ \cos x & -\sin x & \sin x + x\cos x & \cos x - x\sin x \\ 0 & 0 & 2\cos x & -2\sin x \\ 0 & 0 & -2\sin x & -2\cos x \end{bmatrix} \\
&= (-\sin^2 x - \cos^2 x)(-4\cos^2 x - 4\sin^2 x) \\
&= 4
\end{aligned}$$

Each of the functions is a solution of the differential equation

$$y^{\text{iv}} + 2y'' + y = 0$$

a linear homogeneous equation with continuous coefficients. Thus we can conclude that the set of functions $\{\sin x, \cos x, x\sin x, x\cos x\}$ is a linearly independent set. ■

Although in general the Wronskian cannot be used to test a set of functions for linear independence, it does provide a handy criterion for functions in P_n, since every function in P_n is a solution of the linear homogeneous equation $y^{(n+1)} = 0$.

Example 22

Let $y_1 = 1$, $y_2 = x$, $y_3 = x^2$. $W(y_1, y_2, y_3) = \det\begin{bmatrix} 1 & x & x^2 \\ 0 & 1 & 2x \\ 0 & 0 & 2 \end{bmatrix} = 2.$

The set $\{1, x, x^2\}$ is linearly independent.

As a less trivial example, consider $y_1 = x^2$, $y_2 = x^2 - 2x$, $y_3 = x^2 - 4x - 1$.

$$\begin{aligned}
W(y_1, y_2, y_3) &= \det\begin{bmatrix} x^2 & x^2 - 2x & x^2 - 4x - 1 \\ 2x & 2x - 2 & 2x - 4 \\ 2 & 2 & 2 \end{bmatrix} \\
&= \det\begin{bmatrix} 0 & -2x & -4x - 1 \\ 0 & -2 & -4 \\ 2 & 2 & 2 \end{bmatrix} \quad \begin{matrix} \left(\frac{-x^2}{2}\right) R_3 + R_1 \to R_1 \\ (-x)\, R_3 + R_2 \to R_2 \end{matrix} \\
&= -4
\end{aligned}$$

The set $\{x^2, x^2 - 2x, x^2 - 4x - 1\}$ is linearly independent.

Now consider the set $y_1 = x^2 + 1$, $y_2 = x^2 - 2x$, $y_3 = x^2 - 4x - 1$. Again,

$$\begin{aligned}
W(y_1, y_2, y_3) &= \det\begin{bmatrix} x^2 + 1 & x^2 - 2x & x^2 - 4x - 1 \\ 2x & 2x - 2 & 2x - 4 \\ 2 & 2 & 2 \end{bmatrix} \\
&= \det\begin{bmatrix} 1 & -2x & -4x - 1 \\ 0 & -2 & -4 \\ 2 & 2 & 2 \end{bmatrix} = -4 + 8 + 2(8x - 8x - 2) = 0.
\end{aligned}$$

The set $\{x^2 + 1,\ x^2 - 2x,\ x^2 - 4x - 1\}$ is linearly dependent. In fact, $x^2 - 4x - 1 = 2(x^2 - 2x) - (x^2 + 1)$. ■

SUMMARY Let $U = \{\mathbf{u}_1, \mathbf{u}_2, \ldots, \mathbf{u}_k\}$ be a set of vectors in the vector space V. The set of all vectors of the form $c_1\mathbf{u}_1 + c_2\mathbf{u}_2 + \cdots + c_k\mathbf{u}_k$ is a vector space called the space spanned by U. The notation $\text{lin}\{\mathbf{u}_1, \mathbf{u}_2, \ldots, \mathbf{u}_k\}$ is used to represent this space. The set U is a spanning set for $\text{lin}\{\mathbf{u}_1, \mathbf{u}_2, \ldots, \mathbf{u}_k\}$.

A set of vectors $\{\mathbf{u}_1, \mathbf{u}_2, \ldots, \mathbf{u}_k\}$ is a **linearly independent** set if the equation $c_1\mathbf{u}_1 + c_2\mathbf{u}_2 + \cdots + c_k\mathbf{u}_k = \mathbf{0}$ is true only when $c_1 = 0, c_2 = 0, \ldots, c_k = 0$. If a set is not linearly independent, it is linearly dependent. If $\{\mathbf{u}_1, \mathbf{u}_2, \ldots, \mathbf{u}_k\}$ is a linearly dependent set, at least one vector in the set is a linear combination of the remaining vectors.

A set $\{\mathbf{u}_1, \mathbf{u}_2, \ldots, \mathbf{u}_k\}$ from R^n is linearly independent if and only if $\text{rank}(\mathbf{M}) = k$, where $\mathbf{M}$ is the matrix whose columns are $\mathbf{u}_1, \mathbf{u}_2, \mathbf{u}_3, \ldots, \mathbf{u}_k$.

The set $U = \{\mathbf{u}_1, \mathbf{u}_2, \ldots, \mathbf{u}_k\}$ is a **basis** for a linear space V if (1) it spans V and (2) it is a linearly independent set.

EXERCISES 4.2

1. Let $\mathbf{u}_1 = (1,2,1)$, $\mathbf{u}_2 = (2,1,1)$, and $\mathbf{u}_3 = (3,3,2)$. Does $(1,0,0)$ belong to the space spanned by $\{\mathbf{u}_1, \mathbf{u}_2, \mathbf{u}_3\}$? Does $(-1,1,0)$ belong to this space? Does $\{\mathbf{u}_1, \mathbf{u}_2, \mathbf{u}_3\}$ span R^3? Give reasons for your answers.

2. Let $\mathbf{u}_1 = (1,1,1)$ and $\mathbf{u}_2 = (1,0,1)$.
   a. Write several vectors that belong to the space spanned by $\{\mathbf{u}_1, \mathbf{u}_2\}$.
   b. Show that $\mathbf{u}_1, \mathbf{u}_2, \mathbf{0}$ each belong to the space spanned by $\{\mathbf{u}_1, \mathbf{u}_2\}$ by finding appropriate values of c_1 and c_2 in each case.
   c. Find a vector in R^3 that is not in the space spanned by $\{\mathbf{u}_1, \mathbf{u}_2\}$.

3. Recall that $\mathbf{e}_1 = (1,0,0)$, $\mathbf{e}_2 = (0,1,0)$ in R^3.
   a. Give a geometric description of the space spanned by $\{\mathbf{e}_1, \mathbf{e}_2\}$.
   b. Show that $\mathbf{e}_1$ and $\mathbf{e}_2$ belong to $\text{lin}\{\mathbf{u}_1, \mathbf{u}_2\}$, where $\mathbf{u}_1 = (2,3,0)$ and $\mathbf{u}_2 = (1,-1,0)$.

4. Let $\mathbf{u}_1 = (0,0,1)$, $\mathbf{u}_2 = (1,2,5)$ and $\mathbf{v}_1 = (1,2,1)$, $\mathbf{v}_2 = (1,2,3)$, $\mathbf{v}_3 = (3,6,5)$.
   a. Show that $\mathbf{v}_1$, $\mathbf{v}_2$, and $\mathbf{v}_3$ are in the space spanned by $\{\mathbf{u}_1, \mathbf{u}_2\}$.
   b. Show that $\mathbf{u}_1$ and $\mathbf{u}_2$ are in the space spanned by $\{\mathbf{v}_1, \mathbf{v}_2, \mathbf{v}_3\}$.
   c. Use **a.** and **b.** to show that the space spanned by $\{\mathbf{u}_1, \mathbf{u}_2\}$ is the same as the space spanned by $\{\mathbf{v}_1, \mathbf{v}_2, \mathbf{v}_3\}$.

5. Let $\mathbf{u}_1 = (1,0,1)$, $\mathbf{u}_2 = (-1,-1,0)$, $\mathbf{v}_1 = (1,2,0)$, $\mathbf{v}_2 = (0,0,1)$.
   a. For what values of c_1, c_2, d_1, d_2 does $c_1\mathbf{u}_1 + c_2\mathbf{u}_2 = d_1\mathbf{v}_1 + d_2\mathbf{v}_2$?
   b. Use **a.** to show that the space spanned by $\{\mathbf{u}_1, \mathbf{u}_2\}$ is not the same as the space spanned by $\{\mathbf{v}_1, \mathbf{v}_2\}$.

6. Let $p_1 = 1 + x + x^2$, $p_2 = 1 + x - x^2$, and $p_3 = x^2$.
   a. Does $u = 3 + 3x - 4x^2$ belong to the space spanned by $\{p_1, p_2, p_3\}$?
   b. Does $u = 4 + 3x + 2x^2$ belong to the space spanned by $\{p_1, p_2, p_3\}$?
   c. If $a_0 + a_1x + a_2x^2$ belongs to this space, what condition must be satisfied by a_0, a_1, a_2?

7. Let $p_1 = 1 + x - x^2$ and $p_2 = 2 - x$.
   a. Describe the vectors in $\text{lin}\{p_1, p_2\}$.
   b. Verify that $p_3 = 4 + x - 3x^2$ is not in $\text{lin}\{p_1, p_2\}$.
   c. Show that $\{p_1, p_2, p_3\}$ does span P_2.

8. Let S be the space spanned by $\{1, x^2\}$. Let T be the space spanned by $\{1 - x^2, 1 + x^2\}$. Show that every vector in S is also in T. Show that every vector in T is also in S, and hence that S and T are the same space.

9. Let $p_1 = 1 + x$, $p_2 = 2 - x^2$, $p_3 = 5 + 2x + x^2$, and $p_4 = 2 + x$.
  a. Write the form of a vector in the space $\text{lin}\{p_1, p_2\}$.
  b. Write the form of a vector in $\text{lin}\{p_3, p_4\}$.
  c. Show that $a_1p_1 + a_2p_2$ belongs to $\text{lin}\{p_3, p_4\}$ if and only if $3a_2 = a_1$.
  d. What relation must hold between c_1 and c_2 if $c_1p_3 + c_2p_4$ is in $\text{lin}\{p_1, p_2\}$?

10. Find a set that spans P_2 and contains the vectors $p_1 = 1 + x^2$ and $p_2 = 2 - x$. Is there more than one such set? Give a reason for your answer.

11. **a.** Let $p_1 = 1 + x - 2x^2$, $p_2 = 1 - x + x^2$, $p_3 = 2x + 3x^2$, and $p_4 = 1 - 2x$. Show that $\{p_1, p_2, p_3, p_4\}$ is a linearly dependent set.
  b. Show that any set of four vectors in P_2 is linearly dependent.

12. Let $\mathbf{A}_1 = \begin{bmatrix} 1 & 0 & 0 \\ 1 & 1 & 0 \end{bmatrix}$ and $\mathbf{A}_2 = \begin{bmatrix} 1 & 1 & 0 \\ 0 & 1 & 0 \end{bmatrix}$. The matrices $\mathbf{A}_1$ and $\mathbf{A}_2$ are vectors in $M_{2\times 3}$. Write the form of a vector in the subspace of $M_{2\times 3}$ spanned by $\{\mathbf{A}_1, \mathbf{A}_2\}$.

13. Let $\mathbf{A}_1 = \begin{bmatrix} 1 & 0 & 0 \\ 0 & 0 & 0 \end{bmatrix}$, $\mathbf{A}_2 = \begin{bmatrix} 0 & 1 & 0 \\ 0 & 0 & 0 \end{bmatrix}$, and $\mathbf{A}_3 = \begin{bmatrix} 0 & 0 & 1 \\ 0 & 0 & 0 \end{bmatrix}$.
  a. Show that $\{\mathbf{A}_1, \mathbf{A}_2, \mathbf{A}_3\}$ is a linearly independent set.
  b. Show that $\text{lin}\{\mathbf{A}_1, \mathbf{A}_2, \mathbf{A}_3\}$ is a subspace of $M_{2\times 3}$ that is not the entire space.

14. Let $\mathbf{A}_1 = \begin{bmatrix} 1 & 0 & 0 \\ 0 & 0 & 0 \end{bmatrix}$, $\mathbf{A}_2 = \begin{bmatrix} 1 & 0 & 0 \\ 0 & 1 & 0 \end{bmatrix}$, and $\mathbf{A}_3 = \begin{bmatrix} 0 & 0 & 0 \\ 0 & 0 & 1 \end{bmatrix}$. Let $\mathbf{B} = \begin{bmatrix} 3 & 0 & 0 \\ 4 & 5 & 6 \end{bmatrix}$.
  a. Does $\mathbf{B}$ belong to $\text{lin}\{\mathbf{A}_1, \mathbf{A}_2, \mathbf{A}_3\}$?
  b. Write the general form of a vector in $M_{2\times 3}$ that belongs to $\text{lin}\{\mathbf{A}_1, \mathbf{A}_2, \mathbf{A}_3\}$.
  c. Write $\mathbf{C} = \begin{bmatrix} 3 & 0 & 0 \\ 0 & 5 & 6 \end{bmatrix}$ as a linear combination of $\mathbf{A}_1, \mathbf{A}_2, \mathbf{A}_3$.

15. Which of the following sets in $M_{2\times 2}$ are linearly independent? Justify your answer.
  a. $\left\{\begin{bmatrix} 1 & 0 \\ 0 & 1 \end{bmatrix}, \begin{bmatrix} 1 & 0 \\ 1 & 1 \end{bmatrix}, \begin{bmatrix} 1 & 1 \\ 0 & 1 \end{bmatrix}, \begin{bmatrix} 1 & 1 \\ 1 & 1 \end{bmatrix}\right\}$
  b. $\left\{\begin{bmatrix} 1 & 0 \\ 0 & 0 \end{bmatrix}, \begin{bmatrix} 0 & 1 \\ 0 & 0 \end{bmatrix}, \begin{bmatrix} 0 & 0 \\ 1 & 0 \end{bmatrix}, \begin{bmatrix} 0 & 0 \\ 0 & 1 \end{bmatrix}\right\}$
  c. $\left\{\begin{bmatrix} 1 & 1 \\ 0 & 0 \end{bmatrix}, \begin{bmatrix} -1 & 1 \\ 0 & 0 \end{bmatrix}, \begin{bmatrix} 1 & 1 \\ 1 & 1 \end{bmatrix}, \begin{bmatrix} -1 & -1 \\ -1 & 1 \end{bmatrix}\right\}$
  d. $\left\{\begin{bmatrix} 1 & 0 \\ 0 & 0 \end{bmatrix}, \begin{bmatrix} 0 & 1 \\ 0 & 0 \end{bmatrix}, \begin{bmatrix} 0 & 0 \\ 1 & 1 \end{bmatrix}\right\}$
  e. $\left\{\begin{bmatrix} 1 & 0 \\ 0 & 0 \end{bmatrix}, \begin{bmatrix} 0 & 1 \\ 0 & 0 \end{bmatrix}, \begin{bmatrix} 0 & 1 \\ 1 & 0 \end{bmatrix}, \begin{bmatrix} 1 & 0 \\ 0 & 1 \end{bmatrix}, \begin{bmatrix} 1 & 1 \\ 1 & 1 \end{bmatrix}\right\}$

16. **a.** Which of the sets in Problem 15 spans $M_{2\times 2}$?
  b. Which of the sets in Problem 15 forms a basis for $M_{2\times 2}$? Justify your answer.

17. Show that if $\{\mathbf{u}_1, \mathbf{u}_2, \ldots, \mathbf{u}_n\}$ is a linearly dependent set of vectors in V, then one of the vectors can be expressed as a linear combination of the others.

18. Show that if a set of n vectors contains the zero vector, it must be a linearly dependent set.

***19.** Prove that a set of n vectors in R^n is linearly independent if $\det \mathbf{M} \neq 0$. (Corollary 1, Theorem 4.)

***20.** Prove that any set of more than n vectors in R^n is linearly dependent. (Corollary 2, Theorem 4.)

21. Show that any set of more than $n + 1$ vectors in P_n is a linearly dependent set.

22. Show that a set of more than 6 vectors in $M_{2\times 3}$ is a linearly dependent set.

23. Show that the set $\left\{\begin{bmatrix} 1 & 0 \\ 0 & 0 \end{bmatrix}, \begin{bmatrix} 0 & 1 \\ 1 & 0 \end{bmatrix}, \begin{bmatrix} 0 & 0 \\ 0 & 1 \end{bmatrix}\right\}$ spans the subspace of symmetric matrices in $M_{2\times 2}$.

24. Show that a set of more than three symmetric matrices is a linearly dependent set in $M_{2\times 2}$.

25. Show that in any vector space V, $\text{lin}\{\mathbf{u}_{i_1}, \mathbf{u}_{i_2}, \ldots, \mathbf{u}_{i_k}\} \subseteq \text{lin}\{\mathbf{u}_1, \mathbf{u}_2, \ldots, \mathbf{u}_n\}$, where $\{i_1, i_2, \ldots, i_k\}$ is a subset of $\{1, 2, \ldots, n\}$, and $\mathbf{u}_i$, $i = 1, 2, \ldots, n$, are vectors in V.

4.3 Coordinates, Dimension

Definition 5, Section 4.2 lists two requirements for U to be a basis of a vector space S:

1. U is a linearly independent set.
2. U spans the vector space S.

Recall (Section 1.3) that $\mathbf{e}_i = (0, 0, \ldots, 1, \ldots, 0)$ is the vector in R^n with the property that the ith component is 1 and every other component is zero. The set $\{\mathbf{e}_1, \mathbf{e}_2, \ldots, \mathbf{e}_n\}$ forms a very simple basis for R^n. In the case $n = 4$, for example:

$$\mathbf{e}_1 = (1,0,0,0), \qquad \mathbf{e}_2 = (0,1,0,0), \qquad \mathbf{e}_3 = (0,0,1,0), \qquad \mathbf{e}_4 = (0,0,0,1)$$

$$c_1\mathbf{e}_1 + c_2\mathbf{e}_2 + c_3\mathbf{e}_3 + c_4\mathbf{e}_4 = \mathbf{0} \quad \text{if and only if} \quad c_1 = c_2 = c_3 = c_4 = 0$$

Also, any element of R^4, (a_1, a_2, a_3, a_4) has the form $a_1\mathbf{e}_1 + a_2\mathbf{e}_2 + a_3\mathbf{e}_3 + a_4\mathbf{e}_4$. Thus, $\{\mathbf{e}_1, \mathbf{e}_2, \mathbf{e}_3, \mathbf{e}_4\}$ is a linearly independent set and spans R^4. This set is a basis for R^4. However, it is not the only basis for R^4. In this section we identify the properties common to different bases for the same vector space.

A basis is important because of two properties illustrated in the following examples and stated in Theorems 5 and 6.

Example 23 Let $\mathbf{u}_1 = (1,0,0,1,0)$, $\mathbf{u}_2 = (1,1,1,1,1)$, $\mathbf{u}_3 = (0,1,0,1,1)$, and $\mathbf{u}_4 = (0,0,0,1,1)$. Let S be the space spanned by $\{\mathbf{u}_1, \mathbf{u}_2, \mathbf{u}_3, \mathbf{u}_4\}$. This set is a basis for S if it is linearly independent. It is linearly independent if the equation $c_1\mathbf{u}_1 + c_2\mathbf{u}_2 + c_3\mathbf{u}_3 + c_4\mathbf{u}_4 = \mathbf{0}$ has only the trivial solution $c_1 = 0, c_2 = 0, c_3 = 0, c_4 = 0$. The equation $c_1\mathbf{u}_1 + c_2\mathbf{u}_2 + c_3\mathbf{u}_3 + c_4\mathbf{u}_4 = \mathbf{0}$ in matrix form is $\mathbf{MC} = \mathbf{0}$, where

$$\mathbf{M} = \begin{bmatrix} 1 & 1 & 0 & 0 \\ 0 & 1 & 1 & 0 \\ 0 & 1 & 0 & 0 \\ 1 & 1 & 1 & 1 \\ 0 & 1 & 1 & 1 \end{bmatrix} \Leftrightarrow \begin{bmatrix} 1 & 0 & 0 & 0 \\ 0 & 1 & 0 & 0 \\ 0 & 0 & 1 & 0 \\ 0 & 0 & 0 & 1 \\ 0 & 0 & 0 & 0 \end{bmatrix}$$

Any vector in S can be written $\mathbf{v} = c_1\mathbf{u}_1 + c_2\mathbf{u}_2 + c_3\mathbf{u}_3 + c_4\mathbf{u}_4$. For a particular $\mathbf{v}$, such as $\mathbf{v} = (5,4,3,5,3)$, we find c_1, c_2, c_3, and c_4 by solving the equations

$c_1\mathbf{u}_1 + c_2\mathbf{u}_2 + c_3\mathbf{u}_3 + c_4\mathbf{u}_4 = (5,4,3,5,3)$, that is, $\mathbf{MC} = \begin{bmatrix} 5 \\ 4 \\ 3 \\ 5 \\ 3 \end{bmatrix}$. The coefficient

matrix is the same as that of the previous system, since it depends only on the vectors $\mathbf{u}_1, \mathbf{u}_2, \mathbf{u}_3$, and $\mathbf{u}_4$, but the system is nonhomogeneous. Row reduction yields

$$\left[\begin{array}{cccc|c} 1 & 1 & 0 & 0 & 5 \\ 0 & 1 & 1 & 0 & 4 \\ 0 & 1 & 0 & 0 & 3 \\ 1 & 1 & 1 & 1 & 5 \\ 0 & 1 & 1 & 1 & 3 \end{array}\right] \Leftrightarrow \left[\begin{array}{cccc|c} 1 & 0 & 0 & 0 & 2 \\ 0 & 1 & 0 & 0 & 3 \\ 0 & 0 & 1 & 0 & 1 \\ 0 & 0 & 0 & 1 & -1 \\ 0 & 0 & 0 & 0 & 0 \end{array}\right]$$

The equations have the unique solution $c_1 = 2$, $c_2 = 3$, $c_3 = 1$, $c_4 = -1$. The uniqueness of the solution comes from the fact that the rank of the coefficient matrix is 4 and the number of unknowns is also 4. This is exactly the property that is needed to guarantee that $\{\mathbf{u}_1, \mathbf{u}_2, \mathbf{u}_3, \mathbf{u}_4\}$ is a linearly independent set (Theorem 4). ■

Example 23 illustrates that if the set $\{\mathbf{u}_1, \mathbf{u}_2, \ldots, \mathbf{u}_k\}$ is a basis for a linear space S, every vector in S has a **unique** representation in the form $\mathbf{v} = c_1\mathbf{u}_1 + c_2\mathbf{u}_2 + \cdots + c_k\mathbf{u}_k$. The argument in the example used the properties of linear systems of equations. However, the uniqueness of the c_i's does not depend on systems of equations. The proof of Theorem 5 uses only the definition of linear independence.

Theorem 5 The set $\{\mathbf{u}_1, \mathbf{u}_2, \ldots, \mathbf{u}_k\}$ is a basis for the vector space S if and only if every vector $\mathbf{v}$ in S has a unique representation of the form

$$\mathbf{v} = c_1\mathbf{u}_1 + c_2\mathbf{u}_2 + \cdots + c_k\mathbf{u}_k$$

Proof This theorem is an "if and only if" theorem, so its proof has two parts.

First assume every vector in S has a unique representation of the form $\mathbf{v} = c_1\mathbf{u}_1 + c_2\mathbf{u}_2 + \cdots + c_k\mathbf{u}_k$ and prove that $\{\mathbf{u}_1, \mathbf{u}_2, \ldots, \mathbf{u}_k\}$ is a basis for S. We already know that $\{\mathbf{u}_1, \mathbf{u}_2, \ldots, \mathbf{u}_k\}$ spans S since every vector in S is a linear combination of $\{\mathbf{u}_1, \mathbf{u}_2, \ldots, \mathbf{u}_k\}$. We need only prove that $\{\mathbf{u}_1, \mathbf{u}_2, \ldots, \mathbf{u}_k\}$ is linearly independent. We do this by contradiction. Assume $\{\mathbf{u}_1, \mathbf{u}_2, \ldots, \mathbf{u}_k\}$ is linearly dependent. Then there are scalars $d_1, d_2, \ldots, d_k$ not all zero such that

$$\mathbf{0} = d_1\mathbf{u}_1 + d_2\mathbf{u}_2 + \cdots + d_k\mathbf{u}_k$$

A vector $\mathbf{v}$ in S has one representation $\mathbf{v} = a_1\mathbf{u}_1 + a_2\mathbf{u}_2 + \cdots + a_k\mathbf{u}_k$ and also a different representation formed by adding $\mathbf{0}$ to $\mathbf{v}$:

$$\mathbf{v} = (a_1 + d_1)\mathbf{u}_1 + (a_2 + d_2)\mathbf{u}_2 + \cdots + (a_k + d_k)\mathbf{u}_k$$

This contradicts the assumption that the representation of $\mathbf{v}$ is unique. So $\{\mathbf{u}_1, \mathbf{u}_2, \ldots, \mathbf{u}_k\}$ must be a linearly independent set and therefore a basis for S.

Now we must assume $\{\mathbf{u}_1, \mathbf{u}_2, \ldots, \mathbf{u}_k\}$ is a basis for S and prove that every vector $\mathbf{v}$ in S has a unique representation in the form $\mathbf{v} = c_1\mathbf{u}_1 + c_2\mathbf{u}_2 + \cdots + c_k\mathbf{u}_k$. Again we use contradiction. Suppose there is some $\mathbf{v}$ in S that has two representations,

$$\mathbf{v} = a_1\mathbf{u}_1 + a_2\mathbf{u}_2 + \cdots + a_k\mathbf{u}_k \quad \text{and} \quad \mathbf{v} = b_1\mathbf{u}_1 + b_2\mathbf{u}_2 + \cdots + b_k\mathbf{u}_k$$

where $a_i \neq b_i$ for at least one i, $i = 1, 2, \ldots, k$. Subtract these two representations. We get

$$(a_1 - b_1)\mathbf{u}_1 + (a_2 - b_2)\mathbf{u}_2 + \cdots + (a_k - b_k)\mathbf{u}_k = \mathbf{0}$$

where at least one of the coefficients is not zero. This shows that $\{\mathbf{u}_1, \mathbf{u}_2, \ldots, \mathbf{u}_k\}$ is a linearly dependent set (Definition 4), which contradicts the fact that $\{\mathbf{u}_1, \mathbf{u}_2, \ldots, \mathbf{u}_k\}$ is a basis. □

The uniqueness of $c_1, c_2, \ldots, c_k$ means that, given a basis, these scalars can be used to identify the particular vector $\mathbf{v}$. They are called coordinates of $\mathbf{v}$ relative to the basis U.

Definition 6

Let $U = \{\mathbf{u}_1, \mathbf{u}_2, \ldots, \mathbf{u}_k\}$ be a basis for the vector space S, and let $\mathbf{v}$ be a vector in S. The unique k-tuple of numbers $(c_1, c_2, \ldots, c_k)$ such that

$$\mathbf{v} = c_1\mathbf{u}_1 + c_2\mathbf{u}_2 + \cdots + c_k\mathbf{u}_k$$

Coordinate Vector

is called the **coordinate vector** of $\mathbf{v}$ relative to the basis U. We write

$$(\mathbf{v})_U = (c_1, c_2, \ldots, c_k)$$

Coordinates

The numbers $c_1, c_2, \ldots, c_k$ are called the **coordinates of v** relative to the basis U.

Notice that the vector $\mathbf{v}$ belongs to the vector space S, whereas the coordinate vector $(\mathbf{v})_U$ is a k-tuple of real numbers. The actual numbers depend on the vector $\mathbf{v}$ and also on the basis chosen. This is indicated by the notation $(\mathbf{v})_U$.

Example 24

In Example 23 we found that if $\mathbf{u}_1 = (1, 0, 0, 1, 0)$, $\mathbf{u}_2 = (1, 1, 1, 1, 1)$, $\mathbf{u}_3 = (0, 1, 0, 1, 1)$, and $\mathbf{u}_4 = (0, 0, 0, 1, 1)$, then the set $U = \{\mathbf{u}_1, \mathbf{u}_2, \mathbf{u}_3, \mathbf{u}_4\}$ is a basis for the space spanned by U. In particular, we saw that $\mathbf{v} = (5, 4, 3, 5, 3)$ can be written uniquely as $\mathbf{v} = 2\mathbf{u}_1 + 3\mathbf{u}_2 + \mathbf{u}_3 - \mathbf{u}_4$. In this case, $(\mathbf{v})_U = (2, 3, 1, -1)$ is the coordinate vector of $\mathbf{v}$ relative to the basis U.

On the other hand, the statement $(\mathbf{w})_U = (1, 2, -1, 1)$ means that $\mathbf{w} = \mathbf{u}_1 + 2\mathbf{u}_2 - \mathbf{u}_3 + \mathbf{u}_4 = (3, 1, 2, 3, 2)$. ■

The word *coordinate* is borrowed from geometry. Example 25 illustrates three possible bases in R^2. (There are, of course, many more.)

Example 25

The standard vectors $E = \{\mathbf{e}_1, \mathbf{e}_2\}$ form the simplest basis in R^2. They are unit vectors lying along the coordinate axes. The vector $\mathbf{v} = (3, -1) = 3\mathbf{e}_1 + (-1)\mathbf{e}_2$ and $(\mathbf{v})_E = (3, -1)$. Thus, the coordinate vector of $\mathbf{v}$ relative to the standard basis E is simply the pair of coordinates of P relative to the coordinate axes.

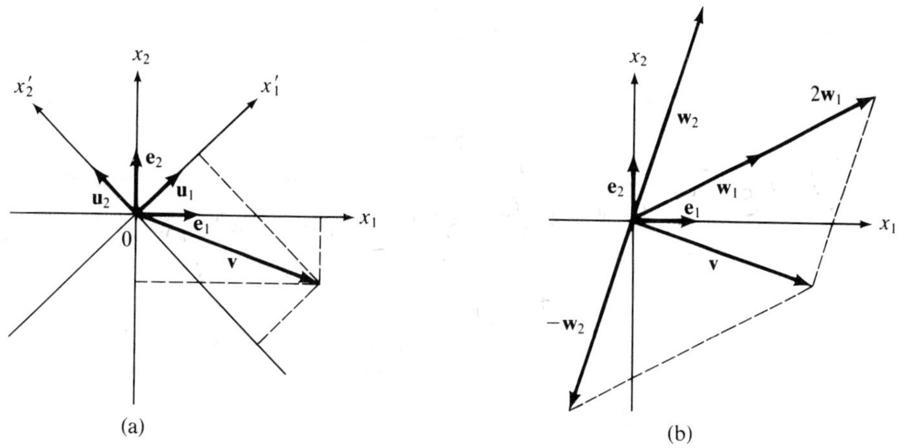

FIGURE 4.3

Now let $U = \{\mathbf{u}_1, \mathbf{u}_2\}$, where $\mathbf{u}_1 = (1/\sqrt{2}, 1/\sqrt{2})$ and $\mathbf{u}_2 = (-1/\sqrt{2}, 1/\sqrt{2})$. The coordinates of $\mathbf{v}$ relative to V are found from the system

$$c_1\mathbf{u}_1 + c_2\mathbf{u}_2 = \mathbf{v}$$

$$\begin{bmatrix} \frac{1}{\sqrt{2}} & -\frac{1}{\sqrt{2}} \\ \frac{1}{\sqrt{2}} & \frac{1}{\sqrt{2}} \end{bmatrix} \begin{bmatrix} c_1 \\ c_2 \end{bmatrix} = \begin{bmatrix} 3 \\ -1 \end{bmatrix}$$

from which $c_1 = \sqrt{2}$ and $c_2 = -2\sqrt{2}$. The coordinate vector $(\mathbf{v})_U = (\sqrt{2}, -2\sqrt{2})$. This represents the coordinates of P relative to the coordinate axes Ox_1', Ox_2', which make an angle of 45° with the original coordinate axes (Figure 4.3a).

Each of the bases considered has two vectors of unit length and perpendicular to each other. Changing from one to the other is accomplished simply by a rotation of the axes about the origin.

A basis in R^2 *need not* consist of orthogonal unit vectors. Let $W = \{\mathbf{w}_1, \mathbf{w}_2\}$, where $\mathbf{w}_1 = (2, 1)$ and $\mathbf{w}_2 = (1, 3)$. The coordinates of $\mathbf{v}$ relative to W are found from the equations

$$\begin{bmatrix} 2 & 1 \\ 1 & 3 \end{bmatrix} \begin{bmatrix} d_1 \\ d_2 \end{bmatrix} = \begin{bmatrix} 3 \\ -1 \end{bmatrix}$$

We have $(\mathbf{v})_W = (2, -1)$. These are also coordinates, but the coordinate axes are not rectangular (Figure 4.3b). ■

A second important property of a basis is the following: Although a given vector space can have many different bases, the *number* of vectors in each basis is the same. Example 26 establishes this fact in the case of a vector space that has a basis containing three vectors.

Example 26 Let S be a vector space with basis $U = \{\mathbf{u}_1, \mathbf{u}_2, \mathbf{u}_3\}$. Any set of vectors from S that has more than three vectors must be a dependent set. To see this consider the set $\{\mathbf{v}_1, \mathbf{v}_2, \mathbf{v}_3, \mathbf{v}_4\}$. Since all of these vectors are in S, each can be written as a linear combination of the basis vectors $\mathbf{u}_1, \mathbf{u}_2, \mathbf{u}_3$. Thus:

$$\begin{aligned}
\mathbf{v}_1 &= a_{11}\mathbf{u}_1 + a_{12}\mathbf{u}_2 + a_{13}\mathbf{u}_3 \\
\mathbf{v}_2 &= a_{21}\mathbf{u}_1 + a_{22}\mathbf{u}_2 + a_{23}\mathbf{u}_3 \\
\mathbf{v}_3 &= a_{31}\mathbf{u}_1 + a_{32}\mathbf{u}_2 + a_{33}\mathbf{u}_3 \\
\mathbf{v}_4 &= a_{41}\mathbf{u}_1 + a_{42}\mathbf{u}_2 + a_{43}\mathbf{u}_3
\end{aligned}$$

Is the set $\{\mathbf{v}_1, \mathbf{v}_2, \mathbf{v}_3, \mathbf{v}_4\}$ a linearly independent set? To answer this we consider the vector equation $c_1\mathbf{v}_1 + c_2\mathbf{v}_2 + c_3\mathbf{v}_3 + c_4\mathbf{v}_4 = \mathbf{0}$. If we substitute the values of $\mathbf{v}_1, \mathbf{v}_2, \mathbf{v}_3, \mathbf{v}_4$ and collect terms, we obtain

$$\begin{aligned}
(c_1a_{11} + c_2a_{21} + c_3a_{31} + c_4a_{41})\mathbf{u}_1 + (c_1a_{12} + c_2a_{22} + c_3a_{32} + c_4a_{42})\mathbf{u}_2 \\
+ (c_1a_{13} + c_2a_{23} + c_3a_{33} + c_4a_{43})\mathbf{u}_3 = \mathbf{0}
\end{aligned}$$

Since the set $\{\mathbf{u}_1, \mathbf{u}_2, \mathbf{u}_3\}$ is a basis, it is linearly independent. Each of the coefficients in the vector equation must be zero. That is,

$$\begin{aligned}
c_1a_{11} + c_2a_{21} + c_3a_{31} + c_4a_{41} &= 0 \\
c_1a_{12} + c_2a_{22} + c_3a_{32} + c_4a_{42} &= 0 \\
c_1a_{13} + c_2a_{23} + c_3a_{33} + c_4a_{43} &= 0
\end{aligned}
\quad \text{or} \quad
\mathbf{A}\begin{bmatrix} c_1 \\ c_2 \\ c_3 \\ c_4 \end{bmatrix} = \begin{bmatrix} 0 \\ 0 \\ 0 \end{bmatrix}$$

This system of three equations in four unknowns must have a nontrivial solution. This says that there are numbers c_1, c_2, c_3, c_4, not all zero, such that

$$c_1\mathbf{v}_1 + c_2\mathbf{v}_2 + c_3\mathbf{v}_3 + c_4\mathbf{v}_4 = \mathbf{0}$$

Thus, the set $\{\mathbf{v}_1, \mathbf{v}_2, \mathbf{v}_3, \mathbf{v}_4\}$ is linearly dependent.

What we have just shown is that if S has a basis of three vectors, no other basis can have *more* than three vectors. Now we must ask whether another basis can have fewer than three vectors. If $U = \{\mathbf{u}_1, \mathbf{u}_2, \mathbf{u}_3\}$ is a basis, can there be a set of two vectors, say, $V = \{\mathbf{v}_1, \mathbf{v}_2\}$, that is also a basis for S? This question has already been answered since if V were a basis with two vectors, the same type of argument given in the first part of this example would show that no other basis can have more than two vectors. We must conclude that every basis for S has exactly three vectors. ■

An argument analogous to that of Example 26 proves the following theorem.

Theorem 6 Let S be a vector space for which the set $U = \{\mathbf{u}_1, \mathbf{u}_2, \ldots, \mathbf{u}_k\}$ is a basis. Then every basis for S has exactly k vectors. □

The uniqueness of the number k makes it a property of the space S and not of the particular basis. Again we borrow a word from geometry and call k the *dimension* of S.

Dimension

Definition 7

The number of vectors in a basis for S is called the **dimension** of the space S. The space consisting of only the zero vector has dimension zero. The dimension of S depends on S itself and not on any particular basis.

We have seen that $\mathbf{e}_1, \mathbf{e}_2, \ldots, \mathbf{e}_n$ is a basis for R^n. Thus R^n is an n-dimensional space. In particular, we have identified R^2 with the plane. Since the dimension of R^2 is two, this agrees with our geometric knowledge that the plane is a two-dimensional region. Similarly, R^3 is identified with the geometry of three dimensions.

The following theorem is an immediate consequence of Theorem 6. Its proof is left as an exercise (Problem 16).

Theorem 7 Let S be a vector space of dimension n, and let U be a set of n vectors in S.

1. If U spans S, it is a basis for S.
2. If U is linearly independent, it is a basis for S. □

In Example 26, we saw that a set of four vectors from a space of three dimensions must be a linearly dependent set. In other words, subspaces of a space of dimension three cannot have dimension more than three. In general, subspaces of a space of dimension n cannot have dimension more than n.

Example 27 What are the possible subspaces of R^3? One subspace has only the zero vector. Suppose S is a subspace that contains nonzero vectors. Choose one of these nonzero vectors, $\mathbf{u}_1$. Two situations are possible. (1) All the vectors in S have the form $k\mathbf{u}_1$, where k is a real number. In this case S is a one-dimensional subspace, corresponding to a line through the origin (see Example 11). (2) There is in S a nonzero vector $\mathbf{u}_2 \neq k\mathbf{u}_1$. The set $\{\mathbf{u}_1, \mathbf{u}_2\}$ is a linearly independent set and $\text{lin}\{\mathbf{u}_1, \mathbf{u}_2\}$ is contained in S. Again two situations are possible. If $S = \text{lin}\{\mathbf{u}_1, \mathbf{u}_2\}$, that is, every vector in S is a linear combination of $\mathbf{u}_1$ and $\mathbf{u}_2$, then S is a two-dimensional subspace of R^3 corresponding to a plane through the origin. (3) If $S \neq \text{lin}\{\mathbf{u}_1, \mathbf{u}_2\}$ there is a nonzero vector $\mathbf{u}_3$ such that $\{\mathbf{u}_1, \mathbf{u}_2, \mathbf{u}_3\}$ is a linearly independent set. In this case S is all of R^3. The subspaces of R^3 described in Example 11 are all the possible subspaces of R^3. ■

An analysis similar to Example 27 can be done to describe the subspaces of any space V provided V has a finite dimension. Among the general vector spaces discussed in Section 4.1, there are spaces that have no finite basis. For example, the space P consisting of all possible polynomials cannot have a finite basis. Suppose that $\{p_1, p_2, \ldots, p_k\}$ is a basis for the set of all polynomials. Let n be the largest of the degrees of the k polynomials in this basis. Every linear combination of the set $\{p_1, p_2, \ldots, p_k\}$ must have degree not exceeding n. Thus, the simple polynomial x^{n+1} is not in the space spanned by $\{p_1, p_2, \ldots, p_k\}$ so this set cannot be a basis for P. The study of spaces of infinite dimension is beyond the scope of this book.

SUMMARY $U = \{\mathbf{u}_1, \mathbf{u}_2, \ldots, \mathbf{u}_k\}$ is a basis for a vector space V if and only if every vector in V can be written uniquely in the form $\mathbf{v} = c_1\mathbf{u}_1 + c_2\mathbf{u}_2 + \cdots + c_k\mathbf{u}_k$. The unique k-tuple $(c_1, c_2, \ldots, c_k)$ is called the **coordinate vector** of $\mathbf{v}$ relative to the basis U and written $(\mathbf{v})_U$.

A space V can have many different bases, but the number of vectors in each basis is the same. The number of vectors in a basis is called the **dimension** of the space.

The simplest basis in R^n is $E = \{\mathbf{e}_1, \mathbf{e}_2, \ldots, \mathbf{e}_n\}$. This is called the **standard basis** in R^n. The n-tuple $\mathbf{x} = (x_1, x_2, \ldots, x_n)$ is a vector in R^n and also the coordinate vector $(\mathbf{x})_E$.

The space R^n has dimension n. Any subspace of R^n has dimension $\leqslant n$. The subspace consisting of only the zero vector has dimension zero.

EXERCISES 4.3

1. Let $\mathbf{u}_1 = (1, 0, 1)$, $\mathbf{u}_2 = (2, 1, 0)$, $\mathbf{u}_3 = (-1, -1, 1)$.
a. Express $(4, 1, 2)$ in the form $c_1\mathbf{u}_1 + c_2\mathbf{u}_2 + c_3\mathbf{u}_3$. Is the choice of c_1, c_2, c_3 unique?
b. Write the matrix equation that must be solved to express (a, b, c) as a linear combination of $\mathbf{u}_1, \mathbf{u}_2, \mathbf{u}_3$. What is the rank of the coefficient matrix?
c. Is $\{\mathbf{u}_1, \mathbf{u}_2, \mathbf{u}_3\}$ a basis for the space spanned by these vectors?

2. Represent $(1, 1, 1)$ as a linear combination of $(1, 0, 1)$, $(0, 1, 0)$ and $(-1, 1, -1)$ in three different ways.

3. Let $\mathbf{v}_1 = (1, 1, -1, 2)$, $\mathbf{v}_2 = (0, 1, 0, 3)$, and $\mathbf{v}_3 = (1, 2, 2, 5)$. Let T be the space spanned by $\{\mathbf{v}_1, \mathbf{v}_2, \mathbf{v}_3\}$.
a. Express $(2, 1, 1, 1)$ in the form $c_1\mathbf{v}_1 + c_2\mathbf{v}_2 + c_3\mathbf{v}_3$. Is the choice of c_1, c_2, c_3 unique?
b. Is $\{\mathbf{v}_1, \mathbf{v}_2, \mathbf{v}_3\}$ a linearly independent set? Is it a basis for T?
c. Is it possible to express $(2, 1, 1, -1)$ in the form $c_1\mathbf{v}_1 + c_2\mathbf{v}_2 + c_3\mathbf{v}_3$? Explain the meaning of your answer.

4. In each case, determine whether the set is a basis for the vector space spanned by the set. Write the matrix **M** with the given vectors as columns and find the rank of **M**.
a. $(1, 2, 1)$, $(1, 2, 3)$, $(1, 0, 1)$
b. $(1, 2, 1)$, $(1, 2, 3)$, $(0, 0, 1)$
c. $(1, 1, 1, 1)$, $(1, -1, 1, 1)$, $(1, 1, -1, 1)$, $(1, -1, -1, -1)$

5. $U = \{\mathbf{u}_1, \mathbf{u}_2, \mathbf{u}_3\}$ is a basis for R^3, where $\mathbf{u}_1 = (1, 1, 2)$, $\mathbf{u}_2 = (2, 2, 1)$, and $\mathbf{u}_3 = (1, 2, 2)$.
a. Find the coordinates of $\mathbf{v} = (1, 1, 0)$ relative to the basis U.
b. The coordinates of $\mathbf{v}$ relative to U are $(\mathbf{v})_U = (1, 1, 2)$. What is $\mathbf{v}$?
c. If $(\mathbf{w})_U = (-2, 4, -1)$, what is $\mathbf{w}$?

6. Let $\mathbf{u}_1 = (1, 1, 1, 1)$, $\mathbf{u}_2 = (1, -1, 1, 1)$, $\mathbf{u}_3 = (1, 1, -1, 1)$, $\mathbf{u}_4 = (1, -1, -1, -1)$ and $U = \{\mathbf{u}_1, \mathbf{u}_2, \mathbf{u}_3, \mathbf{u}_4\}$.
a. Find $(\mathbf{v})_U$ if $\mathbf{v} = (2, 1, 3, 6)$.
b. Find $\mathbf{v}$ given that $(\mathbf{v})_U = (1, 0, -1, 4)$. Find $\mathbf{w}$ given that $(\mathbf{w})_U = (1, 1, 3, 1)$. Verify that $(\mathbf{v} + \mathbf{w})_U = (\mathbf{v})_U + (\mathbf{w})_U$.
c. Let $\mathbf{w} = (2, -4, 4, -2)$. Find $(\mathbf{w})_U$. Find $(2\mathbf{w})_U$. Verify that $(2\mathbf{w})_U = 2(\mathbf{w})_U$.

7. Let $U = \{\mathbf{u}_1, \mathbf{u}_2, \mathbf{u}_3\}$ be a basis for a vector space S. Show that $(\mathbf{z})_U = (\mathbf{x})_U + (\mathbf{y})_U$ if and only if $\mathbf{z} = \mathbf{x} + \mathbf{y}$.

8. Let $\mathbf{U} = \{\mathbf{u}_1, \mathbf{u}_2, \mathbf{u}_3\}$ be a basis for a vector space S. Show that $(\mathbf{v})_U = k(\mathbf{w})_U$ if and only if $\mathbf{v} = k\mathbf{w}$.

9. Show that $E = \{1, x, x^2\}$ is a basis for P_2. What is the dimension of P_2? What is $(p)_E$ if $p = 3 - 4x + x^2$. Write p if $(p)_E = (2, 0, 1)$.

10. **a.** Give an example of a subspace of P_2 of dimension one.
b. Give an example of a subspace of P_2 of dimension two.
c. Show that there is only one subspace of P_2 of dimension three.

11. **a.** Find the coordinates of $3x^2 + 2x - 5$ relative to the basis $\{1, x + x^2, 2 - x + x^2\}$.
b. Find the coordinates of $a_0 + a_1x + a_2x^2$ relative to the basis $\{1, x + x^2, 2 - x + x^2\}$.

12. Let $p_1 = a_0 + a_1x + a_2x^2$, $p_2 = b_0 + b_1x + b_2x^2$, $p_3 = c_0 + c_1x + c_2x^2$. Write a condition on p_1, p_2, p_3 that ensures that the set $\{p_1, p_2, p_3\}$ is linearly independent. What matrix must have rank 3?

13. Let $U = \{p_1, p_2, p_3\}$ be a basis for P_2, where p_1, p_2, p_3 are defined as in Problem 12. Express in matrix form a method for calculating $(p)_U$, where $p = d_0 + d_1x + d_2x^2$.

14. In Exercises 4.2, Problem 16, the set $\{\mathbf{E}_1, \mathbf{E}_2, \mathbf{E}_3, \mathbf{E}_4\}$ was shown to be a basis for $M_{2\times2}$, where $\mathbf{E}_1 = \begin{bmatrix} 1 & 0 \\ 0 & 0 \end{bmatrix}$, $\mathbf{E}_2 = \begin{bmatrix} 0 & 1 \\ 0 & 0 \end{bmatrix}$, $\mathbf{E}_3 = \begin{bmatrix} 0 & 0 \\ 1 & 0 \end{bmatrix}$, and $\mathbf{E}_4 = \begin{bmatrix} 0 & 0 \\ 0 & 1 \end{bmatrix}$. This is called the standard basis for $M_{2\times2}$.
a. What is the dimension of $M_{2\times2}$?
b. If $\mathbf{A} = \begin{bmatrix} 2 & 3 \\ 4 & 5 \end{bmatrix}$, what are the coordinates of $\mathbf{A}$ relative to the standard basis?

15. Show that $\mathbf{B}_1 = \begin{bmatrix} 1 & 0 \\ 0 & 0 \end{bmatrix}$, $\mathbf{B}_2 = \begin{bmatrix} 1 & 0 \\ 1 & 0 \end{bmatrix}$, $\mathbf{B}_3 = \begin{bmatrix} 1 & 0 \\ 1 & 1 \end{bmatrix}$, $\mathbf{B}_4 = \begin{bmatrix} 1 & 1 \\ 1 & 1 \end{bmatrix}$ is also a basis for $M_{2\times2}$. Find the coordinates of $\mathbf{A}$ (from Problem 14) relative to this basis.

*16. Develop a proof of Theorem 7.

17. Show that any linearly independent set of n vectors from R^n is a basis for R^n.

18. Show that any linearly independent set of four vectors from P_3 is a basis for P_3.

19. Recall Theorem 15, Chapter 3. Show that the following statement can be added to the list of equivalent statements given in this theorem:

 9. The set of n-tuples that form the columns of $\mathbf{A}$ is a basis for R^n.

20. Let $\mathbf{u}_1 = (1, 1, 1, 1)$, $\mathbf{u}_2 = (1, 0, 1, 0)$, $\mathbf{u}_3 = (2, 2, 2, 2)$, $\mathbf{u}_4 = (2, 1, 2, 1)$, $\mathbf{u}_5 = (1, -1, 1, 0)$, and $\mathbf{u}_6 = (3, 0, 3, 1)$. Let S be the space spanned by $\{\mathbf{u}_1, \mathbf{u}_2, \mathbf{u}_3, \mathbf{u}_4, \mathbf{u}_5, \mathbf{u}_6\}$. From these six vectors pick a basis for S by the following steps:
a. Form the 4×6 matrix $\mathbf{M}$ with columns $\mathbf{u}_1, \mathbf{u}_2, \mathbf{u}_3, \mathbf{u}_4, \mathbf{u}_5, \mathbf{u}_6$. Row-reduce $\mathbf{M}$ and show that it has rank 3.
b. $\mathbf{M}$ is the coefficient matrix in the equation $c_1\mathbf{u}_1 + c_2\mathbf{u}_2 + c_3\mathbf{u}_3 + c_4\mathbf{u}_4 + c_5\mathbf{u}_5 + c_6\mathbf{u}_6 = \mathbf{0}$ Verify that the columns 1, 2, and 5 are leading columns and that $\mathbf{u}_1, \mathbf{u}_2, \mathbf{u}_5$ is a linearly independent set.
c. Verify that, in the solution of the equation in **b.**, c_3, c_4, c_6 can be assigned arbitrarily. By assigning the values $c_3 = 1$, $c_4 = 0$, $c_6 = 0$, show that $\mathbf{u}_3$ is a linear combination of $\mathbf{u}_1, \mathbf{u}_2, \mathbf{u}_5$.
d. Show that $\mathbf{u}_4$ and $\mathbf{u}_6$ are also linear combinations of $\mathbf{u}_1, \mathbf{u}_2$, and $\mathbf{u}_5$.
e. Using **b.**, **c.**, and **d.**, show that $\{\mathbf{u}_1, \mathbf{u}_2, \mathbf{u}_5\}$ is a basis for S.

21. For the vectors defined in Problem 20, find a different basis for S by using the same technique but writing the columns in $\mathbf{M}$ in the order $\mathbf{u}_5, \mathbf{u}_2, \mathbf{u}_4, \mathbf{u}_6, \mathbf{u}_3, \mathbf{u}_1$. Is the rank of $\mathbf{M}$ changed?

22. Let S be a subspace of R^n spanned by $\{\mathbf{u}_1, \mathbf{u}_2, \ldots, \mathbf{u}_k\}$. Let $\mathbf{M}$ be the $n \times k$ matrix with columns $\mathbf{u}_1, \mathbf{u}_2, \ldots, \mathbf{u}_k$. Show that the dimension of S is the rank of $\mathbf{M}$.

4.4 Spaces Associated with a Matrix: Null Space, Row Space, Column Space

In the two preceding sections we have studied the meaning of linear independence, basis, and dimension. In this section we apply these concepts to a particular set of vector spaces associated with an $m \times n$ matrix $\mathbf{A}$.

First consider the solution set of the equation $\mathbf{AX} = \mathbf{0}$.

Example 28 Let $\mathbf{A} = \begin{bmatrix} 1 & 2 & 1 \\ 2 & 5 & 3 \end{bmatrix}$. Show that the solution set of $\mathbf{AX} = \mathbf{0}$ is a vector space.

Solution

Method 1: We can find the solution set explicitly by solving $\mathbf{AX} = \mathbf{0}$. Row reduction gives

$$\left[\begin{array}{ccc|c} 1 & 2 & 1 & 0 \\ 2 & 5 & 3 & 0 \end{array}\right] \Leftrightarrow \left[\begin{array}{ccc|c} 1 & 0 & -1 & 0 \\ 0 & 1 & 1 & 0 \end{array}\right]$$

The solution set is the set of triples $\{k(1, -1, 1), k \text{ a real number}\}$. A set of this form has already been shown to be a one-dimensional subspace of R^3.
Method 2: We can argue as follows. Since $\mathbf{A}$ is 2×3, then $\mathbf{X}$ is 3×1. The solution set is a subset of R^3. Since $\mathbf{0}$ is in the set, it is nonempty. Let $\mathbf{X}_1$ and $\mathbf{X}_2$ be two elements of the set. Then $\mathbf{AX}_1 = \mathbf{0}$ and $\mathbf{AX}_2 = \mathbf{0}$. Thus $\mathbf{A}(\mathbf{X}_1 + \mathbf{X}_2) = \mathbf{AX}_1 + \mathbf{AX}_2 = \mathbf{0}$. The set is closed with respect to addition. For any scalar k, $\mathbf{A}(k\mathbf{X}_1) = k\mathbf{AX}_1 = \mathbf{0}$. The set is closed with respect to scalar multiplication. By Theorem 2, the set is a subspace of R^3. ■

The argument in the second method of Example 28 does not depend on the particular matrix $\mathbf{A}$ except to determine the space to which $\mathbf{X}$ belongs. An identical argument can be used to prove Theorem 8.

Theorem 8 Let $\mathbf{A}$ be an $m \times n$ matrix. The set of $n \times 1$ arrays $\mathbf{X}$ such that $\mathbf{AX} = \mathbf{0}$ is a subspace of R^n. □

The name "null space of $\mathbf{A}$" is given to this subspace. The word *null* is sometimes used to mean zero and indicates here that multiplying $\mathbf{A}$ and $\mathbf{X}$ yields the vector $\mathbf{0}$.

Null Space

Definition 8

Let $\mathbf{A}$ be an $m \times n$ matrix. The set of $n \times 1$ arrays $\mathbf{X}$ such that $\mathbf{AX} = \mathbf{0}$ is called the **null space** of $\mathbf{A}$.

The vectors in the null space of $\mathbf{A}$ can be calculated by simply solving the corresponding system of homogeneous equations as the following example illustrates.

Example 29A Let

$$\mathbf{A} = \begin{bmatrix} 1 & -1 & -1 & 1 & 0 \\ 1 & 1 & 1 & -3 & 2 \\ 1 & 4 & 4 & -9 & 5 \end{bmatrix}$$

The null space of **A** is the set of 5-tuples that are solutions of the system of equations $\mathbf{AX} = \mathbf{0}$, that is:

$$\begin{aligned} x_1 - x_2 - x_3 + x_4 &= 0 \\ x_1 + x_2 + x_3 - 3x_4 + 2x_5 &= 0 \\ x_1 + 4x_2 + 4x_3 - 9x_4 + 5x_5 &= 0 \end{aligned}$$

The solution of this system by the method of row reduction proceeds as follows: write the augmented matrix of the system, and by row operations, put this into row-reduced form. In this case,

$$\left[\begin{array}{rrrrr|r} 1 & -1 & -1 & 1 & 0 & 0 \\ 1 & 1 & 1 & -3 & 2 & 0 \\ 1 & 4 & 4 & -9 & 5 & 0 \end{array}\right] \Leftrightarrow \left[\begin{array}{rrrrr|r} 1 & 0 & 0 & -1 & 1 & 0 \\ 0 & 1 & 1 & -2 & 1 & 0 \\ 0 & 0 & 0 & 0 & 0 & 0 \end{array}\right]$$

The leading columns are 1 and 2, so x_3, x_4, and x_5 can be given arbitrary values, and x_1 and x_2 can be expressed in terms of them. In this way, we obtain

$$\begin{aligned} x_1 &= k_2 - k_3 \\ x_2 &= -k_1 + 2k_2 - k_3 \\ x_3 &= k_1 \\ x_4 &= k_2 \\ x_5 &= k_3 \end{aligned}$$

or

$$\begin{bmatrix} x_1 \\ x_2 \\ x_3 \\ x_4 \\ x_5 \end{bmatrix} = k_1 \begin{bmatrix} 0 \\ -1 \\ 1 \\ 0 \\ 0 \end{bmatrix} + k_2 \begin{bmatrix} 1 \\ 2 \\ 0 \\ 1 \\ 0 \end{bmatrix} + k_3 \begin{bmatrix} -1 \\ -1 \\ 0 \\ 0 \\ 1 \end{bmatrix}$$

The solution set is the set of 5-tuples,

$$\{k_1\mathbf{u}_1 + k_2\mathbf{u}_2 + k_3\mathbf{u}_3, \text{ where } k_1, k_2, \text{ and } k_3 \text{ are real numbers and}$$
$$\mathbf{u}_1 = (0, -1, 1, 0, 0), \mathbf{u}_2 = (1, 2, 0, 1, 0), \mathbf{u}_3 = (-1, -1, 0, 0, 1)\}$$

Written in this form, the solution set is seen to be exactly the subspace of R^5 spanned by $\{\mathbf{u}_1, \mathbf{u}_2, \mathbf{u}_3\}$. ■

By solving the system of equations $\mathbf{AX} = \mathbf{0}$, we write the vectors in the null space in terms of a spanning set. In order to find the dimension of the null space, we need a basis.

Example 29B To see whether or not the set $\{\mathbf{u}_1, \mathbf{u}_2, \mathbf{u}_3\}$ is linearly independent, we look at the rank of the matrix $\mathbf{M}$, which has as columns the 5-tuples $\mathbf{u}_1, \mathbf{u}_2, \mathbf{u}_3$.

$$\mathbf{M} = \begin{bmatrix} 0 & 1 & -1 \\ -1 & 2 & -1 \\ 1 & 0 & 0 \\ 0 & 1 & 0 \\ 0 & 0 & 1 \end{bmatrix} \Leftrightarrow \begin{bmatrix} 1 & 0 & 0 \\ 0 & 1 & 0 \\ 0 & 0 & 1 \\ 0 & 1 & -1 \\ -1 & 2 & -1 \end{bmatrix} \Leftrightarrow \begin{bmatrix} 1 & 0 & 0 \\ 0 & 1 & 0 \\ 0 & 0 & 1 \\ 0 & 0 & 0 \\ 0 & 0 & 0 \end{bmatrix}$$

The rank of $\mathbf{M}$ is 3, which is equal to the number of columns, so $\{\mathbf{u}_1, \mathbf{u}_2, \mathbf{u}_3\}$ is a linearly independent set. (Theorem 4.) ■

Let $\mathbf{A}$ be an $m \times n$ matrix of rank r. The solution set of the system $\mathbf{AX} = \mathbf{0}$ can be found by row reduction. This method yields a set of $n - r$ vectors that span the null space of $\mathbf{A}$. In Example 29, the vectors found in this way also form a basis. This is not just luck. The method of row reduction always yields a spanning set that is linearly independent.

The final form of a row-reduced matrix of rank r is

$$\begin{array}{c} \\ \\ \\ \\ \\ \\ \text{row } r \\ \\ \text{row } m \end{array} \begin{bmatrix} & & j_1 & & j_2 & & j_3 & & j_r & \\ \cdots & 0 & 1 & \cdots & 0 & \cdots & 0 & \cdots & 0 & \cdots \\ \cdots & 0 & 0 & \cdots & 1 & \cdots & 0 & \cdots & 0 & \cdots \\ \cdots & 0 & 0 & \cdots & 0 & \cdots & 1 & \cdots & 0 & \cdots \\ & \vdots & \vdots & & \vdots & & \vdots & & \vdots & \\ \cdots & 0 & 0 & \cdots & 0 & \cdots & 0 & \cdots & 1 & \cdots \\ & & & & \text{(all zeros)} & & & & & \\ \cdots & 0 & 0 & \cdots & 0 & \cdots & 0 & \cdots & 0 & \cdots \end{bmatrix}$$

If the $m \times n$ matrix $\mathbf{A}$ is the coefficient matrix of a homogeneous system, the solution set is found by writing $x_{j_1}, x_{j_2}, \ldots, x_{j_r}$ in terms of the other $n - r$ unknowns to which arbitrary values are assigned. The solution set is then a linear combination of $n - r$ n-tuples, each corresponding to an arbitrarily assigned x_i. To determine whether these n-tuples form a linearly independent set, form the matrix $\mathbf{M}$ with these n-tuples as columns. It is an $n \times (n - r)$ matrix with $n - r$ rows that are standard vectors. $\mathbf{M}$ must have rank $n - r$. This argument establishes the following theorem.

Theorem 9 Let $\mathbf{A}$ be an $m \times n$ matrix of rank r. If the solution set of the system $\mathbf{AX} = \mathbf{0}$ is found by the method of row reduction, the spanning set of $n - r$ vectors obtained is a basis for the null space of $\mathbf{A}$. □

An important consequence of this theorem is the relation between the rank of $\mathbf{A}$ and the dimension of the null space of $\mathbf{A}$.

Theorem 10 If $\mathbf{A}$ is an $m \times n$ matrix of rank r, the null space of $\mathbf{A}$ has dimension $n - r$. □

The equation $\mathbf{AX} = \mathbf{0}$ implies a special relationship between $\mathbf{X}$ and the rows of $\mathbf{A}$.

Example 30 Let

$$\mathbf{A} = \begin{bmatrix} 1 & -1 & -1 & 1 & 0 \\ 1 & 1 & 1 & -3 & 2 \\ 1 & 4 & 4 & -9 & 5 \end{bmatrix}$$

Then $\mathbf{AX} = \mathbf{0}$ is equivalent to

$$\begin{aligned} x_1 - x_2 - x_3 + x_4 \qquad &= 0 \\ x_1 + x_2 + x_3 - 3x_4 + 2x_5 &= 0 \\ x_1 + 4x_2 + 4x_3 - 9x_4 + 5x_5 &= 0 \end{aligned} \quad \text{or} \quad \begin{aligned} \mathbf{u}_1 \cdot \mathbf{x} &= 0 \\ \mathbf{u}_2 \cdot \mathbf{x} &= 0 \\ \mathbf{u}_3 \cdot \mathbf{x} &= 0 \end{aligned}$$

where $\mathbf{u}_1 = (1, -1, -1, 1, 0)$, $\mathbf{u}_2 = (1, 1, 1, -3, 2)$, $\mathbf{u}_3 = (1, 4, 4, -9, 5)$, and $\mathbf{x} = (x_1, x_2, x_3, x_4, x_5)$. This shows that $\mathbf{x}$ is orthogonal to each of the rows of $\mathbf{A}$. Since it is orthogonal to $\mathbf{u}_1, \mathbf{u}_2, \mathbf{u}_3$, it is orthogonal to every linear combination of these vectors. ■

Row Space

Definition 9

Let $\mathbf{A}$ be an $m \times n$ matrix. The space spanned by the rows of $\mathbf{A}$ is a subspace of R^n called the **row space** of $\mathbf{A}$.

Theorem 11 Each vector in the null space of $\mathbf{A}$ is orthogonal to every vector in the row space of $\mathbf{A}$, and conversely.

Proof Let $\mathbf{A}$ be an $m \times n$ matrix; $\mathbf{u}_1, \mathbf{u}_2, \mathbf{u}_3, \ldots, \mathbf{u}_m$ be the rows of $\mathbf{A}$, and $\mathbf{x} = (x_1, x_2, \ldots, x_n)$ be any vector in the null space of $\mathbf{A}$. Since $\mathbf{AX} = \mathbf{0}$, $\mathbf{u}_i \cdot \mathbf{x} = 0$, $i = 1, 2, \ldots, n$. If $\mathbf{v}$ is in the row space, $\mathbf{v} = \sum_{i=1}^{m} c_i\mathbf{u}_i$. Then $\mathbf{v} \cdot \mathbf{x} = \left(\sum_{i=1}^{m} c_i\mathbf{u}_i\right) \cdot \mathbf{x} = \sum_{i=1}^{m} c_i\mathbf{u}_i \cdot \mathbf{x} = 0$. A similar argument shows that the converse is also true. □

We must now ask: What is the dimension of the row space of $\mathbf{A}$? The definition of the row space of $\mathbf{A}$ gives a spanning set for the space. One of the most instructive techniques for finding a basis is the familiar process of row reduction. At each step in this procedure the row space of the matrix remains unchanged. To see this consider the row operations: (1) interchange two rows; (2) multiply a row by a nonzero scalar; (3) add k times row j to row i, where $i \neq j$. Let the rows of $\mathbf{A}$ be $U = \{\mathbf{r}_1, \mathbf{r}_2, \ldots, \mathbf{r}_m\}$. The first two operations clearly do not change the space spanned by U. In the third case, suppose $i = 2$ and $j = 1$. Then the set U is replaced by $V = \{\mathbf{r}_1, \mathbf{r}_2 + k\mathbf{r}_1, \mathbf{r}_3, \ldots, \mathbf{r}_m\}$. A linear combination of the vectors in V is $c_1\mathbf{r}_1 + c_2(\mathbf{r}_2 + k\mathbf{r}_1) + c_3\mathbf{r}_3 + \cdots + c_m\mathbf{r}_m$, which can also be written

$(c_1 + kc_2)\mathbf{r}_1 + c_2\mathbf{r}_2 + c_3\mathbf{r}_3 + \cdots + c_m\mathbf{r}_m$. Thus every linear combination of the vectors in V is a linear combination of the vectors in U. Similarly, we can see that every linear combination of the vectors in U is a linear combination of the vectors in V. A basis for the row space of **A** is therefore the set of nonzero rows in the row-reduced form of **A**. The row space of **A** has dimension r, where r is the rank of **A**.

Since any vector space has many possible bases, it is possible that in the process of row reduction a basis in the row space of **A** can be identified before the process is complete.

Example 31

Let $\mathbf{A} = \begin{bmatrix} 2 & 1 & 8 & 5 \\ 1 & 0 & 5 & 2 \\ 1 & 4 & -3 & 6 \end{bmatrix}$

$$\mathbf{A} \Leftrightarrow \begin{bmatrix} 1 & 0 & 5 & 2 \\ 1 & 4 & -3 & 6 \\ 2 & 1 & 8 & 5 \end{bmatrix} \Leftrightarrow \begin{bmatrix} 1 & 0 & 5 & 2 \\ 0 & 4 & -8 & 4 \\ 0 & 1 & -2 & 1 \end{bmatrix} \Leftrightarrow \begin{bmatrix} 1 & 0 & 5 & 2 \\ 0 & 1 & -2 & 1 \\ 0 & 0 & 0 & 0 \end{bmatrix}$$

The set $\{(1,0,5,2), (0,1,-2,1)\}$ is a basis for the row space of **A**. The set $\{(1,0,5,2), (0,4,-8,4)\}$ could also be used as a basis. Once the rank r of **A** is known, any set of r linearly independent vectors from the row space can be used as a basis. For practical purposes, however, the process of row reduction is the most direct way of obtaining a basis for the row space. ■

In order to study the relationship between the row space and the null space of a matrix, we consider geometrically the subspaces related to an $m \times 3$ matrix **A**. In this case the null space and the row space are subspaces of R^3.

Example 32

1. **A** has rank 0—that is, **A** is the zero matrix. The solution set of $\mathbf{AX} = \mathbf{0}$ is the entire space. The null space has dimension 3.
2. **A** has rank 1. For example, let $\mathbf{A} = [1 \quad -2 \quad 3]$. The solution set of $\mathbf{AX} = \mathbf{0}$ is the solution set of $x_1 - 2x_2 + 3x_3 = 0$. This set is

$$\mathbf{X} = \left\{ k_1 \begin{bmatrix} 2 \\ 1 \\ 0 \end{bmatrix} + k_2 \begin{bmatrix} -3 \\ 0 \\ 1 \end{bmatrix},\ k_1, k_2 \text{ arbitrary real numbers} \right\}$$

   A basis for the null space is $\{\mathbf{u}_1, \mathbf{u}_2\}$ where $\mathbf{u}_1 = (2,1,0)$ and $\mathbf{u}_2 = (-3,0,1)$. The null space is the plane through the origin determined by these vectors. This plane is also the plane through the origin orthogonal to $\mathbf{n} = (1,-2,3)$. The row space of **A** is the set $\{k(1,-2,3)\}$—that is, the line through the origin perpendicular to the plane that represents the null space of **A**.
3. **A** has rank 2. For example, let $\mathbf{A} = \begin{bmatrix} 1 & 2 & -9 \\ -1 & -1 & 5 \end{bmatrix}$. The row-reduced form

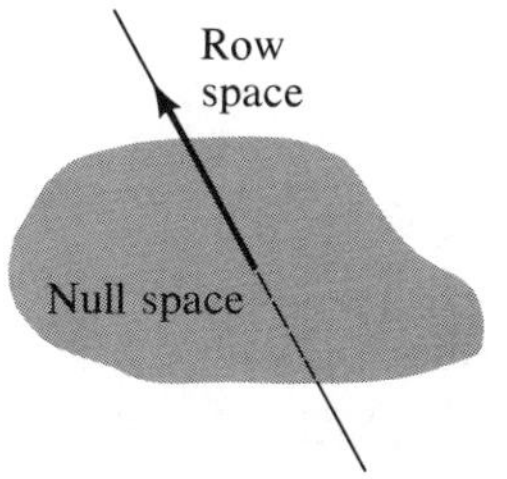

FIGURE 4.4

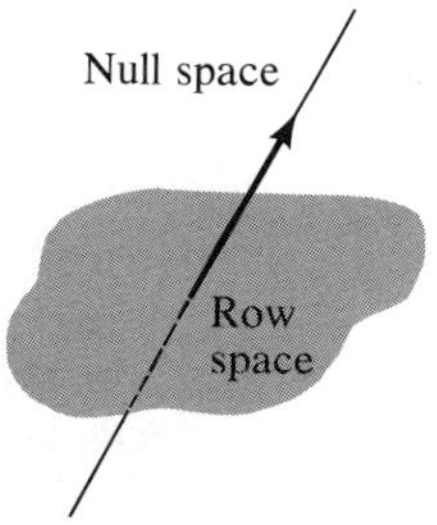

FIGURE 4.5

of **A** is $\begin{bmatrix} 1 & 0 & -1 \\ 0 & 1 & -4 \end{bmatrix}$ and the solution set is $\{k(1, 4, 1), k \text{ a real number}\}$. Thus, the null space of **A** has dimension 1 and consists of the set of multiples of the vector $(1, 4, 1)$. The row space of **A** is the space consisting of vectors of the form $k_1(1, 2, -9) + k_2(-1, -1, 5)$. The row space is the plane determined by these vectors and passing through the origin. This plane is orthogonal to $(1, 4, 1)$.

4. **A** has rank 3. The row space is the entire space R^3, and the null space is the single vector **0**. ■

Two subspaces S_1 and S_2 of the same space R^n are called orthogonal if every **u** in S_1 is orthogonal to every **v** in S_2. The null space of **A** and the row space of **A** are orthogonal spaces. They have a particularly strong type of orthogonality, since the null space contains *every* vector that is orthogonal to the row space. (The null space is *all* the solutions of $\mathbf{AX} = \mathbf{0}$.)

Orthogonal Complement

Definition 10

Given a subspace S of R^n, the space of all vectors orthogonal to S is called the **orthogonal complement** of S.

The null space of **A** and the row space of **A** are orthogonal complements of each other.

The set-theoretic union of two subspaces need not be a subspace. For example, there are certain vectors in R^3 that are not in either the plane or the line normal to the plane. (See Example 32.) However, the set consisting of two basis vectors for the plane and one basis vector for the line is a set of three vectors that is a basis for R^3. In general, the set consisting of $n - r$ basis vectors for the null space and r basis vectors for the row space forms a set of n vectors that is a basis for R^n. For a particular $m \times n$ matrix, **A**, $m \leqslant n$, every vector in R^n can be expressed in exactly one way as the sum of two vectors, one from the row space of **A** and one from the null space of **A**. Example 33 illustrates this.

Example 33 Let $\mathbf{A} = \begin{bmatrix} 1 & 2 & -9 \\ -1 & -1 & 5 \end{bmatrix}$ as in Example 32, part 3. A basis for the row space is $\{(1,0,-1), (0,1,-4)\}$; a basis for the null space is $(1,4,1)$. The vector $(4,3,2)$ in R^3 can be written uniquely in terms of the basis $\{(1,0,-1), (0,1,-4), (1,4,1)\}$. To do this, we solve $\begin{bmatrix} 1 & 0 & 1 \\ 0 & 1 & 4 \\ -1 & -4 & 1 \end{bmatrix}\begin{bmatrix} c_1 \\ c_2 \\ c_3 \end{bmatrix} = \begin{bmatrix} 4 \\ 3 \\ 2 \end{bmatrix}$. By row reduction we find $\begin{bmatrix} c_1 \\ c_2 \\ c_3 \end{bmatrix} = \begin{bmatrix} 3 \\ -1 \\ 1 \end{bmatrix}$, so that $(4,3,2) = 3(1,0,-1) - (0,1,-4) + (1,4,1) = (3,-1,1) + (1,4,1)$, where $(3,-1,1)$ is an element from the row space and $(1,4,1)$ an element from the null space of $\mathbf{A}$. (See Figure 4.6.)

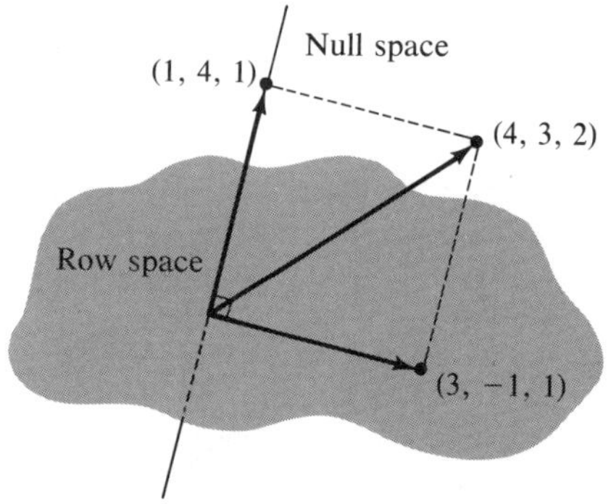

FIGURE 4.6

Notice that $\|(4,3,2)\|^2 = \|(1,4,1)\|^2 + \|(3,-1,1)\|^2$. This is to be expected because of the orthogonality of $(1,4,1)$ and $(3,-1,1)$. ■

Since we have discussed the row space of **A**, it is reasonable to ask what about the space spanned by the columns of **A**? This space is called the column space of **A**. Since the columns are m-tuples, the column space is a subset of R^m.

Column Space

Definition 11

Let **A** be an $m \times n$ matrix. The space spanned by the columns of **A** is a subspace of R^m called the **column space** of **A**.

Since the column space consists of all possible linear combinations of the columns of **A**, its elements are all possible vectors **B** such that $\mathbf{B} = \mathbf{AX}$ for some **X**. If **A** is an $m \times n$ matrix, **B** is an element of R^m and **X** belongs to R^n. The column space has dimension r, the rank of **A**. A basis consists of those columns of the matrix **A** that are found to be leading columns by the row-reduction process.

Example 34 Let **A** be the matrix of Example 31.

$$\mathbf{A} = \begin{bmatrix} 2 & 1 & 8 & 5 \\ 1 & 0 & 5 & 2 \\ 1 & 4 & -3 & 6 \end{bmatrix} \Leftrightarrow \begin{bmatrix} 1 & 0 & 5 & 2 \\ 0 & 1 & -2 & 1 \\ 0 & 0 & 0 & 0 \end{bmatrix}$$

Since **A** is 3 × 4 and has rank 2, the column space of **A** is a two-dimensional subspace of R^3. A possible basis for the column space is $\mathbf{u}_1 = (2, 1, 1)$, $\mathbf{u}_2 = (1, 0, 4)$—that is, the columns of **A** that are found to be leading columns by the row-reduction process. Although the choice of basis is not unique, note that it is not possible to choose columns from the row-reduced matrix in getting a basis for the column space. ■

It is interesting to note that there is a one-to-one correspondence between the vectors in the *row* space and the vectors in the *column* space. This is not surprising since both spaces have dimension r. What is surprising is that the correspondence is unique.

Example 35 Let **A** be the matrix of Example 32, part 3: $\mathbf{A} = \begin{bmatrix} 1 & 2 & -9 \\ -1 & -1 & 5 \end{bmatrix}$. The null space of **A** consists of multiples of the vector (1, 4, 1). Let $\mathbf{X} = \begin{bmatrix} 4 \\ 3 \\ 2 \end{bmatrix}$. Then

$$\mathbf{AX} = \begin{bmatrix} 1 & 2 & -9 \\ -1 & -1 & 5 \end{bmatrix} \begin{bmatrix} 4 \\ 3 \\ 2 \end{bmatrix} = \begin{bmatrix} -8 \\ 3 \end{bmatrix}.$$

The vector (−8, 3) belongs to the column space of **A**.

As we saw in Example 33, (4, 3, 2) = (3, −1, 1) + (1, 4, 1), where (3, −1, 1) is the row space of **A** and (1, 4, 1) is in the null space of **A**. Notice also that $\begin{bmatrix} 1 & 2 & -9 \\ -1 & -1 & 5 \end{bmatrix} \begin{bmatrix} 3 \\ -1 \\ 1 \end{bmatrix} = \begin{bmatrix} -8 \\ 3 \end{bmatrix}$.

The vector (−8, 3) in the column space of **A** corresponds to (3, −1, 1) in the row space of **A** in the sense that $\mathbf{A}\begin{bmatrix} 3 \\ -1 \\ 1 \end{bmatrix} = \begin{bmatrix} -8 \\ 3 \end{bmatrix}$.

The vector $\mathbf{x} = (4, 3, 2)$ is one of a family of vectors such that $\begin{bmatrix} 1 & 2 & -9 \\ -1 & -1 & 5 \end{bmatrix} \mathbf{X} = \begin{bmatrix} -8 \\ 3 \end{bmatrix}$. The solution set of this equation is

$$\{(2, -5, 0) + k(1, 4, 1),\ k \text{ a real number}\}.$$

The vector (3, −1, 1) is the only vector in the row space that belongs to this set. To express any one of the vectors in the solution set in terms of the basis {(1, 0, −1),

$(0, 1, -4), (1, 4, 1)\}$, we write

$$(2 + k, -5 + 4k, k) = c_1(1, 0, -1) + c_2(0, 1, -4) + c_3(1, 4, 1)$$

We could find c_1, c_2, c_3 from this equation by row reduction. However, since we know that $(1, 4, 1)$ is orthogonal to each of the vectors $(1, 0, -1)$ and $(0, 1, -4)$, we can shorten the work by taking the dot product of the equation by $(1, 0, -1)$ and by $(0, 1, -4)$. We get

$$\begin{aligned} 2 + k - k &= 2c_1 + 4c_2 \\ -5 + 4k - 4k &= 4c_1 + 17c_2 \end{aligned}$$

from which we obtain $c_1 = 3$ and $c_2 = -1$. Thus

$$\begin{aligned} (2 + k, -5 + 4k, k) &= (3, 0, -3) + (0, -1, 4) + c_3(1, 4, 1) \\ &= (3, -1, 1) + c_3(1, 4, 1). \end{aligned}$$

For any k, the vector from the row space must be $(3, -1, 1)$. Thus the relation $\mathbf{AX} = \begin{bmatrix} -8 \\ 3 \end{bmatrix}$ associates a unique vector from the row space with the vector $\begin{bmatrix} -8 \\ 3 \end{bmatrix}$ in the column space.

This result is not surprising if we observe that for any two vectors $\mathbf{u}_1$ and $\mathbf{u}_2$ in the row space of $\mathbf{A}$, if $\mathbf{AU}_1 = \mathbf{AU}_2$ then $\mathbf{u}_1 = \mathbf{u}_2$. To see this let $\mathbf{u}_3 = \mathbf{u}_2 - \mathbf{u}_1$. Then $\mathbf{u}_3$ is also in the row space of $\mathbf{A}$ and $\mathbf{AU}_3 = \mathbf{AU}_2 - \mathbf{AU}_1 = \mathbf{0}$. Since $\mathbf{AU}_3 = \mathbf{0}$, $\mathbf{u}_3$ is in the null space of $\mathbf{A}$. The only vector common to the null space and the row space of $\mathbf{A}$ is the zero vector. Therefore, $\mathbf{u}_3$ must be the zero vector and $\mathbf{u}_1 = \mathbf{u}_2$. This shows that for each vector $\mathbf{v}$ in the column space there is a unique vector $\mathbf{u}$ in the row space such that $\mathbf{AU} = \mathbf{V}$. Conversely, given any vector in the row space, a unique vector in the column space is determined by the product $\mathbf{AU}$. ■

The preceding discussion is summarized in the following theorem.

Theorem 12 Let $\mathbf{A}$ be an $m \times n$ matrix of rank r. The row space of $\mathbf{A}$ is a subspace of R^n of dimension r. The column space of $\mathbf{A}$ is a subspace of R^m of dimension r. There is a unique one-to-one correspondence between the column space of $\mathbf{A}$ and the row space of $\mathbf{A}$. □

In Chapter 2 we calculated the solution set of a matrix equation $\mathbf{AX} = \mathbf{B}$. If $\mathbf{B} \neq \mathbf{0}$, the solution set of $\mathbf{AX} = \mathbf{B}$ is a subset of R^n but *not* a subspace of R^n. (It does not contain the zero vector.) In the following example, we look at the solution set in relation to the row space and the null space.

Example 36 Let $\mathbf{A} = \begin{bmatrix} 1 & 2 & -9 \\ -1 & -1 & 5 \end{bmatrix}$ and let $\mathbf{B} = \begin{bmatrix} -8 \\ 3 \end{bmatrix}$. (See Example 35.) The solution set of $\mathbf{AX} = \mathbf{B}$ has a unique representation in the form

$$\{(3, -1, 1) + k(1, 4, 1),\ k \text{ a real number}\}$$

where $(3, -1, 1)$ is a vector in the row space. This set corresponds to a line in R^3

parallel to the null space and translated by the vector $(3, -1, 1)$ in the row space. (See Figure 4.7.)

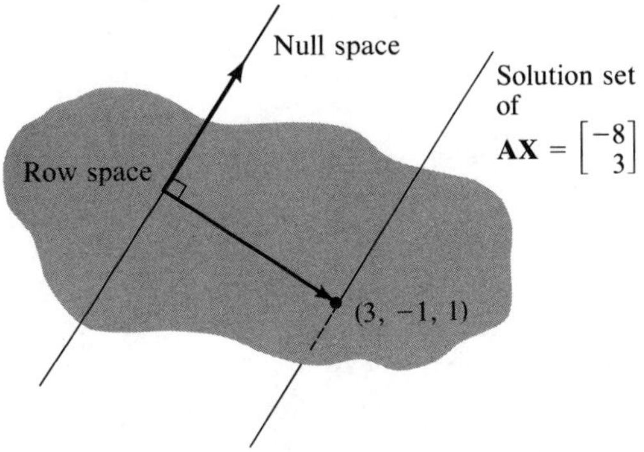

FIGURE 4.7 ■

SUMMARY Let $\mathbf{A}$ be an $m \times n$ matrix. The null space of $\mathbf{A}$ is a subspace of R^n consisting of the solution set of the system of equations $\mathbf{AX} = \mathbf{0}$. The dimension of the null space is $n - r$, where r is the rank of $\mathbf{A}$. To find a basis for the null space, solve the equations $\mathbf{AX} = \mathbf{0}$ by row reduction.

The row space of $\mathbf{A}$ is the subspace of R^n spanned by the rows of $\mathbf{A}$. A basis for the row space is the set of nonzero rows in the row-reduced form of $\mathbf{A}$. The dimension of the row space is r. The row space is the orthogonal complement of the null space in R^n.

The column space of $\mathbf{A}$ is a subspace of R^m spanned by the columns of $\mathbf{A}$. It has dimension r. There is a one-to-one correspondence between the row space and the column space.

EXERCISES 4.4

1. In each case, find a basis for the null space of $\mathbf{A}$. What is the dimension of the null space in each case?

a. $\mathbf{A} = \begin{bmatrix} 1 & 1 & 2 \\ 1 & 0 & 1 \\ 2 & 1 & 3 \end{bmatrix}$

b. $\mathbf{A} = \begin{bmatrix} 1 & 1 & 2 \\ 1 & 0 & 1 \\ 2 & 2 & 4 \end{bmatrix}$

c. $\mathbf{A} = \begin{bmatrix} 1 & 1 & 2 \\ 2 & 2 & 4 \\ -1 & -1 & -2 \end{bmatrix}$

2. a. If $\mathbf{A}$ is a 3×5 matrix, for what n is the null space of $\mathbf{A}$ a subset of R^n?

b. If the null space of $\mathbf{A}$ is a subspace of R^3, what do you know about the size of $\mathbf{A}$?

3. For each of the matrices in Problem 1, find a basis for the row space of $\mathbf{A}$. What is the dimension of the row space of $\mathbf{A}$?

4. Let $\mathbf{A}$ be a 5×9 matrix.

a. For what n is the null space of $\mathbf{A}$ a subspace of R^n?

b. For what n is the row space of $\mathbf{A}$ a subspace of R^n?

c. The rank of $\mathbf{A}$ is 4. What is the dimension of the row space? What is the dimension of the null space?

5. For each of the matrices in Problem 1, give a geometric description of the null space of $\mathbf{A}$ and of the row space of $\mathbf{A}$.

6. Let $\mathbf{A} = \begin{bmatrix} 1 & 2 & -1 \\ 1 & -1 & 1 \end{bmatrix}$. Describe the line that is the null space of **A**. What planes intersect in this line? Describe the plane that is the row space of **A**.

7. Let

$$\mathbf{A} = \begin{bmatrix} 1 & 1 & 2 & 2 \\ 1 & 0 & 2 & -1 \\ 2 & 1 & 4 & 1 \end{bmatrix}$$

Find a basis for the null space of **A** and a basis for the row space of **A**. Write the vector $(6, -7, 3, -3)$ as the sum of a vector from the row space and a vector from the null space.

8. Let $\mathbf{A} = [1\ \ 0\ \ 0]$ and $\mathbf{B} = [0\ \ 1\ \ 0]$. Give a geometric description of the null space of **A** and the row space of **A**. Give a geometric description of the null space of **B** and the row space of **B**. What is the relation between the row space of **B** and the null space of **A**?

9. Let

$$\mathbf{A} = \begin{bmatrix} 1 & 1 & 0 & 0 \\ 0 & 1 & 2 & 3 \end{bmatrix}$$

and

$$\mathbf{B} = \begin{bmatrix} 1 & 1 & 0 & 0 \\ 0 & 1 & 2 & 3 \\ 0 & 0 & 1 & 2 \end{bmatrix}$$

a. What is the dimension of the null space of **A**?
b. What is the dimension of the null space of **B**?
c. Show that the null space of **B** is contained in the null space of **A**.

10. Let

$$\mathbf{A} = \begin{bmatrix} 1 & 1 & 0 & 0 \\ 0 & 0 & 1 & 2 \end{bmatrix}$$

and

$$\mathbf{B} = \begin{bmatrix} 1 & 1 & 0 & 0 \\ 0 & 1 & 2 & 3 \end{bmatrix}$$

a. What is the dimension of the null space of **A**?
b. What is the dimension of the null space of **B**?
c. Show that both of these are contained in the null space of $\mathbf{C} = [1\ \ 1\ \ 0\ \ 0]$.

11. Let

$$\mathbf{A} = \begin{bmatrix} 1 & 1 & 0 & 0 \\ 0 & 0 & 1 & 2 \end{bmatrix}$$

and

$$\mathbf{B} = \begin{bmatrix} 1 & 1 & 0 & 0 \\ 0 & 1 & 2 & 3 \end{bmatrix}$$

What space is the intersection of the null space of **A** and the null space of **B**?

12. Let

$$\mathbf{A} = \begin{bmatrix} 1 & 1 & 0 & 2 \\ 2 & 0 & 1 & 0 \end{bmatrix}$$

and

$$\mathbf{B} = \begin{bmatrix} 1 & 1 & 1 & 1 \\ 3 & 1 & 1 & 2 \end{bmatrix}$$

What vectors are common to the null space of **A** and the null space of **B**?

13. a. Let

$$\mathbf{A} = \begin{bmatrix} 2 & 1 & 1 \\ 0 & 2 & 1 \\ 0 & 0 & 2 \end{bmatrix}$$

Find the dimension of the null space of $\mathbf{A} - 2\mathbf{I}$. Note that 2 is an eigenvalue of **A**.

b. Let

$$\mathbf{A} = \begin{bmatrix} 2 & 0 & 0 \\ 0 & 2 & 1 \\ 0 & 0 & 2 \end{bmatrix}$$

Find the dimension of the null space of $\mathbf{A} - 2\mathbf{I}$.

14. Let

$$\mathbf{A} = \begin{bmatrix} 2 & -1 & 0 \\ 2 & 1 & 1 \\ -2 & 2 & 1 \end{bmatrix}$$

a. Describe the null space of $\mathbf{A} - \mathbf{I}$.
b. Describe the null space of $\mathbf{A} - 2\mathbf{I}$.
c. Describe the null space of $\mathbf{A} - 3\mathbf{I}$.
d. Describe the null space of $\mathbf{A} + 4\mathbf{I}$.
e. What numbers are eigenvalues of **A**?

15. Show that λ is an eigenvalue of **A** if and only if the null space of $\mathbf{A} - \lambda\mathbf{I}$ has dimension greater than zero.

16. Show that $\mathbf{X}_0$ is an eigenvector of **A** corresponding to λ_0 if and only if $\mathbf{X}_0 \neq \mathbf{0}$ and $\mathbf{X}_0$ belongs to the null space of $\mathbf{A} - \lambda_0\mathbf{I}$.

17. Let

$$\mathbf{A} = \begin{bmatrix} 1 & 1 & 0 & 0 \\ 0 & 1 & 2 & 3 \end{bmatrix}$$

and

$$\mathbf{B} = \begin{bmatrix} 1 & 1 & 0 & 0 \\ 0 & 1 & 2 & 3 \\ 0 & 0 & 1 & 2 \end{bmatrix}$$

Show that the row space of **A** is contained in the row space of **B**. (Compare with Problem 9.)

18. Let

$$\mathbf{A} = \begin{bmatrix} 1 & 1 & 0 & 0 \\ 0 & 0 & 1 & 2 \end{bmatrix}$$

and

$$\mathbf{B} = \begin{bmatrix} 1 & 1 & 0 & 0 \\ 0 & 1 & 2 & 3 \end{bmatrix}$$

Show that the intersection of the row space of **A** and the row space of **B** is the row space of [1 1.0 0]. (Compare with Problem 10.)

19. Let

$$\mathbf{A} = \begin{bmatrix} 1 & -1 & -1 & 1 & 0 \\ 1 & 1 & 1 & -3 & 2 \\ 1 & 4 & 4 & -9 & 5 \end{bmatrix}$$

The null space of **A** was found (Example 29A) to have as a basis $\{\mathbf{u}_1, \mathbf{u}_2, \mathbf{u}_3\}$, where $\mathbf{u}_1 = (0, -1, 1, 0, 0)$, $\mathbf{u}_2 = (1, 2, 0, 1, 0)$, and $\mathbf{u}_3 = (-1, -1, 0, 0, 1)$. Show that the row space of **A** is the null space of the matrix

$$\mathbf{B} = \begin{bmatrix} 0 & -1 & 1 & 0 & 0 \\ 1 & 2 & 0 & 1 & 0 \\ -1 & -1 & 0 & 0 & 1 \end{bmatrix}$$

20. Let

$$\mathbf{A} = \begin{bmatrix} 1 & 2 & 1 & 3 \\ 3 & 1 & 1 & 2 \\ 2 & -1 & 0 & -1 \end{bmatrix}$$

a. For what value of k is the column space of **A** a subset of R^k?

b. Do the columns of **A** form a basis for the column space of **A**?

21. Let

$$\mathbf{A} = \begin{bmatrix} 1 & 2 & 1 & 3 \\ 3 & 1 & 1 & 2 \\ 2 & -1 & 0 & -1 \end{bmatrix}$$

Find the dimension of the column space of **A**.

22. Let

$$\mathbf{A} = \begin{bmatrix} 1 & 1 & 1 & -1 & 2 \\ 1 & -1 & 1 & 2 & 1 \\ 0 & -2 & 0 & 3 & -1 \\ 1 & -1 & 1 & 4 & 2 \end{bmatrix}$$

a. Show that the columns of **A** are a linearly dependent set by solving the equations

$$\begin{bmatrix} 1 \\ 1 \\ 0 \\ 1 \end{bmatrix} c_1 + \begin{bmatrix} 1 \\ -1 \\ -2 \\ -1 \end{bmatrix} c_2 + \begin{bmatrix} 1 \\ 1 \\ 0 \\ 1 \end{bmatrix} c_3 + \begin{bmatrix} -1 \\ 2 \\ 3 \\ 4 \end{bmatrix} c_4 + \begin{bmatrix} 2 \\ 1 \\ -1 \\ 2 \end{bmatrix} c_5 = \begin{bmatrix} 0 \\ 0 \\ 0 \\ 0 \end{bmatrix}$$

b. In solving this system by row reduction, columns 1, 2, and 4 are leading columns. Show that the columns 1, 2, 4 of **A** form a linearly independent set and that columns 1, 2, 3, 4 form a linearly dependent set.

23. Let

$$\mathbf{A} = \begin{bmatrix} 1 & 1 & 1 & 1 & 1 \\ 1 & -1 & 1 & 3 & 1 \\ 1 & 1 & 1 & 2 & 0 \\ 1 & 1 & 1 & 3 & -1 \end{bmatrix}$$

The row-reduced form of **A** is

$$\begin{bmatrix} 1 & 0 & 1 & 0 & 3 \\ 0 & 1 & 0 & 0 & -1 \\ 0 & 0 & 0 & 1 & -1 \\ 0 & 0 & 0 & 0 & 0 \end{bmatrix}$$

a. Show that columns 3 and 5 of **A** can be expressed as linear combinations of columns 1, 2, and 4.

b. Hence show that the column space of **A** has as basis the first, second, and fourth columns of **A**.

c. Show that columns 1, 2, 4 of the row-reduced form of **A** do *not* form a basis for the column space of **A** and hence that row reduction of a matrix changes its column space.

24. Use the matrix **A** in Problem 23.

a. Write a basis for the row space of **A**.

b. Write a basis for the null space of **A**.

c. Express the vector (4, 2, 3, 0, 1) as the sum of a vector from the row space and a vector from the null space of **A**.

d. Find the vector in the column space that corresponds to the vector from the row space calculated in **c.**

25. Let

$$\mathbf{A} = \begin{bmatrix} 1 & 2 & 1 & 9 \\ 1 & 1 & 0 & 5 \\ 1 & -1 & -2 & -3 \\ 3 & 1 & -2 & 7 \end{bmatrix}$$

a. Write a basis for the row space of **A**.

b. Write a basis for the null space of **A**.

c. Write the vector $\mathbf{v} = (4, 4, 3, 8)$ in the form $\mathbf{u} + \mathbf{n}$, where $\mathbf{u}$ is in the row space of **A**, and $\mathbf{n}$ is in the null space of **A**.

d. Show that $\mathbf{AV} = \mathbf{AU} = \begin{bmatrix} 87 \\ 48 \\ -30 \\ 66 \end{bmatrix}$.

26. Let **A** be the matrix in Problem 25. You are given the 4-tuple $(87, 48, -30, 66)$ in the column space. Find the corresponding vector in the row space of **A**. To do this you may wish to find a vector **V** such that $\mathbf{AV} = \begin{bmatrix} 87 \\ 48 \\ -30 \\ 66 \end{bmatrix}$.

Will this vector **v** necessarily be $\mathbf{v} = (4, 4, 3, 8)$ as in Problem 25?

4.5 Change of Basis, Orthonormal Bases

The set of standard vectors $E = \{\mathbf{e}_1, \mathbf{e}_2, \ldots, \mathbf{e}_n\}$ forms a basis for R^n called the standard basis. Any vector $\mathbf{x} = (a_1, a_2, \ldots, a_n)$ can be written uniquely in the form $\mathbf{x} = a_1\mathbf{e}_1 + a_2\mathbf{e}_2 + \cdots + a_n\mathbf{e}_n$; so $(\mathbf{x})_E = (a_1, a_2, \ldots, a_n)$. Thus, in R^n the coordinates of **x** relative to the standard basis are the components of **x**.

There are many other possible bases for R^n. In fact, every linearly independent set of n vectors in R^n is a basis for R^n. (See Exercises 4.3, Problem 17.) In R^2 and R^3 a basis plays a role similar to that of the coordinate axes (Example 25). Rotation of the coordinate axes is sometimes quite useful. Example 18, Section 1.2, illustrates a rotation of axes that makes it possible to identify and plot a conic section in the plane by choosing the coordinate axes in an appropriate way. In many situations a particular problem can be handled more easily in a coordinate system different from the standard one. Since the coordinates of a vector depend on the basis used, we need a formula that tells how the coordinates change when the basis changes. With such a formula, we can change from one basis to another in order to simplify a particular problem. Example 37 illustrates a change of basis in R^2.

Example 37 Let $\mathbf{u}_1 = (1, 1)$ and $\mathbf{u}_2 = (-1, 2)$; then $U = \{\mathbf{u}_1, \mathbf{u}_2\}$ is a basis for R^2. Let **x** be the vector $(2, 5)$ and let $(\mathbf{x})_U = (c_1, c_2)$. We can find $(\mathbf{x})_U$ by solving equations $c_1\mathbf{u}_1 + c_2\mathbf{u}_2 = (2, 5)$, that is,

$$\begin{aligned} c_1 - c_2 &= 2 \\ c_1 + 2c_2 &= 5 \end{aligned} \quad \text{or} \quad \begin{bmatrix} 1 & -1 \\ 1 & 2 \end{bmatrix} \begin{bmatrix} c_1 \\ c_2 \end{bmatrix} = \begin{bmatrix} 2 \\ 5 \end{bmatrix}$$

Since U is a basis, $\begin{bmatrix} 1 & -1 \\ 1 & 2 \end{bmatrix}$ has rank 2 (Theorem 4). We can find (c_1, c_2) by row reduction or by multiplying on the left by the inverse of $\begin{bmatrix} 1 & -1 \\ 1 & 2 \end{bmatrix}$. Thus,

$$\begin{bmatrix} c_1 \\ c_2 \end{bmatrix} = \begin{bmatrix} \frac{2}{3} & \frac{1}{3} \\ -\frac{1}{3} & \frac{1}{3} \end{bmatrix} \begin{bmatrix} 2 \\ 5 \end{bmatrix} = \begin{bmatrix} 3 \\ 1 \end{bmatrix}$$

In Figures 4.8a and 4.8b, **x** is the geometric vector OP. In Figure 4.8a, OP is thought of as the diagonal of the parallelogram $OMPN$, $OM = 2\mathbf{e}_1$, and

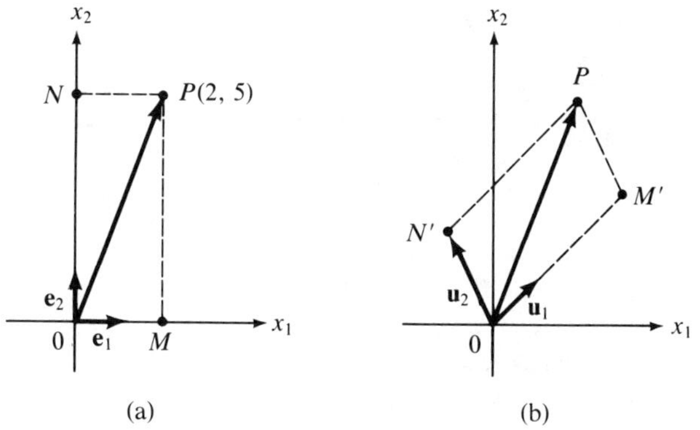

FIGURE 4.8

$ON = 5\mathbf{e}_2$. Because $\mathbf{e}_1$ has length 1, the length of OM is 2, which is the abscissa of the point P. The length of ON is 5, which is the ordinate of P.

Relative to the basis U (Figure 4.8b), OP is thought of as the diagonal of $OM'PN'$, where OM' is $3\mathbf{u}_1$ and ON' is $\mathbf{u}_2$. The coordinate 3 means that the length of OM' is 3 times the length of $\mathbf{u}_1$, and the coordinate 1 means that the length of ON' is the length of $\mathbf{u}_2$.

Given any vector $\mathbf{x} = (a_1, a_2)$ in R^2, we can find $(\mathbf{x})_U = (c_1, c_2)$ by solving the equations $c_1\mathbf{u}_1 + c_2\mathbf{u}_2 = (a_1, a_2)$:

$$\begin{bmatrix} 1 & -1 \\ 1 & 2 \end{bmatrix}\begin{bmatrix} c_1 \\ c_2 \end{bmatrix} = \begin{bmatrix} a_1 \\ a_2 \end{bmatrix} \quad \text{so that} \quad \begin{bmatrix} c_1 \\ c_2 \end{bmatrix} = \begin{bmatrix} \frac{2}{3} & \frac{1}{3} \\ -\frac{1}{3} & \frac{1}{3} \end{bmatrix}\begin{bmatrix} a_1 \\ a_2 \end{bmatrix}$$

Since the coordinates of $\mathbf{x}$ relative to U occur as a column in this equation, it is convenient to use the notation $[\mathbf{x}]_U$ in which [ ] indicates that the coordinates are to be written as a vertical array. Thus the equation relating the coordinates relative to U and the coordinates relative to the standard basis is:

$$\begin{bmatrix} 1 & -1 \\ 1 & 2 \end{bmatrix}[\mathbf{x}]_U = [\mathbf{x}]_E \quad \text{or} \quad [\mathbf{x}]_U = \begin{bmatrix} \frac{2}{3} & \frac{1}{3} \\ -\frac{1}{3} & \frac{1}{3} \end{bmatrix}[\mathbf{x}]_E$$

For example, given $\mathbf{x} = (-5, 1)$ we have

$$[\mathbf{x}]_E = \begin{bmatrix} -5 \\ 1 \end{bmatrix}, \qquad [\mathbf{x}]_U = \begin{bmatrix} \frac{2}{3} & \frac{1}{3} \\ -\frac{1}{3} & \frac{1}{3} \end{bmatrix}\begin{bmatrix} -5 \\ 1 \end{bmatrix} = \begin{bmatrix} -3 \\ 2 \end{bmatrix}$$

Conversely, given $[\mathbf{x}]_U = \begin{bmatrix} -3 \\ 2 \end{bmatrix}$,

$$[\mathbf{x}]_E = \begin{bmatrix} 1 & -1 \\ 1 & 2 \end{bmatrix}\begin{bmatrix} -3 \\ 2 \end{bmatrix} = \begin{bmatrix} -5 \\ 1 \end{bmatrix}$$

■

Notation

If $\mathbf{x}$ is a vector in the vector space V and $U = \{\mathbf{u}_1, \mathbf{u}_2, \ldots, \mathbf{u}_k\}$ is a basis for V, then $(\mathbf{x})_U$ represents the k-tuple of coordinates of $\mathbf{x}$ relative to the basis U and $[\mathbf{x}]_U$ is the $k \times 1$ array formed from this k-tuple of coordinates.

Example 38 illustrates a situation in which neither basis is the standard basis.

Example 38 Let $\mathbf{u}_1 = (1, 1, 2)$, $\mathbf{u}_2 = (1, 0, 1)$, $\mathbf{u}_3 = (0, 1, 0)$; the set $U = \{\mathbf{u}_1, \mathbf{u}_2, \mathbf{u}_3\}$ is a basis for R^3. Let $\mathbf{v}_1 = (1, 1, 1)$, $\mathbf{v}_2 = (1, 1, 0)$, $\mathbf{v}_3 = (1, 0, 0)$; the set $V = \{\mathbf{v}_1, \mathbf{v}_2, \mathbf{v}_3\}$ is also a basis for R^3. Find the change-of-basis matrix $\mathbf{P}$, that is, the matrix $\mathbf{P}$ such that $[\mathbf{x}]_V = \mathbf{P}[\mathbf{x}]_U$ for any vector $\mathbf{x}$ in R^3.

Solution Let

$$[\mathbf{x}]_U = \begin{bmatrix} c_1 \\ c_2 \\ c_3 \end{bmatrix} \quad \text{and} \quad [\mathbf{x}]_V = \begin{bmatrix} d_1 \\ d_2 \\ d_3 \end{bmatrix}$$

Then for any $\mathbf{x}$ in R^3

$$\mathbf{x} = c_1\mathbf{u}_1 + c_2\mathbf{u}_2 + c_3\mathbf{u}_3 \quad \text{and} \quad \mathbf{x} = d_1\mathbf{v}_1 + d_2\mathbf{v}_2 + d_3\mathbf{v}_3$$

This leads to the equation

$$c_1\mathbf{u}_1 + c_2\mathbf{u}_2 + c_3\mathbf{u}_3 = d_1\mathbf{v}_1 + d_2\mathbf{v}_2 + d_3\mathbf{v}_3$$

In matrix form this vector equation is

$$\begin{bmatrix} 1 & 1 & 0 \\ 1 & 0 & 1 \\ 2 & 1 & 0 \end{bmatrix} \begin{bmatrix} c_1 \\ c_2 \\ c_3 \end{bmatrix} = \begin{bmatrix} 1 & 1 & 1 \\ 1 & 1 & 0 \\ 1 & 0 & 0 \end{bmatrix} \begin{bmatrix} d_1 \\ d_2 \\ d_3 \end{bmatrix}$$

or $\mathbf{U}[\mathbf{x}]_U = \mathbf{V}[\mathbf{x}]_V$. Since the columns of $\mathbf{U}$ are the vectors of the basis U the matrix $\mathbf{U}$ is nonsingular. The matrix $\mathbf{V}$ is also nonsingular, since its columns are the vectors of the basis V.

If we multiply both sides of the equation by $\mathbf{V}^{-1}$, we obtain $[\mathbf{x}]_V = \mathbf{V}^{-1}\mathbf{U}[\mathbf{x}]_U$, or $[\mathbf{x}]_V = \mathbf{P}[\mathbf{x}]_U$ where $\mathbf{P} = \mathbf{V}^{-1}\mathbf{U}$. The matrix $\mathbf{P}$ is called the change-of-basis matrix from U to V. In this case

$$\mathbf{P} = \begin{bmatrix} 2 & 1 & 0 \\ -1 & -1 & 1 \\ 0 & 1 & -1 \end{bmatrix}$$

Given

$$[\mathbf{x}]_U = \begin{bmatrix} 1 \\ -1 \\ 3 \end{bmatrix}, \qquad [\mathbf{x}]_V = \begin{bmatrix} 2 & 1 & 0 \\ -1 & -1 & 1 \\ 0 & 1 & -1 \end{bmatrix} \begin{bmatrix} 1 \\ -1 \\ 3 \end{bmatrix} = \begin{bmatrix} 1 \\ 3 \\ -4 \end{bmatrix}$$

Since $\mathbf{U}$ and $\mathbf{V}$ are nonsingular, $\mathbf{P}$ is also nonsingular. We can write $[\mathbf{x}]_U = \mathbf{P}^{-1}[\mathbf{x}]_V$. $\mathbf{P}^{-1}$ is the change-of-basis matrix from V to U.

To emphasize the meaning of the notation used, we write **x** as a triple.

$$[\mathbf{x}]_U = \begin{bmatrix} 1 \\ -1 \\ 3 \end{bmatrix} \text{ means } \mathbf{x} = \mathbf{u}_1 - \mathbf{u}_2 + 3\mathbf{u}_3 = (0, 4, 1)$$

$$[\mathbf{x}]_V = \begin{bmatrix} 1 \\ 3 \\ -4 \end{bmatrix} \text{ means } \mathbf{x} = \mathbf{v}_1 + 3\mathbf{v}_2 - 4\mathbf{v}_3 = (0, 4, 1)$$ ■

A change of basis can be carried out in any n-dimensional vector space and the corresponding change-of-basis matrix found. Theorem 13 states this and describes **P**. The proof of Theorem 13 is stated for R^n. The more general setting is discussed in Section 5.3.

Theorem 13 Let W be an n-dimensional vector space with bases $U = \{\mathbf{u}_1, \mathbf{u}_2, \ldots, \mathbf{u}_n\}$ and $V = \{\mathbf{v}_1, \mathbf{v}_2, \ldots, \mathbf{v}_n\}$. Then $[\mathbf{x}]_V = \mathbf{P}[\mathbf{x}]_U$, where **x** is an element of W and **P** is a matrix with columns $[\mathbf{u}_1]_V, [\mathbf{u}_2]_V, \ldots, [\mathbf{u}_n]_V$.

Proof Let $(c_1, c_2, \ldots, c_n)$ be the coordinates of **x** relative to U. Then $\mathbf{x} = c_1\mathbf{u}_1 + c_2\mathbf{u}_2 + \cdots + c_n\mathbf{u}_n$. Since $\mathbf{u}_i$ is an n-tuple, $i = 1, 2, \ldots, n$, and since $\mathbf{x} = (x_1, x_2, \ldots, x_n) = (\mathbf{x})_E$, the statement $\mathbf{x} = c_1\mathbf{u}_1 + c_2\mathbf{u}_2 + \cdots + c_n\mathbf{u}_n$ can be written as the matrix product $\mathbf{U}[\mathbf{x}]_U = [\mathbf{x}]_E$, where **U** is the matrix with columns the n-tuples $\mathbf{u}_1, \mathbf{u}_2, \ldots, \mathbf{u}_n$. Since U is a basis, the matrix **U** is nonsingular.

In the same way, $\mathbf{V}[\mathbf{x}]_V = [\mathbf{x}]_E$, where **V** is the nonsingular matrix with columns the n-tuples $\mathbf{v}_1, \mathbf{v}_2, \ldots, \mathbf{v}_n$.

Equate these two expressions for $[\mathbf{x}]_E$. We get $\mathbf{U}[\mathbf{x}]_U = \mathbf{V}[\mathbf{x}]_V$ from which $[\mathbf{x}]_V = \mathbf{P}[\mathbf{u}]_U$ where $\mathbf{P} = \mathbf{V}^{-1}\mathbf{U}$.

Now consider the special case $\mathbf{x} = \mathbf{u}_1$. Since $(\mathbf{u}_1)_U = (1, 0, 0, \ldots, 0)$, we have

$$[\mathbf{u}_1]_V = \mathbf{P}\begin{bmatrix} 1 \\ 0 \\ \vdots \\ 0 \end{bmatrix} = \text{the first column of } \mathbf{P}$$

Similarly

$$[\mathbf{u}_2]_V = \mathbf{P}\begin{bmatrix} 0 \\ 1 \\ \vdots \\ 0 \end{bmatrix} = \text{the second column of } \mathbf{P}$$

In general, the ith column of **P** is the coordinate vector of $\mathbf{u}_i$ relative to the basis V. □

Example 39 illustrates Theorem 13 in the setting of P_2.

Example 39 Let $u_1 = 1 + x$, $u_2 = 1 - x$, $u_3 = 1 + 2x + x^2$. Then $U = \{u_1, u_2, u_3\}$ is a basis for P_2. Let $p = a_1 + a_2x + a_3x^2$ be any vector in P_2. Find the change-of-basis matrix from the standard basis E to the basis U.

Solution According to Theorem 13, $[x]_V = \mathbf{P}[x]_U$, where $\mathbf{P}$ is a matrix with columns $[u_1]_V, [u_2]_V, [u_3]_V$. Since it is easy to write coordinates relative to the standard basis, we choose $V = E$. Then

$$[u_1]_E = \begin{bmatrix} 1 \\ 1 \\ 0 \end{bmatrix}, \qquad [u_2]_E = \begin{bmatrix} 1 \\ -1 \\ 0 \end{bmatrix}, \qquad [u_3]_E = \begin{bmatrix} 1 \\ 2 \\ 1 \end{bmatrix}$$

so that

$$[p]_E = \begin{bmatrix} 1 & 1 & 1 \\ 1 & -1 & 2 \\ 0 & 0 & 1 \end{bmatrix} [p]_U$$

Since we are asked to find the change-of-basis matrix from E to U, we must write

$$[p]_U = \begin{bmatrix} 1 & 1 & 1 \\ 1 & -1 & 2 \\ 0 & 0 & 1 \end{bmatrix}^{-1} [p]_E$$

The required matrix is thus

$$\begin{bmatrix} \frac{1}{2} & \frac{1}{2} & -\frac{3}{2} \\ \frac{1}{2} & -\frac{1}{2} & \frac{1}{2} \\ 0 & 0 & 1 \end{bmatrix}$$

As an illustration, let $p = 5 + 5x + 2x^2$

$$[p]_E = \begin{bmatrix} 5 \\ 5 \\ 2 \end{bmatrix} \quad \text{and} \quad [p]_U = \begin{bmatrix} \frac{1}{2} & \frac{1}{2} & -\frac{3}{2} \\ \frac{1}{2} & -\frac{1}{2} & \frac{1}{2} \\ 0 & 0 & 1 \end{bmatrix} \begin{bmatrix} 5 \\ 5 \\ 2 \end{bmatrix} = \begin{bmatrix} 2 \\ 1 \\ 2 \end{bmatrix}$$

Since $2(1 + x) + (1 - x) + 2(1 + 2x + x^2) = 5 + 5x + 2x^2$, our calculations check in this case. ■

In Section 1.5 an orthonormal set of vectors in R^n was defined (Definition 16). This definition applies in any vector space in which length and orthogonality are defined. A basis that is also an orthonormal set of vectors is frequently a desirable choice of basis. The standard basis in R^n is itself such a basis.

Definition 12

Orthonormal Set

An **orthonormal set** is a set of vectors $\{\mathbf{v}_1, \mathbf{v}_2, \ldots, \mathbf{v}_k\}$ with the property

$$\mathbf{v}_i \cdot \mathbf{v}_j = \begin{Bmatrix} 1 & \text{if } i = j \\ 0 & \text{if } i \neq j \end{Bmatrix}$$

Orthonormal Basis

A basis in which the vectors form an orthonormal set is called an **orthonormal basis.**

Example 40

Let $\mathbf{u}_1 = (\frac{2}{3}, \frac{1}{3}, \frac{2}{3})$, $\mathbf{u}_2 = (-\frac{2}{3}, \frac{2}{3}, \frac{1}{3})$, $\mathbf{u}_3 = (\frac{1}{3}, \frac{2}{3}, -\frac{2}{3})$. The set $\{\mathbf{u}_1, \mathbf{u}_2, \mathbf{u}_3\}$ is an orthonormal set since $\mathbf{u}_1 \cdot \mathbf{u}_2 = \mathbf{u}_1 \cdot \mathbf{u}_3 = \mathbf{u}_2 \cdot \mathbf{u}_3 = 0$ and $\mathbf{u}_1 \cdot \mathbf{u}_1 = \mathbf{u}_2 \cdot \mathbf{u}_2 = \mathbf{u}_3 \cdot \mathbf{u}_3 = 1$. The set $\{\mathbf{u}_1, \mathbf{u}_2, \mathbf{u}_3\}$ is a linearly independent set. To show this we assume $c_1\mathbf{u}_1 + c_2\mathbf{u}_2 + c_3\mathbf{u}_3 = \mathbf{0}$ and show that $c_1 = 0$, $c_2 = 0$, $c_3 = 0$.

The special properties of an orthonormal set make it simple to do this. Consider

$$\mathbf{u}_1 \cdot (c_1\mathbf{u}_1 + c_2\mathbf{u}_2 + c_3\mathbf{u}_3) = \mathbf{u}_1 \cdot \mathbf{0}$$

Thus, $c_1\mathbf{u}_1 \cdot \mathbf{u}_1 + c_2\mathbf{u}_1 \cdot \mathbf{u}_2 + c_3\mathbf{u}_1 \cdot \mathbf{u}_3 = 0$. Since $\mathbf{u}_1 \cdot \mathbf{u}_1 = 1$, $\mathbf{u}_1 \cdot \mathbf{u}_2 = 0$ and $\mathbf{u}_1 \cdot \mathbf{u}_3 = 0$, this implies $c_1 = 0$. Similarly, $c_2 = 0$ and $c_3 = 0$.

Since the set $U = \{\mathbf{u}_1, \mathbf{u}_2, \mathbf{u}_3\}$ is a linearly independent set of three vectors in R^3, U is a basis for R^3. Because U is an orthonormal set and a basis, it is an orthonormal basis. The orthonormal property makes it easy to find the coordinates of a vector relative to the basis U. Let $\mathbf{x} = (2, 3, -5)$, and suppose $(\mathbf{x})_U = (d_1, d_2, d_3)$, that is,

$$d_1\mathbf{u}_1 + d_2\mathbf{u}_2 + d_3\mathbf{u}_3 = (2, 3, -5)$$

Dot this equation with $\mathbf{u}_1 = (\frac{2}{3}, \frac{1}{3}, \frac{2}{3})$. We obtain

$$d_1 + 0 + 0 = \tfrac{4}{3} + \tfrac{3}{3} - \tfrac{10}{3} = -1$$

Similarly, dot the equation with $\mathbf{u}_2$ and with $\mathbf{u}_3$. This gives $c_2 = -1$ and $c_3 = 6$, so that

$$[\mathbf{x}]_U = \begin{bmatrix} -1 \\ -1 \\ 6 \end{bmatrix}$$

The same result can be obtained by the method of Example 39.

$$\begin{bmatrix} \frac{2}{3} & -\frac{2}{3} & \frac{1}{3} \\ \frac{1}{3} & \frac{2}{3} & \frac{2}{3} \\ \frac{2}{3} & \frac{1}{3} & -\frac{2}{3} \end{bmatrix} [\mathbf{x}]_U = [\mathbf{x}]_E$$

so that

$$[\mathbf{x}]_U = \begin{bmatrix} \frac{2}{3} & \frac{1}{3} & \frac{2}{3} \\ -\frac{2}{3} & \frac{2}{3} & \frac{1}{3} \\ \frac{1}{3} & \frac{2}{3} & -\frac{2}{3} \end{bmatrix} \begin{bmatrix} 2 \\ 3 \\ -5 \end{bmatrix} = \begin{bmatrix} -1 \\ -1 \\ 6 \end{bmatrix}$$ ■

Theorem 14 Let $U = \{\mathbf{u}_1, \mathbf{u}_2, \ldots, \mathbf{u}_k\}$. If the set U is orthonormal it is linearly independent. If U is an orthonormal basis for W, the coordinates of the vector $\mathbf{x}$ relative to U are $(\mathbf{x} \cdot \mathbf{u}_1, \mathbf{x} \cdot \mathbf{u}_2, \ldots, \mathbf{x} \cdot \mathbf{u}_k)$.

Proof Consider $c_1\mathbf{u}_1 + c_2\mathbf{u}_2 + \cdots + c_k\mathbf{u}_k = \mathbf{0}$. The dot product of this equation with $\mathbf{u}_i$, $i = 1, 2, \ldots, k$, gives $c_i = 0$, $i = 1, 2, \ldots, k$. This shows that U is linearly independent.

Suppose the coordinates of $\mathbf{x}$ are $(d_1, d_2, \ldots, d_k)$. Then $\mathbf{x} = d_1\mathbf{u}_1 + d_2\mathbf{u}_2 + \cdots + d_k\mathbf{u}_k$. The dot product of this equation with $\mathbf{u}_i$ gives $d_i = \mathbf{x} \cdot \mathbf{u}_i$, $i = 1, 2, \ldots, k$. □

Notice that in Example 40, the inverse of the matrix $\mathbf{U}$ is the matrix $\mathbf{U}^T$, where $\mathbf{U}$ is the matrix with columns $\mathbf{u}_1, \mathbf{u}_2, \mathbf{u}_3$. This special property is possessed by any matrix in which the columns form an orthonormal set. As the following theorem shows, every matrix $\mathbf{P}$ such that $\mathbf{P}^T\mathbf{P} = \mathbf{I}$, that is, $\mathbf{P}^{-1} = \mathbf{P}^T$, has the property that its columns form an orthonormal set. It would seem reasonable to call such a matrix an orthonormal matrix. However, accepted terminology gives it the name *orthogonal matrix*.

Orthogonal Matrix

Definition 13

The $n \times n$ matrix $\mathbf{P}$ is an **orthogonal matrix** if $\mathbf{P}^T\mathbf{P} = \mathbf{I}$.

Theorem 15 The square matrix $\mathbf{P}$ is orthogonal if and only if its columns form an orthonormal set. The square matrix $\mathbf{P}$ is orthogonal if and only if its rows form an orthonormal set.

Proof For simplicity we assume that $\mathbf{P}$ is a 3×3 matrix. The columns of $\mathbf{P}$ are $\mathbf{V}_1$, $\mathbf{V}_2$, and $\mathbf{V}_3$, so that the rows of $\mathbf{P}^T$ are $\mathbf{V}_1^T$, $\mathbf{V}_2^T$, and $\mathbf{V}_3^T$. In this notation, the matrix

$$\mathbf{P}^T\mathbf{P} = \begin{bmatrix} \mathbf{V}_1^T\mathbf{V}_1 & \mathbf{V}_1^T\mathbf{V}_2 & \mathbf{V}_1^T\mathbf{V}_3 \\ \mathbf{V}_2^T\mathbf{V}_1 & \mathbf{V}_2^T\mathbf{V}_2 & \mathbf{V}_2^T\mathbf{V}_3 \\ \mathbf{V}_3^T\mathbf{V}_1 & \mathbf{V}_3^T\mathbf{V}_2 & \mathbf{V}_3^T\mathbf{V}_3 \end{bmatrix}$$

This product will be the identity matrix if and only if each of the diagonal elements is 1 and each of the elements not on the diagonal is 0. The condition $\mathbf{V}_i^T\mathbf{V}_i = \mathbf{v}_i \cdot \mathbf{v}_i = 1$ implies that $\mathbf{v}_i$ is a unit vector, $i = 1, 2, 3$. The condition $\mathbf{V}_i^T\mathbf{V}_j = \mathbf{v}_i \cdot \mathbf{v}_j = 0$ when $i \neq j$ implies that the vectors $\mathbf{v}_i$ and $\mathbf{v}_j$ are orthogonal. Together, this tells us that $\mathbf{P}^T\mathbf{P} = \mathbf{I}$ if and only if the vectors $\mathbf{v}_1$, $\mathbf{v}_2$, and $\mathbf{v}_3$ are unit vectors orthogonal in pairs; that is, the set $\{\mathbf{v}_1, \mathbf{v}_2, \mathbf{v}_3\}$ is an orthonormal set. □

Orthogonal matrices have many useful properties. The change-of-basis matrix from basis U to basis V is an orthogonal matrix if U and V are orthonormal bases. In the 3×3 case, for example, the matrix $\mathbf{P}$, according to Theorem 13, is

$$\mathbf{P} = [[\mathbf{u}_1]_V, [\mathbf{u}_2]_V, [\mathbf{u}_3]_V]$$

From Theorem 14 we obtain

$$\mathbf{P} = \begin{bmatrix} \mathbf{u}_1 \cdot \mathbf{v}_1 & \mathbf{u}_2 \cdot \mathbf{v}_1 & \mathbf{u}_3 \cdot \mathbf{v}_1 \\ \mathbf{u}_1 \cdot \mathbf{v}_2 & \mathbf{u}_2 \cdot \mathbf{v}_2 & \mathbf{u}_3 \cdot \mathbf{v}_2 \\ \mathbf{u}_1 \cdot \mathbf{v}_3 & \mathbf{u}_2 \cdot \mathbf{v}_3 & \mathbf{u}_3 \cdot \mathbf{v}_3 \end{bmatrix}$$

Let $\mathbf{u}_i = (u_{i1}, u_{i2}, u_{i3})$, and $\mathbf{v}_i = (v_{i1}, v_{i2}, v_{i3})$, $i = 1, 2, 3$. Then

$$\mathbf{P} = \begin{bmatrix} v_{11} & v_{12} & v_{13} \\ v_{21} & v_{22} & v_{23} \\ v_{31} & v_{32} & v_{33} \end{bmatrix} \begin{bmatrix} u_{11} & u_{21} & u_{31} \\ u_{12} & u_{22} & u_{32} \\ u_{13} & u_{23} & u_{33} \end{bmatrix} = \mathbf{V}^T\mathbf{U}$$

where $\mathbf{V}$ is the matrix with columns $\mathbf{v}_1, \mathbf{v}_2, \mathbf{v}_3$ and $\mathbf{U}$ is the matrix with columns $\mathbf{u}_1, \mathbf{u}_2, \mathbf{u}_3$. Since the product of orthogonal matrices is orthogonal (see Problem 17), $\mathbf{V}^T\mathbf{U}$ is an orthogonal matrix.

We conclude this section by outlining a famous method of constructing an orthonormal basis for the space with basis $\{\mathbf{u}_1, \mathbf{u}_2, \ldots, \mathbf{u}_n\}$. This method is called the Gram-Schmidt method, and it is applicable in any vector space in which the concepts of orthogonality and norm are defined. We begin with a geometric example in R^2.

Example 41 Let $\mathbf{u}_1 = (2, 1)$ and $\mathbf{u}_2 = (1, 2)$. We wish to construct an orthonormal basis for R^2 in which one of the basis vectors is a multiple of $\mathbf{u}_1$. Let $\mathbf{v}_1 = (\frac{2}{\sqrt{5}}, \frac{1}{\sqrt{5}})$, a unit vector that is a multiple of $\mathbf{u}_1$. The vector $(\mathbf{u}_2 \cdot \mathbf{v}_1)\mathbf{v}_1$ is the projection of $\mathbf{u}_2$ on $\mathbf{v}_1$ (OA in Figure 4.9). The vector $\mathbf{w}_2 = \mathbf{u}_2 - (\mathbf{u}_2 \cdot \mathbf{v}_1)\mathbf{v}_1$ is the projection of $\mathbf{u}_2$ orthogonal to $\mathbf{v}_1$. (See Section 1.5, Definition 17 and Theorem 10.) But $\mathbf{w}_2$ may not be a unit vector. In this case $\mathbf{w}_2 = (1, 2) - (\frac{4}{\sqrt{5}})(\frac{2}{\sqrt{5}}, \frac{1}{\sqrt{5}}) = (-\frac{3}{5}, \frac{6}{5})$. Set $\mathbf{v}_2 = \mathbf{w}_2/\|\mathbf{w}_2\|$. Then $\mathbf{v}_2 = (\frac{-1}{\sqrt{5}}, \frac{2}{\sqrt{5}})$. The vectors $\{\mathbf{v}_1, \mathbf{v}_2\}$ form an orthonormal basis in R^2. In geometric terms, the orthonormal basis (in some order) corresponds to a rotation of the coordinate axes.

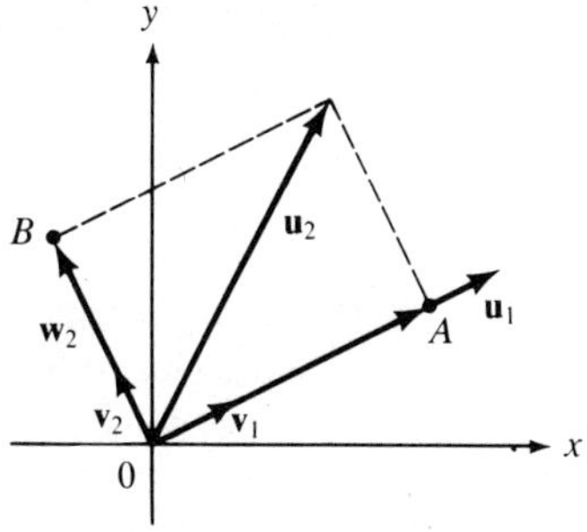

FIGURE 4.9

■

The key to finding $\mathbf{w}_2$ in Example 41 was finding a vector orthogonal to $\mathbf{v}_1$. The idea of projection orthogonal to a unit vector can be extended to projection of a vector orthogonal to a subspace of a vector space.

Theorem 16 Let S be a subspace of a vector space. Let $V = \{\mathbf{v}_1, \mathbf{v}_2, \ldots, \mathbf{v}_k\}$ be an orthonormal basis of S. Let $\mathbf{u}$ be a vector not in S. The vector $\mathbf{w} = \mathbf{u} - (\mathbf{u} \cdot \mathbf{v}_1)\mathbf{v}_1 - (\mathbf{u} \cdot \mathbf{v}_2)\mathbf{v}_2 - \cdots - (\mathbf{u} \cdot \mathbf{v}_k)\mathbf{v}_k$ is orthogonal to every vector in S and is in the space spanned by $\{\mathbf{u}, \mathbf{v}_1, \mathbf{v}_2, \ldots, \mathbf{v}_k\}$.

Proof Because $\mathbf{w}$ is a linear combination of $\{\mathbf{u}, \mathbf{v}_1, \mathbf{v}_2, \ldots, \mathbf{v}_k\}$ it is in the space spanned by this set. The vector $\mathbf{w}$ is orthogonal to each $\mathbf{v}_i$ since

$$\begin{aligned}\mathbf{w} \cdot \mathbf{v}_i &= (\mathbf{u} \cdot \mathbf{v}_i) - (\mathbf{u} \cdot \mathbf{v}_1)(\mathbf{v}_1 \cdot \mathbf{v}_i) - (\mathbf{u} \cdot \mathbf{v}_2)(\mathbf{v}_2 \cdot \mathbf{v}_i) - \cdots - (\mathbf{u} \cdot \mathbf{v}_k)(\mathbf{v}_k \cdot \mathbf{v}_i) \\ &= (\mathbf{u} \cdot \mathbf{v}_i) - (\mathbf{u} \cdot \mathbf{v}_i) \\ &= 0\end{aligned}$$

□

The Gram-Schmidt process extends the technique illustrated in Example 41 by repeated application of Theorem 16. It gives a method of replacing a basis of k vectors by an orthonormal basis of k vectors. In Example 42 the process is demonstrated for a linearly independent set of four vectors. The process can be carried out numerically. This is discussed in Section 4.6.

Example 42 Let $\{\mathbf{u}_1, \mathbf{u}_2, \mathbf{u}_3, \mathbf{u}_4\}$ be a basis for a vector space S. The following method generates an orthonormal basis for the same space:

1. Let $\mathbf{v}_1 = \mathbf{u}_1/\|\mathbf{u}_1\|$.
2. Form the vector $\mathbf{v}_2$ in the following two steps:
   a. $\mathbf{w}_2 = \mathbf{u}_2 - (\mathbf{u}_2 \cdot \mathbf{v}_1)\mathbf{v}_1$ (the projection of $\mathbf{u}_2$ orthogonal to $\mathbf{v}_1$)
   b. $\mathbf{v}_2 = \mathbf{w}_2/\|\mathbf{w}_2\|$ (a unit vector that is a multiple of $\mathbf{w}_2$)
3. Form the vector $\mathbf{v}_3$ in the following two steps:
   a. $\mathbf{w}_3 = \mathbf{u}_3 - (\mathbf{u}_3 \cdot \mathbf{v}_1)\mathbf{v}_1 - (\mathbf{u}_3 \cdot \mathbf{v}_2)\mathbf{v}_2$ (the projection of $\mathbf{u}_3$ orthogonal to the space spanned by $\{\mathbf{v}_1, \mathbf{v}_2\}$)
   b. $\mathbf{v}_3 = \mathbf{w}_3/\|\mathbf{w}_3\|$. The set $\{\mathbf{v}_1, \mathbf{v}_2, \mathbf{v}_3\}$ is orthonormal.
4. Form the vector $\mathbf{v}_4$ in the following two steps:
   a. $\mathbf{w}_4 = \mathbf{u}_4 - (\mathbf{u}_4 \cdot \mathbf{v}_1)\mathbf{v}_1 - (\mathbf{u}_4 \cdot \mathbf{v}_2)\mathbf{v}_2 - (\mathbf{u}_4 \cdot \mathbf{v}_3)\mathbf{v}_3$ (the projection of $\mathbf{u}_4$ orthogonal to the space spanned by $\{\mathbf{v}_1, \mathbf{v}_2, \mathbf{v}_3\}$)
   b. $\mathbf{v}_4 = \mathbf{w}_4/\|\mathbf{w}_4\|$

The set $\{\mathbf{v}_1, \mathbf{v}_2, \mathbf{v}_3, \mathbf{v}_4\}$ is an orthonormal basis for the space spanned by $\{\mathbf{u}_1, \mathbf{u}_2, \mathbf{u}_3, \mathbf{u}_4\}$. The set is orthonormal by Theorem 16 and parts b of steps 2–4. Parts a of steps 2–4 guarantee that $\mathbf{v}_i$ belongs to the space spanned by $\{\mathbf{u}_1, \mathbf{u}_2, \mathbf{u}_3, \mathbf{u}_4\}$. The set is linearly independent by Theorem 14. ■

Example 43 shows how to use the Gram-Schmidt process to find an orthogonal basis for the null space of a matrix.

Example 43 In Example 29a the null space of the matrix

$$\mathbf{A} = \begin{bmatrix} 1 & -1 & -1 & 1 & 0 \\ 1 & 1 & 1 & -3 & 2 \\ 1 & 4 & 4 & -9 & 5 \end{bmatrix}$$

was found to have dimension three and a basis consisting of $\mathbf{u}_1 = (0, -1, 1, 0, 0)$, $\mathbf{u}_2 = (1, 2, 0, 1, 0)$, $\mathbf{u}_3 = (-1, -1, 0, 0, 1)$. To find an orthonormal basis for this null space, we proceed as follows. Let $\mathbf{v}_1 = \mathbf{u}_1/\|\mathbf{u}_1\| = (0, \frac{-1}{\sqrt{2}}, \frac{1}{\sqrt{2}}, 0, 0)$. Since $(\mathbf{u}_2 \cdot \mathbf{v}_1) = \frac{-2}{\sqrt{2}}$, $\mathbf{w}_2 = (1, 2, 0, 1, 0) + \frac{2}{\sqrt{2}}(0, \frac{-1}{\sqrt{2}}, \frac{1}{\sqrt{2}}, 0, 0) = (1, 1, 1, 1, 0)$, so that $\mathbf{v}_2 = (\frac{1}{2}, \frac{1}{2}, \frac{1}{2}, \frac{1}{2}, 0)$. Now $(\mathbf{u}_3 \cdot \mathbf{v}_1) = \frac{1}{\sqrt{2}}$ and $(\mathbf{u}_3 \cdot \mathbf{v}_2) = -1$ so that

$$\begin{aligned} \mathbf{w}_3 &= (-1, -1, 0, 0, 1) - \tfrac{1}{\sqrt{2}}(0, \tfrac{-1}{\sqrt{2}}, \tfrac{1}{\sqrt{2}}, 0, 0) \\ &\quad + (\tfrac{1}{2}, \tfrac{1}{2}, \tfrac{1}{2}, \tfrac{1}{2}, 0) = (-\tfrac{1}{2}, 0, 0, \tfrac{1}{2}, 1) \end{aligned}$$

From this $\mathbf{v}_3 = (\frac{-1}{\sqrt{6}}, 0, 0, \frac{1}{\sqrt{6}}, \frac{2}{\sqrt{6}})$. The set $\{\mathbf{v}_1, \mathbf{v}_2, \mathbf{v}_3\}$ is an orthonormal basis for the null space of $\mathbf{A}$. ■

We saw in Section 4.4 that the null space of a matrix $\mathbf{A}$ and the row space of $\mathbf{A}$ are orthogonal complements of each other. As a consequence of this, if $\{\mathbf{v}_1, \mathbf{v}_2, \ldots, \mathbf{v}_k\}$ is an orthonormal basis for the null space and $\{\mathbf{v}_{k+1}, \mathbf{v}_{k+2}, \ldots, \mathbf{v}_n\}$ is an orthonormal basis for the row space of $\mathbf{A}$, the union of these two sets, $\{\mathbf{v}_1, \mathbf{v}_2, \ldots, \mathbf{v}_n\}$, is an orthonormal basis for R^n.

Example 44 Let $\mathbf{A}$ be the matrix of Example 43.

$$\mathbf{A} \Leftrightarrow \begin{bmatrix} 1 & 0 & 0 & -1 & 1 \\ 0 & 1 & 1 & -2 & 1 \\ 0 & 0 & 0 & 0 & 0 \end{bmatrix},$$

$$\mathbf{u}_4 = (1, 0, 0, -1, 1), \quad \text{and} \quad \mathbf{u}_5 = (0, 1, 1, -2, 1)$$

form a basis for the row space of $\mathbf{A}$. To obtain an orthonormal basis for the row space of $\mathbf{A}$, we follow the procedure of Example 42:

$$\begin{aligned} \mathbf{v}_4 &= (\tfrac{1}{\sqrt{3}}, 0, 0, \tfrac{-1}{\sqrt{3}}, \tfrac{1}{\sqrt{3}}) \\ \mathbf{w}_5 &= (0, 1, 1, -2, 1) - (\tfrac{3}{\sqrt{3}})(\tfrac{1}{\sqrt{3}}, 0, 0, \tfrac{-1}{\sqrt{3}}, \tfrac{1}{\sqrt{3}}) \\ &= (-1, 1, 1, -1, 0) \\ \mathbf{v}_5 &= (-\tfrac{1}{2}, \tfrac{1}{2}, \tfrac{1}{2}, -\tfrac{1}{2}, 0) \end{aligned}$$

The set $\{\mathbf{v}_1, \mathbf{v}_2, \mathbf{v}_3, \mathbf{v}_4, \mathbf{v}_5\}$ is an orthonormal basis for R^5. ■

SUMMARY If $\mathbf{x}$ is a vector in a vector space W and $U = \{\mathbf{u}_1, \mathbf{u}_2, \ldots, \mathbf{u}_k\}$ is a basis for W, $(\mathbf{x})_U$ represents the k-tuple of coordinates of $\mathbf{x}$ relative to the basis U and $[\mathbf{x}]_U$ represents the $k \times 1$ array formed from this k-tuple of coordinates.

If an n-dimensional vector space W has bases U and V, there is a matrix $\mathbf{P}$ such that $[\mathbf{x}]_V = \mathbf{P}[\mathbf{x}]_U$. The columns of $\mathbf{P}$ are the arrays $[\mathbf{u}_1]_V, [\mathbf{u}_2]_V, \ldots, [\mathbf{u}_k]_V$.

An orthonormal set is a set of vectors $\{\mathbf{v}_1, \mathbf{v}_2, \ldots, \mathbf{v}_k\}$ with the properties $\mathbf{v}_i \cdot \mathbf{v}_j = 0$ if $i \neq j$ and $\mathbf{v}_i \cdot \mathbf{v}_i = 1$. An orthonormal basis is a basis in which the vectors form an orthonormal set. The $n \times n$ matrix $\mathbf{P}$ is orthogonal if its columns form an orthonormal set; $\mathbf{P}$ is orthogonal if and only if $\mathbf{P}^T\mathbf{P} = \mathbf{I}$.

An orthonormal basis can be formed for the space with basis $\{\mathbf{u}_1, \mathbf{u}_2, \ldots, \mathbf{u}_k\}$ by a technique called the Gram-Schmidt method.

EXERCISES 4.5

1. Let $\mathbf{u}_1 = (1, 1)$ and $\mathbf{u}_2 = (-1, 2)$, and $U = \{\mathbf{u}_1, \mathbf{u}_2\}$.

a. Express $\mathbf{x} = (3, 6)$ as a linear combination of $\mathbf{u}_1$ and $\mathbf{u}_2$. Find $[\mathbf{x}]_U$.

b. Write $[\mathbf{x}]_U$, where $\mathbf{x} = (a_1, a_2)$.

c. Write the relation between $[\mathbf{x}]_U$ and $[\mathbf{x}]_E$ in the form $[\mathbf{x}]_U = \mathbf{A}[\mathbf{x}]_E$.

d. If $[\mathbf{x}]_U = \begin{bmatrix} 3 \\ -4 \end{bmatrix}$ find $\mathbf{x}$. Write $[\mathbf{x}]_E$.

e. If $[\mathbf{x}]_U = \begin{bmatrix} a \\ b \end{bmatrix}$ find $[\mathbf{x}]_E$.

f. Write the relation between $[\mathbf{x}]_E$ and $[\mathbf{x}]_U$ in the form $[\mathbf{x}]_E = \mathbf{A}[\mathbf{x}]_U$.

2. a. Let $\mathbf{u}_1 = (1, -1, 1)$, $\mathbf{u}_2 = (0, 1, -1)$, $\mathbf{u}_3 = (1, -2, 1)$. Find the equations that relate the coordinates of $\mathbf{x}$ relative to $U = \{\mathbf{u}_1, \mathbf{u}_2, \mathbf{u}_3\}$ and the coordinates of $\mathbf{x}$ relative to the standard basis.

b. Verify that $[\mathbf{e}_1]_U$, $[\mathbf{e}_2]_U$, $[\mathbf{e}_3]_U$ are the columns of the matrix $\mathbf{P}$ such that $[\mathbf{x}]_U = \mathbf{P}[\mathbf{x}]_E$.

3. a. Let $U = \{u_1, u_2, u_3\}$ where $u_1 = 1 + x^2$, $u_2 = x$, and $u_3 = 1 - x^2$. Find the coordinates of $p = 1 + 3x - 4x^2$ relative to the basis $\{u_1, u_2, u_3\}$.

b. Find the matrix $\mathbf{U}$ such that $[p]_E = \mathbf{U}[p]_U$.

c. Verify that the columns of $\mathbf{U}$ are $[u_1]_E$, $[u_2]_E$, $[u_3]_E$.

4. a. Let $V = \{v_1, v_2, v_3\}$, where $v_1 = 1 - x$, $v_2 = x - x^2$, $v_3 = x^2$. Find the matrix $\mathbf{V}$ such that $\mathbf{V}[p]_V = [p]_E$.

b. With U and V defined as in Problems **3** and **4a**, find $\mathbf{C}$ such that $[p]_U = \mathbf{C}[p]_V$. Verify that the columns of $\mathbf{C}$ are $[v_1]_U$, $[v_2]_U$, $[v_3]_U$.

5. Let W be a subspace of R^4 with basis $U = \{\mathbf{u}_1, \mathbf{u}_2, \mathbf{u}_3\}$, where $\mathbf{u}_1 = (1, 1, 1, 1)$, $\mathbf{u}_2 = (1, 0, 1, 1)$, and $\mathbf{u}_3 = (0, 1, 0, 1)$. The set $V = \{\mathbf{v}_1, \mathbf{v}_2, \mathbf{v}_3\}$ is also a basis for W, where $\mathbf{v}_1 = (0, 1, 0, 1)$, $\mathbf{v}_2 = (1, 1, 1, 0)$, and $\mathbf{v}_3 = (1, 0, 1, 1)$.

a. Let $\mathbf{x} = (0, 3, 0, 1)$. Verify that

$$[\mathbf{x}]_U = \begin{bmatrix} 2 \\ -2 \\ 1 \end{bmatrix} \quad \text{and} \quad [\mathbf{x}]_V = \begin{bmatrix} 2 \\ 1 \\ -1 \end{bmatrix}$$

b. Find the matrix $\mathbf{P}$ such that $[\mathbf{x}]_V = \mathbf{P}[\mathbf{x}]_U$ for $\mathbf{x}$ in W.

c. Check using $[\mathbf{x}]_U$ and $[\mathbf{x}]_V$ as calculated in **a.**

6. Let $\mathbf{u}_1 = (1, 0, 0)$, $\mathbf{u}_2 = (1, 1, 0)$, $\mathbf{u}_3 = (1, 1, 1)$, and $\mathbf{v}_1 = (1, 0, -1)$, $\mathbf{v}_2 = (0, 1, 0)$, $\mathbf{v}_3 = (1, 1, 2)$. The set $U = \{\mathbf{u}_1, \mathbf{u}_2, \mathbf{u}_3\}$ and the set $V = \{\mathbf{v}_1, \mathbf{v}_2, \mathbf{v}_3\}$; U is a basis for R^3 and V is also a basis for R^3.

a. Find $\mathbf{P}$ such that $[\mathbf{x}]_U = \mathbf{P}[\mathbf{x}]_V$.

b. If $[\mathbf{x}]_V = \begin{bmatrix} 3 \\ -1 \\ 2 \end{bmatrix}$, find $[\mathbf{x}]_U$.

7. Let $\mathbf{u} = (1, 0, 2, 1)$; find a vector $\mathbf{v}$ such that $\mathbf{u}$ and $\mathbf{v}$ are orthogonal. Is your answer unique? Show that the set of all possible $\mathbf{v}$ orthogonal to $\mathbf{u}$ is a subspace of R^4, and find a basis for this subspace.

8. Let $\mathbf{u} = (1, 2, 1, 1)$ and $\mathbf{v} = (-1, 0, 2, -1)$. Find $\mathbf{w}$ such that $\mathbf{w}$ is orthogonal to $\mathbf{u}$ and $\mathbf{v}$. Find a basis for the set of all possible vectors $\mathbf{w}$.

9. Which of the following sets of vectors are orthonormal sets?

a. $\left(\frac{1}{\sqrt{5}}, 0, \frac{2}{\sqrt{5}}\right)$, $\left(\frac{-2}{\sqrt{6}}, \frac{1}{\sqrt{6}}, \frac{1}{\sqrt{6}}\right)$, $\left(\frac{-2}{\sqrt{30}}, \frac{-5}{\sqrt{30}}, \frac{1}{\sqrt{30}}\right)$

b. $\left(\frac{1}{\sqrt{5}}, 0, \frac{2}{\sqrt{5}}\right)$, $(0, 1, 0)$, $\left(\frac{-2}{\sqrt{6}}, \frac{1}{\sqrt{6}}, \frac{1}{\sqrt{6}}\right)$

c. $\left(\frac{1}{\sqrt{6}}, 0, \frac{2}{\sqrt{6}}, \frac{1}{\sqrt{6}}\right)$, $\left(\frac{-2}{\sqrt{6}}, \frac{1}{\sqrt{6}}, \frac{1}{\sqrt{6}}, 0\right)$, $\left(\frac{-1}{\sqrt{6}}, \frac{-2}{\sqrt{6}}, 0, \frac{1}{\sqrt{6}}\right)$, $\left(0, \frac{1}{\sqrt{6}}, \frac{-1}{\sqrt{6}}, \frac{2}{\sqrt{6}}\right)$

d. $\left(\frac{1}{\sqrt{2}}, 0, \frac{1}{\sqrt{2}}, 0\right)$, $\left(\frac{-1}{\sqrt{3}}, \frac{1}{\sqrt{3}}, \frac{1}{\sqrt{3}}, 0\right)$, $(0, 0, 0, 1)$.

10. Let $U = \{\mathbf{u}_1, \mathbf{u}_2, \mathbf{u}_3\}$, $\mathbf{u}_1 = \left(\frac{-1}{\sqrt{3}}, \frac{1}{\sqrt{3}}, \frac{1}{\sqrt{3}}\right)$, $\mathbf{u}_2 = \left(\frac{2}{\sqrt{6}}, \frac{1}{\sqrt{6}}, \frac{1}{\sqrt{6}}\right)$, $\mathbf{u}_3 = \left(0, \frac{1}{\sqrt{2}}, \frac{-1}{\sqrt{2}}\right)$.
a. Show that $\{\mathbf{u}_1, \mathbf{u}_2, \mathbf{u}_3\}$ is an orthonormal basis for R^3.
b. Find $[\mathbf{x}]_U$ if $\mathbf{x} = (1, 0, 1)$.

11. a. With U defined as in Problem 10, verify that the matrix with columns $\mathbf{U}_1, \mathbf{U}_2, \mathbf{U}_3$ is an orthogonal matrix.
b. Write the equations relating $[\mathbf{x}]_U$ and $[\mathbf{x}]_E$.

12. Let $U = \{\mathbf{u}_1, \mathbf{u}_2, \mathbf{u}_3, \mathbf{u}_4\}$ be an orthonormal basis for R^4. Let $V = \{\mathbf{v}_1, \mathbf{v}_2, \mathbf{v}_3, \mathbf{v}_4\}$ be a second orthonormal basis for R^4. Let $\mathbf{P}$ be the change-of-basis matrix from basis U to basis V. Write the elements of $\mathbf{P}$ in terms of $\mathbf{u}_i$ and $\mathbf{v}_j$.

13. Let

$$\mathbf{A} = \begin{bmatrix} \frac{1}{\sqrt{2}} & 0 & \frac{1}{\sqrt{2}} & 0 \\ 0 & \frac{1}{\sqrt{2}} & 0 & \frac{1}{\sqrt{2}} \\ -\frac{1}{2} & \frac{1}{2} & \frac{1}{2} & -\frac{1}{2} \\ \frac{1}{2} & \frac{1}{2} & -\frac{1}{2} & -\frac{1}{2} \end{bmatrix}$$

Show that $\mathbf{A}$ is an orthogonal matrix by showing that $\mathbf{AA}^T = \mathbf{I}$. Verify that the rows of $\mathbf{A}$ form an orthonormal set. Verify that the columns of $\mathbf{A}$ form an orthonormal set.

14. Consider the 2×4 matrix

$$\mathbf{B} = \begin{bmatrix} -\frac{1}{2} & \frac{1}{2} & \frac{1}{2} & -\frac{1}{2} \\ \frac{1}{2} & \frac{1}{2} & -\frac{1}{2} & -\frac{1}{2} \end{bmatrix}$$

Calculate $\mathbf{BB}^T$ and $\mathbf{B}^T\mathbf{B}$. In what ways is $\mathbf{B}$ like an orthogonal matrix? In what ways is it different from an orthogonal matrix?

15. Find an orthonormal basis for the space spanned by $\{\mathbf{u}_1, \mathbf{u}_2\}$ if $\mathbf{u}_1 = (1, 2, 2)$ and $\mathbf{u}_2 = (1, 1, 1)$.

16. Find an orthonormal basis for the space spanned by $\{\mathbf{u}_1, \mathbf{u}_2, \mathbf{u}_3\}$ if $\mathbf{u}_1 = (1, 1, -1, 1)$, $\mathbf{u}_2 = (1, 0, 1, 1)$, and $\mathbf{u}_3 = (0, 1, 0, 1)$.

17. Show that the product of two orthogonal matrices is orthogonal.

18. Show that the inverse of an orthogonal matrix is orthogonal.

19. Let $\begin{bmatrix} a & b \\ c & d \end{bmatrix}$ be an orthogonal matrix. Show that

$$\mathbf{P} = \begin{bmatrix} 1 & 0 & 0 \\ 0 & a & b \\ 0 & c & d \end{bmatrix}$$

is also an orthogonal matrix.

20. Show that the determinant of an orthogonal matrix is ± 1.

21. If $\{\mathbf{u}_1, \mathbf{u}_2\}$ is an orthonormal set and $\{\mathbf{v}_1, \mathbf{v}_2, \mathbf{v}_3\}$ is an orthonormal set, and if $\mathbf{u}_i \cdot \mathbf{v}_j = 0$ for $i = 1, 2$ and $j = 1, 2, 3$, show that $\{\mathbf{u}_1, \mathbf{u}_2, \mathbf{v}_1, \mathbf{v}_2, \mathbf{v}_3\}$ is an orthonormal set.

Supplemental Topic

The Norm in P_n The following problems are set in P_n and require integration.

22. In P_2 define $\|p\|^2 = \int_{-1}^{1} p^2\,dx$. Using this definition, find the length of $1, x, x^2$.

23. In P_2 define $p \cdot q = \int_{-1}^{1} pq\,dx$. Using this definition show that:
a. 1 and x are orthogonal;
b. 1 and x^2 are not orthogonal;
c. x and x^2 are orthogonal.

24. Generalize, using Problem 23, to show that the standard basis in P_n is not an orthonormal set. What pairs of vectors in the standard basis are orthogonal?

25. Use the Gram-Schmidt process to replace the standard basis in P_3 with an orthonormal basis.

26. The first four Legendre polynomials are: $p_0(x) = 1$, $p_1(x) = x$, $p_2(x) = \frac{1}{2}(3x^2 - 1)$, $p_3(x) = \frac{1}{2}(5x^3 - 3x)$. Show that $\|p_n(x)\|^2 = 2/(2n + 1)$, $n = 0, 1, 2, 3$.

27. Replace the Legendre polynomials in Problem 26 with multiples of these polynomials of length 1. Verify that the normalized Legendre polynomials form the orthonormal set found in Problem 25.

28. Using the orthonormal basis of normalized Legendre polynomials q_0, q_1, q_2, q_3, express the polynomial $p = 1 + x + x^3$ in the form $c_0q_0 + c_1q_1 + c_2q_2 + c_3q_3$.

29. Let p be a polynomial of degree $\leqslant 3$. Show how to calculate c_i, $i = 0, 1, 2, 3$ so that $p = c_0q_0 + c_1q_1 + c_2q_2 + c_3q_3$.

4.6 Applications: An Error-Correcting Code, Homogeneous Coordinates, Orientation in Space

An Error-Correcting Code

This first application is an example in which a particular subspace of a vector space plays an important role in detecting the presence of an error in a transmitted message. By a *message* we mean some sequence of 0s and 1s of a known, fixed length. For example, if the length is ten, then a typical message might be $(0, 0, 1, 0, 1, 0, 1, 1, 1, 0)$. You may think that such messages are too simple to convey any information, but this is precisely how computers on Earth reconstructed the pictures transmitted from the Voyager spacecrafts as they approached Uranus in January 1986.

The major difficulty in transmitting and receiving messages containing 0s and 1s is that they must be detected accurately. Errors can easily enter a transmitted message as noise or interference. Our problem is to pinpoint the existence of an error and, if possible, to correct it. To simplify our discussion, let us agree that a message has an error if the received message differs from the transmitted message in only *one* position. This means that if we send $(0, 0, 1, 1, 0, 1)$ and $(0, 0, 0, 1, 0, 1)$ is received, an error has occurred in the transmission.

One way to detect and correct an error makes use of an appropriately chosen vector space and one of its subspaces. This subspace acts as the decoding space. Then received messages that are not in this subspace are known to have an error. If we are clever enough to choose our subspace carefully, it may be possible to correct the error at the same time.

Up to now we have used only vector spaces over the real numbers. For this application the components of the vectors come from a field other than the real numbers. This field, designated Z_2, has two elements, 0 and 1. The laws of addition and multiplication for Z_2 are:

$$\begin{array}{ll} 0 + 0 = 0 & 0 \cdot 0 = 0 \\ 0 + 1 = 1 & 0 \cdot 1 = 0 \\ 1 + 0 = 1 & 1 \cdot 0 = 0 \\ 1 + 1 = 0 & 1 \cdot 1 = 1 \end{array}$$

From these definitions, we can conclude that the commutative laws of addition and multiplication hold ($a + b = b + a$ and $a \cdot b = b \cdot a$). The distributive law also holds; for example, $1(1 + 0) = 1 \cdot 1 = 1$ and $1 \cdot 1 + 1 \cdot 0 = 1 + 0 = 1$, so that $1(1 + 0) = 1 \cdot 1 + 1 \cdot 0$. Thus, we can operate with the symbols 0 and 1 according to these rules just as if they were real numbers—except we must remember that, in addition, $1 + 1 = 0$.

For $n \geqslant 2$, let V_n denote the set of all possible n-tuples consisting of elements from Z_2. Thus, V_n is the set of all vectors $\mathbf{v} = (a_1, a_2, \ldots, a_n)$, where $a_i = 0$ or 1 for all $i = 1, 2, \ldots, n$. Since there are two choices for the value of each a_i, the set V_n contains 2^n elements.

Example 45 V_3 contains vectors (0, 0, 0), (1, 0, 0), (0, 1, 0), (0, 0, 1), (1, 0, 1), (0, 1, 1), (1, 1, 0), and (1, 1, 1). ■

Equality of vectors, addition of vectors, and multiplication of a vector by a scalar are defined in V_n exactly the same way as in R^n. The scalars in this case, however, must be chosen only from Z_2.

Example 46 Let $\mathbf{v}_1 = (1, 0, 1, 1, 0)$ and $\mathbf{v}_2 = (1, 1, 1, 0, 0)$. Then

$$\mathbf{v}_1 + \mathbf{v}_2 = (1 + 1, 0 + 1, 1 + 1, 1 + 0, 0 + 0) = (0, 1, 0, 1, 0)$$

The vector $\mathbf{v}_1 + \mathbf{v}_2$ is an element of V_5. Let $\mathbf{0} = (0, 0, 0, 0, 0)$. Then $0\mathbf{v}_1 = \mathbf{0}$, $1\mathbf{v}_1 = \mathbf{v}_1$, and $\mathbf{v}_1 + \mathbf{0} = \mathbf{v}_1$. ■

In general, let $\mathbf{v}_1 = (a_1, a_2, \ldots, a_n)$ and $\mathbf{v}_2 = (b_1, b_2, \ldots, b_n)$. Since $a_i + b_i = 0$ or 1 for every possible choice of a_i and b_i, it follows that $\mathbf{v}_1 + \mathbf{v}_2$ belongs to V_n, so V_n is closed under vector addition. Also, since $1 \cdot a_i = a_i$ and $0 \cdot a_i = 0$ for all i, V_n is closed under scalar multiplication.

The set V_n with the operations of addition and multiplication by a scalar is a vector space. One of the major differences between V_n and R^n is that V_n has only a finite set of vectors. However, the definitions of subspace, linear independence, spanning sets, bases, and dimension can all be carried over to the space V_n. In this setting, they are somewhat simpler to apply since, for example, the only possible linear combinations of $\mathbf{u}_1$ and $\mathbf{u}_2$ are $\mathbf{0}, \mathbf{u}_1, \mathbf{u}_2$, and $\mathbf{u}_1 + \mathbf{u}_2$. The subspace spanned by $\mathbf{u}_1$, $\mathbf{u}_2$, and $\mathbf{u}_3$ has eight possible vectors: $\mathbf{0}, \mathbf{u}_1, \mathbf{u}_2, \mathbf{u}_3, \mathbf{u}_1 + \mathbf{u}_2, \mathbf{u}_1 + \mathbf{u}_3, \mathbf{u}_2 + \mathbf{u}_3$, $\mathbf{u}_1 + \mathbf{u}_2 + \mathbf{u}_3$.

Recall that our basic goal is to define a subspace of V_n that will detect the presence of errors and, possibly, correct them. In general, suppose a message of length k is sent. Extra positions are added to make n positions in all. The information in the extra positions is chosen in such a way as to reveal the existence of an error. The set of messages used in this way is a k-dimensional subspace of V_n designated by $\mathscr{C}_{n,k}$ and referred to as a *code*. To illustrate how this can be done we will use $n = 7$ and discuss the *Hamming code* $\mathscr{C}_{7,4}$.

The Hamming code $\mathscr{C}_{7,4}$ is a four-dimensional subspace of V_7. The basis vectors for this subspace are

$$\mathbf{u}_1 = (1, 0, 0, 0, 0, 1, 1) \qquad \mathbf{u}_2 = (0, 1, 0, 0, 1, 0, 1)$$
$$\mathbf{u}_3 = (0, 0, 1, 0, 1, 1, 0) \qquad \mathbf{u}_4 = (0, 0, 0, 1, 1, 1, 1)$$

Example 47 Show that the set $\{\mathbf{u}_1, \mathbf{u}_2, \mathbf{u}_3, \mathbf{u}_4\}$ just defined is linearly independent.

Solution $c_1\mathbf{u}_1 + c_2\mathbf{u}_2 + c_3\mathbf{u}_3 + c_4\mathbf{u}_4 = (c_1, c_2, c_3, c_4, c_2 + c_3 + c_4, c_1 + c_3 + c_4, c_1 + c_2 + c_4)$. This is $\mathbf{0}$ only if $c_1 = 0$, $c_2 = 0$, $c_3 = 0$, $c_4 = 0$, which implies the set $\{\mathbf{u}_1, \mathbf{u}_2, \mathbf{u}_3, \mathbf{u}_4\}$ is linearly independent. ■

The subspace $\mathscr{C}_{7,4}$ generated by $\{\mathbf{u}_1, \mathbf{u}_2, \mathbf{u}_3, \mathbf{u}_4\}$ has 16 vectors in all. They are

$$\begin{array}{rcl@{\qquad}rcl}
\mathbf{0} & = & (0,0,0,0,0,0,0) & \mathbf{u}_2 + \mathbf{u}_3 & = & (0,1,1,0,0,1,1) \\
\mathbf{u}_1 & = & (1,0,0,0,0,1,1) & \mathbf{u}_2 + \mathbf{u}_4 & = & (0,1,0,1,0,1,0) \\
\mathbf{u}_2 & = & (0,1,0,0,1,0,1) & \mathbf{u}_3 + \mathbf{u}_4 & = & (0,0,1,1,0,0,1) \\
\mathbf{u}_3 & = & (0,0,1,0,1,1,0) & \mathbf{u}_1 + \mathbf{u}_2 + \mathbf{u}_3 & = & (1,1,1,0,0,0,0) \\
\mathbf{u}_4 & = & (0,0,0,1,1,1,1) & \mathbf{u}_1 + \mathbf{u}_3 + \mathbf{u}_4 & = & (1,0,1,1,0,1,0) \\
\mathbf{u}_1 + \mathbf{u}_2 & = & (1,1,0,0,1,1,0) & \mathbf{u}_2 + \mathbf{u}_3 + \mathbf{u}_4 & = & (0,1,1,1,1,0,0) \\
\mathbf{u}_1 + \mathbf{u}_3 & = & (1,0,1,0,1,0,1) & \mathbf{u}_1 + \mathbf{u}_2 + \mathbf{u}_4 & = & (1,1,0,1,0,0,1) \\
\mathbf{u}_1 + \mathbf{u}_4 & = & (1,0,0,1,1,0,0) & \mathbf{u}_1 + \mathbf{u}_2 + \mathbf{u}_3 + \mathbf{u}_r & = & (1,1,1,1,1,1,1)
\end{array}$$

In this case, there are 16 possible correct messages, one corresponding to each of the elements in the subspace $\mathscr{C}_{7,4}$. When a message of some sequence of seven 0s or 1s is sent, it will be received in the form of some element of V_7. The code $\mathscr{C}_{7,4}$ is called an *error-correcting code*, because for each $\mathbf{w}$ in V_7 not in $\mathscr{C}_{7,4}$ there is exactly one element in $\mathscr{C}_{7,4}$ that differs from $\mathbf{w}$ in just one position. If the message received is not an element of $\mathscr{C}_{7,4}$, it is then known that an error must be present in the message. Furthermore, if there is an error in only one position, it is possible to identify the correct message. The remainder of this section will show why these statements are true. First, an example.

Example 48 Suppose the message received is $\mathbf{w} = (1,0,1,1,1,1,0)$. This message is not an element of $\mathscr{C}_{7,4}$, so some error is present. Comparison with the elements of $\mathscr{C}_{7,4}$ shows that $\mathbf{u}_1 + \mathbf{u}_3 + \mathbf{u}_4 = (1,0,1,1,0,1,0)$, which differs from $\mathbf{w}$ in the fifth position. It therefore follows that the correct message is $(1,0,1,1,0,1,0)$. Furthermore, all the messages that differ from $(1,0,1,1,0,1,0)$ in exactly one position are: $(0,0,1,1,0,1,0)$, $(1,1,1,1,0,1,0)$, $(1,0,0,1,0,1,0)$, $(1,0,1,0,0,1,0)$, $(1,0,1,1,1,1,0)$, $(1,0,1,1,0,0,0)$, and $(1,0,1,1,0,1,1)$. Notice that none of these messages is an element of $\mathscr{C}_{7,4}$. ■

To establish the statements made above about the nature of the subspace $\mathscr{C}_{7,4}$, we define a *distance* between two elements in V_n. Let $\mathbf{v}$ and $\mathbf{w}$ be vectors in V_n. Then $d(\mathbf{v}, \mathbf{w})$ is defined to be the number of entries in $\mathbf{v}$ that are different from the corresponding entries in $\mathbf{w}$. By definition, $d(\mathbf{v}, \mathbf{w})$ is always a nonnegative integer.

Example 49 Let $\mathbf{v} = (1,1,0,1,1,0,0)$ and $\mathbf{w} = (1,0,1,1,0,1,1)$. Since $\mathbf{v}$ and $\mathbf{w}$ differ in the second, third, fifth, sixth, and seventh positions, $d(\mathbf{v}, \mathbf{w}) = 5$. Notice also that $\mathbf{v} + \mathbf{w} = (0,1,1,0,1,1,1)$ and $d(\mathbf{0}, \mathbf{v} + \mathbf{w}) = 5$. ■

The following statements follow easily from the definition of distance:

1. $d(\mathbf{v}, \mathbf{v}) = 0$
2. $d(\mathbf{v}, \mathbf{w}) = d(\mathbf{w}, \mathbf{v})$
3. $d(\mathbf{v}, \mathbf{w}) = d(\mathbf{0}, \mathbf{v} + \mathbf{w})$
4. $d(\mathbf{v}, \mathbf{w}) \leqslant d(\mathbf{v}, \mathbf{u}) + d(\mathbf{u}, \mathbf{w})$

The fourth statement is called the *triangle inequality*. An argument to show that this is true could go like this: Let $\mathbf{v} = (a_1, a_2, \ldots, a_n)$, $\mathbf{w} = (b_1, b_2, \ldots, b_n)$, and $\mathbf{u} = (c_1, c_2, \ldots, c_n)$. If $a_1 \neq b_1$, then 1 is contributed to the term $d(\mathbf{v}, \mathbf{w})$. However, c_1 must be either 0 or 1; hence, either $a_1 = c_1$ and $c_1 \neq b_1$ or $a_1 \neq c_1$ and $c_1 = b_1$. Thus, 1 is contributed to either $d(\mathbf{v}, \mathbf{u})$ or $d(\mathbf{u}, \mathbf{w})$, and the left-hand side is no bigger than the right-hand side. Now suppose $a_1 = b_1$. This contributes 0 to the term $d(\mathbf{v}, \mathbf{w})$. Either of two cases might hold: $a_1 = b_1 = c_1$, which contributes 0 to the right-hand side; or $a_1 \neq c_1$ and $b_1 \neq c_1$, in which case 2 is added to the right-hand side. In all cases, $d(\mathbf{v}, \mathbf{w})$ is no bigger than $d(\mathbf{v}, \mathbf{u}) + d(\mathbf{u}, \mathbf{w})$. Since this argument is the same in all components, the inequality is established.

We now define a *sphere* of radius r about a vector $\mathbf{v}$. The sphere consists of all the vectors $\mathbf{w}$ such that $d(\mathbf{v}, \mathbf{w}) \leqslant r$.

Example 50 Let $\mathbf{v} = (1, 0, 0, 0)$. The sphere of radius 2 about $\mathbf{v}$ consists of the vectors $(0, 0, 0, 0)$, $(1, 1, 0, 0)$, $(1, 0, 1, 0)$, $(1, 0, 0, 1)$, $(0, 1, 0, 0)$, $(1, 1, 1, 0)$, $(1, 0, 0, 0)$, $(1, 1, 0, 1)$, $(0, 0, 1, 0)$, $(0, 0, 0, 1)$, and $(1, 0, 1, 1)$. ■

Theorem 17 The numbers of vectors in the sphere of radius r about a vector $\mathbf{v}$ is equal to the number of vectors in the sphere of radius r about $\mathbf{0}$.

Proof Because $d(\mathbf{v}, \mathbf{w}) = d(\mathbf{0}, \mathbf{v} + \mathbf{w})$, $\mathbf{w}$ is in the sphere of radius r about $\mathbf{v}$ if and only if $\mathbf{v} + \mathbf{w}$ is in the sphere of radius r about $\mathbf{0}$. □

Consider a subspace of V_n and the distances $d(\mathbf{0}, \mathbf{v})$ for all vectors $\mathbf{v}$ in this subspace. Let δ represent the smallest *positive* number among these distances. Then δ is called the *minimum weight* of the code.

Example 51 Consider the code $\mathscr{C}_{7,4}$ listed on page 228. For the nonzero vectors in this code, $d(\mathbf{0}, \mathbf{v})$ has these values: 3, 3, 3, 4, 4, 4, 3, 4, 3, 3, 3, 4, 4, 4, 7. The minimum weight is therefore 3. ■

Theorem 18 The spheres of radius r about the code vectors are disjoint when $r = [(\delta - 1)/2]$, that is, the greatest integer less than or equal to $(\delta - 1)/2$.

Proof Assume two of the spheres are indeed not disjoint. Then there is a vector $\mathbf{u}$ in the sphere of radius r about $\mathbf{v}$ and also in the sphere of radius r about $\mathbf{w}$. This means that $d(\mathbf{u}, \mathbf{v}) \leqslant r$ and $d(\mathbf{u}, \mathbf{w}) \leqslant r$. But we know that $d(\mathbf{v}, \mathbf{w}) \leqslant d(\mathbf{v}, \mathbf{u}) + d(\mathbf{u}, \mathbf{w}) \leqslant r + r \leqslant \delta - 1$. However, we also know that $d(\mathbf{v}, \mathbf{w}) = d(\mathbf{0}, \mathbf{v} + \mathbf{w})$. But $d(\mathbf{0}, \mathbf{v} + \mathbf{w})$ must be greater than or equal to δ because $\mathbf{v} + \mathbf{w}$ is an element of the *subspace* and δ is the minimum weight of the code. Thus the assumption that the spheres are not disjoint leads to a contradiction, establishing that they are all disjoint. □

Note, that for the Hamming code, $r = [(3 - 1)/2] = 1$.

Theorem 19 Every vector in V_7 is in a sphere of radius 1 about some element in the *subspace* $\mathscr{C}_{7,4}$.

Proof This theorem is easily established with a counting process. How many elements are in a sphere of radius 1 about **0**? There are seven elements that differ from **0** in exactly one position. These plus the zero vector itself make up the sphere, so the sphere contains eight elements. But according to Theorem 17, the spheres of radius 1 all have the same number of elements. Theorem 18 assures us that spheres about the code vectors do not have common elements. Thus the elements in the 16 spheres about the code vectors contain exactly $16 \times 8 = 128$ different vectors. But this is 2^7, the number of vectors in V_7! □

Theorem 19 is the key to the error-correcting ability of the code $\mathscr{C}_{7,4}$. Any message received that consists of a 7-tuple made up of 0s and 1s is an element of V_7. By Theorem 19, it is in exactly one sphere of radius 1 about a code vector. Thus we can identify the unique code vector that is at distance 1 from the received vector. On the assumption that there is no more than one error in the message received, the code vector gives the corrected message.

The example described here is a very simple one. The Golay code $\mathscr{C}_{23,12}$ contains 12 information positions and 11 extra positions. The minimum weight of this particular code is 7, so it will correct $\delta = [(7 - 1)/2] = 3$ errors.

Homogeneous Coordinates

In Chapter 1 we showed how matrices can be used to represent changes in a video image stored in computer memory. One difficulty we saw immediately is that a translation of a set of points cannot be handled by the matrix products we had introduced. For example, suppose we consider the translation that moves every point (x, y) to $(x - 2, y + 3)$. We can think of this as just sliding (x, y) first two units left to $(x - 2, y)$ and then three units up to $(x - 2, y + 3)$. If the matrix $\begin{bmatrix} a & b \\ c & d \end{bmatrix}$ represents this action for some choices of real numbers a, b, c, d, then

$$\begin{bmatrix} a & b \\ c & d \end{bmatrix} \begin{bmatrix} x \\ y \end{bmatrix} = \begin{bmatrix} x - 2 \\ y + 3 \end{bmatrix} \tag{1}$$

must be true for all x and y. However, when $x = 0$ and $y = 0$, equation (1) becomes

$$\begin{bmatrix} a & b \\ c & d \end{bmatrix} \begin{bmatrix} 0 \\ 0 \end{bmatrix} = \begin{bmatrix} -2 \\ 3 \end{bmatrix} \tag{2}$$

which clearly cannot be true for *any* choices of $a, b, c,$ or d.

How can we salvage the situation? In this case, "bigger" is truly better! Suppose we identify points (x, y) in R^2 with the points $(x, y, 1)$ in the plane P_1, $z = 1$. If we represent $(x, y, 1)$ by $\begin{bmatrix} x \\ y \\ 1 \end{bmatrix}$, the fact that $\mathbf{I}_3$ leaves points unchanged is given by the matrix equation

$$\begin{bmatrix} 1 & 0 & 0 \\ 0 & 1 & 0 \\ 0 & 0 & 1 \end{bmatrix} \begin{bmatrix} x \\ y \\ 1 \end{bmatrix} = \begin{bmatrix} x \\ y \\ 1 \end{bmatrix} \tag{3}$$

However, can such a matrix product define a translation of points (x, y)? Yes —a simple modification of $\mathbf{I}_3$ will do the job. If the translation is a units in the x-direction and b units in the y-direction, the matrix product we seek is:

$$\begin{bmatrix} 1 & 0 & a \\ 0 & 1 & b \\ 0 & 0 & 1 \end{bmatrix} \begin{bmatrix} x \\ y \\ 1 \end{bmatrix} = \begin{bmatrix} x + a \\ y + b \\ 1 \end{bmatrix} \tag{4}$$

We can also use this concept to represent rotations, scaling changes, and shears. Suppose we wish to rotate the points (x, y) through an angle θ. The 2×2 matrix that defines the rotation is:

$$\begin{bmatrix} \cos\theta & -\sin\theta \\ \sin\theta & \cos\theta \end{bmatrix}$$

To set up the 3×3 matrix that gives this rotation in the plane P_1, we envision a partitioned matrix:

$$\left[\begin{array}{cc|c} \cos\theta & -\sin\theta & 0 \\ \sin\theta & \cos\theta & 0 \\ \hline 0 & 0 & 1 \end{array}\right]$$

Thus, the matrix

$$\begin{bmatrix} 0 & -1 & 0 \\ 1 & 0 & 0 \\ 0 & 0 & 1 \end{bmatrix}$$

represents a rotation by 90° of points $\begin{bmatrix} x \\ y \\ 1 \end{bmatrix}$ about the origin $\begin{bmatrix} 0 \\ 0 \\ 1 \end{bmatrix}$, and

$$\begin{bmatrix} 0 & -1 & 0 \\ 1 & 0 & 0 \\ 0 & 0 & 1 \end{bmatrix} \begin{bmatrix} x \\ y \\ 1 \end{bmatrix} = \begin{bmatrix} -y \\ x \\ 1 \end{bmatrix} \tag{5}$$

In addition, we have a reward: We can combine *both* the rotation and translation into one matrix. Suppose we wish to construct the matrix that would represent a rotation by 90° followed by a translation of 2 units right in the x-direction and 5 units down in the y-direction. This matrix would be:

$$\begin{bmatrix} 0 & -1 & 2 \\ 1 & 0 & -5 \\ 0 & 0 & 1 \end{bmatrix} \quad \text{so that} \quad \begin{bmatrix} 0 & -1 & 2 \\ 1 & 0 & -5 \\ 0 & 0 & 1 \end{bmatrix} \begin{bmatrix} x \\ y \\ 1 \end{bmatrix} = \begin{bmatrix} -y + 2 \\ x - 5 \\ 1 \end{bmatrix} \tag{6}$$

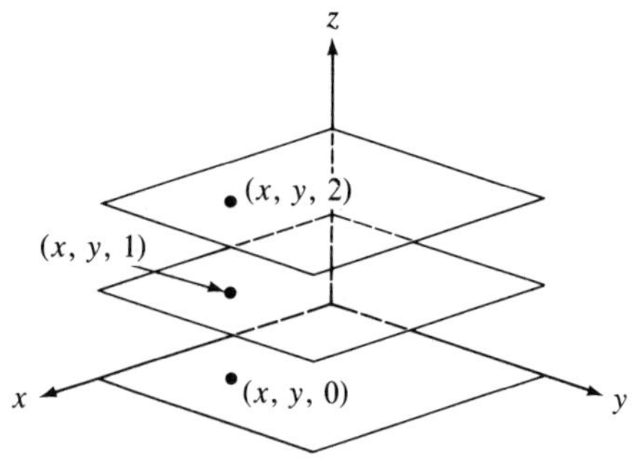

FIGURE 4.10

We have accomplished what we set out to do: define translations of points (x, y) in the plane using a matrix product. The matrices we use to represent such changes are 3×3, and they require that our points be represented by the matrices $\begin{bmatrix} x \\ y \\ 1 \end{bmatrix}$. More importantly, we can still use such matrices for rotations of points, scale changes, and shears. The representation of points (x, y) by $\begin{bmatrix} x \\ y \\ 1 \end{bmatrix}$ is called *homogeneous coordinates*. We have chosen the plane P_1 in which to do our work.

There are many planes other than $z = 1$ that we might use; the planes $z = k$ are all parallel to $z = 1$ (see Figure 4.10). Would some other plane do as well? Suppose we choose P_2, so all points (x, y) are represented by $\begin{bmatrix} x \\ y \\ 2 \end{bmatrix}$. Then equation (6) would become

$$\begin{bmatrix} 0 & -1 & 2 \\ 1 & 0 & -5 \\ 0 & 0 & 1 \end{bmatrix}\begin{bmatrix} x \\ y \\ 2 \end{bmatrix} = \begin{bmatrix} -y + 4 \\ x - 10 \\ 2 \end{bmatrix} \tag{7}$$

which does not appear to agree with our previous result. This difficulty is resolved to our advantage if we use the convention that (x, y) is represented in the plane $z = k$ $(k \neq 0)$ by $\begin{bmatrix} kx \\ ky \\ k \end{bmatrix}$.

Then (7) becomes

$$\begin{bmatrix} 0 & -1 & 2 \\ 1 & 0 & -5 \\ 0 & 0 & 1 \end{bmatrix}\begin{bmatrix} 2x \\ 2y \\ 2 \end{bmatrix} = \begin{bmatrix} 2(-y + 2) \\ 2(\ x - 5) \\ 2(1) \end{bmatrix} \tag{8}$$

which gives results corresponding to those in the plane $z = 1$, except that all coordinates are magnified by a factor of 2. Notice that we did not need to change the matrix itself in equations (6) and (8). The only adjustment was in the particular choice of k in $\begin{bmatrix} kx \\ ky \\ k \end{bmatrix}$. For this reason, the value of k is called the *scaling factor* in the homogeneous coordinates used to represent (x, y). However, $k = 0$ is not used, since no point of the form $\begin{bmatrix} x \\ y \\ 0 \end{bmatrix}$ can be translated to a different point $\begin{bmatrix} x + a \\ y + b \\ 0 \end{bmatrix}$ by the matrix product

$$\begin{bmatrix} 1 & 0 & a \\ 0 & 1 & b \\ 0 & 0 & 1 \end{bmatrix} \begin{bmatrix} x \\ y \\ 0 \end{bmatrix}$$

The standard choice for k is $k = 1$. However, scaling with values of k other than 1 can be very useful in computer graphics: We can enlarge or diminish the scope of the drawings held in memory by choosing the plane $z = k$ carefully. But in any of these planes, rotations, translations, shears, and (local) scaling can be done by the use of matrix products. One benefit of using k other than 1 occurs in an application where the numbers are extremely large; in such cases, rounding errors can be controlled by keeping the numbers within the capacity of the computer being used. For example, the point $(67000, -85000)$ can be represented by $\begin{bmatrix} 670 \\ -850 \\ 0.01 \end{bmatrix}$ or $\begin{bmatrix} 0.67 \\ -0.85 \\ 0.00001 \end{bmatrix}$.

Orientation in Space

When a spacecraft moves in a circular orbit around Earth, its location in orbit is not difficult to track. However, it is also important to identify its orientation relative to Earth and perhaps to make changes in this orientation. To do this, two coordinate systems are needed: One must be fixed relative to the spacecraft, and the other must be fixed relative to Earth.

Choose a spacecraft coordinate system as shown in Figure 4.11. The origin is at a convenient point in the spacecraft; the x- and y-axes are at right angles to each other, representing some plane that might be thought of as the level position; and the z-axis completes the usual right-handed coordinate system. This reference system is fixed relative to the spacecraft.

The angular motions of the spacecraft can be analyzed in terms of roll, pitch, and yaw. (See Figure 4.11.) Roll is a rotation around the x-axis, pitch is a rotation around the y-axis, and yaw is a rotation around the z-axis. Since the spacecraft coordinate system undergoes the same rotation as the spacecraft, we need a reference system that remains fixed.

A fixed reference system, called the terrestrial coordinate system, can be chosen as follows: The origin is the same as the spacecraft coordinate origin, the z-axis is

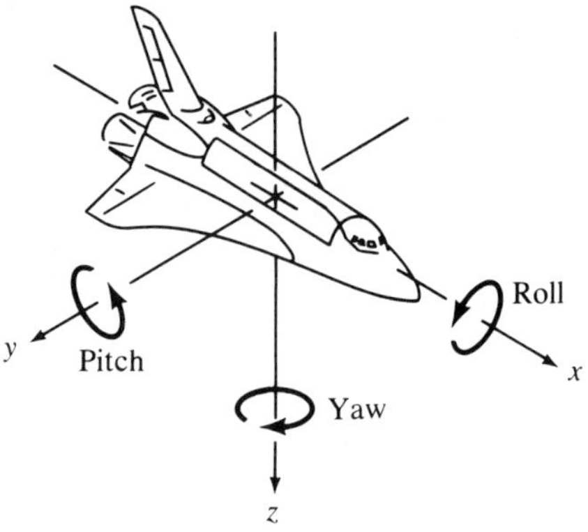

FIGURE 4.11

directed toward the center of Earth, and the x- and y-axes lie in a plane perpendicular to the z-axis.

Although the origin has been chosen to be the same in both systems, it is not fixed, since the spacecraft is moving in orbit. However, our main interest is not in the position of the spacecraft but in its orientation. Thus, the situation is described best in terms of sets of basis vectors. Designate the unit vectors in the directions of the spacecraft coordinate axes by $\{\mathbf{s}_1, \mathbf{s}_2, \mathbf{s}_3\}$ and the unit vectors in the directions of the terrestrial coordinate axes by $\{\mathbf{t}_1, \mathbf{t}_2, \mathbf{t}_3\}$. Observe that both sets are orthonormal sets. When the spacecraft performs a set of rotations, its new orientation corresponds to a change of basis from $\{\mathbf{t}_1, \mathbf{t}_2, \mathbf{t}_3\}$ to $\{\mathbf{s}_1, \mathbf{s}_2, \mathbf{s}_3\}$.

The change-of-basis matrix is easily calculated:

$$[\mathbf{x}]_S = \begin{bmatrix} \mathbf{t}_1 \cdot \mathbf{s}_1 & \mathbf{t}_2 \cdot \mathbf{s}_1 & \mathbf{t}_3 \cdot \mathbf{s}_1 \\ \mathbf{t}_1 \cdot \mathbf{s}_2 & \mathbf{t}_2 \cdot \mathbf{s}_2 & \mathbf{t}_3 \cdot \mathbf{s}_2 \\ \mathbf{t}_1 \cdot \mathbf{s}_3 & \mathbf{t}_2 \cdot \mathbf{s}_3 & \mathbf{t}_3 \cdot \mathbf{s}_3 \end{bmatrix} [\mathbf{x}]_T$$

We need only identify the elements of the matrix in each particular case.

Consider a roll of angle R in a counterclockwise direction around $\mathbf{t}_1$. Then (Figure 4.12) we have $\mathbf{t}_1 = \mathbf{s}_1$, $\mathbf{t}_2 \cdot \mathbf{s}_2 = \cos R$, $\mathbf{t}_2 \cdot \mathbf{s}_3 = -\sin R$, $\mathbf{t}_3 \cdot \mathbf{s}_2 = \sin R$, and

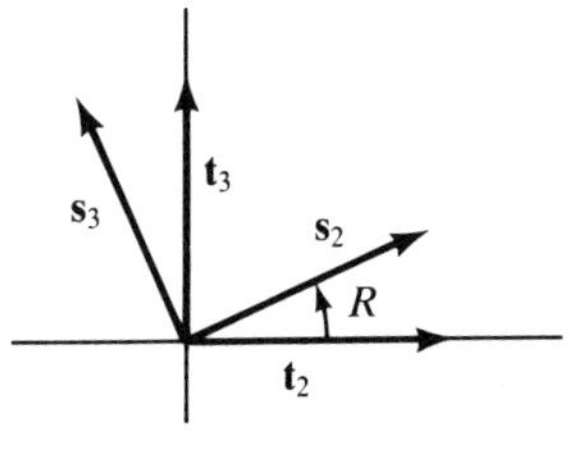

FIGURE 4.12

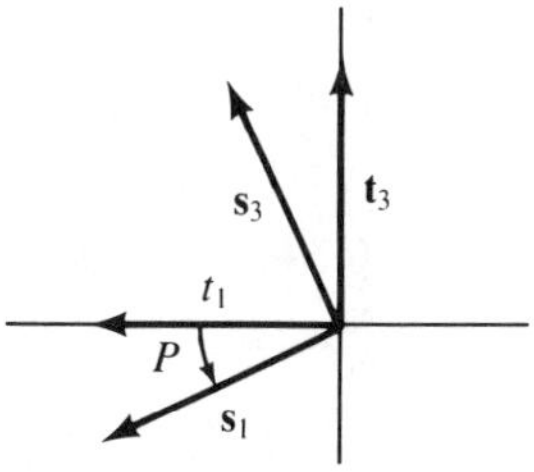

FIGURE 4.13

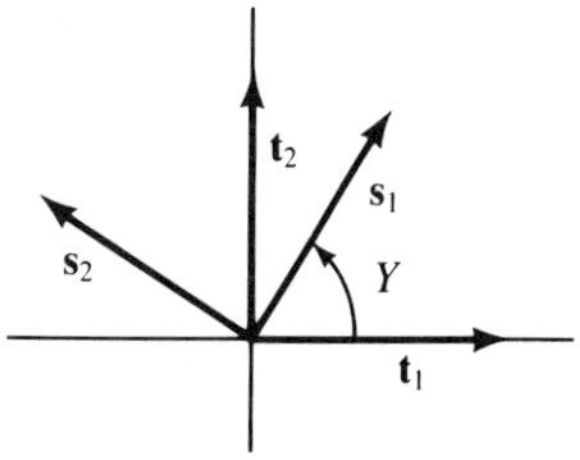

FIGURE 4.14

$\mathbf{t}_3 \cdot \mathbf{s}_3 = \cos R$. The change-of-basis matrix is

$$\mathbf{M}_R = \begin{bmatrix} 1 & 0 & 0 \\ 0 & \cos R & \sin R \\ 0 & -\sin R & \cos R \end{bmatrix}$$

Similarly, a pitch through an angle P around the $\mathbf{t}_2$ direction is described by the matrix $\mathbf{M}_P$. Again, counterclockwise is considered positive. (See Figure 4.13.)

$$\mathbf{M}_P = \begin{bmatrix} \cos P & 0 & -\sin P \\ 0 & 1 & 0 \\ \sin P & 0 & \cos P \end{bmatrix}$$

Finally, yaw is around $\mathbf{t}_3$. In the $\mathbf{t}_1\mathbf{t}_2$ plane, $\mathbf{t}_1$ makes an angle Y with $\mathbf{s}_1$. (See Figure 4.14.) The change-of-basis matrix is

$$\mathbf{M}_Y = \begin{bmatrix} \cos Y & \sin Y & 0 \\ -\sin Y & \cos Y & 0 \\ 0 & 0 & 1 \end{bmatrix}$$

Example 52 Suppose the spacecraft and the terrestrial systems are initially concurrent and the spacecraft performs in sequence a roll through an angle of 10°, a pitch through an angle of 20°, and a yaw through an angle of 15°. Find the resulting angles made by each of the spacecraft basis vectors with the terrestrial basis vectors.

Using $R = 10°$, $P = 20°$, $Y = 15°$ we have

$$\mathbf{M}_R = \begin{bmatrix} 1 & 0 & 0 \\ 0 & 0.9848 & 0.1736 \\ 0 & -0.1736 & 0.9848 \end{bmatrix} \qquad \mathbf{M}_P = \begin{bmatrix} 0.9397 & 0 & -0.3420 \\ 0 & 1 & 0 \\ 0.3420 & 0 & 0.9397 \end{bmatrix}$$

$$\mathbf{M}_Y = \begin{bmatrix} 0.9659 & 0.2588 & 0 \\ -0.2588 & 0.9659 & 0 \\ 0 & 0 & 1 \end{bmatrix}$$

The matrix representing the sequence of operations is

$$\mathbf{M} = \mathbf{M}_Y\mathbf{M}_P\mathbf{M}_R = \begin{bmatrix} 0.9077 & 0.3122 & -0.2804 \\ -0.2432 & 0.9358 & 0.2548 \\ 0.3420 & -0.1631 & 0.9254 \end{bmatrix}$$

The new orientation of the spacecraft vectors is given by

$$\mathbf{M}\begin{bmatrix} 1 \\ 0 \\ 0 \end{bmatrix} = \begin{bmatrix} 0.9077 \\ -0.2432 \\ 0.3420 \end{bmatrix} = \begin{bmatrix} \cos 24.8° \\ \cos(-75.9°) \\ \cos 70° \end{bmatrix}$$

$$\mathbf{M}\begin{bmatrix} 0 \\ 1 \\ 0 \end{bmatrix} = \begin{bmatrix} 0.3122 \\ 0.9358 \\ -0.1631 \end{bmatrix} = \begin{bmatrix} \cos 71.8° \\ \cos 20.6° \\ \cos(-80.6°) \end{bmatrix}$$

$$\mathbf{M}\begin{bmatrix} 0 \\ 0 \\ 1 \end{bmatrix} = \begin{bmatrix} -0.2804 \\ 0.2548 \\ 0.9254 \end{bmatrix} = \begin{bmatrix} \cos(-73.7°) \\ \cos 75.2° \\ \cos 22.3° \end{bmatrix}$$ ■

The result obtained, as one would expect, depends on the order in which the operations are performed. You are asked to verify this in Problem 17.

EXERCISES 4.6

1. How many computations must be verified before we can say the distributive law really holds in Z_2? Verify some of them.

2. In Z_2, verify the associative law for addition for all choices of 0s and 1s. How many computations did this exercise require?

3. Write the four possible vectors in V_2 and form all possible sums to see that the set is closed under vector addition.

4. In each case, identify the correct message if the message received is listed. Use $\mathscr{C}_{7,4}$

a. $(1, 1, 0, 1, 1, 0, 1)$ **b.** $(1, 0, 1, 1, 1, 1, 0)$
c. $(1, 1, 1, 0, 0, 1, 1)$ **d.** $(1, 0, 0, 1, 1, 1, 1)$
e. $(1, 0, 1, 1, 0, 0, 1)$ **f.** $(1, 1, 1, 0, 1, 1, 1)$

5. In the space V_{23}, how many elements are there in a sphere of radius 1 about $\mathbf{0}$?

6. What is the sphere of radius $\frac{1}{2}$ about $(1, 0, 1, 0)$? Find the sphere of radius 1 about $(1, 0, 0, 0)$.

7. In $\mathscr{C}_{23,12}$, the subspace of V_{23} is spanned by 12 vectors. How many vectors are there in this subspace? This number is the number of messages that can be identified correctly if there are no more than three errors in transmission.

8. Verify that $d(\mathbf{v}, \mathbf{w}) = d(\mathbf{0}, \mathbf{v} + \mathbf{w})$.

9. *Gram-Schmidt Orthogonalization Process.* In Section 4.5, a procedure was discussed whereby a given set of linearly independent vectors can be replaced by an orthonormal set that spans the same space. This means that if we are given a set of k linearly independent vectors in R^n, $(\mathbf{u}_1, \mathbf{u}_2, \ldots, \mathbf{u}_k\}$, we can replace this with a new set $\{\mathbf{v}_1, \mathbf{v}_2, \ldots, \mathbf{v}_k\}$ so that the following conditions are met:

1. $\|\mathbf{v}_i\| = 1$ for all $i = 1, 2, \ldots, k$ (normal condition).
2. $\mathbf{v}_i \cdot \mathbf{v}_j = 0$ for all $i, j = 1, 2, \ldots, k$ $(i \neq j)$ (orthogonal condition).
3. Any vector that can be written as a linear combination of the $\mathbf{u}_i$'s can be written as a linear combination of the $\mathbf{v}_i$'s, and conversely. (The two sets are bases of the same vector space.)

It is possible to carry out this process using

MAX or a matrix algebra program. (A BASIC program is provided in the Appendix.) Replace the set $\{\mathbf{u}_1, \mathbf{u}_2, \mathbf{u}_3, \mathbf{u}_4\}$ with an orthonormal set, where $\mathbf{u}_1 = (1, -2, 0, -1)$, $\mathbf{u}_2 = (1, 0, 0, -1)$, $\mathbf{u}_3 = (0, 1, 0, 1)$, and $\mathbf{u}_4 = (-2, 0, 1, 2)$, using such a program.

10. Let $\mathbf{u}_1 = (1.4, -2.0, 3.5, 4.2, -1.7)$, $\mathbf{u}_2 = (-0.1, 0.2, 3.3, 1.4, -5.1)$, and $\mathbf{u}_3 = (1.7, -2.1, 0.7, -15.2, 2.4)$. Find an orthonormal basis for the space spanned by $\{\mathbf{u}_1, \mathbf{u}_2, \mathbf{u}_3\}$.

11. Find the homogeneous coordinates for the following points using the scaling factors $1, 10, \frac{1}{2}$, and 0.05:

a. $(5, 6)$
b. $(-100, 5)$
c. $(1000, -5000)$
d. $(255000, -562000)$

12. The matrix for a translation

$(x, y) \to (x + a, y + b)$ is $\mathbf{A} = \begin{bmatrix} 1 & 0 & a \\ 0 & 1 & b \\ 0 & 0 & 1 \end{bmatrix}$

when using homogeneous coordinates $\begin{bmatrix} x \\ y \\ 1 \end{bmatrix}$.

a. Based purely on the concept of translation of points, find $\mathbf{A}^{-1}$.
b. Find $\mathbf{A}^{-1}$ using matrix methods, and show that it must exist for any values of a and b.

13. Find the 3×3 matrices that define the following actions on the points $\begin{bmatrix} x \\ y \\ 1 \end{bmatrix}$:

a. Rotate the plane 90° clockwise.
b. Translate all points (x, y) to $(x + 2, y - 3)$.
c. Translate all points (x, y) to $(x + 1, y - 1)$ and then rotate 90° clockwise.
d. Shear by a factor of 2 in the x-direction.
e. Shear by a factor of 2 in the x-direction and then translate all points 5 units left.
f. Reflect all points in the y-axis followed by a shear in the y-direction by a factor of 3.

14. The subspaces $y = mx$ of R^2 remain subspaces under a general rotation of the plane through a positive angle. Show this is true using homogeneous coordinates.

15. In the plane P_1, consider the translation that moves all points (x, y) to $(x + 2, y - 3)$. Show that such a translation moves the line $y = 3x - 4$ to $y' = 3x' - 13$. Use homogeneous coordinates.

16. Homogeneous coordinates $\begin{bmatrix} kx \\ ky \\ k \end{bmatrix}$ have, by definition, $k \neq 0$. Give a rationale for requiring $k \neq 0$.

17. Verify that if the changes in direction in Example 52 are performed in the order pitch, roll, and yaw, the resulting orientation will be different.

18. Find a sequence of operations that will return the spacecraft from its position at the end of Example 52 to coincidence with the terrestrial basis.

19. After a sequence of roll, pitch, and yaw (in that order), the coordinates of the terrestrial basis relative to $\{\mathbf{s}_1, \mathbf{s}_2, \mathbf{s}_3\}$ were $(0.35, -0.61, 0.71)$, $(0.93, 0.13, -0.35)$, $(0.13, 0.78, 0.61)$. The angle of roll was 30°, and the angle of pitch was 45°. What was the angle of yaw?

20. Verify that the matrix $\mathbf{M}$ in Example 52 is an orthogonal matrix.

21. What are the possible forms of the matrix $\mathbf{M}$ if only pitch and yaw are used?

5 Functions from One Vector Space to Another

5.1 Linear Transformations

When we use mathematical techniques and ideas to solve problems, we must first analyze these problems in terms of relations among the quantities involved. In this chapter we study the special type of relation called a linear transformation and see how the ideas of the preceding chapters relate to such transformations. The words function, mapping, and transformation all mean the same thing—the special type of pairing that Definition 1 describes.

Definition 1

Function Let D and R be sets. A **function** f from D to R is a set of pairs (x, y) such that x is an element of D, y is an element of R, and no two different pairs have the same first element. For each x in D there is a pair (x, y) in f. The set D is called the **domain** of the function. The subset of R containing all elements y from the pairs (x, y) in f is called the **range** of the function.

Domain
Range

Function	*Domain*	*Range*
Length of a vector $\|\mathbf{u}\| = \sqrt{\mathbf{u} \cdot \mathbf{u}}$	R^n	Nonnegative real numbers
Rank of a matrix	Set of all matrices	Nonnegative integers
Determinant of a matrix	Set of square matrices	Real numbers
The coordinate function: coordinates of a vector $\mathbf{v}$ relative to a given basis	n-dimensional vector space V	R^n
Transpose of a matrix, $\mathbf{A}^T$	Set of $m \times n$ matrices	Set of $n \times m$ matrices
Translation $T(\mathbf{X}) = \mathbf{X} + \mathbf{A}$, where $\mathbf{X}$ and $\mathbf{A}$ are $m \times n$ matrices, $\mathbf{A} \neq \mathbf{0}$	Set of $m \times n$ matrices	Set of $m \times n$ matrices

The important point is that a function associates with each element of its domain a single element of its range. In elementary algebra, the domain and the range are usually sets of real numbers, but they can be much more general sets. We have already used several types of functions in this book, some examples are listed in the preceding table.

Example 1 Let V be the space P_2 consisting of polynomials of degree less than or equal to 2. The set $U = \{1, 1 + x, 1 + x + x^2\}$ is a basis for V. The coordinates of $v = a_0 + a_1x + a_2x^2$ relative to U are c_1, c_2, c_3. Then $a_0 + a_1x + a_2x^2 = c_1(1) + c_2(1 + x) + c_3(1 + x + x^2)$, so that

$$\begin{bmatrix} 1 & 1 & 1 \\ 0 & 1 & 1 \\ 0 & 0 & 1 \end{bmatrix} \begin{bmatrix} c_1 \\ c_2 \\ c_3 \end{bmatrix} = \begin{bmatrix} a_0 \\ a_1 \\ a_2 \end{bmatrix}$$

Thus,

$$[v]_U = \begin{bmatrix} c_1 \\ c_2 \\ c_3 \end{bmatrix} = \begin{bmatrix} 1 & -1 & 0 \\ 0 & 1 & -1 \\ 0 & 0 & 1 \end{bmatrix} \begin{bmatrix} a_0 \\ a_1 \\ a_2 \end{bmatrix} = \begin{bmatrix} a_0 - a_1 \\ a_1 - a_2 \\ a_2 \end{bmatrix} = \mathbf{P} \begin{bmatrix} a_0 \\ a_1 \\ a_2 \end{bmatrix}$$

where

$$\mathbf{P} = \begin{bmatrix} 1 & -1 & 0 \\ 0 & 1 & -1 \\ 0 & 0 & 1 \end{bmatrix}$$

The coordinate function C, which associates with each v its triple of coordinates relative to U, is a function from P_2 to R^3, and $C(v) = (v)_U$. The following table gives some particular values of C.

v	$C(v)$
$4 + 3x + 2x^2$	$(1, 1, 2)$
$1 + x - x^2$	$(0, 2, -1)$
$5 + 4x + x^2$	$(1, 3, 1)$
$2 + 2x - 2x^2$	$(0, 4, -2)$
0	$(0, 0, 0)$

Notice in the table that: $C(u + v) = C(u) + C(v)$, the first three entries; $C(ku) = kC(u)$, entries two and four; $C(0) = \mathbf{0}$, entry five. These properties are true in general. Let $u = a_0 + a_1x + a_2x^2$ and $v = b_0 + b_1x + b_2x^2$. Then $u + v = (a_0 + b_0) + (a_1 + b_1)x + (a_2 + b_2)x^2$, so that

$$C(u + v) = \mathbf{P} \begin{bmatrix} a_0 + b_0 \\ a_1 + b_1 \\ a_2 + b_2 \end{bmatrix} = \mathbf{P} \begin{bmatrix} a_0 \\ a_1 \\ a_2 \end{bmatrix} + \mathbf{P} \begin{bmatrix} b_0 \\ b_1 \\ b_2 \end{bmatrix} = [u]_U + [v]_U = C(u) + C(v)$$

A similar argument shows that $C(ku) = kC(u)$ and $C(0) = \mathbf{0}$. ■

The three properties illustrated in Example 1 make a function a *linear* function, usually referred to as a linear transformation.

Linear Transformation

Definition 2

Let T be a function from the vector space D to the vector space R. Then T is a **linear transformation** if and only if

$$T(a\mathbf{u} + b\mathbf{v}) = aT(\mathbf{u}) + bT(\mathbf{v})$$

for every $\mathbf{u}$ and $\mathbf{v}$ in D and for every pair of real numbers a and b.

In particular, Definition 2 implies three properties easy to check:

1. $T(\mathbf{0}) = \mathbf{0}$ $\qquad a = b = 0$
2. $T(\mathbf{u} + \mathbf{v}) = T(\mathbf{u}) + T(\mathbf{v})$ $\qquad a = b = 1$
3. $T(k\mathbf{u}) = kT(\mathbf{u})$ $\qquad a = k,\ b = 0$

If any of these properties fails to hold, the T is not a linear transformation. For example, a translation cannot be a linear transformation, since $T(\mathbf{0}) = \mathbf{A} \neq \mathbf{0}$, so condition 1. is not true.

The length of a vector cannot be a linear transformation. When $\mathbf{u} \neq \mathbf{0}$ and $\mathbf{v} \neq k\mathbf{u}$, $\|\mathbf{u} + \mathbf{v}\| \neq \|\mathbf{u}\| + \|\mathbf{v}\|$. This shows that 2. is not satisfied.

Det $\mathbf{A}$ cannot be a linear transformation, since $\det k\mathbf{A} = k^n \det \mathbf{A}$. Thus, 3. is not true for $n > 1$.

The coordinate function *is* a linear transformation. Let $U = \{\mathbf{u}_1, \mathbf{u}_2, \ldots, \mathbf{u}_n\}$ be a basis in D. For any $\mathbf{v}$ and $\mathbf{w}$ in D and any real numbers a and b,

$$\begin{aligned}
\mathbf{v} &= a_1\mathbf{u}_1 + a_2\mathbf{u}_2 + \cdots + a_n\mathbf{u}_n \\
\mathbf{w} &= b_1\mathbf{u}_1 + b_2\mathbf{u}_2 + \cdots + b_n\mathbf{u}_n \\
a\mathbf{v} + b\mathbf{w} &= (aa_1 + bb_1)\mathbf{u}_1 + (aa_2 + bb_2)\mathbf{u}_2 + \cdots + (aa_n + bb_n)\mathbf{u}_n.
\end{aligned}$$

These three statements imply:

$$\begin{aligned}
C(\mathbf{v}) &= (a_1, a_2, \ldots, a_n); \quad C(\mathbf{w}) = (b_1, b_2, \ldots, b_n) \quad \text{and} \\
C(a\mathbf{v} + b\mathbf{w}) &= (aa_1 + bb_1,\ aa_2 + bb_2, \ldots,\ aa_n + bb_n) = aC(\mathbf{v}) + bC(\mathbf{w})
\end{aligned}$$

Examples 2 and 3 illustrate other transformations that are linear transformations. In one case the definition is algebraic; in the other, it is geometric.

Example 2 Let T be a function from R^3 to R^2 defined as follows: For each $\mathbf{x}$ in R^3, $T(\mathbf{x})$ is the pair in R^2 calculated by the rule

$$T(x_1, x_2, x_3) = (2x_1 + 3x_2 + x_3,\ x_1 - x_3)$$

Let $\mathbf{u} = (u_1, u_2, u_3)$ and $\mathbf{v} = (v_1, v_2, v_3)$, so that

$$a\mathbf{u} + b\mathbf{v} = (au_1 + bv_1,\ au_2 + bv_2,\ au_3 + bv_3)$$

Then

$$\begin{aligned} T(a\mathbf{u} + b\mathbf{v}) &= (2au_1 + 2bv_1 + 3au_2 + 3bv_2 + au_3 + bv_3, au_1 + bv_1 - au_3 - bv_3) \\ &= (2au_1 + 3au_2 + au_3, au_1 - au_3) + (2bv_1 + 3bv_2 + bv_3, bv_1 - bv_3) \\ &= a(2u_1 + 3u_2 + u_3, u_1 - u_3) + b(2v_1 + 3v_2 + v_3, v_1 - v_3) \\ &= aT(\mathbf{u}) + bT(\mathbf{v}) \end{aligned}$$

This property makes T a linear transformation. ■

Example 3 Let OP be the geometric vector representing $\mathbf{x}$ in R^2. Define $T(\mathbf{x})$ as follows. Let OQ be the vector obtained by rotating OP in a counterclockwise direction through an angle of 90°. Let $\mathbf{y}$ be the vector in R^2 whose geometric representation is OQ. The transformation $T(\mathbf{x}) = \mathbf{y}$ is a transformation from R^2 to R^2 defined by a rotation of the plane about the origin in a counterclockwise direction through an angle of 90°. (See Figure 5.1.) The following geometric argument shows that T is linear.

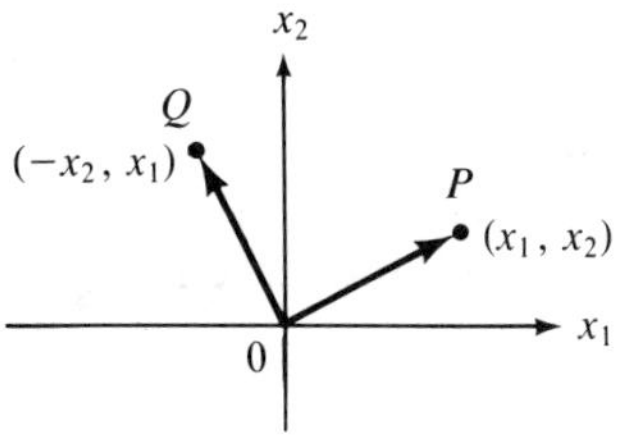

FIGURE 5.1

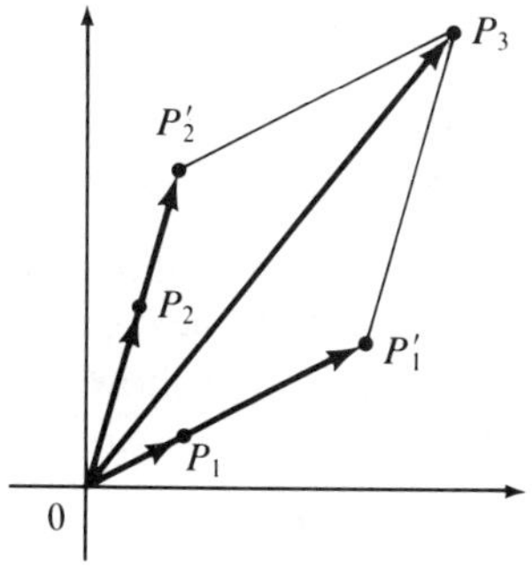

FIGURE 5.2

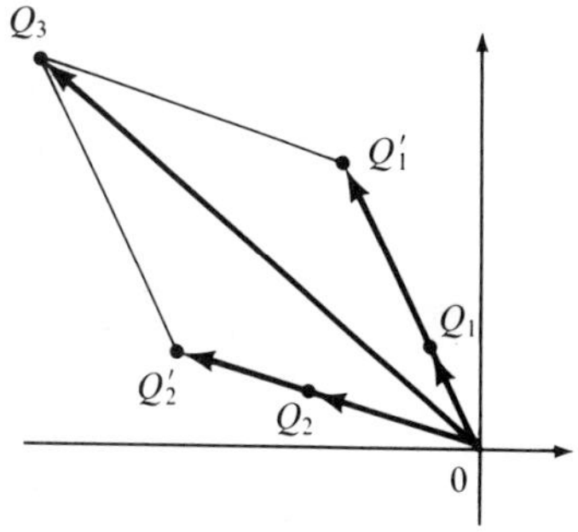

FIGURE 5.3

Let $\mathbf{u} = OP_1, \mathbf{v} = OP_2$, $a\mathbf{u} = OP_1'$, $b\mathbf{v} = OP_2'$, and $a\mathbf{u} + b\mathbf{v} = OP_3$. (See Figure 5.2.) Rotation of the plane through 90° carries the parallelogram $OP_1'P_3P_2'$ into the congruent parallelogram $OQ_1'Q_3Q_2'$. (See Figure 5.3.) We have $T(a\mathbf{u} + b\mathbf{v}) = T(OP_3) = OQ_3 = OQ_1' + OQ_2'$. Now $OP_1 = \mathbf{u}$, $OP_1' = a\mathbf{u}$, and $T(a\mathbf{u}) = OQ_1' = aOQ_1 = aT(\mathbf{u})$. Also, $OP_2 = \mathbf{v}$, $OP_2' = b\mathbf{v}$, and $T(b\mathbf{v}) = OQ_2' = bOQ_2 = bT(\mathbf{v})$. Thus, $OQ_3 = OQ_1' + OQ_2'$ implies $T(a\mathbf{u} + b\mathbf{v}) = aT(\mathbf{u}) + bT(\mathbf{v})$ and T is a linear transformation. ■

An important type of linear transformation from R^n to R^m is defined by a matrix product of the form $\mathbf{AX}$, where $\mathbf{A}$ is an $m \times n$ matrix and $\mathbf{X}$ is a vector from R^n written as an $n \times 1$ array. In Example 4, T is a linear transformation from R^3 to R^2.

Example 4 Let

$$T(\mathbf{X}) = \mathbf{AX}, \qquad \text{where } \mathbf{X} = \begin{bmatrix} x_1 \\ x_2 \\ x_3 \end{bmatrix} \text{ and } \mathbf{A} = \begin{bmatrix} 2 & 3 & 1 \\ 1 & 0 & -1 \end{bmatrix}$$

Then $T(\mathbf{X})$ is a 2×1 array for each $\mathbf{X}$. For example,

$$T\left(\begin{bmatrix} 1 \\ 2 \\ 3 \end{bmatrix}\right) = \begin{bmatrix} 2 & 3 & 1 \\ 1 & 0 & -1 \end{bmatrix}\begin{bmatrix} 1 \\ 2 \\ 3 \end{bmatrix} = \begin{bmatrix} 11 \\ -2 \end{bmatrix}$$

Notice that

$$T\left(\begin{bmatrix} x_1 \\ x_2 \\ x_3 \end{bmatrix}\right) = \begin{bmatrix} 2 & 3 & 1 \\ 1 & 0 & -1 \end{bmatrix}\begin{bmatrix} x_1 \\ x_2 \\ x_3 \end{bmatrix} = \begin{bmatrix} 2x_1 + 3x_2 + x_3 \\ x_1 - x_3 \end{bmatrix}$$

Compare this with Example 2. The transformations defined in Example 2 and in Example 4 are the same, where an $n \times 1$ array is used to represent an n-tuple from R^n. ■

Theorem 1 Let $\mathbf{A}$ be an $m \times n$ matrix. The transformation T defined by $T(\mathbf{X}) = \mathbf{AX}$ is a linear transformation from R^n to R^m.

Proof Let $\mathbf{X}$ be an $n \times 1$ array that represents a vector in R^n. The matrix product $\mathbf{AX}$ gives an $m \times 1$ array that is the column representation of a vector in R^m. The properties of matrix multiplication show that T is linear as follows: Let a and b be scalars and let $\mathbf{U}$ and $\mathbf{V}$ be vectors from R^n, written as columns. We have

$T(a\mathbf{U} + b\mathbf{V})$	$= \mathbf{A}(a\mathbf{U} + b\mathbf{V})$	By the definition of T
	$= \mathbf{A}a\mathbf{U} + \mathbf{A}b\mathbf{V}$	By the distributive property of matrix multiplication
	$= a\mathbf{AU} + b\mathbf{AV}$	By the commutative property of scalar multiplication
	$= aT(\mathbf{U}) + bT(\mathbf{V})$	By the definition of T □

The condition $T(a\mathbf{u} + b\mathbf{v}) = aT(\mathbf{u}) + bT(\mathbf{v})$ can be extended by the associative law to

$$T(a_1\mathbf{u}_1 + a_2\mathbf{u}_2 + \cdots + a_k\mathbf{u}_k) = a_1T(\mathbf{u}_1) + a_2T(\mathbf{u}_2) + \cdots + a_kT(\mathbf{u}_k)$$

This fact makes it natural to express a linear transformation in terms of the basis vectors of the domain. Suppose that D is a vector space with basis $\{\mathbf{u}_1, \mathbf{u}_2, \ldots, \mathbf{u}_k\}$, and that T is a linear transformation from D to R. Any vector $\mathbf{x}$ in D can be written in the form $\mathbf{x} = c_1\mathbf{u}_1 + c_2\mathbf{u}_2 + \cdots + c_k\mathbf{u}_k$. Since T is linear, $T(\mathbf{x}) = c_1T(\mathbf{u}_1) + c_2T(\mathbf{u}_2) + \cdots + c_kT(\mathbf{u}_k)$. This implies that $T(\mathbf{x})$ can be calculated as soon as the value of T for each of the basis vectors is known. The result is stated in the following theorem.

Theorem 2 Let D be a vector space with basis $U = \{\mathbf{u}_1, \mathbf{u}_2, \ldots, \mathbf{u}_n\}$. Let T be a linear transformation from D to R. Then for any $\mathbf{x}$ in D,

$$T(\mathbf{x}) = c_1T(\mathbf{u}_1) + c_2T(\mathbf{u}_2) + \cdots + c_nT(\mathbf{u}_n),$$

where $(c_1, c_2, \ldots, c_n)$ is the coordinate vector of $\mathbf{x}$ relative to U. □

When D and R are the spaces R^n and R^m, Theorem 2 implies that the linear transformation T can be written in matrix form. If the basis is the standard basis $\{\mathbf{e}_1, \mathbf{e}_2, \ldots, \mathbf{e}_n\}$, $\mathbf{x} = (x_1, x_2, \ldots, x_n)$ in R^n can be written $x_1\mathbf{e}_1 + x_2\mathbf{e}_2 + \cdots + x_n\mathbf{e}_n$. Thus $T(\mathbf{x}) = x_1T(\mathbf{e}_1) + x_2T(\mathbf{e}_2) + \cdots + x_nT(\mathbf{e}_n)$. The expressions $T(\mathbf{e}_i)$, $i = 1, 2, \ldots, n$ are vectors in R^m. If these vectors are written as columns, then $T(\mathbf{X}) = x_1T(\mathbf{E}_1) + x_2T(\mathbf{E}_2) + \cdots + x_nT(\mathbf{E}_n) = \mathbf{AX}$, where $\mathbf{A}$ is the $m \times n$ matrix with columns $T(\mathbf{E}_1), T(\mathbf{E}_2), \ldots, T(\mathbf{E}_n)$ and $\mathbf{X}$ is the column array

$$\begin{bmatrix} x_1 \\ x_2 \\ \vdots \\ x_n \end{bmatrix}$$

Corollary (Theorem 2) If T is a linear transformation from R^n to R^m, then $T(\mathbf{X}) = \mathbf{AX}$, where $\mathbf{A}$ is the $m \times n$ matrix with columns $T(\mathbf{E}_1), T(\mathbf{E}_2), \ldots, T(\mathbf{E}_n)$. □

When the standard basis is used in D and R, the matrix $\mathbf{A}$ is called the **standard matrix** for T. The procedure for finding the standard matrix can be summarized as follows: Let U and V be the standard bases for D and R, and let T be a linear transformation from D to R.

1. For each $\mathbf{u}_i$ in U, find $[T(\mathbf{u}_i)]_V$.
2. Form the matrix $\mathbf{A}$ whose columns are $[T(\mathbf{u}_i)]_V$.
3. To find $T(\mathbf{u})$
   a. Find $[\mathbf{u}]_U$.
   b. Calculate $[T(\mathbf{u})]_V = \mathbf{A}[\mathbf{u}]_U$.
   c. Write $T(\mathbf{u})$.

Example 5 Let T be a linear transformation from R^3 to R^2 for which $T(\mathbf{e}_1) = (1, 3)$, $T(\mathbf{e}_2) = (1, -1)$, and $T(\mathbf{e}_3) = (0, 5)$. The standard basis in R^2 is $V = \{(1, 0), (0, 1)\}$.

1. $[T(\mathbf{e}_1)]_V = \begin{bmatrix} 1 \\ 3 \end{bmatrix}$, $[T(\mathbf{e}_2)]_V = \begin{bmatrix} 1 \\ -1 \end{bmatrix}$, $[T(\mathbf{e}_3)]_V = \begin{bmatrix} 0 \\ 5 \end{bmatrix}$.
2. $\mathbf{A} = \begin{bmatrix} 1 & 1 & 0 \\ 3 & -1 & 5 \end{bmatrix}$.
3. If $\mathbf{u} = x_1\mathbf{e}_1 + x_2\mathbf{e}_2 + x_3\mathbf{e}_3$, $[\mathbf{u}]_U = \begin{bmatrix} x_1 \\ x_2 \\ x_3 \end{bmatrix}$, and $[T(\mathbf{u})]_V = \begin{bmatrix} 1 & 1 & 0 \\ 3 & -1 & 5 \end{bmatrix} \begin{bmatrix} x_1 \\ x_2 \\ x_3 \end{bmatrix}$.

That is,

$$T(\mathbf{u}) = (x_1 + x_2)(1,0) + (3x_1 - x_2 + 5x_3)(0,1)$$
$$= (x_1 + x_2, 3x_1 - x_2 + 5x_3)$$ ■

Example 6 By rotation about the origin in a counterclockwise direction through 90°, the vector $\mathbf{e}_1$ is carried into $\mathbf{e}_2$; thus $T(\mathbf{e}_1) = (0,1)$. The vector $\mathbf{e}_2$ is carried into $-\mathbf{e}_1$; thus $T(\mathbf{e}_2) = (-1,0)$. The matrix form of this transformation is

$$T(\mathbf{X}) = \begin{bmatrix} 0 & -1 \\ 1 & 0 \end{bmatrix} \mathbf{X}$$

This agrees with Example 3, since Figure 5.1 shows that

$$T(\mathbf{X}) = \begin{bmatrix} -x_2 \\ x_1 \end{bmatrix}$$ ■

In the next section we use the coordinate function to write any linear transformation from one finite-dimensional space to another in matrix form.

In the set of real-valued functions there are two that play special roles. One, the zero function, is defined by $f(x) = 0$ for all x in D. The other, the identity function, is defined by $f(x) = x$ for all x in D. The linear transformation defined in Definition 3 are the natural counterparts of these functions.

Zero Identity Transformations

Definition 3

The **zero transformation**, Z, from the vector space V to the vector space W is defined by $Z(\mathbf{x}) = \mathbf{0}$ for every $\mathbf{x}$ in V. The **identity transformation**, I, from the vector space V to itself is defined by $I(\mathbf{x}) = \mathbf{x}$ for every $\mathbf{x}$ in V.

SUMMARY A function with domain a vector space D and range a vector space R is a linear transformation if for any scalars a and b and for any vectors $\mathbf{u}, \mathbf{v}$ in D, $T(a\mathbf{u} + b\mathbf{v}) = aT(\mathbf{u}) + bT(\mathbf{v})$.

The coordinate function from an n-dimensional space D to R^n associates with each vector $\mathbf{v}$ in D its coordinate vector in R^n. This function is a linear transformation.

If $\mathbf{A}$ is an $m \times n$ matrix, the function defined by $T(\mathbf{X}) = \mathbf{AX}$ is a linear transformation with domain R^n and range contained in R^m.

EXERCISES 5.1

1. Let $T(\mathbf{X}) = \mathbf{AX}$, where $\mathbf{A} = \begin{bmatrix} -1 & 1 \\ 2 & 3 \\ -4 & 5 \end{bmatrix}$. Let $\mathbf{u} = (1,1)$ and $\mathbf{v} = (-1,3)$.
   a. Calculate $T(\mathbf{U})$, $T(\mathbf{V})$.
   b. Calculate $\mathbf{w} = 4\mathbf{u} - 5\mathbf{v}$. Calculate $T(\mathbf{W})$.
   c. Verify that $T(\mathbf{W}) = 4T(\mathbf{U}) - 5T(\mathbf{V})$.

2. Let T be a function defined by $T(\mathbf{x}) = (x_1 + 3x_2 + 2x_3, -x_1 + x_2)$; let $\mathbf{u} = (-1, 1, 3)$ and $\mathbf{v} = (3, 0, 4)$.
a. Calculate $T(\mathbf{u})$ and $T(\mathbf{v})$.
b. Let $\mathbf{w} = 3\mathbf{u} - 4\mathbf{v}$. Calculate $T(\mathbf{w})$.
c. Verify that $T(\mathbf{w}) = 3T(\mathbf{u}) - 4T(\mathbf{v})$.

3. Let S be a function from R^2 to R^2 defined by $S(\mathbf{x}) = (x_1^2, x_1x_2)$. Show that S has the property $S(\mathbf{0}) = \mathbf{0}$, but that S is not a linear transformation.

4. Let F be a function from R^2 to R^2 defined by

$$F(\mathbf{X}) = \begin{bmatrix} 1 & 2 \\ 1 & 3 \end{bmatrix}\mathbf{X} + \begin{bmatrix} 3 \\ 4 \end{bmatrix}$$

Show that F is not a linear transformation.

5. Let T be a linear transformation from R^3 to R^3 such that $T(1, 0, 0) = (1, 2, 3)$, $T(0, 1, 0) = (2, 4, 6)$, and $T(0, 0, 1) = (3, 6, 9)$. Show that $T(\mathbf{x}) = k(1, 2, 3)$ for every $\mathbf{x}$ in R^3.

6. a. Let T be a linear transformation from R^3 to R^3. If $T(1, 4, 3) = (1, 0, 1)$ and $T(0, 2, 0) = (4, 1, 1)$, find $T(1, 0, 3)$.
b. For T in **a.**, we also know that $T(3, 1, 5) = (2, 0, 2)$. Find a nonzero vector $\mathbf{z}$ such that $T(\mathbf{z}) = (0, 0, 0)$.

7. Let T be a linear transformation and let $T(1, 0) = (5, 6)$ and $T(0, 1) = (1, 2)$. Calculate $T(2, 3)$. Calculate $T(1, -4)$. Calculate $T(a, b)$. Write T in matrix form.

8. Let F be a function from R^2 to R^2 defined by $F(\mathbf{x}) = (2x_1 + 3x_2, x_2)$. Show that F is a linear transformation. Write F in matrix form.

9. Let T be the function from P_2 to P_2 such that $T(a_0 + a_1x + a_2x^2) = a_0 + a_1(x + 1) + a_2(x + 1)^2$.
a. Calculate $T(1 + 2x - x^2)$.
b. Show that $T(ap + bq) = aT(p) + bT(q)$.

10. Let T be the function from P_2 to P_1 such that $T(a_0 + a_1x + a_2x^2) = a_1 + 2a_2x$. Determine whether or not T is a linear transformation.

11. We have seen that if $T(a\mathbf{u} + b\mathbf{v}) = aT(\mathbf{u}) + bT(\mathbf{v})$ for every a, b, then 1. $T(\mathbf{u} + \mathbf{v}) = T(\mathbf{u}) + T(\mathbf{v})$ and 2. $T(a\mathbf{u}) = aT(\mathbf{u})$. Show that the converse is true; that is, if 1. and 2. hold, then $T(a\mathbf{u} + b\mathbf{v}) = aT(\mathbf{u}) + bT(\mathbf{v})$ for every a, b.

12. Let T from P_2 to P_3 be defined by $T(a_0 + a_1x + a_2x^2) = a_0x + a_1x^2 + a_2x^3$. Determine whether or not T is a linear transformation.

13. Let T from P_2 to P_3 be defined by $T(a_0 + a_1x + a_2x^2) = 1 + a_0x + a_1x^2 + a_2x^3$. Determine whether or not T is a linear transformation.

14. Let T be the transpose function from the set of $m \times n$ matrices to the set of $n \times m$ matrices: $T(\mathbf{A}) = \mathbf{A}^T$. Is T a linear transformation?

15. Let

$$T(\mathbf{X}) = \mathbf{AX}, \quad \text{where } \mathbf{A} = \begin{bmatrix} 1 & 3 & 1 \\ 4 & 0 & 2 \end{bmatrix}$$

a. Find $T(\mathbf{X})$ for each of the following $\mathbf{X}$:

$$\begin{bmatrix} 1 \\ 0 \\ 0 \end{bmatrix}, \begin{bmatrix} 0 \\ 1 \\ 0 \end{bmatrix}, \begin{bmatrix} 1 \\ 1 \\ 0 \end{bmatrix}, \begin{bmatrix} 1 \\ 1 \\ 1 \end{bmatrix},$$

$$\begin{bmatrix} 2 \\ -1 \\ 0 \end{bmatrix}, \begin{bmatrix} 1 \\ -1 \\ 1 \end{bmatrix}, \begin{bmatrix} -1 \\ \frac{5}{3} \\ 5 \end{bmatrix}$$

b. Find

$$T\left(\begin{bmatrix} a \\ 0 \\ 0 \end{bmatrix}\right), \quad T\left(\begin{bmatrix} 0 \\ b \\ 0 \end{bmatrix}\right), \quad \text{and} \quad T\left(\begin{bmatrix} a \\ b \\ 0 \end{bmatrix}\right)$$

How should these be related to each other?

16. Let T be the linear transformation $T(\mathbf{X}) = \mathbf{AX}$, where

$$\mathbf{A} = \begin{bmatrix} 1 & 2 & 1 & 1 \\ 0 & 1 & 1 & 1 \\ 0 & -2 & -2 & -2 \\ 0 & 3 & 3 & 3 \end{bmatrix}$$

a. Find $T(\mathbf{X})$ for $\mathbf{X}$ equal to

$$\begin{bmatrix} 1 \\ 0 \\ 1 \\ 0 \end{bmatrix}, \begin{bmatrix} -1 \\ -1 \\ -1 \\ -1 \end{bmatrix}, \begin{bmatrix} 1 \\ 0 \\ 0 \\ 0 \end{bmatrix}, \begin{bmatrix} 2 \\ 4 \\ 1 \\ 2 \end{bmatrix}, \begin{bmatrix} x_1 \\ x_2 \\ x_3 \\ x_4 \end{bmatrix}$$

b. Is there an $\mathbf{X}$ such that the following is true?

$$T(\mathbf{X}) = \begin{bmatrix} c_1 \\ c_2 \\ c_3 \\ c_4 \end{bmatrix}$$

What conditions must be satisfied by the numbers c_1, c_2, c_3, c_4?

17. Let T be the linear transformation $T(\mathbf{X}) = \mathbf{AX}$, where

$$\mathbf{A} = \begin{bmatrix} 1 & 3 & 2 \\ 4 & 1 & 6 \\ 2 & 5 & 3 \end{bmatrix}$$

Calculate $T(\mathbf{E}_1), T(\mathbf{E}_2), T(\mathbf{E}_3)$, where $\mathbf{E}_1, \mathbf{E}_2, \mathbf{E}_3$ are the standard columns in R^3.

18. Let T be the linear transformation $T(\mathbf{X}) = \mathbf{AX}$, where

$$\mathbf{A} = \begin{bmatrix} 1 & -1 & 2 & 4 \\ 3 & 1 & 0 & 2 \\ 1 & 1 & 3 & 0 \end{bmatrix}$$

Calculate $T(\mathbf{E}_1)$, $T(\mathbf{E}_2)$, $T(\mathbf{E}_3)$, and $T(\mathbf{E}_4)$.

19. Let T be a linear transformation from R^3 to R^2 with the property $T(\mathbf{e}_1) = (4, 1)$, $T(\mathbf{e}_2) = (1, 1)$, and $T(\mathbf{e}_3) = (-1, 1)$. Write $T(\mathbf{x})$ for $\mathbf{x} = (x_1, x_2, x_3)$. Write the matrix representation of T.

20. A simple geometric linear transformation from R^2 to R^2 is projection on the x_1-axis. This is described by $P(x_1, x_2) = (x_1, 0)$. What is $P(0, 1)$? What is $P(1, 0)$? Write this transformation in matrix form.

21. Let T be the transformation from R^2 to R^2 described by reflection with respect to the x_1-axis, that is, $T(x_1, x_2) = (x_1, -x_2)$. What is $T(1, 0)$? What is $T(0, 1)$? Write T in matrix form.

22. Let T be a linear transformation from R^3 to R^2. What will be the size of the matrix of T? Explain how this matrix is found. Is the matrix unique? Why?

23. Verify that the transformations Z and I (Definition 3) satisfy the definition of a linear transformation.

24. Let R be the linear transformation from R^2 to R^2 defined as follows: For any geometric vector OP, the vector $R(OP)$ is the vector OQ determined by rotating OP through 45° in the counterclockwise direction.

a. Show that

$$R(\mathbf{X}) = \begin{bmatrix} \frac{\sqrt{2}}{2} & -\frac{\sqrt{2}}{2} \\ \frac{\sqrt{2}}{2} & \frac{\sqrt{2}}{2} \end{bmatrix} \mathbf{X}$$

b. Let

$$\mathbf{V} = \begin{bmatrix} 1 \\ 1 \end{bmatrix} \quad \text{and} \quad \mathbf{W} = \begin{bmatrix} 0 \\ 1 \end{bmatrix}.$$

Show that the length of $\mathbf{V}$ and the length of $R(\mathbf{V})$ are the same. Also show that the length of $\mathbf{W}$ and the length of $R(\mathbf{W})$ are the same.

c. Let θ_1 be the angle between $\mathbf{V}$ and $\mathbf{W}$, and let θ_2 be the angle between $R(\mathbf{V})$ and $R(\mathbf{W})$. Show that $\cos\theta_1 = \cos\theta_2$.

d. Why does geometric intuition suggest that the lengths of vectors and the angles between them should be unchanged by the transformation R?

25. In each case T is a transformation from the linear space $M_{2\times 2}$ to $M_{2\times 2}$. (Recall that $M_{2\times 2}$ is the space of 2×2 matrices.) Which of the following are linear transformations? Justify your answer in **d.** and **e.**

a. $\mathbf{X} = \begin{bmatrix} a & b \\ c & d \end{bmatrix}$, k a scalar, $T(\mathbf{X}) = \begin{bmatrix} a + kb & b \\ c + kd & d \end{bmatrix}$

b. $\mathbf{X} = \begin{bmatrix} a & b \\ c & d \end{bmatrix}$, $T(\mathbf{X}) = \begin{bmatrix} a + 2 & b + 4 \\ c + 3 & d + 5 \end{bmatrix}$

c. $\mathbf{X} = \begin{bmatrix} a & b \\ c & d \end{bmatrix}$, $T(\mathbf{X}) = \begin{bmatrix} 2a & 4b \\ 3c & 5d \end{bmatrix}$

d. $\mathbf{X} = \begin{bmatrix} a & b \\ c & d \end{bmatrix}$, $T(\mathbf{X}) = \begin{bmatrix} a & 0 \\ 0 & d \end{bmatrix}$

e. $\mathbf{X} = \begin{bmatrix} a & b \\ c & d \end{bmatrix}$, $T(\mathbf{X}) = \begin{bmatrix} ab & 0 \\ 0 & cd \end{bmatrix}$

26. Let $\mathbf{X}$ be an $n \times n$ matrix in the linear space $M_{n\times n}$. Show that the transformation $T(\mathbf{X}) = \mathbf{X}^T$ is a linear transformation, where $\mathbf{X}^T$ is the transpose of $\mathbf{X}$.

5.2 Matrix Representation of a Transformation, Range, Null Space

Let $\mathbf{A}$ be an $m \times n$ matrix. The equation $T(\mathbf{X}) = \mathbf{AX}$ represents a linear transformation from R^n to R^m (Theorem 1) and any linear transformation from R^n to R^m can be written in the form $T(\mathbf{X}) = \mathbf{AX}$ (Corollary, Theorem 2). We now consider a linear transformation from a more general space, W, to another, W'. We assume throughout that the spaces are finite dimensional so that in each space the elements can be written as linear combinations of basis vectors.

Example 7 T is a linear transformation from P_2 to P_3 defined as follows:

$$\begin{aligned} p &= a_0 + a_1 x + a_2 x^2 \\ T(p) &= a_0(x+1) + a_1(x+1)^2 + a_2(x+1)^3 \\ &= (a_0 + a_1 + a_2) + (a_0 + 2a_1 + 3a_2)x + (a_1 + 3a_2)x^2 + a_2 x^3. \end{aligned}$$

Direct application of Definition 2 shows that T is linear. We write T in matrix form using the standard basis in P_2, $U = \{1, x, x^2\}$ and the standard basis in P_3, $V = \{1, x, x^2, x^3\}$.

1. $T(1) = x + 1$, so that $[T(1)]_V = \begin{bmatrix} 1 \\ 1 \\ 0 \\ 0 \end{bmatrix}$

   $T(x) = (x+1)^2$, so that $[T(\mathbf{x})]_V = \begin{bmatrix} 1 \\ 2 \\ 1 \\ 0 \end{bmatrix}$

   $T(x^2) = (x+1)^3$, so that $[T(x^2)]_V = \begin{bmatrix} 1 \\ 3 \\ 3 \\ 1 \end{bmatrix}$

2. The matrix $\mathbf{A}$ is

$$\mathbf{A} = \begin{bmatrix} 1 & 1 & 1 \\ 1 & 2 & 3 \\ 0 & 1 & 3 \\ 0 & 0 & 1 \end{bmatrix}$$

3. If $[p]_U = \begin{bmatrix} c_1 \\ c_2 \\ c_3 \end{bmatrix}$, $p = c_1(1) + c_2(x) + c_3(x^2)$ and

   $T(p) = c_1 T(1) + c_2 T(x) + c_3 T(x^2)$.

Because of the linearity of the coordinate function,

$$[T(p)]_V = c_1[T(1)]_V + c_2[T(x)]_V + c_3[T(x^2)]_V = \mathbf{A}[p]_U$$

Thus T is described by a matrix product $[T(p)]_V = \mathbf{A}[p]_U$ that relates the coordinates of $T(p)$ relative to the standard basis in P_3 and the coordinates of p relative to the standard basis in P_2.

For example, if $p = 3 + 4x - x^2$, $[p]_U = \begin{bmatrix} 3 \\ 4 \\ -1 \end{bmatrix}$ and

$$[T(p)]_V = \begin{bmatrix} 1 & 1 & 1 \\ 1 & 2 & 3 \\ 0 & 1 & 3 \\ 0 & 0 & 1 \end{bmatrix} \begin{bmatrix} 3 \\ 4 \\ -1 \end{bmatrix} = \begin{bmatrix} 6 \\ 8 \\ 1 \\ -1 \end{bmatrix}$$

Thus $T(p) = 6 + 8x + x^2 - x^3$. This is the same result as we would obtain by applying the definition $T(p) = 3(x + 1) + 4(x + 1)^2 - (x + 1)^3$. ■

Example 7 illustrates how the coordinate function enables us to write a linear transformation from D to R in matrix form. Theorem 3 states the general situation.

Theorem 3 Let D be an n-dimensional vector space with basis $U = \{\mathbf{u}_1, \mathbf{u}_2, \ldots, \mathbf{u}_n\}$. Let R be an m-dimensional vector space with basis $V = \{\mathbf{v}_1, \mathbf{v}_2, \ldots, \mathbf{v}_m\}$. Let T be a linear transformation from D to R. Then for any $\mathbf{x}$ in D,

$$[T(\mathbf{x})]_V = \mathbf{A}[\mathbf{x}]_U$$

where $\mathbf{A}$ is the $m \times n$ matrix with columns $[T(\mathbf{u}_1)]_V, [T(\mathbf{u}_2)]_V, \ldots, [T(\mathbf{u}_n)]_V$.

Proof Since U is a basis for D, any vector $\mathbf{x}$ in D can be written

$$\mathbf{x} = c_1\mathbf{u}_1 + c_2\mathbf{u}_2 + \cdots + c_n\mathbf{u}_n$$

Because T is linear,

$$T(\mathbf{x}) = c_1T(\mathbf{u}_1) + c_2T(\mathbf{u}_2) + \cdots + c_nT(\mathbf{u}_n)$$

Because the coordinate function is linear,

$$[T(\mathbf{x})]_V = c_1[T(\mathbf{u}_1)]_V + c_2[T(\mathbf{u}_2)]_V + \cdots + c_n[T(\mathbf{u}_n)]_V$$

The right hand side is the matrix product

$$\mathbf{A}\begin{bmatrix} c_1 \\ c_2 \\ \vdots \\ c_n \end{bmatrix} = \mathbf{A}[\mathbf{x}]_U$$

where $\mathbf{A}$ is the matrix with columns $[T(\mathbf{u}_1)]_V, [T(\mathbf{u}_2)]_V, \ldots, [T(\mathbf{u}_n)]_V$. □

Notice that the representation described in Theorem 3 depends on the particular bases chosen for the spaces D and R. If different bases were chosen, a different matrix would result.

Matrix of T

Definition 4

If a linear transformation T from D with basis U to R with basis V is written in matrix form $[T(\mathbf{x})]_V = \mathbf{A}[\mathbf{x}]_U$, the matrix $\mathbf{A}$ is called the **matrix of T relative to the bases** U, V.

If the standard basis is used in both D and R, the matrix $\mathbf{A}$ is frequently referred to simply as **the matrix of T**.

In the next section we study the way in which the matrix of T is affected by a change of basis in one or both of the spaces involved. Before doing so it is helpful to see how the matrix representation provides useful information about the transformation T. For simplicity we omit a designation of a basis and write $T(\mathbf{X}) = \mathbf{AX}$. First, recall some terms connected with the study of functions.

Image
Range
Preimage

Definition 5

Let T be a function from D to R. For each $\mathbf{x}$ in D, $T(\mathbf{x})$ is called the **image of x under T**. The set of all possible images for $\mathbf{x}$ in D is called the **range of T**. Given any element $\mathbf{y}$ in the range of T, the set of $\mathbf{x}$ in D such that $T(\mathbf{x}) = \mathbf{y}$ is called the **preimage of y**.

Example 8

Let T be the transformation $T(\mathbf{X}) = \mathbf{AX}$, where $\mathbf{A} = \begin{bmatrix} 2 & 3 & 1 \\ 1 & 0 & -1 \end{bmatrix}$. The domain of T is R^3. For any $\mathbf{X}$ in R^3, the image of $\mathbf{X}$ is $\mathbf{AX}$, that is,

$$\begin{bmatrix} 2 & 3 & 1 \\ 1 & 0 & -1 \end{bmatrix} \begin{bmatrix} x_1 \\ x_2 \\ x_3 \end{bmatrix} = \begin{bmatrix} 2x_1 + 3x_2 + x_3 \\ x_1 + 0x_2 - x_3 \end{bmatrix}$$

$$= x_1 \begin{bmatrix} 2 \\ 1 \end{bmatrix} + x_2 \begin{bmatrix} 3 \\ 0 \end{bmatrix} + x_3 \begin{bmatrix} 1 \\ -1 \end{bmatrix}$$

Thus the image of a given $\mathbf{X}$ is a particular linear combination of the columns of $\mathbf{A}$. The range of T, which is the set of all possible images, is the set of all possible linear combinations of these columns—that is, the column space of $\mathbf{A}$. ■

An analysis similar to that in Example 8 can be carried out in the case of a general transformation T. The set of $\mathbf{AX}$ for all choices of $\mathbf{X}$ is simply the set of all linear combinations of the columns of $\mathbf{A}$. Thus the range of T is the set of vectors whose coordinates belong to the column space of $\mathbf{A}$ (Section 4.4).

Theorem 4 Let $\mathbf{A}$ be an $m \times n$ matrix and T the linear transformation $T(\mathbf{X}) = \mathbf{AX}$. The range of T is the set of vectors whose coordinates belong to the column space of $\mathbf{A}$. The dimension of the range is equal to the rank of $\mathbf{A}$. □

To find whether a particular vector is in the range of T, we need the machinery set up in Chapter 2. The question "Is $\mathbf{U}_0$ in the range of T?" is the same as the question "Is there an $\mathbf{X}$ such that $\mathbf{AX} = \mathbf{U}_0$?" and this in turn is the same as "Can the system of equations $\mathbf{AX} = \mathbf{U}_0$ be solved?" If this system can be solved, the solution set obtained is exactly the preimage of $\mathbf{U}_0$.

Example 9 illustrates the process.

Example 9

$T(\mathbf{X}) = \mathbf{AX}$, where $\mathbf{A} = \begin{bmatrix} 1 & 0 & 1 \\ 2 & 1 & 2 \\ 0 & 1 & 0 \end{bmatrix}$. Is $\begin{bmatrix} 1 \\ 1 \\ 1 \end{bmatrix}$ in the range of T? "Is there an

X such that $\begin{bmatrix} 1 & 0 & 1 \\ 2 & 1 & 2 \\ 0 & 1 & 0 \end{bmatrix} \begin{bmatrix} x_1 \\ x_2 \\ x_3 \end{bmatrix} = \begin{bmatrix} 1 \\ 1 \\ 1 \end{bmatrix}$?" Augmented matrix: $\left[\begin{array}{ccc|c} 1 & 0 & 1 & 1 \\ 2 & 1 & 2 & 1 \\ 0 & 1 & 0 & 1 \end{array}\right] \Leftrightarrow$ $\left[\begin{array}{ccc|c} 1 & 0 & 1 & 1 \\ 0 & 1 & 0 & -1 \\ 0 & 0 & 0 & 2 \end{array}\right]$. No solution; $\begin{bmatrix} 1 \\ 1 \\ 1 \end{bmatrix}$ is not in the range of T.

Is $\begin{bmatrix} 2 \\ 7 \\ 3 \end{bmatrix}$ in the range of T? The system of equations: $\begin{bmatrix} 1 & 0 & 1 \\ 2 & 1 & 2 \\ 0 & 1 & 0 \end{bmatrix} \begin{bmatrix} x_1 \\ x_2 \\ x_3 \end{bmatrix} = \begin{bmatrix} 2 \\ 7 \\ 3 \end{bmatrix}$ has augmented matrix $\left[\begin{array}{ccc|c} 1 & 0 & 1 & 2 \\ 2 & 1 & 2 & 7 \\ 0 & 1 & 0 & 3 \end{array}\right] \Leftrightarrow \left[\begin{array}{ccc|c} 1 & 0 & 1 & 2 \\ 0 & 1 & 0 & 3 \\ 0 & 0 & 0 & 0 \end{array}\right]$; the solution set is

$$\left\{ \mathbf{X} = \begin{bmatrix} 2 \\ 3 \\ 0 \end{bmatrix} + k \begin{bmatrix} -1 \\ 0 \\ 1 \end{bmatrix}, k \text{ a real number} \right\}$$

This set is the preimage of $\begin{bmatrix} 2 \\ 7 \\ 3 \end{bmatrix}$. ■

The preimage of an element **C** in the range is the solution set of the system of equations **AX** = **C**. In particular, to find the preimage of the zero vector, the system of equations **AX** = **0** must be solved. The preimage of **0** is simply the null space of the matrix **A**. If **A** is an $m \times n$ matrix of rank r, its null space is a subspace of R^n and has dimension $n - r$. The preimage of **0** then is a subspace of the domain and has dimension $n - r$.

Example 10

Let $T(\mathbf{X}) = \mathbf{AX}$, where $\mathbf{A} = \begin{bmatrix} 1 & 0 & 1 \\ 2 & 1 & 2 \\ 0 & 1 & 0 \end{bmatrix}$. The preimage of **0** is the solution set of

$\mathbf{AX} = \mathbf{0}$; $\left[\begin{array}{ccc|c} 1 & 0 & 1 & 0 \\ 2 & 1 & 2 & 0 \\ 0 & 1 & 0 & 0 \end{array}\right] \Leftrightarrow \left[\begin{array}{ccc|c} 1 & 0 & 1 & 0 \\ 0 & 1 & 0 & 0 \\ 0 & 0 & 0 & 0 \end{array}\right]$; the solution set is

$$\left\{ k \begin{bmatrix} 1 \\ 0 \\ -1 \end{bmatrix}, k \text{ a real number} \right\}$$

The rank of **A** is 2, the dimension of the domain is 3, and the preimage of zero has dimension 1.

Definition 6

Null Space of T

If T is a linear transformation from D to R, the subspace of D that is the preimage of $\mathbf{0}$ is called the **null space of T**.

An important relationship exists among the dimensions of the three linear spaces associated with T: domain, range, and null space. Compare the following theorem with Theorem 10, Chapter 4.

Theorem 5 Let T be a linear transformation from D to R. Then (dimension of range of T) + (dimension of null space of T) = (dimension of D). □

The following geometric example illustrates *null space*, *range*, *dimension*, *image*, and *preimage* for the transformation P that is a projection of a point in R^3 on the x_1, x_2-plane.

Example 11 Let $\mathbf{x} = (x_1, x_2, x_3)$ correspond to the geometric vector OQ (Figure 5.4).

The projection of OQ on the x_1, x_2-plane is the geometric vector OM.

Since $\mathbf{e}_1$ and $\mathbf{e}_2$ lie in the x_1, x_2-plane, $P(\mathbf{e}_1) = \mathbf{e}_1$ and $P(\mathbf{e}_2) = \mathbf{e}_2$. Since $\mathbf{e}_3$ lies along the x_3-axis, $P(\mathbf{e}_3) = \mathbf{0}$. The matrix of P is $\begin{bmatrix} 1 & 0 & 0 \\ 0 & 1 & 0 \\ 0 & 0 & 0 \end{bmatrix}$.

The projection of a vector is $\mathbf{0}$ if and only if the vector lies on the x_3-axis (Figure 5.5). The null space, the preimage of $\mathbf{0}$, is thus the x_3-axis, a one-dimensional subspace spanned by $\mathbf{e}_3$. The range is the entire $x_1 x_2$ plane, since every point $(x_1, x_2, 0)$ is the projection of at least one point, say $(x_1, x_2, 1)$. The range has dimension two. The domain of P is R^3 and has dimension three. Compare this with Theorem 5.

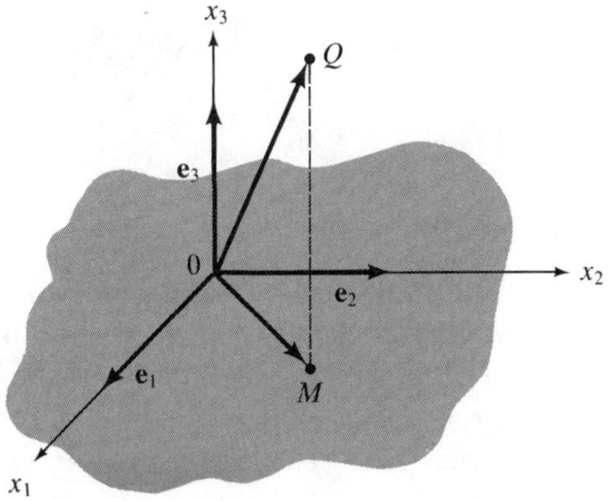

FIGURE 5.4

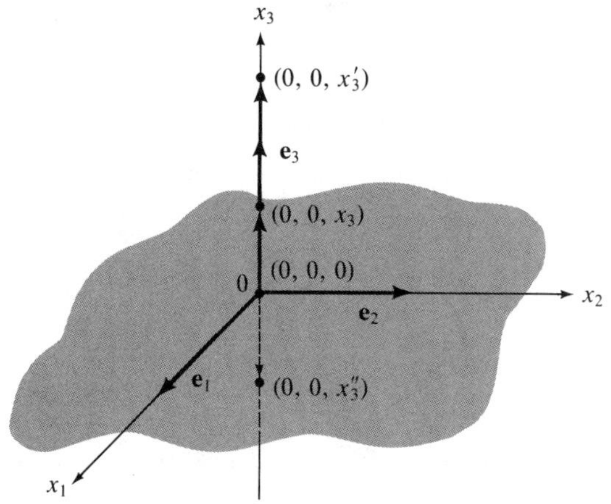

FIGURE 5.5

The preimage of a nonzero vector (OM in Figure 5.6) is an infinite set of vectors OQ with endpoints on the line through $(x_1, x_2, 0)$ and perpendicular to the x_1x_2 plane.

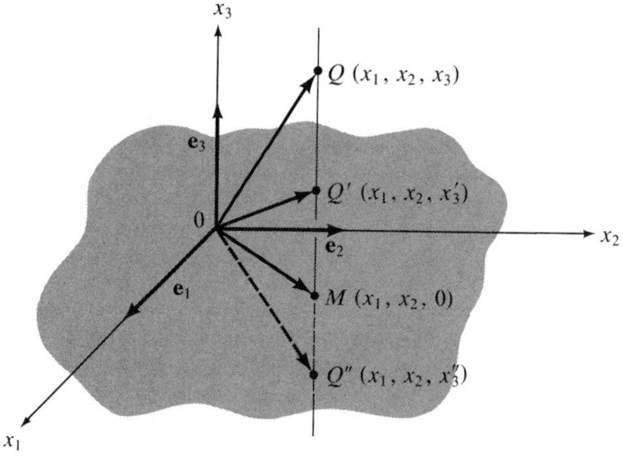

FIGURE 5.6 ■

The following problem involves a linear transformation. Experimental data have been collected, and we wish to find a polynomial that will pass through all the data obtained. We can represent the observed data by points in a plane: (x_1, y_1), $(x_2, y_2), \ldots, (x_m, y_m)$. Is there a polynomial $p(x) = a_1 + a_2x + \cdots + a_nx^n$ that has the property that its graph passes through each of these points? If so, $p(x_1) = y_1, p(x_2) = y_2, \ldots, p(x_m) = y_m$.

This calls for a transformation from some polynomial space P_n to the space of m-tuples R^m such that $T(p) = (p(x_1), p(x_2), \ldots, p(x_m))$. This transformation associates with a polynomial p the m-tuple of real numbers that are the values of p at the

m fixed numbers $x_1, x_2, \ldots, x_m$. We choose the polynomial space in which to work and look for the polynomial p with the property that $T(p) = (y_1, y_2, \ldots, y_m)$. The question is, What is the preimage of the m-tuple $(y_1, y_2, \ldots, y_m)$? Examples 12, 13, and 14 illustrate this in the case of a polynomial of degree 2 or less.

Example 12 Find a polynomial of degree 2 or less passing through the points (0, 1), (1, 2), and (−1, 4). Here T is from P_2 to R^3; the fixed numbers x_1, x_2, x_3 are $0, 1, -1$; $T(p) = (p(0), p(1), p(-1))$. We use the standard basis in both spaces.

$$[T(1)] = \begin{bmatrix} 1 \\ 1 \\ 1 \end{bmatrix}, \qquad [T(x)] = \begin{bmatrix} 0 \\ 1 \\ -1 \end{bmatrix}, \qquad [T(x^2)] = \begin{bmatrix} 0 \\ 1 \\ 1 \end{bmatrix}$$

and

$$[T(p)] = \begin{bmatrix} 1 & 0 & 0 \\ 1 & 1 & 1 \\ 1 & -1 & 1 \end{bmatrix} [p] = \mathbf{A}[p]$$

We want to find those p with the property $\mathbf{A}[p] = \begin{bmatrix} 1 \\ 2 \\ 4 \end{bmatrix}$. Since $\mathbf{A}$ is nonsingular, the preimage of $\begin{bmatrix} 1 \\ 2 \\ 4 \end{bmatrix}$ is

$$[p] = \mathbf{A}^{-1} \begin{bmatrix} 1 \\ 2 \\ 4 \end{bmatrix} = \begin{bmatrix} 1 & 0 & 0 \\ 0 & \frac{1}{2} & -\frac{1}{2} \\ -1 & \frac{1}{2} & \frac{1}{2} \end{bmatrix} \begin{bmatrix} 1 \\ 2 \\ 4 \end{bmatrix} = \begin{bmatrix} 1 \\ -1 \\ 2 \end{bmatrix}$$

The unique second-degree polynomial passing through these points is $p = 1 - x + 2x^2$. ■

Example 13 What polynomials in P_2 pass through the points (0, 1) and (1, 2)? In this case, T is from P_2 to R^2; $T(1) = (1, 1)$, $T(x) = (0, 1)$, $T(x^2) = (0, 1)$. The matrix of T is $\begin{bmatrix} 1 & 0 & 0 \\ 1 & 1 & 1 \end{bmatrix}$ and $[T(p)] = \begin{bmatrix} 1 & 0 & 0 \\ 1 & 1 & 1 \end{bmatrix} [p]$. For what p is $[T(p)] = \begin{bmatrix} 1 \\ 2 \end{bmatrix}$? The system of equations

$$\begin{bmatrix} 1 & 0 & 0 \\ 1 & 1 & 1 \end{bmatrix} \begin{bmatrix} a_0 \\ a_1 \\ a_2 \end{bmatrix} = \begin{bmatrix} 1 \\ 2 \end{bmatrix}$$

has augmented matrix

$$\left[\begin{array}{ccc|c} 1 & 0 & 0 & 1 \\ 1 & 1 & 1 & 2 \end{array}\right] \Leftrightarrow \left[\begin{array}{ccc|c} 1 & 0 & 0 & 1 \\ 0 & 1 & 1 & 1 \end{array}\right]$$

so that $a_0 = 1$, $a_1 = 1 - k$, and $a_2 = k$, where k is any real number. The family of polynomials $p = 1 + (1 - k)x + kx^2$ passes through the two points (0, 1) and (1, 2). Notice that the polynomial found in Example 12 is one of this family. The additional condition that $(-1, 4)$ is on the graph is satisfied by the choice $k = 2$. ■

Example 14 What second-degree polynomials pass through (0, 1), (1, 2), $(-1, 4)$, and (2, 5)? Here, T is from P_2 to R^4; the matrix of T is

$$\mathbf{A} = \begin{bmatrix} 1 & 0 & 0 \\ 1 & 1 & 1 \\ 1 & -1 & 1 \\ 1 & 2 & 4 \end{bmatrix} \quad \text{so that} \quad \begin{bmatrix} 1 & 0 & 0 \\ 1 & 1 & 1 \\ 1 & -1 & 1 \\ 1 & 2 & 4 \end{bmatrix} [p] = \begin{bmatrix} 1 \\ 2 \\ 4 \\ 5 \end{bmatrix}$$

The augmented matrix of this system is

$$\left[\begin{array}{ccc|c} 1 & 0 & 0 & 1 \\ 1 & 1 & 1 & 2 \\ 1 & -1 & 1 & 4 \\ 1 & 2 & 4 & 5 \end{array}\right] \Leftrightarrow \left[\begin{array}{ccc|c} 1 & 0 & 0 & 1 \\ 0 & 1 & 1 & 1 \\ 0 & 0 & 2 & 4 \\ 0 & 0 & 0 & -2 \end{array}\right]$$

The system of equations has no solution. The 4-tuple (1, 2, 4, 5) is not in the range of T and there is no second-degree polynomial passing through the four points (0, 1), (1, 2), $(-1, 4)$, and (2, 5). ■

In general, if $m = n + 1$ distinct points are given with distinct first components, a unique polynomial in P_n passes through the points. If $m < n + 1$, a family of polynomials passing through the points can be found; if $m > n + 1$, it is quite possible that there is no polynomial in P_n with a graph that passes through all these points. (See Problems 15–22.) In case no polynomial passes through all the points, it is still useful to ask what polynomial of degree n comes nearest to passing through the m points. A method frequently used for deciding the "best" choice is referred to as the method of least squares and is discussed in the applications in Section 5.4.

SUMMARY If D is an n-dimensional vector space with basis U, and R is an m-dimensional vector space with basis V, and T is a linear transformation from D to R, then for any $\mathbf{x}$ in D, $[T(\mathbf{x})]_V = \mathbf{A}[\mathbf{x}]_U$, where $\mathbf{A}$ is the $m \times n$ matrix with columns $[T(\mathbf{u}_1)]_V, [T(\mathbf{u}_2)]_V, \ldots, [T(\mathbf{u}_n)]_V$. $\mathbf{A}$ is called the matrix of T relative to the bases U and V.

For each $\mathbf{x}$ in D, $T(\mathbf{x})$ is called the image of $\mathbf{x}$ under T. The set of all images for $\mathbf{x}$ in D is a subspace of R called the range of T.

For each $\mathbf{y}$ in the range of T, the set of $\mathbf{x}$ such that $T(\mathbf{x}) = \mathbf{y}$ is called the preimage of $\mathbf{y}$. The preimage of $\mathbf{0}$ is a subspace of D called the null space of T.

If $\mathbf{A}$ is the matrix of T, the range of T is the set of all vectors in R whose coordinates are in the column space of $\mathbf{A}$. The null space of T is the set of vectors in D whose coordinates are in the null space of $\mathbf{A}$—that is, the solution set of $\mathbf{AX} = \mathbf{0}$. If the rank $\mathbf{A}$ is r, the dimension of the range of T is r and the dimension of the null space of T is $n - r$. Thus: (dimension of range) + (dimension of null space) = (dimension of domain).

EXERCISES 5.2

1. Let W be a vector space with basis $U = \{\mathbf{u}_1, \mathbf{u}_2, \mathbf{u}_3\}$ and let T be a linear transformation from W to W. The matrix of T relative to U is

$$\mathbf{A} = \begin{bmatrix} 1 & 1 & 0 \\ 2 & 1 & 3 \\ -1 & 0 & 1 \end{bmatrix}$$

a. What is $T(\mathbf{u}_1)$? What is $T(\mathbf{u}_2)$? What is $T(\mathbf{u}_3)$?
b. What is $T(\mathbf{w})$ if $\mathbf{w} = 3\mathbf{u}_1 - 4\mathbf{u}_2 + \mathbf{u}_3$?
c. What is $\mathbf{w}$ if $T(\mathbf{w}) = -\mathbf{u}_1 + 3\mathbf{u}_2$?
d. What is the preimage of $\mathbf{0}$?

2. Let W be a vector space with basis $U = \{\mathbf{u}_1, \mathbf{u}_2\}$ and let T be a linear transformation from W to W for which $T(\mathbf{u}_1) = 3\mathbf{u}_1 + 4\mathbf{u}_2$ and $T(\mathbf{u}_2) = -\mathbf{u}_1 - 2\mathbf{u}_2$.
a. Write $[T(\mathbf{u}_1)]_U$ and $[T(\mathbf{u}_2)]_U$.
b. Write the matrix T relative to U.
c. Let $\mathbf{w} = 4\mathbf{u}_1 - 2\mathbf{u}_2$. Write $[\mathbf{w}]_U$ and find $[T(\mathbf{w})]_U$ using **b.**
d. Calculate $T(\mathbf{w})$ from the linearity of T and compare your answer with **c.**

3. The projection of $\mathbf{x}$ on a fixed nonzero vector $\mathbf{u}$ is defined to be the vector

$$\frac{(\mathbf{x} \cdot \mathbf{u})}{(\mathbf{u} \cdot \mathbf{u})}\mathbf{u}$$

Show that the projection of $\mathbf{x}$ on $(1, 3)$ is

$$P(\mathbf{x}) = \left(\frac{x_1 + 3x_2}{10}, \frac{3x_1 + 9x_2}{10}\right)$$

Write this transformation in matrix form. Give a geometric description of the range of the transformation and of the preimage of an element in the range.

4. Let T be the transformation from R^2 to R^2 in which $T(x_1, x_2)$ is obtained by reflection in the line $x_1 = x_2$.
a. Write the matrix of T relative to the standard basis.
b. What vectors belong to the null space of T?
c. What is the range of T?

5. Let T be the transformation from P_1 to R^2 defined by $T(p) = (p(0), p(1))$.
a. What is $T(1)$? What is $T(x)$? Write the matrix of T relative to the standard basis.
b. What is the null space of T?

6. Let T be the transformation from P_2 to R^2 defined by $T(p) = (p(0), p(1))$.
a. What is $T(1)$? What is $T(x)$? What is $T(x^2)$?
b. Write the matrix of T relative to the standard basis.
c. What is the null space of T? (Compare with Problem 5.)

7. Describe the range of T for each of the transformations $T(\mathbf{X}) = \mathbf{AX}$ below. If the range is not all of R^3, give a basis for the range.

a. $\mathbf{A} = \begin{bmatrix} 1 & -1 & 3 \\ 0 & 1 & 1 \\ 1 & 0 & 4 \end{bmatrix}$

b. $\mathbf{A} = \begin{bmatrix} 1 & -1 & 3 \\ 0 & 1 & 1 \\ 1 & 1 & 4 \end{bmatrix}$

c. $\mathbf{A} = \begin{bmatrix} 1 & -1 & 3 \\ 2 & -2 & 6 \\ 3 & -3 & 6 \end{bmatrix}$

d. $\mathbf{A} = \begin{bmatrix} 1 & 0 & 0 & 0 & 0 \\ 0 & 1 & 0 & 0 & 0 \\ 0 & 0 & 1 & 0 & 0 \end{bmatrix}$

e. $\mathbf{A} = \begin{bmatrix} 1 & 1 & 2 & 1 & 4 \\ 0 & 0 & 1 & 3 & 3 \\ 0 & 0 & 0 & 0 & 1 \end{bmatrix}$

8. The transformation T is defined by

$$T(\mathbf{X}) = \begin{bmatrix} 1 & 1 & 2 \\ 2 & 1 & 0 \\ 1 & 0 & -2 \end{bmatrix}\mathbf{X}$$

a. Find the image of each of the following:

$$\begin{bmatrix} 1 \\ -1 \\ 0 \end{bmatrix}, \begin{bmatrix} 1 \\ 0 \\ 1 \end{bmatrix}, \begin{bmatrix} 2 \\ -4 \\ 1 \end{bmatrix}, \begin{bmatrix} 4 \\ -8 \\ 2 \end{bmatrix}, \begin{bmatrix} 2k \\ -4k \\ k \end{bmatrix}$$

b. Find a spanning set for the range of T.

c. Find a basis for the range of T.

9. Let T from R^3 to R^2 be defined by

$$T(\mathbf{X}) = \begin{bmatrix} 1 & 3 & 1 \\ 4 & 0 & 2 \end{bmatrix} \mathbf{X}$$

a. Describe the range of T.

b. Find the preimage of each of the following:

$$\begin{bmatrix} 1 \\ 0 \end{bmatrix}, \begin{bmatrix} 0 \\ 1 \end{bmatrix}, \begin{bmatrix} 0 \\ 0 \end{bmatrix}, \begin{bmatrix} -1 \\ 6 \end{bmatrix}$$

c. Describe the null space of T. Compare your answers with Theorem 5.

10. Let $T(\mathbf{X}) = \mathbf{AX}$, where

$$\mathbf{A} = \begin{bmatrix} 1 & 2 & -1 & -1 \\ 0 & 1 & 1 & 1 \\ 1 & 1 & 0 & 0 \\ 1 & 0 & -1 & -1 \end{bmatrix}$$

a. Find the preimage of each of the following:

$$\begin{bmatrix} 2 \\ 0 \\ 2 \\ 2 \end{bmatrix}, \begin{bmatrix} 1 \\ 1 \\ 0 \\ -1 \end{bmatrix}, \begin{bmatrix} 0 \\ 1 \\ -1 \\ -2 \end{bmatrix}$$

$$\begin{bmatrix} 1 \\ 0 \\ 1 \\ 1 \end{bmatrix}, \begin{bmatrix} 1 \\ 3 \\ -1 \\ -4 \end{bmatrix}, \begin{bmatrix} 1 \\ 3 \\ -2 \\ -5 \end{bmatrix}$$

b. Find the null space of T.

c. Compare the dimension of the range, the number of columns of $\mathbf{A}$, and the dimension of the null space of T.

11. Let T be the transformation $T(\mathbf{X}) = \mathbf{AX}$, where $\mathbf{A}$ is an $m \times n$ matrix of rank r.

a. What is the dimension of the range of T?

b. Under what conditions will a vector in the range have a unique preimage?

c. Under what conditions will the null space of T have dimension 0?

12. Let T be defined by

$$T(\mathbf{X}) = \begin{bmatrix} 1 & 2 \\ 1 & 1 \\ 1 & -1 \end{bmatrix} \mathbf{X}$$

Show that the null space of T has dimension 0, but that the range of T is not all of R^3.

13. Show that the matrix of the zero transformation (Definition 3) is a zero matrix, for any choice of basis in the domain and in the range.

14. Show that the matrix of the identity transformation is an identity matrix, if the same basis is used in the domain and in the range.

15. What polynomial in P_2 passes through the points $(0, -1)$, $(1, 4)$, and $(-1, 0)$?

16. What polynomial in P_2 passes through $(0, 0)$, $(1, 3)$, $(-1, -3)$?

17. What polynomial in P_2 passes through $(0, -1)$, $(1, 4)$, $(-1, 0)$, and $(2, 15)$?

18. What polynomial in P_2 passes through $(0, -1)$, $(1, 3)$, $(-1, -5)$, and $(2, 7)$?

19. Let T be the transformation from P_2 to R^3 given by

$$T(p) = (p(x_1), p(x_2), p(x_3)) = (y_1, y_2, y_3)$$

where x_1, x_2, x_3 are fixed numbers (Examples 12–14).

a. Write the matrix of T relative to the standard bases.

b. Show that the determinant of the matrix is

$$(x_1 - x_2)(x_3 - x_1)(x_2 - x_3) \neq 0$$

if x_1, x_2, x_3 are distinct.

c. Show that the preimage of (y_1, y_2, y_3) is unique.

20. Let T be the transformation from P_2 to R^2 given by $T(p) = (p(x_1), p(x_2))$, $x_1 \neq x_2$.

a. Write the matrix of T relative to the standard bases.

b. Find the preimage of (y_1, y_2).

21. Let T be the transformation from P_2 to R^4 given by $T(p) = (p(x_1), p(x_2), p(x_3), p(x_4))$

a. Write the matrix of T relative to the standard bases.

b. Show that the range of T has dimension less than or equal to 3 and hence there are some 4-tuples (y_1, y_2, y_3, y_4) in R^4 for which the preimage does not exist.

22. Let T be the transformation from P_n to R^m with

$$T(p) = (p(x_1), p(x_2), \ldots, p(x_m))$$

where $x_1, x_2, \ldots, x_m$ are distinct fixed numbers.

a. Write the matrix of T.

b. Show that if $m < n + 1$, the preimage of $(y_1, y_2, \ldots, y_m)$ exists but is not unique for each m-tuple in R^m. (*Hint:* Use Problem 30, Section 3.2.)

c. Show that if $m = n + 1$, each m-tuple in R^m has a unique preimage.

d. Show that if $m > n + 1$, the range of T is a subspace of R^m of dimension $\leqslant n + 1$.

The following exercises use calculus.

23. Recall that the derivative with respect to x of a polynomial $p(x) = a_0 + a_1x + a_2x^2 + \cdots + a_nx^n$ is

$$p'(x) = a_1 + 2a_2x + 3a_3x^2 + \cdots + na_nx^{n-1}$$

a. Show that the transformation from P_n to P_{n-1} given by $D(p) = p'(x)$ is a linear transformation.

b. Write the matrix of D relative to the standard basis.

24. For the transformation D in Problem 23,

a. Find the null space of D. Compare this answer with the rules of differentiation.

b. Find the preimage of $1 + 2x$. Compare your answer with integration.

25. Let $T(p) = p'' - 3p' + 4p$ (where p'' means the second derivative of p with respect to x).

a. Show that T is a linear transformation from P_2 to P_2.

b. Find the matrix of T relative to the standard basis.

c. Calculate $T(p)$ for $p = 2 - 4x + x^2$.

d. What p are in the null space of T?

e. Find the preimage of $p = 1 + 2x - 3x^2$.

26. Let V be the vector space with basis $U = \{\sin x, \cos x\}$. Let $T(p) = p'' - 3p' + 4p$.

a. Show that T is a linear transformation from V to V.

b. Find the matrix of T relative to U.

c. Calculate $T(p)$ for $p = 2\sin x - \cos x$.

d. Find the preimage of $p = 3\sin x + 4\cos x$.

27. Recall (Exercises 4.3, Problem 14) that the standard basis for $M_{2\times 2}$ is $\mathbf{E}_1 = \begin{bmatrix} 1 & 0 \\ 0 & 0 \end{bmatrix}$,

$\mathbf{E}_2 = \begin{bmatrix} 0 & 1 \\ 0 & 0 \end{bmatrix}$, $\mathbf{E}_3 = \begin{bmatrix} 0 & 0 \\ 1 & 0 \end{bmatrix}$ and $\mathbf{E}_4 = \begin{bmatrix} 0 & 0 \\ 0 & 1 \end{bmatrix}$.

Let T be the linear transformation from $M_{2\times 2}$ to $M_{2\times 2}$ defined by

$$T\left(\begin{bmatrix} a & b \\ c & d \end{bmatrix}\right) = \begin{bmatrix} a & \dfrac{b + c}{2} \\ \dfrac{b + c}{2} & d \end{bmatrix}$$

a. Write the matrix of T relative to the standard basis.

b. What is the dimension of the null space?

c. Identify the elements of the null space.

d. Show that every element of $M_{2\times 2}$ can be written as the sum of an element from the range of T and a suitably chosen element from the null space of T.

5.3 Composition of Transformations, Change of Basis

Real-valued functions can be combined into new functions in a variety of ways. The same definitions hold for linear transformations.

Definition 7

Let T and S be linear transformations.

kT 1. For any real number k, the transformation $\boldsymbol{kT}$ is defined by $(kT)(\mathbf{x}) = kT(\mathbf{x})$.

$T + S$ 2. If T and S have the same domain, the sum $\boldsymbol{T + S}$ is defined by $(T + S)(\mathbf{x}) = T(\mathbf{x}) + S(\mathbf{x})$, provided that $T(\mathbf{x})$ and $S(\mathbf{x})$ are in the same space.

$T \circ S$ 3. If the range of S is a subset of the domain of T, the composition $\boldsymbol{T \circ S}$ is defined by $(T \circ S)(\mathbf{x}) = T[S(\mathbf{x})]$.

The functions defined in this way are linear transformations, and the matrices of kT, $T + S$, and $T \circ S$ are related to the matrices of T and S in a natural way. Addition and multiplication by a scalar are discussed in the exercises. Example 15 illustrates $T \circ S$.

Example 15 Let S be the linear transformation from R^3 to R^2 defined by $S(\mathbf{X}) = \mathbf{BX}$, and T be the linear transformation from R^2 to R^4 defined by $T(\mathbf{X}) = \mathbf{AX}$, where

$$\mathbf{B} = \begin{bmatrix} 1 & 0 & 1 \\ -1 & 2 & 3 \end{bmatrix} \quad \text{and} \quad \mathbf{A} = \begin{bmatrix} 1 & 0 \\ -1 & 2 \\ 1 & 5 \\ 0 & 1 \end{bmatrix}$$

To calculate $(T \circ S)(\mathbf{X})$, we first calculate $S(\mathbf{X})$ and then $T(S(\mathbf{X}))$. For example:

$$\mathbf{X} = \begin{bmatrix} 1 \\ 2 \\ 1 \end{bmatrix}; \qquad S(\mathbf{X}) = S\left(\begin{bmatrix} 1 \\ 2 \\ 1 \end{bmatrix}\right) = \begin{bmatrix} 1 & 0 & 1 \\ -1 & 2 & 3 \end{bmatrix}\begin{bmatrix} 1 \\ 2 \\ 1 \end{bmatrix} = \begin{bmatrix} 2 \\ 6 \end{bmatrix}$$

and

$$(T \circ S)(\mathbf{X}) = T(S(\mathbf{X})) = T\left(\begin{bmatrix} 2 \\ 6 \end{bmatrix}\right) = \begin{bmatrix} 1 & 0 \\ -1 & 2 \\ 1 & 5 \\ 0 & 1 \end{bmatrix}\begin{bmatrix} 2 \\ 6 \end{bmatrix} = \begin{bmatrix} 2 \\ 10 \\ 32 \\ 6 \end{bmatrix}$$

This can also be written as the product

$$\begin{bmatrix} 1 & 0 \\ -1 & 2 \\ 1 & 5 \\ 0 & 1 \end{bmatrix}\begin{bmatrix} 1 & 0 & 1 \\ -1 & 2 & 3 \end{bmatrix}\begin{bmatrix} 1 \\ 2 \\ 1 \end{bmatrix} = \begin{bmatrix} 1 & 0 & 1 \\ -3 & 4 & 5 \\ -4 & 10 & 16 \\ -1 & 2 & 3 \end{bmatrix}\begin{bmatrix} 1 \\ 2 \\ 1 \end{bmatrix}$$

Thus $T \circ S$ is a linear transformation from R^3 to R^4 and is represented by the matrix product **AB**. In general, $S(\mathbf{X}) = \mathbf{BX}$ and $(T \circ S)(\mathbf{X}) = T(\mathbf{BX}) = \mathbf{A}(\mathbf{BX}) = (\mathbf{AB})\mathbf{X}$. The product **AB** is defined, since the range of S is a subset of the domain of T, which implies in this example that **A** has two columns and **B** has two rows. ■

Theorem 6 Let S be a linear transformation from R^n to R^m with matrix **B**, and let T be a linear transformation from R^m to R^k with matrix **A**. The composition $T \circ S$ is a linear transformation from R^n to R^k with matrix **AB**.

Proof The linearity follows directly from Definitions 2 and 7. (See Problem 3.)

By Definition 7, $(T \circ S)(\mathbf{X}) = T[S(\mathbf{X})]$. Now $S(\mathbf{X}) = \mathbf{BX}$, a vector in R^m. Thus, $T(S(\mathbf{X}))$ is defined and is equal to $\mathbf{A}(\mathbf{BX})$, which by the associative law is $(\mathbf{AB})\mathbf{X}$. Thus, $(T \circ S)(\mathbf{X}) = (\mathbf{AB})\mathbf{X}$ and the matrix of $T \circ S$ is **AB**. Since S is from R^n to R^m, the matrix **B** is $m \times n$, and since T is from R^m to R^k, the matrix **A** is $k \times m$. This means that **AB** will be defined and will be a $k \times n$ matrix, so that $T \circ S$ is a transformation from R^n to R^k. □

One composition of transformations is of particular interest. Let T be a linear transformation from R^n to R^n. Is there a linear transformation S from R^n to R^n with the property that $S \circ T$ is the identity? Such a transformation S would pair a vector in the range of T with its preimage in the domain T. This requires that the preimage of each vector be a single vector in the domain, since S must be a function. If $T(\mathbf{X}) = \mathbf{AX}$ and $S(\mathbf{X}) = \mathbf{BX}$, $(S \circ T)(\mathbf{X}) = \mathbf{BAX}$. Thus, $S \circ T$ is the identity if and only if $\mathbf{BA} = \mathbf{I}_n$. Since **A** and **B** are both $n \times n$, this means that **A** is nonsingular and $\mathbf{B} = \mathbf{A}^{-1}$. Also, T and S are one-to-one if such a transformation exists.

T^{-1}

Definition 8

If T is a linear transformation from R^n to R^n and if a linear transformation S exists such that $S \circ T$ is the identity transformation, S is called the **inverse** of T and is denoted by $\boldsymbol{T^{-1}}$.

Theorem 7 If T is a linear transformation from R^n to R^n with nonsingular matrix **A**, T^{-1} exists. The matrix of T^{-1} is $\mathbf{A}^{-1}$. □

Example 16 Let T from R^2 to R^2 be a rotation of the plane about the origin in a counterclockwise direction through an angle of 90°. (See Example 3.)

It is clear geometrically that the inverse of T is a rotation of the plane about the origin in a clockwise direction through an angle of 90°. The matrix of T is $\begin{bmatrix} 0 & -1 \\ 1 & 0 \end{bmatrix}$ (Example 6). Since rotation in the clockwise direction through 90° takes $\mathbf{e}_1$ into

$(0, -1)$ and $\mathbf{e}_2$ into $(1, 0)$, the matrix of the inverse transformation is $\begin{bmatrix} 0 & 1 \\ -1 & 0 \end{bmatrix}$. As expected, $\begin{bmatrix} 0 & -1 \\ 1 & 0 \end{bmatrix}\begin{bmatrix} 0 & 1 \\ -1 & 0 \end{bmatrix} = \begin{bmatrix} 1 & 0 \\ 0 & 1 \end{bmatrix}$.

Projection of (x_1, x_2, x_3) on the x_1x_2-plane (Example 11) does not have an inverse, since the preimage of each vector in the x_1x_2-plane is an infinite set. The matrix of this projection is $\begin{bmatrix} 1 & 0 & 0 \\ 0 & 1 & 0 \\ 0 & 0 & 0 \end{bmatrix}$, which has no inverse. ■

The matrix of a linear transformation T from D to R depends on the choice of basis in both D and R. Recall the process of creating this matrix (Section 5.2). Let U be the basis in D and V the basis in R.

1. For each $\mathbf{u}_i$ in U, find $[T(\mathbf{u}_i)]_V$.
2. Form the matrix $\mathbf{A}$ with columns the coordinate columns $[T(\mathbf{u}_i)]_V$.

Thus $\mathbf{A} = \big[[T(\mathbf{u}_1)]_V\ [T(\mathbf{u}_2)]_V \cdots [T(\mathbf{u}_n)]_V\big]$. This clearly involves both U and V.

There are many possible choices of basis in each of the vector spaces D and R. In order to study which choice is best for a particular purpose, we must first see how a change of basis in D or R (or both) affects the matrix $\mathbf{A}$.

Consider the vector space W. Let U be a basis for W, and V a basis for W. Let J be a linear transformation such that: (1) The domain of J is W (basis U), (2) the range of J is W (basis V), (3) $J(\mathbf{x}) = \mathbf{x}$. Thus J maps each vector into itself, but $\mathbf{x}$ is represented relative to U in the domain and relative to V in the range. To find the matrix of J we proceed in the usual way:

1. For each $\mathbf{u}_i$ in U, $[J(\mathbf{u}_i)]_V = [\mathbf{u}_i]_V$.
2. The matrix of J is the matrix $\mathbf{P} = \big[[\mathbf{u}_1]_V\ [\mathbf{u}_2]_V \cdots [\mathbf{u}_n]_V\big]$.
3. The transformation J in matrix form is $[\mathbf{x}]_V = \mathbf{P}[\mathbf{x}]_U$.

This is the same matrix obtained in Section 4.5, Theorem 13.

Example 17 illustrates a change of basis related to a linear transformation from R^2 to R^2.

Example 17

Let T from R^2 to R^2 be defined by $[T(\mathbf{x})]_E = \begin{bmatrix} 1 & -2 \\ -2 & -2 \end{bmatrix} [\mathbf{x}]_E$. Here the standard basis is used in domain and range. The basis U consists of the vectors $\mathbf{u}_1 = (1, 1)$, $\mathbf{u}_2 = (1, -1)$. To express T relative to the basis U three transformations are involved:

1. J, domain R^2 (basis U), range R^2 (basis E), changes basis in the domain.
2. T, domain R^2 (basis E), range R^2 (basis E), is the given linear transformation.
3. J^{-1}, domain R^2 (basis E), range R^2 (basis U), changes basis from E to U.

Write the matrices in each case:

1. (a) $[\mathbf{u}_1]_E = \begin{bmatrix} 1 \\ 1 \end{bmatrix}$, $[\mathbf{u}_2]_E = \begin{bmatrix} 1 \\ -1 \end{bmatrix}$.

   (b) Matrix of J is $\mathbf{P} = \begin{bmatrix} 1 & 1 \\ 1 & -1 \end{bmatrix}$.

2. Matrix of T relative to E is $\mathbf{A} = \begin{bmatrix} 1 & -2 \\ -2 & -2 \end{bmatrix}$.

3. (a) $[\mathbf{e}_1]_U = \begin{bmatrix} \frac{1}{2} \\ \frac{1}{2} \end{bmatrix}$, $[\mathbf{e}_2]_U = \begin{bmatrix} \frac{1}{2} \\ -\frac{1}{2} \end{bmatrix}$.

   (b) Matrix of J^{-1} is $\mathbf{P}^{-1} = \begin{bmatrix} \frac{1}{2} & \frac{1}{2} \\ \frac{1}{2} & -\frac{1}{2} \end{bmatrix}$.

Since T relative to U is: (1) J followed by (2) T (basis E), followed by (3) J^{-1},

$$T\,(\text{basis } U) = J^{-1} \circ T \circ J.$$

The matrix of T (basis U) is

$$\mathbf{B} = \mathbf{P}^{-1}\mathbf{AP} = \begin{bmatrix} \frac{1}{2} & \frac{1}{2} \\ \frac{1}{2} & -\frac{1}{2} \end{bmatrix}\begin{bmatrix} 1 & -2 \\ -2 & -2 \end{bmatrix}\begin{bmatrix} 1 & 1 \\ 1 & -1 \end{bmatrix} = \begin{bmatrix} -\frac{5}{2} & \frac{3}{2} \\ \frac{3}{2} & \frac{3}{2} \end{bmatrix}$$

As a check of our work, find $T(\mathbf{x})$ for $\mathbf{x} = (-1, 3)$. Here $[\mathbf{x}]_E = \begin{bmatrix} -1 \\ 3 \end{bmatrix}$, and, using (2), $[T(\mathbf{x})]_E = \begin{bmatrix} 1 & -2 \\ -2 & -2 \end{bmatrix}\begin{bmatrix} -1 \\ 3 \end{bmatrix} = \begin{bmatrix} -7 \\ -4 \end{bmatrix}$. To calculate $[T(\mathbf{x})]_U$ we take the product $\begin{bmatrix} -\frac{5}{2} & \frac{3}{2} \\ \frac{3}{2} & \frac{3}{2} \end{bmatrix}[\mathbf{x}]_U$. We can find $[\mathbf{x}]_U$ either from the product $\begin{bmatrix} \frac{1}{2} & \frac{1}{2} \\ \frac{1}{2} & -\frac{1}{2} \end{bmatrix}[\mathbf{x}]_E$ or directly by observing that $(-1, 3) = (1, 1) - 2(1, -1)$. In either case, $[\mathbf{x}]_U = \begin{bmatrix} 1 \\ -2 \end{bmatrix}$, and $[T(\mathbf{x})]_U = \begin{bmatrix} -\frac{5}{2} & \frac{3}{2} \\ \frac{3}{2} & \frac{3}{2} \end{bmatrix}\begin{bmatrix} 1 \\ -2 \end{bmatrix} = \begin{bmatrix} -\frac{11}{2} \\ -\frac{3}{2} \end{bmatrix}$. To express this in terms of the standard basis in R^2, we write $-(\frac{11}{2})(1, 1) - (\frac{3}{2})(1, -1) = (-\frac{14}{2}, -\frac{8}{2}) = (-7, -4)$. This agrees with our previous calculation. ■

Recall that a matrix **B** is **similar** to a matrix **A** if there exists a nonsingular matrix **P** such that $\mathbf{B} = \mathbf{P}^{-1}\mathbf{AP}$ (Definition 6, Chapter 3). In Example 17, the matrix of T (basis U) is similar to the matrix of T (basis E); the matrix **P** in this case is $\begin{bmatrix} 1 & 1 \\ 1 & -1 \end{bmatrix}$.

The importance of this is seen in Chapter 6 when we use eigenvalues and eigenvectors to obtain a diagonal representation for the transformation T. Example 18 gives a preview of the use of eigenvectors as a basis.

Example 18 The transformation T defined in Example 17 has matrix, relative to the standard basis, $\begin{bmatrix} 1 & -2 \\ -2 & -2 \end{bmatrix}$. The eigenvalues of $\begin{bmatrix} 1 & -2 \\ -2 & -2 \end{bmatrix}$ are $2, -3$, and the corresponding eigenvectors are $\mathbf{v}_1 = (2, -1)$ and $\mathbf{v}_2 = (1, 2)$. Let $V = \{\mathbf{v}_1, \mathbf{v}_2\}$. The change-of-basis transformation from R^2 (basis V) to R^2 (basis E) has matrix $\mathbf{P} = \begin{bmatrix} 2 & 1 \\ -1 & 2 \end{bmatrix}$. The matrix of T relative to V is given by $\mathbf{P}^{-1}\mathbf{AP}$. Here

$$\mathbf{P}^{-1}\mathbf{AP} = \begin{bmatrix} \frac{2}{5} & -\frac{1}{5} \\ \frac{1}{5} & \frac{2}{5} \end{bmatrix} \begin{bmatrix} 1 & -2 \\ -2 & -2 \end{bmatrix} \begin{bmatrix} 2 & 1 \\ -1 & 2 \end{bmatrix} = \begin{bmatrix} 2 & 0 \\ 0 & -3 \end{bmatrix}$$

The matrix of T relative to the basis V is diagonal and thus considerably simpler than either the matrix of T relative to U or the matrix of T relative to E.

The new matrix of the transformation is diagonal, so it is not difficult to get a geometric picture of the effect of the transformation. (See Figure 5.7.) The vector $\mathbf{v}_1$ is mapped into $2\mathbf{v}_1$, and the vector $\mathbf{v}_2$ is mapped into $-3\mathbf{v}_2$. The linear combinations of $\mathbf{v}_1$ and $\mathbf{v}_2$ are mapped into the same linear combinations of $2\mathbf{v}_1$ and $-3\mathbf{v}_2$. Thus, the vectors that lie in the portion of the right half-plane between the rays containing $\mathbf{v}_1$ and $\mathbf{v}_2$ are mapped into the portion of the lower half-plane between the rays containing $2\mathbf{v}_1$ and $-3\mathbf{v}_2$.

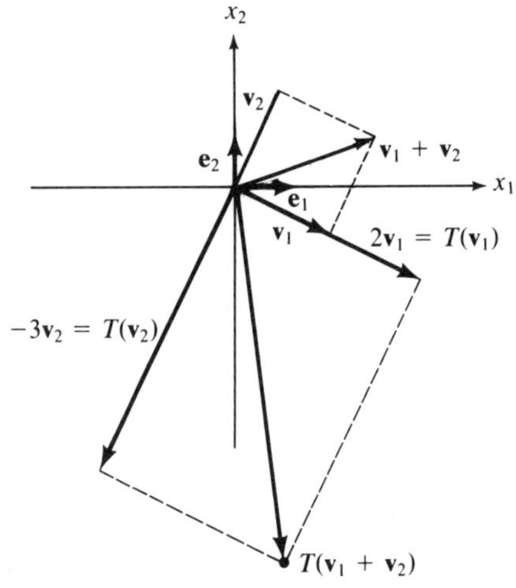

FIGURE 5.7 ■

In the discussion so far we have assumed that one of the bases in the vector space W is the standard basis. This restriction is unnecessary. Before stating and proving Theorem 8 we outline the linear transformations and corresponding matrix equations involved.

	Matrix Equation	**Corresponding Transformation**
1.	$[\mathbf{x}]_U = \mathbf{P}[\mathbf{x}]_V$	$J(\mathbf{x}) = \mathbf{x}$,
	$[J(\mathbf{x})]_U = [\mathbf{x}]_U = \mathbf{P}[\mathbf{x}]_V$	J: W (Basis V) $\to$ W (Basis U)
2.	$[\mathbf{x}]_V = \mathbf{P}^{-1}[\mathbf{x}]_U$	$J^{-1}(\mathbf{x}) = \mathbf{x}$,
	$[J^{-1}(\mathbf{x})]_V = [\mathbf{x}]_V = \mathbf{P}^{-1}[\mathbf{x}]_U$	J^{-1}: W (Basis U) $\to$ W (Basis V)
3.	$[T(\mathbf{x})]_U = \mathbf{A}[\mathbf{x}]_U$	T: W (Basis U) $\to$ W (Basis U)
4.	$[T(\mathbf{x})]_V = \mathbf{B}[\mathbf{x}]_V$	T: W (Basis V) $\to$ W (Basis V)

Theorem 8 Let W be an n-dimensional vector space. Let U and V be bases for W. Let T be a linear transformation from W to W. If the matrix of T relative to U is $\mathbf{A}$, and the matrix of T relative to V is $\mathbf{B}$, then $\mathbf{A}$ and $\mathbf{B}$ are similar.

Proof Let J be the transformation 1. above from W (Basis V) to W (Basis U). The matrix of J is $\mathbf{P}$: $[\mathbf{x}]_U = \mathbf{P}[\mathbf{x}]_V$.

The given linear transformation T from W to W relative to U has the matrix representation $[T(\mathbf{x})]_U = \mathbf{A}[\mathbf{x}]_U$. This is transformation 3. Then $T \circ J$, that is, 1. followed by 3., is given by $[T(\mathbf{x})]_U = \mathbf{AP}[\mathbf{x}]_V$.

The transformation J^{-1}, 2. above, changes from W (Basis U) to W (Basis V). Its equation is $[\mathbf{x}]_V = \mathbf{P}^{-1}[\mathbf{x}]_U$. The transformation $J^{-1} \circ T \circ J$, that is, 1. followed by 3. followed by 2., has the matrix representation:

$$[T(\mathbf{x})]_V = \mathbf{P}^{-1}\mathbf{AP}[\mathbf{x}]_V$$

But this is exactly the transformation 4., T from W to W relative to V, and has matrix $\mathbf{B}$. Thus, $\mathbf{B} = \mathbf{P}^{-1}\mathbf{AP}$. This means that the matrix of T relative to V is similar to the matrix of T relative to U. □

Exercises 5.3 contain several problems illustrating a change of basis in the vector spaces with which we are familiar. The computations involved in a change of basis are much simpler when we are dealing with orthonormal bases because of the ease of taking inverses of an orthogonal matrix. (See Problems 24–26.)

The more general case of a transformation from one vector space into another vector space can be handled in a similar way. In this situation, two bases are involved in the representation of the transformation. A change of basis can be performed independently both in the domain and in the range. This case is discussed in Problems 28–30.

SUMMARY Linear transformations T and S can be combined by addition, scalar multiplication, and composition. The composition $(T \circ S)(\mathbf{x}) = T(S(\mathbf{x}))$ is defined if the range of S is a subset of the domain of T. If the matrix of S is $\mathbf{B}$ and the matrix of T is $\mathbf{A}$, the matrix of $T \circ S$ is $\mathbf{AB}$.

If T is one-to-one, the matrix $\mathbf{A}$ of T is nonsingular. There is a linear transformation T^{-1} such that $T^{-1} \circ T = T \circ T^{-1} = I$. The matrix of T^{-1} is $\mathbf{A}^{-1}$.

The change-of-basis transformation J is a transformation from W (basis U) to W (basis V): $[J(\mathbf{x})]_V = \mathbf{P}[\mathbf{x}]_U$. The matrix $\mathbf{P}$ is nonsingular with columns $[\mathbf{u}_1]_V, [\mathbf{u}_2]_V, \ldots, [\mathbf{u}_n]_V$. Let T be a linear transformation from W to W. If the matrix of T relative to U is $\mathbf{A}$, the matrix of T relative to V is $\mathbf{B} = \mathbf{P}^{-1}\mathbf{AP}$.

EXERCISES 5.3

1. Let

$$T(\mathbf{X}) = \begin{bmatrix} 1 & 1 \\ 2 & 3 \end{bmatrix}\mathbf{X} \quad \text{and} \quad S(\mathbf{X}) = \begin{bmatrix} 2 & 2 \\ 1 & 4 \end{bmatrix}\mathbf{X}$$

a. Write $S \circ T(\mathbf{X})$ in matrix form.

b. Write $T \circ S(\mathbf{X})$ in matrix form.

c. Is $S \circ T = T \circ S$?

2. Let T be defined by $T(\mathbf{X}) = \begin{bmatrix} 1 & 1 \\ 2 & 3 \end{bmatrix}\mathbf{X}$. Find S such that $S \circ T = I$.

3. Show that $(T \circ S)(a\mathbf{u} + b\mathbf{v}) = a(T \circ S)(\mathbf{u}) + b(T \circ S)(\mathbf{v})$.

4. Let T be defined by

$$T(\mathbf{X}) = \begin{bmatrix} 1 & 2 & 1 \\ 1 & 1 & 3 \\ 1 & 0 & -1 \end{bmatrix} \mathbf{X}$$

Find the matrix of T^{-1}.

5. Let T be the transformation

$$T(\mathbf{X}) = \begin{bmatrix} 1 & 2 & 1 \\ c & 1 & 0 \\ 0 & 0 & 1 \end{bmatrix} \mathbf{X}$$

where c is a real number. For what values of c does T have an inverse?

6. Show that if S is the inverse of T, then T is the inverse of S.

7. Let

$$S(\mathbf{X}) = \begin{bmatrix} 1 & 1 \\ 0 & 0 \end{bmatrix} \mathbf{X}$$

Find a transformation T such that $S \circ T = Z$. Is it possible to find a T different from Z that has this property?

8. Let

$$T(\mathbf{X}) = \begin{bmatrix} 1 & 1 & 2 \\ 2 & 1 & 0 \\ 1 & 0 & -2 \end{bmatrix} \mathbf{X}$$

Write the transformation $2T$ in matrix form. What is the range of T? What is the range of $2T$?

9. Let

$$T_1(\mathbf{X}) = \begin{bmatrix} 1 & 2 & 1 \\ 1 & 1 & 3 \end{bmatrix} \mathbf{X},$$

$$T_2(\mathbf{X}) = \begin{bmatrix} 1 & 1 \\ 0 & 2 \end{bmatrix} \mathbf{X}$$

and

$$T_3(\mathbf{X}) = \begin{bmatrix} -1 & 2 & 1 \\ 1 & 1 & 2 \\ 1 & 1 & 5 \end{bmatrix} \mathbf{X}$$

a. Compare the domain of T_1 and the domain of T_2. Compare the range of T_1 and the range of T_2. Why is $T_1 + T_2$ not defined?

b. Compare the domain of T_1 and the domain of T_3. Compare the range of T_1 and the range of T_3. Why is $T_1 + T_3$ not defined?

10. Let $T_1(\mathbf{X}) = \mathbf{AX}$ and $T_2(\mathbf{X}) = \mathbf{BX}$.

a. Under what conditions is $\mathbf{A} + \mathbf{B}$ defined?

b. Under what conditions is $T_1 + T_2$ defined?

c. Show that the conditions in **a.** hold if and only if the conditions in **b.** hold.

11. Let

$$T(\mathbf{X}) = \begin{bmatrix} 2 & 1 \\ 4 & 5 \end{bmatrix} \mathbf{X}$$

Write a transformation S such that $T + S = Z$.

12. Let T_1 be a linear transformation with matrix $\begin{bmatrix} 1 & 2 & 1 \\ 1 & 1 & 3 \end{bmatrix}$ and let T_2 be a linear transformation with matrix $\begin{bmatrix} -1 & 1 & 2 \\ 1 & 0 & -1 \end{bmatrix}$. Write the matrix of $2T_1 - 3T_2$. Find a transformation T_3 such that $T_1 + T_3 = Z$.

13. Verify that the set of all linear transformations from R^3 to R^2 is a vector space, with the transformation Z as the additive identity.

14. Let P_1 represent projection on the x_1-axis in R^2, and let P_2 represent projection on the x_2-axis in R^2. What is $P_1 + P_2$? Describe this geometrically and check your intuition by writing the projections in matrix form.

15. Let P_1 be projection on the x_3-axis in R^3 and P_2 be projection on the x_1x_2-plane in R^3. Describe $P_1 + P_2$ geometrically and check your intuition by writing the projections in matrix form.

16. Let P be the transformation projection on the x_1-axis in R^2. Find a transformation T such that $T \circ P = Z$ and describe it geometrically.

17. Let R_1 be reflection in the x_1-axis and let R_2 be reflection in the x_2-axis. Interpret $R_1 + R_2$ geometrically. Interpret $R_1 \circ R_2$ geometrically.

18. Let

$$T(\mathbf{X}) = \begin{bmatrix} 1 & 1 & 2 \\ 2 & 1 & 0 \\ 1 & 0 & -2 \end{bmatrix} \mathbf{X}$$

and

$$S(\mathbf{X}) = \begin{bmatrix} 1 & 1 & 1 \\ 0 & 1 & 1 \\ 0 & 0 & 1 \end{bmatrix} \mathbf{X}$$

a. What is the range of T? What is the range of S?

b. Write $S \circ T$ in matrix form. What is the range of $S \circ T$?

c. Why is the range of $S \circ T$ a proper subset of the range of S?

19. Let

$$T(\mathbf{X}) = \begin{bmatrix} 1 & 1 & 0 \\ 2 & 2 & 1 \\ 3 & 3 & 1 \end{bmatrix} \mathbf{X}$$

and

$$S(\mathbf{X}) = \begin{bmatrix} 1 & 1 & 0 \\ 1 & 1 & 0 \\ 0 & 0 & 1 \end{bmatrix} \mathbf{X}$$

a. Find the null space of S.
b. Find the null space of $S \circ T$.
c. Show that the null space of $S \circ T$ is the set of vectors $\mathbf{v}$ such that $T(\mathbf{v})$ lies in the null space of S.

20. Let T be a transformation from R^2 to R^2 with matrix $\mathbf{A} = \begin{bmatrix} 3 & 3 \\ 2 & 4 \end{bmatrix}$. Let $U = \{\mathbf{u}_1, \mathbf{u}_2\}$ where $\mathbf{u}_1 = (1, 0)$, $\mathbf{u}_2 = (1, 1)$.
a. Write the change-of-basis transformation J from R^2 (basis U) to R^2 (basis E).
b. Write the matrix of T relative to the basis U.
c. Check by direct calculation.

21. The matrix of T relative to the standard basis is $\mathbf{A} = \begin{bmatrix} 3 & 3 \\ 2 & 4 \end{bmatrix}$. Let $V = \{\mathbf{v}_1, \mathbf{v}_2\}$, where $\mathbf{v}_1 = (1, 1)$ and $\mathbf{v}_2 = (3, -2)$.
a. Write the change-of-basis transformation J from R^2 (basis V) to R^2 (basis E).
b. Write the matrix of T relative to the basis V.

22. Let T be defined by

$$T(\mathbf{X}) = \begin{bmatrix} 8 & 7 & 7 \\ -5 & -6 & -9 \\ 5 & 7 & 10 \end{bmatrix} \mathbf{X}$$

Let $U = \{\mathbf{u}_1, \mathbf{u}_2, \mathbf{u}_3\}$, where $\mathbf{u}_1 = (1, -1, 1)$, $\mathbf{u}_2 = (0, 1, -1)$, and $\mathbf{u}_3 = (1, -2, 1)$. Find the matrix representation of T relative to the basis U.

23. Show that the determinant of the matrix of a transformation is unchanged by a change of basis.

24. Let $U = \{\mathbf{u}_1, \mathbf{u}_2\}$, where $\mathbf{u}_1 = \left(\frac{1}{\sqrt{2}}, \frac{-1}{\sqrt{2}}\right)$ and $\mathbf{u}_2 = \left(\frac{1}{\sqrt{2}}, \frac{1}{\sqrt{2}}\right)$

$V = \{\mathbf{v}_1, \mathbf{v}_2\}$, where $\mathbf{v}_1 = \left(\frac{2}{\sqrt{5}}, \frac{1}{\sqrt{5}}\right)$ and $\mathbf{v}_2 = \left(\frac{1}{\sqrt{5}}, \frac{-2}{\sqrt{5}}\right)$

and T be a linear transformation with matrix, relative to basis U, $\mathbf{A} = \begin{bmatrix} 1 & 2 \\ 1 & -1 \end{bmatrix}$.

a. What special property do the basis U and the basis V have?
b. Find the coordinates of $\mathbf{u}_1$ and the coordinates of $\mathbf{u}_2$ relative to V.
c. Let J be the linear transformation from R^2 basis U to R^2 basis V. Write the matrix $\mathbf{P}$ of J. What special property does $\mathbf{P}$ have?
d. Calculate the matrix of T relative to basis V.

25. Let U and V be the bases described in Problem 24. Let the matrix of T relative to U be $\mathbf{A} = \begin{bmatrix} -\frac{5}{2} & \frac{3}{2} \\ \frac{3}{2} & \frac{3}{2} \end{bmatrix}$.
a. Find the matrix of T relative to V. Call this matrix $\mathbf{B}$.
b. Find the matrix of T relative to E. Call this matrix $\mathbf{C}$.
c. Calculate the eigenvalues and eigenvectors of the matrix $\mathbf{C}$.
d. Compare the basis V with your answer in **c.**
e. Find the eigenvalues and eigenvectors of the matrix $\mathbf{A}$.
f. Show that the eigenvectors of $\mathbf{A}$ are the coordinates relative to U of vectors proportional to $\mathbf{v}_1$ and $\mathbf{v}_2$.

26. Let U and $\mathbf{A}$ be defined as in Problem 24, and let V be the basis with $\mathbf{v}_1 = \left(\frac{2}{\sqrt{13}}, \frac{3}{\sqrt{13}}\right)$ and $\mathbf{v}_2 = \left(\frac{-3}{\sqrt{13}}, \frac{2}{\sqrt{13}}\right)$. Find the matrix of T relative to V.

27. Let T be defined from P_2 to P_2 by $T(p) = p'' + p' + 2p$. Relative to the standard basis the matrix of T is

$$\begin{bmatrix} 2 & 1 & 2 \\ 0 & 2 & 2 \\ 0 & 0 & 2 \end{bmatrix}$$

a. Find the change-of-basis transformation J from P_2 (basis U) to P_2 (basis E), where $U = \{\mathbf{u}_1, \mathbf{u}_2, \mathbf{u}_3\}$ and $\mathbf{u}_1 = 1 + x$, $\mathbf{u}_2 = 1 - x$, $\mathbf{u}_3 = 1 + x + x^2$.
b. Find the matrix of T relative to U.
c. Check using Theorem 3.

28. Let T be a transformation from P_2 to R^3 in which $T(p) = (p(0), p(1), p(-1))$.
a. Verify that the matrix of T, relative to the standard basis in each space, is

$$\mathbf{A} = \begin{bmatrix} 1 & 0 & 0 \\ 1 & 1 & 1 \\ 1 & -1 & 1 \end{bmatrix}$$

b. Let $U = \{\mathbf{u}_1, \mathbf{u}_2, \mathbf{u}_3\}$ be a basis in R^3, where $\mathbf{u}_1 = (1,0,0)$, $\mathbf{u}_2 = (1,1,0)$, $\mathbf{u}_3 = (1,1,1)$. Write the change-of-basis transformation J_1 from R^3 (basis U) to R^3 (basis E).

c. Let $Q = \{p_1, p_2, p_3\}$ be a basis in P_2, where $p_1 = 1 + x$, $p_2 = 1 - x$, and $p_3 = 1 + x + x^2$. Write the change-of-basis transformation J_2 from P_2 (basis Q) to P_2 (basis E).

d. Verify that the matrix of T relative to U and Q is the matrix of $J_1^{-1} \circ T \circ J_2$. Calculate this matrix.

29. Using T as defined in Problem 28, let U be the basis in R^3 for which $\mathbf{u}_1 = (1,0,0)$, $\mathbf{u}_2 = (0,1,0)$, and $\mathbf{u}_3 = (0, -\frac{1}{2}, \frac{1}{2})$, and let Q be the basis in P_2 for which $q_1 = 1 + x + x^2$, $q_2 = x - x^2$, $q_3 = x^2$. Find the matrix of T relative to the bases U and Q.

30. Using T as defined in Problem 28, let U be the basis in R^3 for which $\mathbf{u}_1 = (1,0,0)$, $\mathbf{u}_2 = (0,1,-1)$, $\mathbf{u}_3 = (0,0,2)$. Let Q be the basis in P_2 for which $q_1 = 1 - x^2$, $q_2 = x$, $q_3 = -x + x^2$. Find the matrix of T relative to the bases U and Q.

Supplemental Topic

Row Reduction as a Composition of Linear Transformations. Consider the transformations on $M_{m \times n}$:

$T_{i,j,k}(\mathbf{A}) = \mathbf{B}$, where $\mathbf{B}$ is the $m \times n$ matrix obtained from $\mathbf{A}$ by adding k times row j to row i, $k \neq 0$.

$R_{i,c}(\mathbf{A}) = \mathbf{B}$, where $\mathbf{B}$ is the $m \times n$ matrix obtained from $\mathbf{A}$ by multiplying row i by c, $c \neq 0$

$S_{i,j}(\mathbf{A}) = \mathbf{B}$, where $\mathbf{B}$ is the $m \times n$ matrix obtained from $\mathbf{A}$ by interchanging rows i and j

For example: $T_{1,2,5}\left(\begin{bmatrix} 2 & 4 & 3 \\ 1 & -1 & 0 \end{bmatrix}\right) = \begin{bmatrix} 7 & -1 & 3 \\ 1 & -1 & 0 \end{bmatrix}$,

$R_{2,2}\left(\begin{bmatrix} 2 & 4 & 3 \\ 1 & -1 & 0 \end{bmatrix}\right) = \begin{bmatrix} 2 & 4 & 3 \\ 2 & -2 & 0 \end{bmatrix}$;

$S_{1,2}\left(\begin{bmatrix} 2 & 4 & 3 \\ 1 & -1 & 0 \end{bmatrix}\right) = \begin{bmatrix} 1 & -1 & 0 \\ 2 & 4 & 3 \end{bmatrix}$. A basis for $M_{m \times n}$ consists of mn matrices, the entries of which are all zero except for a 1 in the ijth position. For simplicity, we consider $M_{2 \times 3}$. The basis vectors are:

$$\begin{bmatrix} 1 & 0 & 0 \\ 0 & 0 & 0 \end{bmatrix}, \quad \begin{bmatrix} 0 & 1 & 0 \\ 0 & 0 & 0 \end{bmatrix},$$
$$\begin{bmatrix} 0 & 0 & 1 \\ 0 & 0 & 0 \end{bmatrix}, \quad \begin{bmatrix} 0 & 0 & 0 \\ 1 & 0 & 0 \end{bmatrix},$$
$$\begin{bmatrix} 0 & 0 & 0 \\ 0 & 1 & 0 \end{bmatrix}, \quad \begin{bmatrix} 0 & 0 & 0 \\ 0 & 0 & 1 \end{bmatrix}$$

The matrix of any of the transformations T, R, or S in this space will be 6×6.

31. a. Show that the matrix of the transformation $T_{1,2,5}$ is

$$\begin{bmatrix} 1 & 0 & 0 & 5 & 0 & 0 \\ 0 & 1 & 0 & 0 & 5 & 0 \\ 0 & 0 & 1 & 0 & 0 & 5 \\ 0 & 0 & 0 & 1 & 0 & 0 \\ 0 & 0 & 0 & 0 & 1 & 0 \\ 0 & 0 & 0 & 0 & 0 & 1 \end{bmatrix}$$

b. What is the dimension of the null space of the transformation in **a.**?

c. What is the coordinate vector of the matrix $\begin{bmatrix} 2 & 4 & 3 \\ 1 & -1 & 0 \end{bmatrix}$?

d. Use the matrix in **a.** and the coordinate vector in **c.** to find the coordinate vector of $T_{1,2,5}\left(\begin{bmatrix} 2 & 4 & 3 \\ 1 & -1 & 0 \end{bmatrix}\right)$ and hence the matrix this transformation produces.

(*Note:* If you have studied partitioned matrices, Chapter 1, you will see that the calculations can be simplified by writing $\begin{bmatrix} \mathbf{I} & 5\mathbf{I} \\ \mathbf{0} & \mathbf{I} \end{bmatrix}$ for the matrix in **a.**)

32. Use a technique similar to that of Problem 31 to find the row-reduced form of the matrix $\begin{bmatrix} 1 & 3 & -1 \\ 2 & 8 & 4 \end{bmatrix}$.

33. Apply the same technique to the space $M_{2 \times 2}$.

a. Consider the matrix $\begin{bmatrix} 2 & 5 \\ 1 & 1 \end{bmatrix}$ and find a composition of transformations such that $T\left(\begin{bmatrix} 2 & 5 \\ 1 & 1 \end{bmatrix}\right) = \begin{bmatrix} 1 & 0 \\ 0 & 1 \end{bmatrix}$.

b. Write the matrix of each transformation used, and obtain the matrix of T.
c. Write the transformation T in matrix form.

34. Use the result of Problem 33 to write $T\left(\begin{bmatrix} 1 & 0 \\ 0 & 1 \end{bmatrix}\right)$. Verify that $T\left(\begin{bmatrix} 1 & 0 \\ 0 & 1 \end{bmatrix}\right)$ gives the coordinates of the matrix that is the inverse of $\begin{bmatrix} 2 & 5 \\ 1 & 1 \end{bmatrix}$.

35. Show that:
a. $(T_{i,j,k})^{-1} = T_{i,j,-k}$
b. $(R_{i,c})^{-1} = R_{i,1/c}$
c. $(S_{i,j})^{-1} = S_{i,j}$

5.4 Applications: The Method of Least Squares, Differential Equations, Robotics, The Scrambler Transformation

The Method of Least Squares

In Section 5.2 we illustrated the use of a transformation from P_n to R^m in finding a polynomial graph that passes through m distinct points. Whether such a graph exists depends on the relative size of m and n. If $m > n + 1$, it is possible that there is no polynomial of degree n with a graph that passes through all these points. It is still useful, however, to ask what polynomial of degree n comes nearest to passing through the m points. A method frequently used for deciding the "best" choice of the polynomial p is referred to as the *method of least squares.*

Let the m points be $(x_1, y_1), (x_2, y_2), \ldots, (x_m, y_m)$. Then $p(x_i) - y_i$ is the vertical distance from the point (x_i, y_i) to the graph of p. (See Figure 5.8.) The method of least squares consists of choosing the polynomial p for which the sum of the squares of these distances is the least. Let

$$D^2 = [p(x_1) - y_1]^2 + [p(x_2) - y_2]^2 + \cdots + [p(x_m) - y_m]^2$$

We want to choose p so that D^2 is a minimum.

Let T be the transformation from P_n to R^m defined by $T(p) = (p(x_1), p(x_2), \ldots, p(x_m))$, and let $\mathbf{y} = (y_1, y_2, \ldots, y_m)$. The number D^2 is the square of the length of the vector $T(p) - \mathbf{y}$. If $\mathbf{y}$ is not in the range of T, we have to find an element $T(p)$ in the range such that $\|T(p) - \mathbf{y}\|$ is a minimum. Example 19 illustrates how this can be done.

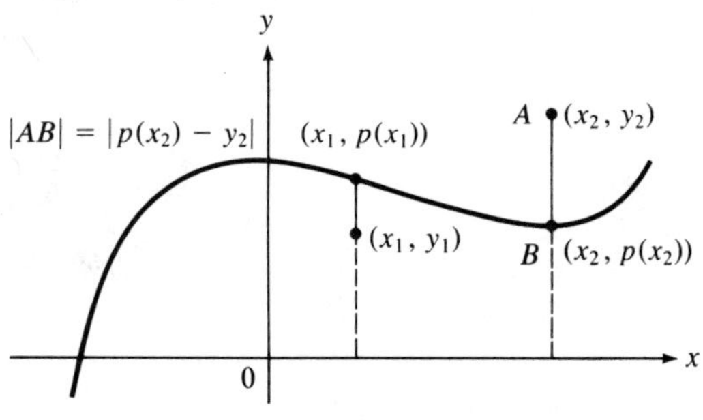

FIGURE 5.8

Example 19 Find the first-degree polynomial that is the best fit for the set of points (x_1, y_1), (x_2, y_2), (x_3, y_3), (x_4, y_4).

Solution The transformation T is from P_1 to R^4 in this case. Its matrix is

$$\mathbf{A} = \begin{bmatrix} 1 & x_1 \\ 1 & x_2 \\ 1 & x_3 \\ 1 & x_4 \end{bmatrix}$$

We want to choose p so that $\| T(p) - \mathbf{y} \|$ is a minimum. Now $T(p) = \mathbf{A}[p]$ and

$$\mathbf{A}[p] - [\mathbf{y}] = \mathbf{A}\begin{bmatrix} a_0 \\ a_1 \end{bmatrix} - [\mathbf{y}] = \begin{bmatrix} a_0 + a_1x_1 - y_1 \\ a_0 + a_1x_2 - y_2 \\ a_0 + a_1x_3 - y_3 \\ a_0 + a_1x_4 - y_4 \end{bmatrix}$$

so that

$$\begin{aligned} D^2 &= (a_0 + a_1x_1 - y_1)^2 + (a_0 + a_1x_2 - y_2)^2 \\ &\quad + (a_0 + a_1x_3 - y_3)^2 + (a_0 + a_1x_4 - y_4)^2 \end{aligned}$$

From calculus, we know that the values of a_0 and a_1 that make D^2 a minimum can be found by setting the partial derivative of D^2 with respect to a_0 equal to zero and the partial derivative of D^2 with respect to a_1 equal to zero. The equations are

$$a_0 + a_1x_1 - y_1 + a_0 + a_1x_2 - y_2 + a_0 + a_1x_3 - y_3 + a_0 + a_1x_4 - y_4 = 0$$

and

$$\begin{aligned} &x_1(a_0 + a_1x_1 - y_1) + x_2(a_0 + a_1x_2 - y_2) \\ &+x_3(a_0 + a_1x_3 - y_3) + x_4(a_0 + a_1x_4 - y_4) = 0 \end{aligned}$$

In matrix form, these equations are

$$\begin{bmatrix} 1 & 1 & 1 & 1 \\ x_1 & x_2 & x_3 & x_4 \end{bmatrix} \begin{bmatrix} a_0 + a_1x_1 - y_1 \\ a_0 + a_1x_2 - y_2 \\ a_0 + a_1x_3 - y_3 \\ a_0 + a_1x_4 - y_4 \end{bmatrix} = \mathbf{0}$$

or

$$\mathbf{A}^T(\mathbf{A}[p] - [\mathbf{y}]) = \mathbf{0}$$

In this example, the matrix $\mathbf{A}^T\mathbf{A}$ is a 2×2 matrix. If the values x_1, x_2, x_3, x_4 are distinct, $\mathbf{A}^T\mathbf{A}$ is nonsingular (Exercises 7–10). We can solve for $[p]$:

$$[p] = (\mathbf{A}^T\mathbf{A})^{-1}\mathbf{A}^T[\mathbf{y}]$$

Remember that $(\mathbf{A}^T\mathbf{A})^{-1}$ cannot be simplified, since $\mathbf{A}^T$ and $\mathbf{A}$ individually do not have inverses. ■

A similar argument shows that, in general, the polynomial of best fit is found from $[p] = (\mathbf{A}^T\mathbf{A})^{-1}\mathbf{A}^T[\mathbf{y}]$, where T is the transformation from P_n to R^m such that $T(p) = (p(x_1), p(x_2), \ldots, p(x_m))$, and $\mathbf{A}$ is the matrix of T.

Example 20 Find the second-degree polynomial that best fits the four points $(0, 1)$, $(1, 2)$, $(-1, 4)$, and $(2, 5)$. (Compare with Example 14.)

Solution

$$\mathbf{A} = \begin{bmatrix} 1 & 0 & 0 \\ 1 & 1 & 1 \\ 1 & -1 & 1 \\ 1 & 2 & 4 \end{bmatrix}, \qquad \mathbf{A}^T\mathbf{A} = \begin{bmatrix} 4 & 2 & 6 \\ 2 & 6 & 8 \\ 6 & 8 & 18 \end{bmatrix}$$

and

$$(\mathbf{A}^T\mathbf{A})^{-1} = \frac{1}{20}\begin{bmatrix} 11 & 3 & -5 \\ 3 & 9 & -5 \\ -5 & -5 & 5 \end{bmatrix}$$

Thus,

$$[p] = \frac{1}{20}\begin{bmatrix} 11 & 3 & -5 \\ 3 & 9 & -5 \\ -5 & -5 & 5 \end{bmatrix}\begin{bmatrix} 1 & 1 & 1 & 1 \\ 0 & 1 & -1 & 2 \\ 0 & 1 & 1 & 4 \end{bmatrix}\begin{bmatrix} 1 \\ 2 \\ 4 \\ 5 \end{bmatrix} = \begin{bmatrix} 1.3 \\ -1.1 \\ 1.5 \end{bmatrix}$$

The second-degree polynomial that best fits the four points is $p = 1.3 - 1.1x + 1.5x^2$. This polynomial passes through $(0, 1.3)$, $(1, 1.7)$, $(-1, 3.9)$, and $(2, 5.1)$. (See Figure 5.9.)

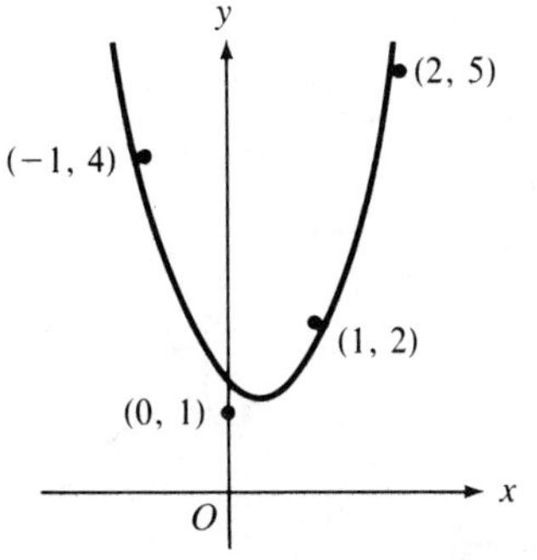

FIGURE 5.9

■

Example 21 Computer matrix algebra packages can take much of the drudgery out of finding a best-fit polynomial. The various steps in solving the following problem were carried out using such a computer program.

Find the third-degree polynomial that best fits the ten points $(-3, -24)$, $(-2, 0)$, $(-1, 6)$, $(0, 5)$, $(0.5, 3)$, $(1, 0)$, $(1.5, -2)$, $(2, -4)$, $(3, 0)$, and $(4, 16)$.

Solution

$$\mathbf{A} = \begin{bmatrix} 1 & -3 & 9 & -27 \\ 1 & -2 & 4 & -8 \\ 1 & -1 & 1 & -1 \\ 1 & 0 & 0 & 0 \\ 1 & \frac{1}{2} & \frac{1}{4} & \frac{1}{8} \\ 1 & 1 & 1 & 1 \\ 1 & \frac{3}{2} & \frac{9}{4} & \frac{27}{8} \\ 1 & 2 & 4 & 8 \\ 1 & 3 & 9 & 27 \\ 1 & 4 & 16 & 64 \end{bmatrix}, \qquad \mathbf{YVAL} = \begin{bmatrix} -24 \\ 0 \\ 6 \\ 5 \\ 3 \\ 0 \\ -2 \\ -4 \\ 0 \\ 16 \end{bmatrix}$$

The following matrices are found in the stated order ($*$ indicates matrix multiplication):

1. $\mathbf{A}^T$ = transpose of $\mathbf{A}$
2. $\mathbf{P} = \mathbf{A}^T * \mathbf{A}$
3. $\mathbf{Q} = \mathbf{P}^{-1}$
4. $\mathbf{R} = \mathbf{Q} * \mathbf{A}^T$
5. $\mathbf{ANS} = \mathbf{R} * \mathbf{YVAL}$

The matrix algebra program MAX will find the result of this computation in one single command:

```
COMPUTE (A' * A)^(-1) * A' * YVAL ANS
```

In the context of the COMPUTE command, MAX understands that $\mathbf{A}'$ means $\mathbf{A}^T$. The result of the computation is put in the matrix **ANS**. However, do not assume that such a simple-appearing computation is without its difficulties. A standard approach to finding an inverse matrix via computer uses row-reduction methods. Usually, $(\mathbf{A}^T * \mathbf{A})^{-1}$ is ill-conditioned (see Section 2.5) in least squares problems. There are, however, some sophisticated techniques for overcoming this difficulty. In any event, using *exact rational arithmetic* via computer, we find that

$$(\mathbf{A}^T * \mathbf{A})^{-1} = (1/3351348)\begin{bmatrix} 809091 & -228201 & -115524 & 29652 \\ -228301 & 439066 & 53796 & -42280 \\ -115524 & 53796 & 30096 & -8400 \\ 29652 & -42280 & -8400 & 5152 \end{bmatrix}$$

and then

$$[p] = (\mathbf{A}^T * \mathbf{A})^{-1} * \mathbf{A}^T * \mathbf{YVAL} = \begin{bmatrix} 5.290 \\ -4.325 \\ -1.909 \\ 0.916 \end{bmatrix}$$

(using three-decimal-place accuracy).

The cubic polynomial that best fits the ten given points is

$$p = 5.290 - 4.325x - 1.909x^2 + 0.916x^3$$

(See Figure 5.10.)

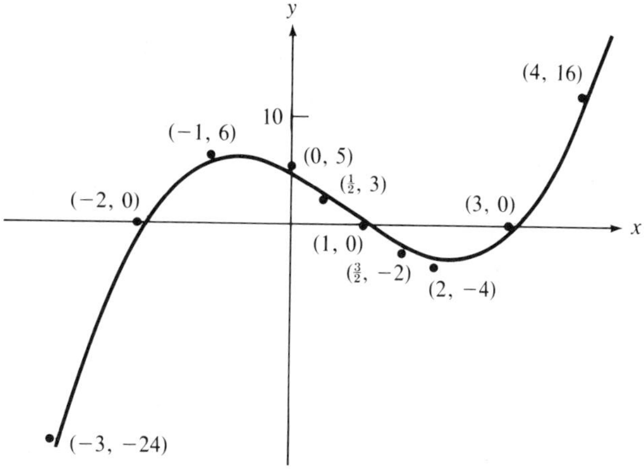

FIGURE 5.10 ∎

A Particular Solution of a Linear Differential Equation

A linear differential operator with constant coefficients is a linear transformation from one function space to another. (See Section 5.2, Problems 23–26). This fact can be used to find a particular solution of a nonhomogeneous linear differential equation. Let $T(y) = f(x)$ be a linear differential equation of order n with constant coefficients. The general solution of this equation is the sum of the general solution of the corresponding homogeneous equation, $T(y) = 0$, and a particular solution of the equation $T(y) = f(x)$. Any particular solution is the preimage of $f(x)$ under the transformation T. This can be found by the methods of this chapter provided a suitable finite-dimensional subspace can be chosen in the domain of T. Example 22 illustrates the method.

Example 22 Find a particular solution of $y'' - 4y' + 3y = x \sin x + 2 \cos x$.

Solution $T(y) = y'' - 4y' + 3y$. The function space that contains the preimage of $x \sin x + 2 \cos x$ must be a space containing linear combinations of all functions that are in this expression, and all the derivatives of these functions. A good spanning set is $B = \{x \sin x, x \cos x, \sin x, \cos x\}$. The set B is a linearly independent set and is the basis of a function space. Relative to this basis, the matrix of

T is found from the following calculations:

$$\begin{aligned} T(x\sin x) &= 2x\sin x - 4x\cos x + 2\cos x - 4\sin x \\ T(x\cos x) &= 4x\sin x + 2x\cos x - 4\cos x - 2\sin x \\ T(\sin x) &= 2\sin x - 4\cos x \\ T(\cos x) &= 2\cos x + 4\sin x \end{aligned}$$

Relative to B the matrix of T is

$$\mathbf{A} = \begin{bmatrix} 2 & 4 & 0 & 0 \\ -4 & 2 & 0 & 0 \\ -4 & -2 & 2 & 4 \\ 2 & -4 & -4 & 2 \end{bmatrix}$$

Since $T(y) = x\sin x + 2\cos x$,

$$[T(y)]_B = \begin{bmatrix} 1 \\ 0 \\ 0 \\ 2 \end{bmatrix}$$

Since $[T(y)]_B = \mathbf{A}[y]_B$, to find $[y]_B$ we must solve the equation

$$\mathbf{A}[y]_B = \begin{bmatrix} 1 \\ 0 \\ 0 \\ 2 \end{bmatrix}$$

In this case, $\mathbf{A}$ is nonsingular, so that

$$[y]_B = \mathbf{A}^{-1}\begin{bmatrix} 1 \\ 0 \\ 0 \\ 2 \end{bmatrix}$$

$$= \begin{bmatrix} \frac{1}{10} & -\frac{1}{5} & 0 & 0 \\ \frac{1}{5} & \frac{1}{10} & 0 & 0 \\ -\frac{2}{50} & -\frac{11}{50} & \frac{1}{10} & -\frac{1}{5} \\ \frac{11}{50} & -\frac{2}{50} & \frac{1}{5} & \frac{1}{10} \end{bmatrix} \begin{bmatrix} 1 \\ 0 \\ 0 \\ 2 \end{bmatrix} = \begin{bmatrix} \frac{1}{10} \\ \frac{1}{5} \\ -\frac{11}{25} \\ \frac{21}{50} \end{bmatrix}$$

A particular solution of the linear differential equation is thus

$$y(x) = \tfrac{1}{10}x\sin x + \tfrac{1}{5}x\cos x - \tfrac{11}{25}\sin x + \tfrac{21}{50}\cos x \qquad \blacksquare$$

In elementary differential equations the method of undetermined coefficients is usually used to arrive at the particular solution for equations like that discussed in Example 22. In both approaches, one of the difficulties is finding the appropriate function space for the problem. The following example illustrates this.

Example 23 Find a particular solution of $y'' - 3y' + 2y = xe^x + 3e^{3x}$.

Solution Let $B = \{xe^x, e^x, e^{3x}\}$. This set contains the functions on the right-hand side of the equation, along with all functions that can be obtained from them by differentiation. The set B is a linearly independent set. Relative to B, the matrix of T is

$$\mathbf{A} = \begin{bmatrix} 0 & 0 & 0 \\ -1 & 0 & 0 \\ 0 & 0 & 2 \end{bmatrix}$$

The differential equation in matrix form is $[T(y)]_B = \mathbf{A}[y]_B$.

For $T(y) = xe^x + 3e^{3x}$,

$$[T(y)]_B = \begin{bmatrix} 1 \\ 0 \\ 3 \end{bmatrix}$$

To find the preimage of $xe^x + 3e^{3x}$, we must solve the equations

$$\begin{bmatrix} 0 & 0 & 0 \\ -1 & 0 & 0 \\ 0 & 0 & 2 \end{bmatrix}[y]_B = \begin{bmatrix} 1 \\ 0 \\ 3 \end{bmatrix}$$

These equations are inconsistent, which shows that $\begin{bmatrix} 1 \\ 0 \\ 3 \end{bmatrix}$ is not in the range of T relative to B; that is, the function space chosen for the representation of T does not include the preimage of the function $xe^x + 3e^{3x}$.

We must enlarge the function space considered. Instead of B, use $B' = \{x^2e^x, xe^x, e^x, e^{3x}\}$. The matrix of T relative to B' is

$$\begin{bmatrix} 0 & 0 & 0 & 0 \\ -2 & 0 & 0 & 0 \\ 2 & -1 & 0 & 0 \\ 0 & 0 & 0 & 2 \end{bmatrix} \quad \text{and} \quad [T(y)]_{B'} = \begin{bmatrix} 0 \\ 1 \\ 0 \\ 3 \end{bmatrix}$$

To find the preimage of $xe^x + 3e^{3x}$, we solve

$$\begin{bmatrix} 0 & 0 & 0 & 0 \\ -2 & 0 & 0 & 0 \\ 2 & -1 & 0 & 0 \\ 0 & 0 & 0 & 2 \end{bmatrix}[y]_{B'} = \begin{bmatrix} 0 \\ 1 \\ 0 \\ 3 \end{bmatrix}$$

This system of equations is consistent and has the solution

$$[y]_{B'} = \begin{bmatrix} -\frac{1}{2} \\ -1 \\ c \\ \frac{3}{2} \end{bmatrix}$$

The preimage of $xe^x + 3e^{3x}$ is thus $y(x) = -\frac{1}{2}x^2e^x - xe^x + ce^x + \frac{3}{2}e^{3x}$. The fact that the coefficient of e^x can be chosen arbitrarily indicates that the preimage is not a single function but an infinite set of functions. This arises from the inclusion of e^x, which is a solution of the associated homogeneous equation. ■

The method of finding a particular solution illustrated in Examples 22 and 23 is equivalent to the method of undetermined coefficients. The linear algebra setting gives some insight into the meaning of the calculations involved.

Robotics

The techniques of linear algebra play an important role in the field of robotics. Much attention has been focused recently on this subject, especially in industry, where machines controlled by microprocessors can be programmed to repeat precisely a sequence of motions in a plane or three-space. These motions can be described as translations or rotations of sets of points being moved by the robot, or a so-called manipulator arm. Such machines can be quite complex (for example, industrial robots used in automated manufacturing or the space shuttle robot arm). To give an introduction to some of the problems in this fascinating field, we will simplify a robot system in order to study how to compute motions of it using linear algebra.

In Chapter 4 we resolved the difficulty of representing a translation using a matrix product by the use of homogeneous coordinates. There, points (x, y) in the plane were represented by the column matrices $\begin{bmatrix} x \\ y \\ k \end{bmatrix}$, $k \neq 0$. This idea can be readily used for points in three-space: We will represent (x, y, z) by the column $\begin{bmatrix} x \\ y \\ z \\ 1 \end{bmatrix}$. Then a translation of (x, y, z) to $(x + \Delta x, y + \Delta y, z + \Delta z)$ can be found using the matrix product

$$\begin{bmatrix} 1 & 0 & 0 & \Delta x \\ 0 & 1 & 0 & \Delta y \\ 0 & 0 & 1 & \Delta z \\ 0 & 0 & 0 & 1 \end{bmatrix} \begin{bmatrix} x \\ y \\ z \\ 1 \end{bmatrix} = \begin{bmatrix} x + \Delta x \\ y + \Delta y \\ z + \Delta z \\ 1 \end{bmatrix} \tag{1}$$

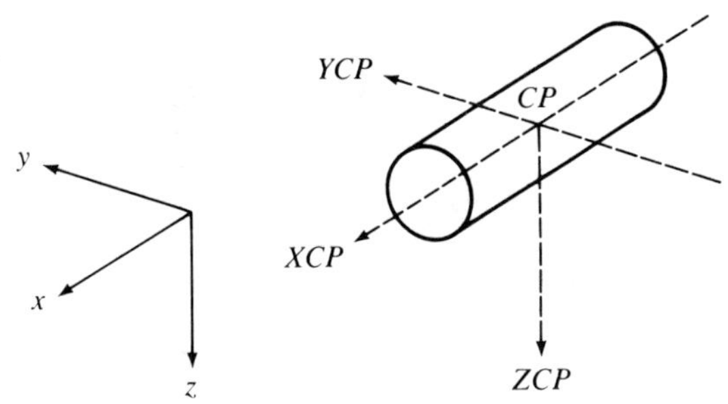

FIGURE 5.11

Let us idealize a robot to a cylinder and choose a convenient fixed central point *CP* inside the robot. All manipulations to the robot will be to the point *CP* with respect to an axis system *XCP*, *YCP*, *ZCP* chosen through *CP*. Comparisons to a fixed-axis system *xyz* (see Figure 5.11) are also possible.

Whereas translations of the robot to new points in three-space can be found using the matrix product (1), the *attitude* of the robot is described by three angles *A*, *B*, *C* known as pitch, yaw, and roll (see Figure 5.12). First, a positive pitch angle *A* will rotate the robot *counterclockwise* about *YCP*. A positive yaw angle *B* will rotate the robot counterclockwise about *ZCP*. A positive roll angle *C* will rotate the robot counterclockwise about *XCP*.

Since yaw is rotation essentially in the *xy* plane, the matrix that effects a rotation by the yaw angle *B* is

$$Y_B = \begin{bmatrix} \cos B & -\sin B & 0 & 0 \\ \sin B & \cos B & 0 & 0 \\ 0 & 0 & 1 & 0 \\ 0 & 0 & 0 & 1 \end{bmatrix}$$

similar to what we discussed in Section 4.6.
Also it can be shown that the rotation by the pitch angle *A* is given by the matrix

$$\mathbf{P}_A = \begin{bmatrix} \cos A & 0 & \sin A & 0 \\ 0 & 1 & 0 & 0 \\ -\sin A & 0 & \cos A & 0 \\ 0 & 0 & 0 & 1 \end{bmatrix}$$

Finally, the matrix

$$\mathbf{R}_C = \begin{bmatrix} 1 & 0 & 0 & 0 \\ 0 & \cos C & -\sin C & 0 \\ 0 & \sin C & \cos C & 0 \\ 0 & 0 & 0 & 1 \end{bmatrix}$$

represents a rotation by the roll angle *C*.

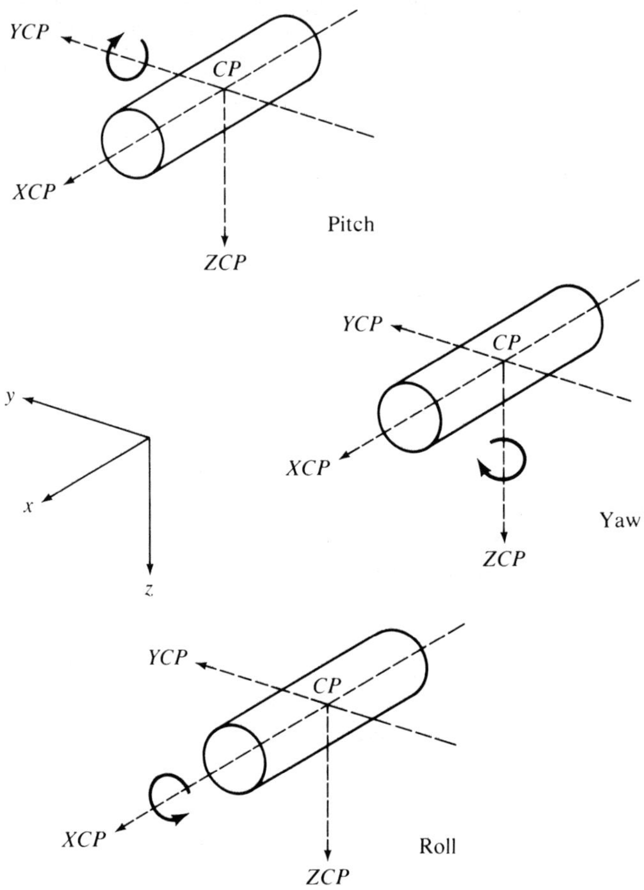

FIGURE 5.12

For example, the point $\begin{bmatrix}1\\0\\0\\1\end{bmatrix}$ in the *XCP*, *YCP*, *ZCP*-axis system, when subjected to a pitch of $\pi/4$, would be located at:

$$\begin{bmatrix} \frac{\sqrt{2}}{2} & 0 & \frac{\sqrt{2}}{2} & 0 \\ 0 & 1 & 0 & 0 \\ -\frac{\sqrt{2}}{2} & 0 & \frac{\sqrt{2}}{2} & 0 \\ 0 & 0 & 0 & 1 \end{bmatrix}\begin{bmatrix}1\\0\\0\\1\end{bmatrix} = \begin{bmatrix}\frac{\sqrt{2}}{2}\\0\\-\frac{\sqrt{2}}{2}\\1\end{bmatrix}$$

Theoretically, then, we can completely describe the location and attitude of the robot, through the point *CP*, by a matrix product. The order of multiplication of these matrices is, of course, important, since in general they do not commute. (For example, you might wish to experiment with a model to show that a yaw of $\pi/4$ followed by a pitch of $\pi/4$ will give an attitude different from a pitch of $\pi/4$ followed by a yaw of $\pi/4$.) However, suppose we agree that the order of operations in modulating the robot shall be first translations, then pitch, yaw, and roll in that order.

Example 24 Suppose we wish to translate the robot CP at (x, y, z) to a new position $(x + 1, y - 1, z + 2)$ and then subject the robot to a pitch, yaw, and roll of 30°. The matrices involved would be:

$$\mathbf{T} = \begin{bmatrix} 1 & 0 & 0 & 1 \\ 0 & 1 & 0 & -1 \\ 0 & 0 & 1 & 2 \\ 0 & 0 & 0 & 1 \end{bmatrix}$$

$$\mathbf{Y}_{\pi/6} = \tfrac{1}{2}\begin{bmatrix} \sqrt{3} & -1 & 0 & 0 \\ 1 & \sqrt{3} & 0 & 0 \\ 0 & 0 & 2 & 0 \\ 0 & 0 & 0 & 2 \end{bmatrix}, \qquad \mathbf{P}_{\pi/6} = \tfrac{1}{2}\begin{bmatrix} \sqrt{3} & 0 & 1 & 0 \\ 0 & 2 & 0 & 0 \\ -1 & 0 & \sqrt{3} & 0 \\ 0 & 0 & 0 & 2 \end{bmatrix}$$

and

$$\mathbf{R}_{\pi/6} = \tfrac{1}{2}\begin{bmatrix} 2 & 0 & 0 & 0 \\ 0 & \sqrt{3} & -1 & 0 \\ 0 & 1 & \sqrt{3} & 0 \\ 0 & 0 & 0 & 2 \end{bmatrix}$$

Then the new location of the point $\begin{bmatrix} 1 \\ 0 \\ 0 \\ 1 \end{bmatrix}$ (with respect to the current axis system XCP, YCP, ZCP) would be given by the matrix products

$$\mathbf{R}_{\pi/6}\mathbf{Y}_{\pi/6}\mathbf{P}_{\pi/6}\mathbf{T}\begin{bmatrix} 1 \\ 0 \\ 0 \\ 1 \end{bmatrix} = \begin{bmatrix} 2 + \frac{1}{2}\sqrt{3} \\ \frac{1}{2} - \frac{1}{4}\sqrt{3} \\ \frac{1}{4} - \frac{1}{2}\sqrt{3} \\ 1 \end{bmatrix}$$

■

The Scrambler Transformation

The idea of sending messages that cannot be read except by those who know a coding secret is universally appealing, whether one looks at the exercise as a puzzle, as a part of "intelligence" and intrigue, or simply as a mundane process of transmitting restricted information. Nations have gone to great lengths to develop effective coding procedures. Equally important are efforts to decipher other governments' codes. For example, the successful cracking of a German code during World War II by British intelligence was so important and secret that it was code-named "Ultra." Some of the best mathematical talent Britain could summon were asked to work on this project, including the famous A. M. Turing. In this section, we show how linear algebra can be used in coding procedures.

First, it is necessary to devise a way to set up a message so it fits into a vector space. As a first example, let us choose R^3 as the space in which to work. Our messages must be put in the form of ordered triples of real numbers. To do this, letters must correspond to numbers in some way. There are many ways to do this, of course, but the most convenient method would be to use a standard numbering scheme that has been adopted by the computer industry: the ASCII[1] alphabetic codes. We will use only a portion of the codes that represent the 26 letters of our alphabet. We will rarely encounter a problem because we lack punctuation marks or numerals since punctuation can be inferred from context and numerals can be written out. The codes are:

A	B	C	D	E	F	G	H	I	J	K	L	M
65	66	67	68	69	70	71	72	73	74	75	76	77
N	O	P	Q	R	S	T	U	V	W	X	Y	Z
78	79	80	81	82	83	84	85	86	87	88	89	90

A message becomes a string of integers that then can be grouped into ordered triples. One or two X's may be added to the last triple as needed.

Example 25 The phrase

IT CAN BE DONE

translates into numbers from the ASCII code as

73 84 67 65 78 66 69 68 79 78 69

that is,

$$(73, 84, 67), \quad (65, 78, 66), \quad (69, 68, 79), \quad (78, 69, 88)$$

A code for X is added to complete the last triple. The message is now a set of four vectors in R^3. ■

With the message represented as a set of vectors in R^3, we need a transformation that will put the message into an unreadable form, but one that can be deciphered only by the receiver who has the coding key. To accomplish this without confusion, the image of the message must have a unique preimage. One way to make this happen is to use a transformation $\mathbf{Y} = \mathbf{AX}$ for which an inverse transformation exists. A little extra care is needed here to make certain that the preimage will be a set of vectors with integer entries. If $\mathbf{A}$ is a matrix with integer entries and so is

[1]ASCII = American Standard Code for Information Interchange.

a vector $\mathbf{X}$, then $\mathbf{AX}$ will also have integer entries. However, $\mathbf{A}^{-1}$ may not be a matrix with integer entries. To ensure that it is, we may select matrices $\mathbf{A}$ so that $\det \mathbf{A} = \pm 1$.

Example 26 Let

$$\mathbf{A} = \begin{bmatrix} 1 & 1 & 1 \\ -1 & 0 & 1 \\ 0 & 1 & 1 \end{bmatrix}$$

Then $\det \mathbf{A} = -1$, and

$$\mathbf{A}^{-1} = \begin{bmatrix} 1 & 0 & -1 \\ -1 & -1 & 2 \\ 1 & 1 & -1 \end{bmatrix}$$

The elements in R^3 are transformed into elements in R^3 by the transformation defined by $T(\mathbf{X}) = \mathbf{AX}$. In particular, we find that the images of the vectors in Example 23 are

$$\mathbf{A}\begin{bmatrix} 73 \\ 84 \\ 67 \end{bmatrix} = \begin{bmatrix} 224 \\ -6 \\ 151 \end{bmatrix}, \quad \mathbf{A}\begin{bmatrix} 65 \\ 78 \\ 66 \end{bmatrix} = \begin{bmatrix} 209 \\ 1 \\ 144 \end{bmatrix}, \quad \mathbf{A}\begin{bmatrix} 69 \\ 68 \\ 79 \end{bmatrix} = \begin{bmatrix} 216 \\ 10 \\ 147 \end{bmatrix}, \quad \mathbf{A}\begin{bmatrix} 78 \\ 69 \\ 88 \end{bmatrix} = \begin{bmatrix} 235 \\ 10 \\ 157 \end{bmatrix}$$

A more efficient way to do this is to write the four vectors that constitute the message as the four columns of a matrix $\mathbf{B}$. Then if $\mathbf{AB} = \mathbf{C}$, the matrix $\mathbf{C}$ has as columns the four vectors that are the images of the columns of $\mathbf{A}$:

$$\mathbf{AB} = \begin{bmatrix} 224 & 209 & 216 & 235 \\ -6 & 1 & 10 & 10 \\ 151 & 144 & 147 & 157 \end{bmatrix}$$

The message can now be sent in numerical form, but it will look more authentic if the vectors are translated back into letters. In doing so, a difficulty can arise if the image of the message contains integers outside the range 65–90. The entry 224, for instance, is not one of the numbers to which symbols have been assigned.

This problem can be overcome by deciding that for our purposes two integers are equivalent if they differ by a multiple of 26, the total number of symbols we are using. Furthermore, every integer is equivalent to exactly one integer in the range 65–90. For example, 224 is equivalent to 68 and -6 is equivalent to 72. When each integer in our transformed message is replaced by an equivalent number in the set $\{65, 66, 67, \ldots, 90\}$, the matrix $\mathbf{C} = \mathbf{AB}$ becomes

$$\mathbf{C}' = \begin{bmatrix} 68 & 79 & 86 & 79 \\ 72 & 79 & 88 & 88 \\ 73 & 66 & 69 & 79 \end{bmatrix}$$

This can now be written in letters as DHIOOBVXEOXO. ■

Why is this a more effective coding of the message than the familiar letter replacement code (where each letter is replaced by some other letter, which in effect scrambles the alphabet)? The answer lies in known facts about the frequency of use of the letters in the English language. For example, it is known that in a book containing several thousand words, the letter E will appear most frequently. Thus, in trying to crack a letter replacement code, one would find the letter that appears most often and assume it stood for E. But note in the above message there are two X's and four O's. The transformation used here maps D to X and E to X. What about the preimages of the four O's?

The message in coded form is sent to the receiver. With the key, the message can now be decoded. How is this done? First, the letters in the received message are converted to their integer equivalents from the set $\{65, 66, \dots, 90\}$. These numbers are then grouped in three's and placed in columns in order to form a matrix $\mathbf{C}'$. To decode the message, we multiply $\mathbf{C}'$ by $\mathbf{A}^{-1}$ (taking care to multiply in the order $\mathbf{A}^{-1}\mathbf{C}'$, since $\mathbf{A}^{-1}\mathbf{C}' = \mathbf{A}^{-1}\mathbf{A}\mathbf{C} = \mathbf{C}$). This will transform $\mathbf{C}'$ to the preimage matrix $\mathbf{B}$.

Example 27 Decipher the message DHIOOBVXEOXO using $\mathbf{A}^{-1}$ in Example 26. First, change the letters to their integer form:

$$68 \quad 72 \quad 73 \quad 79 \quad 79 \quad 66 \quad 86 \quad 88 \quad 69 \quad 79 \quad 88 \quad 79$$

List these numbers in the columns of a three-row matrix; then premultiply by $\mathbf{A}^{-1}$. We get:

$$\mathbf{A}^{-1}\begin{bmatrix} 68 & 79 & 86 & 79 \\ 72 & 79 & 88 & 88 \\ 73 & 66 & 69 & 79 \end{bmatrix} = \begin{bmatrix} -5 & 13 & 17 & 0 \\ 6 & -26 & -36 & -9 \\ 67 & 92 & 105 & 88 \end{bmatrix}$$

When the entries in this product are replaced with their equivalent values in the range 65–90, we obtain the matrix

$$\begin{bmatrix} 73 & 65 & 69 & 78 \\ 84 & 78 & 68 & 69 \\ 67 & 66 & 79 & 88 \end{bmatrix}$$

which gives the original message ITCANBEDONE.

Our ciphering process does not contain a technique for separating the words of the message. We could do this by inserting the triple XYZ (or some other constant sequence of letters) between all words. ■

Example 28 The following message is received: HUGPFQCJEZZBIQOVMWKD. Without the key matrix or even a hint that it is a matrix cipher, decoding this message would be difficult indeed. Suppose we know the coding matrix **A**:

$$\mathbf{A} = \begin{bmatrix} 1 & 2 & -1 & 3 \\ -1 & -1 & 1 & 2 \\ 1 & 2 & 0 & 7 \\ 0 & 1 & 1 & 10 \end{bmatrix} \quad \text{and} \quad \mathbf{A}^{-1} = \begin{bmatrix} -2 & -5 & -2 & 3 \\ 1 & 6 & 5 & -5 \\ -1 & 4 & 5 & -4 \\ 0 & -1 & -1 & 1 \end{bmatrix}$$

We now know that the range of the message is in R^4, and therefore that the message should be divided into 4-tuples. (Without this, we couldn't even have begun!) When the letters are given number equivalents and the resulting set is expressed as the columns of a $4 \times n$ matrix, we obtain

$$\mathbf{C}' = \begin{bmatrix} 72 & 70 & 69 & 73 & 77 \\ 85 & 81 & 90 & 81 & 87 \\ 71 & 67 & 90 & 79 & 75 \\ 80 & 74 & 66 & 86 & 68 \end{bmatrix}$$

Now, find the preimage **C** of $\mathbf{C}'$ by calculating $\mathbf{A}^{-1}\mathbf{C}'$:

$$\mathbf{C} = \begin{bmatrix} -471 & -457 & -520 & -451 & -535 \\ 537 & 521 & 729 & 524 & 634 \\ 303 & 293 & 477 & 302 & 374 \\ -76 & -74 & -114 & -74 & -94 \end{bmatrix}$$

When the entries of $\mathbf{A}^{-1}\mathbf{C}'$ are changed to equivalent integers in the range $65, 66, \ldots, 90$, the uncoded, preimage matrix becomes

$$\begin{bmatrix} 75 & 89 & 80 & 69 & 89 \\ 69 & 79 & 79 & 82 & 88 \\ 69 & 85 & 87 & 68 & 88 \\ 80 & 82 & 68 & 82 & 88 \end{bmatrix}$$

All that remains is to replace the numbers by the letters assigned to them. ■

Computers have played an important role in the past several decades in message encryption. Even though a matrix coding scheme is challenging to break, modern high-speed computers can sample coded text and suggest methods of breaking the code. To ensure enhanced security of matrix codes used to encrypt long messages, many matrices of varying size can be used to encode the message. In fact, some of the exercises invite you to try to design a computer program to implement the matrix coding method. In any event, by now you should be convinced that coding procedures are far from elementary. However, a rather simple type of coding method involves defining a linear transformation $T(\mathbf{X}) = \mathbf{AX}$ from R^n to R^n, where **A** is an $n \times n$ matrix with determinant ± 1. The transformation T^{-1} then uncodes the coded message.

EXERCISES 5.4

1. Use the method of least squares to find the straight line that best fits the set of points (0, 4), (1, 2), (2, 2), and (3, 1).

2. Find the best line to fit the set of points (0, 4), (1, 2), (2, 3), (3, 1), and (−1, 4).

3. Use the method of least squares to find the second-degree polynomial that best fits the points of Problem 1. Compare the given data points with the corresponding points calculated from the polynomial.

4. Find the second-degree polynomial that best fits the points in Problem 2.

5. Find the second-degree polynomial that best fits the points (0, 1), (1, 2), and (−1, 4). Compare your work with Example 12.

6. State University's enrollment figures over the years 1976–1980 are (in thousands)

Year	**Enrollment**
1976	19.0
1977	20.5
1978	20.8
1979	21.3
1980	22.1

What line best fits these figures? (Assume $x = 0$ at 1976.) If the linear increase continues at the same rate, in what year will the enrollment surpass 25,000?

7. Calculate the product

$$\begin{bmatrix} 1 & 1 & 1 \\ x_1 & x_2 & x_3 \end{bmatrix} \begin{bmatrix} 1 & x_1 \\ 1 & x_2 \\ 1 & x_3 \end{bmatrix}$$

and show that its determinant is $(x_1 - x_2)^2 + (x_1 - x_3)^2 + (x_2 - x_3)^2$.

8. Let

$$\mathbf{A} = \begin{bmatrix} 1 & 1 & 1 & 1 \\ x_1 & x_2 & x_3 & x_4 \end{bmatrix}$$

Show that

$$\det \mathbf{A}\mathbf{A}^T = (x_1 - x_2)^2 + (x_1 - x_3)^2 + (x_1 - x_4)^2 + (x_2 - x_3)^2 + (x_2 - x_4)^2 + (x_3 - x_4)^2$$

9. Show that if

$$\mathbf{A} = \begin{bmatrix} 1 & 1 & 1 & \cdots & 1 \\ x_1 & x_2 & x_3 & & x_n \end{bmatrix}$$

then

$$\det \mathbf{A}\mathbf{A}^T = \sum (x_i - x_j)^2, \quad i, j = 1, 2, \ldots, n,\ i < j$$

10. Let T be the transformation from P_2 to R^4 such that $T(p) = (p(x_1), p(x_2), p(x_3), p(x_4))$. In this case the matrix of T is

$$\mathbf{A} = \begin{bmatrix} 1 & x_1 & x_1^2 \\ 1 & x_2 & x_2^2 \\ 1 & x_3 & x_3^2 \\ 1 & x_4 & x_4^2 \end{bmatrix}$$

Show that

$$\det \mathbf{A}^T\mathbf{A} = (\det \mathbf{A}_{123})^2 + (\det \mathbf{A}_{134})^2 + (\det \mathbf{A}_{124})^2 + (\det \mathbf{A}_{234})^2$$

where

$$\mathbf{A}_{ijk} = \begin{bmatrix} 1 & 1 & 1 \\ x_i & x_j & x_k \\ x_i^2 & x_j^2 & x_k^2 \end{bmatrix}$$

11. Find the location of the point (1, 0, 0) in the XCP, YCP, ZCP-axis system when subjected first to a pitch of 45° and then a roll of 45°. Find the location of the same point when subjected first to a roll of 45° and then a pitch of 45°. Compare your results.

12. Show, in general, that for an arbitrary pitch angle A and yaw angle B the matrices $\mathbf{Y}_B$ and $\mathbf{P}_A$ do not commute.

13. The following problem illustrates in a simple setting the effect of interchanging the order of the fundamental robotics operations: translation, yaw, pitch, and roll. In each case find the final location of the point (1, 0, 0) using matrices. Then examine the operation in detail geometrically. Notice that the operations chosen make changes only in the xy plane.

a. A yaw of 45° is followed by a translation of three units in the x-direction and two units in the y-direction.

b. A translation of three units in the x-direction and two units in the y-direction is followed by a yaw of 45°.

14. a. Show that after a sequence of yaw, roll, and pitch transformations in any order the new position of the coordinate axes is an orthonormal set. (*Hint:* Consider orthogonal matrices.)

b. Will the final position of the coordinate axes be the same if the order of the transformations is changed? Prove your answer.

15. Design a computer program in a language of your choice so that a message may be entered at the computer keyboard and either coded or decoded using the matrix coding method. Allow for spaces to separate words in the message.

16. Use the program of Problem 15 and the matrix **A** of Example 28 to code the message: WE HOLD THESE TRUTHS TO BE SELF-EVIDENT, THAT ALL MEN ARE CREATED EQUAL. Use the standard ASCII codes with spaces between words (but no other punctuation allowed).

17. Use the program of Problem 15 to decode the message

SPMLVDOD AMNPZQKMNIJ
VQHPPQZXDEUJKYHHKMNI
JVWFFUSUUXOWZU

You are given that the coding matrix was

$$\mathbf{A} = \begin{bmatrix} -1 & 2 & 4 \\ 2 & -1 & -4 \\ 1 & 0 & -1 \end{bmatrix}$$

18. (*Computer Project*) The matrix coding method developed in this section depends strongly on the availability of matrices of arbitrary size with determinant ± 1. Describe a method for generating such matrices. Construct a computer program to carry out your design.

19. Find a particular solution for each of the following equations.

a. $y'' + y' - 2y = 2x$
b. $y'' + y' - 2y = 2e^x + x$
c. $y'' + y = 3\sin 2x + x\cos 2x$
d. $y'' + 4y = 3\sin 2x + x\cos 2x$

20. Find a particular solution for each of the following equations.

a. $y'' + 4y = x^2 + 3e^x$
b. $y'' + 2y' = 3 + 4\sin 2x$
c. $y'' - 9y = x^2e^{3x}$
d. $y'' - 2y' + y = xe^x + 4$

6 Diagonalization

6.1 Representation of a Linear Transformation by a Diagonal Matrix

In Chapter 5 we saw that a linear transformation T from an n-dimensional vector space S to itself can be written in the form $[T(\mathbf{x})]_U = \mathbf{A}[\mathbf{x}]_U$, where U is a basis for S. The matrix $\mathbf{A}$ depends on the basis U; in fact, the columns of $\mathbf{A}$ are coordinates of $T(\mathbf{u}_1), T(\mathbf{u}_2), \ldots, T(\mathbf{u}_n)$ with respect to U (Theorem 3, Chapter 5). If the basis is changed from U to V, the matrix of T is $\mathbf{B} = \mathbf{P}^{-1}\mathbf{AP}$, where $\mathbf{P}$ is the change-of-basis matrix $[\mathbf{x}]_U = \mathbf{P}[\mathbf{x}]_V$ (Section 5.3). Since a diagonal matrix has many desirable properties, we look for a diagonal matrix representation of T.

Theorem 1 Let S be an n-dimensional vector space, $U = \{\mathbf{u}_1, \mathbf{u}_2, \ldots, \mathbf{u}_n\}$ a basis for S, and T a linear transformation from S to S. The matrix of T relative to U is diagonal if and only if there exist scalars $\lambda_1, \lambda_2, \ldots, \lambda_n$ such that $T(\mathbf{u}_i) = \lambda_i \mathbf{u}_i$, $i = 1, 2, \ldots, n$.

Proof A matrix is diagonal if and only if its ith column is a multiple of the ith standard vector $\mathbf{e}_i$, for each $i = 1, 2, \ldots, n$. The ith column of $\mathbf{A}$ is $[T(\mathbf{u}_i)]_U$. The theorem follows from the fact that $[T(\mathbf{u}_i)]_U = \lambda_i \mathbf{E}_i$ if and only if $T(\mathbf{u}_i) = \lambda_i \mathbf{u}_i$. □

According to Theorem 1, the basis we should use is related to T by the property $T(\mathbf{x}) = \lambda\mathbf{x}$. If the matrix of T relative to the basis U is $\mathbf{A}$, then $T(\mathbf{x}) = \lambda\mathbf{x}$ implies $\mathbf{A}[\mathbf{x}]_U = \lambda[\mathbf{x}]_U$. This is an equation of the form $\mathbf{AY} = \lambda\mathbf{Y}$, or $(\mathbf{A} - \lambda\mathbf{I})\mathbf{Y} = \mathbf{0}$. Nontrivial solutions exist if λ is an eigenvalue of $\mathbf{A}$ (Theorem 16, Chapter 3). The corresponding nontrivial $\mathbf{Y}$ is an eigenvector of $\mathbf{A}$. Example 1 illustrates the use of eigenvectors as a basis.

Example 1 Let T be a linear transformation from R^2 to R^2. Let $U = \{\mathbf{u}_1, \mathbf{u}_2\}$ be a basis for R^2, and let $\mathbf{A} = \begin{bmatrix} 1 & 3 \\ 2 & 2 \end{bmatrix}$ be the matrix of T relative to U. Find a basis that diagonalizes T.

Solution The eigenvalues of **A** are -1 and 4. An eigenvector corresponding to -1 is $(3, -2)$, and an eigenvector corresponding to 4 is $(1, 1)$. For the transformation T, we have $T(\mathbf{x}) = -\mathbf{x}$ if $[\mathbf{x}]_U = \begin{bmatrix} 3 \\ -2 \end{bmatrix}$, that is, if $\mathbf{x} = 3\mathbf{u}_1 - 2\mathbf{u}_2$. Also, $T(\mathbf{x}) = 4\mathbf{x}$ if $[\mathbf{x}]_U = \begin{bmatrix} 1 \\ 1 \end{bmatrix}$, that is, $\mathbf{x} = \mathbf{u}_1 + \mathbf{u}_2$.

Let $\mathbf{v}_1 = 3\mathbf{u}_1 - 2\mathbf{u}_2$, $\mathbf{v}_2 = \mathbf{u}_1 + \mathbf{u}_2$, and $V = \{\mathbf{v}_1, \mathbf{v}_2\}$. Write the matrix of T relative to the basis V. The columns of this matrix are $[T(\mathbf{v}_1)]_V$ and $[T(\mathbf{v}_2)]_V$. Since $T(\mathbf{v}_1) = -\mathbf{v}_1$ and $T(\mathbf{v}_2) = 4\mathbf{v}_2$, $[T(\mathbf{v}_1)]_V = \begin{bmatrix} -1 \\ 0 \end{bmatrix}$ and $[T(\mathbf{v}_2)]_V = \begin{bmatrix} 0 \\ 4 \end{bmatrix}$. The matrix of T relative to this basis is the diagonal matrix $\begin{bmatrix} -1 & 0 \\ 0 & 4 \end{bmatrix}$. ■

Theorem 8, Chapter 5, assures us that the matrix of T relative to the basis U is similar to the matrix of T relative to V for any two bases U and V. Similar matrices have the same eigenvalues (Theorem 18, Chapter 3). Thus, the matrix corresponding to a linear transformation T has the same eigenvalues no matter what basis is used. It makes sense, then, to call these eigenvalues the eigenvalues of the transformation T.

Definition 1

Eigenvalues
Eigenvectors

Let T be a linear transformation from a vector space S to itself. The **eigenvalues of T** are the scalars λ for which $T(\mathbf{x}) = \lambda\mathbf{x}$ has a nontrivial solution. For a particular eigenvalue λ, the **eigenvectors of T corresponding to** λ are the nonzero vectors $\mathbf{x}$ such that $T(\mathbf{x}) = \lambda\mathbf{x}$.

Although the eigenvalues and eigenvectors of T are unchanged by a change of basis, we must keep in mind that when we use a particular matrix representation of T to obtain its eigenvectors, this gives us the coordinates of the eigenvectors relative to the basis used in this representation. Theorem 2 states this formally.

Theorem 2 If T has the representation $[T(\mathbf{x})]_U = \mathbf{A}[\mathbf{x}]_U$, the eigenvalues of T are the eigenvalues of **A**. If λ is an eigenvalue of **A**, a corresponding eigenvector $[\mathbf{x}]_U$ gives the coordinate column relative to the basis U of an eigenvector of T. □

The set of all $\mathbf{x}$ such that $T(\mathbf{x}) = \lambda\mathbf{x}$—that is, the set of $\mathbf{x}$ such that $(T - \lambda I)(\mathbf{x}) = \mathbf{0}$—is the preimage of $\mathbf{0}$ under the transformation $T - \lambda I$. This set is a subspace of the domain, the null space of $T - \lambda I$ (Section 5.2). This subspace is called the eigenspace of T corresponding to λ.

If **A** is a matrix of T, then $\mathbf{A} - \lambda\mathbf{I}$ is the corresponding matrix of $T - \lambda I$. The vectors **X** such that $(\mathbf{A} - \lambda\mathbf{I})\mathbf{X} = \mathbf{0}$ form a subspace of R^n—namely, the null space of the matrix $\mathbf{A} - \lambda\mathbf{I}$ (Section 4.4). This subspace of R^n is called the eigenspace of **A** corresponding to λ.

Eigenspace of T

Definition 2

Let T be a linear transformation from S to S, and let λ be an eigenvalue of T. The set of vectors such that $T(\mathbf{x}) = \lambda\mathbf{x}$ is called the **eigenspace of T** corresponding to λ. Every nonzero vector in this space is an eigenvector of T corresponding to λ.

Eigenspace of A

Definition 3

Let $\mathbf{A}$ be an $n \times n$ matrix and λ an eigenvalue of $\mathbf{A}$. The set of all $\mathbf{X}$ such that $(\mathbf{A} - \lambda\mathbf{I})\mathbf{X} = \mathbf{0}$ is a subspace of R^n called the **eigenspace of A** corresponding to λ. Every nonzero n-tuple in this space is an eigenvector of $\mathbf{A}$ corresponding to λ.

Example 2 gives a picture of eigenspaces and eigenvectors in a simple geometric setting.

Example 2 Let T be the transformation from R^2 to R^2 defined by reflection in the line L with equation $x_1 = x_2$. (See Figure 6.1.)

Geometrically, if $\mathbf{x} = OP$, $T(\mathbf{x}) = OQ$, where Q is obtained by drawing PM perpendicular to the line L and extending it so that $PM = MQ$. This implies that triangles OPR and QOS are congruent so that $|OR| = |QS|$ and $|PR| = |OS|$. If the coordinates of P are (x_1, x_2), the coordinates of Q are (x_2, x_1).

The matrix of T relative to the standard basis is easy to obtain since $T(\mathbf{e}_1) = \mathbf{e}_2$ and $T(\mathbf{e}_2) = \mathbf{e}_1$. Thus, T is given by

$$T(\mathbf{X}) = \mathbf{AX}, \qquad \text{where } \mathbf{A} = \begin{bmatrix} 0 & 1 \\ 1 & 0 \end{bmatrix}$$

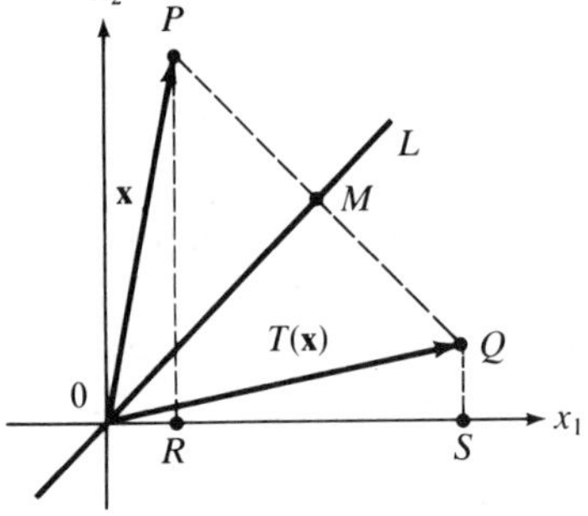

FIGURE 6.1

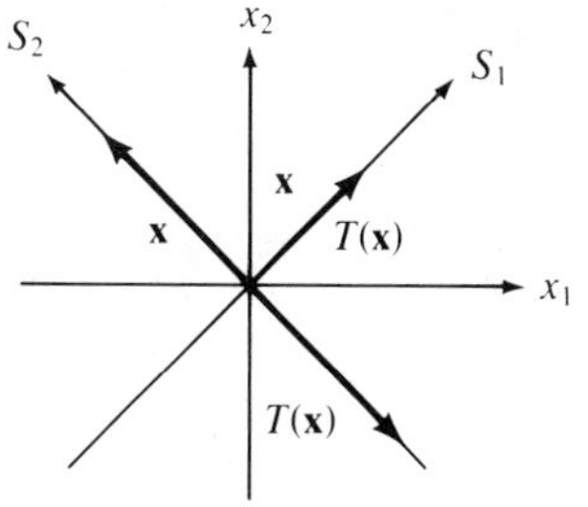

FIGURE 6.2

The eigenvalues of **A** are found from the equation $\det\begin{bmatrix} -\lambda & 1 \\ 1 & -\lambda \end{bmatrix} = 0$, that is, $\lambda^2 - 1 = 0$. The eigenvalues are ± 1.

If $\lambda = 1$, the corresponding eigenspace, S_1, is the solution set of

$$\begin{bmatrix} -1 & 1 \\ 1 & -1 \end{bmatrix}\mathbf{X} = \mathbf{0}$$

that is, $\{k(1, 1), k \text{ a real number}\}$. (See Figure 6.2.)

If $\lambda = -1$, the corresponding eigenspace, S_2, is the solution set of

$$\begin{bmatrix} 1 & 1 \\ 1 & 1 \end{bmatrix}\mathbf{X} = \mathbf{0}$$

that is, $\{k(1, -1), k \text{ a real number}\}$.

Geometrically, S_1 is the one-dimensional subspace consisting of the line L itself; $T(\mathbf{x}) = \mathbf{x}$ for any vector $\mathbf{x}$ in the space S_1. Any nonzero vector in this space is an eigenvector of T.

The eigenspace S_2 consists of the line through the origin with equation $x_2 = -x_1$; $T(\mathbf{x}) = -\mathbf{x}$ for any vector $\mathbf{x}$ on this line. ■

We get a diagonal representation of T by using the eigenvectors T as a basis for the domain. To settle the question of whether T has a diagonal representation, we must return to the question that arose first in Section 3.5: "What can we say about the eigenvalues and eigenvectors of a matrix **A**?"

Suppose **A** is an $n \times n$ matrix. The eigenvalues of **A** are the roots of the nth-degree polynomial

$$\lambda^n - s_1\lambda^{n-1} + s_2\lambda^{n-2} - \cdots + (-1)^n s_n$$

According to the Fundamental Theorem of Algebra, such a polynomial has n roots. These n roots may be real or imaginary numbers, and repeated roots must be counted as often as they occur. If the coefficients of the polynomial are real, imaginary roots must occur in pairs $a + bi$ and $a - bi$. Example 3 illustrates each of these possibilities.

Example 3

a. $\mathbf{A} = \begin{bmatrix} 1 & 4 & 4 \\ 0 & 1 & 0 \\ -1 & 4 & 1 \end{bmatrix}$ $\quad \det(\mathbf{A} - \lambda\mathbf{I}) = \det\begin{bmatrix} 1-\lambda & 4 & 4 \\ 0 & 1-\lambda & 0 \\ -1 & 4 & 1-\lambda \end{bmatrix}$

$$= (1 - \lambda)(5 - 2\lambda + \lambda^2)$$

The three eigenvalues are 1, $1 + 2i$, $1 - 2i$. There is only one real eigenvalue.

b. $\mathbf{A} = \begin{bmatrix} 1 & 4 & -1 \\ 0 & 1 & 0 \\ 1 & 4 & 3 \end{bmatrix}$ $\quad \det(\mathbf{A} - \lambda\mathbf{I}) = \det\begin{bmatrix} 1-\lambda & 4 & -1 \\ 0 & 1-\lambda & 0 \\ 1 & 4 & 3-\lambda \end{bmatrix}$

$$= (1 - \lambda)(4 - 4\lambda + \lambda^2)$$
$$= (1 - \lambda)(2 - \lambda)^2$$

There are three eigenvalues: 1, 2, 2. There are two *distinct* eigenvalues: 1 and 2.

c. $\mathbf{A} = \begin{bmatrix} 5 & 4 & 3 \\ 0 & 1 & 0 \\ -1 & 4 & 1 \end{bmatrix}$ $\quad \det(\mathbf{A} - \lambda\mathbf{I}) = \det\begin{bmatrix} 5-\lambda & 4 & 3 \\ 0 & 1-\lambda & 0 \\ -1 & 4 & 1-\lambda \end{bmatrix}$

$$= (1 - \lambda)(8 - 6\lambda + \lambda^2)$$
$$= (1 - \lambda)(4 - \lambda)(2 - \lambda)$$

There are three distinct real eigenvalues: 1, 2, 4. ■

In the study of linear algebra over the complex field—that is, the field in which scalars are assumed to be any complex numbers—the use of imaginary eigenvalues would present no problem. We are confining ourselves to the study of linear algebra over the real numbers, so we require that our eigenvalues be real. Eigenvalues in general, do *not* turn out to be integers. For the most part our examples involve integers or, at worst, simple fractions, so that the simplicity of the theory is not lost in complicated arithmetic. As we have mentioned throughout this book, you should use available computer software to aid you in more realistic problems, especially those in the applications sections.

Recall:

1. The matrix **A** is similar to a diagonal matrix if and only if there is a nonsingular matrix **C** whose columns are eigenvectors of **A**. (Theorem 19, Chapter 3.)
2. An $n \times n$ matrix **C** is nonsingular if and only if its columns are linearly independent (Chapter 3, Theorem 15).
3. A linearly independent set of n vectors in R^n forms a basis for R^n (Exercises 4.3, Problem 17).

In order to have a diagonal representation of the linear transformation T, what is needed is a basis for R^n consisting of eigenvectors.

If λ_0 is an eigenvalue of **A**, $\det(\mathbf{A} - \lambda_0\mathbf{I}) = 0$, and $\mathbf{A} - \lambda_0\mathbf{I}$ has rank less than or equal to $n - 1$. The null space of $\mathbf{A} - \lambda_0\mathbf{I}$ has dimension greater than or equal to 1 (Theorem 10, Section 4.4). The dimension of the eigenspace of **A** corresponding to λ_0 determines the maximum number of eigenvectors in a linearly independent set from that space. Example 4 illustrates a set of eigenvectors corresponding to distinct eigenvalues.

Example 4 Let T be the transformation from R^3 to R^3 given by $T(\mathbf{X}) = \mathbf{AX}$, where

$$\mathbf{A} = \begin{bmatrix} 3 & -1 & -1 \\ -2 & 3 & 2 \\ 4 & -1 & -2 \end{bmatrix}$$

The characteristic equation of $\mathbf{A}$ is $\lambda^3 - 4\lambda^2 + \lambda + 6 = 0$, so the eigenvalues of T (and of $\mathbf{A}$) are $2, 3$, and -1. Next we need a basis for each eigenspace.

Let $\lambda = 2$. The eigenspace corresponding to 2 is the null space of $\mathbf{A} - 2\mathbf{I}$. Since

$$\mathbf{A} - 2\mathbf{I} = \begin{bmatrix} 1 & -1 & -1 \\ -2 & 1 & 2 \\ 4 & -1 & -4 \end{bmatrix} \Leftrightarrow \begin{bmatrix} 1 & 0 & -1 \\ 0 & 1 & 0 \\ 0 & 0 & 0 \end{bmatrix}$$

its null space has dimension $3 - 2 = 1$. A basis for this space is $\mathbf{u}_1 = (1, 0, 1)$.

Let $\lambda = 3$.

$$\mathbf{A} - 3\mathbf{I} = \begin{bmatrix} 0 & -1 & -1 \\ -2 & 0 & 2 \\ 4 & -1 & -5 \end{bmatrix} \Leftrightarrow \begin{bmatrix} 1 & 0 & -1 \\ 0 & 1 & 1 \\ 0 & 0 & 0 \end{bmatrix}$$

Again the null space has dimension 1, and a basis is $\mathbf{u}_2 = (1, -1, 1)$.

Let $\lambda = -1$.

$$\mathbf{A} + \mathbf{I} = \begin{bmatrix} 4 & -1 & -1 \\ -2 & 4 & 2 \\ 4 & -1 & -1 \end{bmatrix} \Leftrightarrow \begin{bmatrix} 1 & 0 & -\frac{1}{7} \\ 0 & 1 & \frac{3}{7} \\ 0 & 0 & 0 \end{bmatrix}$$

The null space has dimension 1 and a basis is $\mathbf{u}_3 = (1, -3, 7)$. Since

$$\det \begin{bmatrix} 1 & 1 & 1 \\ 0 & -1 & -3 \\ 1 & 1 & 7 \end{bmatrix} = -6 \neq 0$$

the set $U = \{\mathbf{u}_1, \mathbf{u}_2, \mathbf{u}_3\}$ is linearly independent and forms a basis for R^3. Since $T(\mathbf{u}_1) = 2\mathbf{u}_1$, $T(\mathbf{u}_2) = 3\mathbf{u}_2$, and $T(\mathbf{u}_3) = -\mathbf{u}_3$, the matrix of T relative to U is

$$\begin{bmatrix} 2 & 0 & 0 \\ 0 & 3 & 0 \\ 0 & 0 & -1 \end{bmatrix}$$

■

It is easy to check in a numerical case whether a set of vectors is linearly independent. We have already seen (Theorem 20, Chapter 3) that a set of eigenvectors, no two from the same eigenspace, is a linearly independent set. We repeat this theorem here.

Theorem 3 Let $\mathbf{A}$ be an $n \times n$ matrix, $\lambda_1, \lambda_2, \ldots, \lambda_k$ distinct eigenvalues of $\mathbf{A}$, and $\mathbf{u}_1, \mathbf{u}_2, \ldots, \mathbf{u}_k$ eigenvectors of $\mathbf{A}$ corresponding to $\lambda_1, \lambda_2, \ldots, \lambda_k$. The set $\{\mathbf{u}_1, \mathbf{u}_2, \ldots, \mathbf{u}_k\}$ is linearly independent.

The proof of this theorem for the case $n = 3$ was given in Section 3.5. The proof in the general case follows the same technique. The steps in this proof are outlined in Problem 25. □

Theorem 3 can be extended (Problems 26, 27, 28) to show that if $\lambda_1, \lambda_2, \ldots, \lambda_k$ is a set of distinct eigenvalues and S_i is a linearly independent set of eigenvectors corresponding to λ_i, then the set $S_1 \cup S_2 \cup \cdots \cup S_k$ is a linearly independent set.

If the eigenvalues of $\mathbf{A}$ are real but not distinct, it may or may not be possible to find a basis for R^n consisting of eigenvectors; that is, the matrix $\mathbf{A}$ may or may not be similar to a diagonal matrix. Example 5 illustrates that both situations can occur.

Example 5

a.

$$\mathbf{A} = \begin{bmatrix} 1 & 3 & 0 \\ 0 & 1 & 0 \\ 0 & 0 & 2 \end{bmatrix}$$

Eigenvalues 1, 1, 2

$$\mathbf{A} - 2\mathbf{I} = \begin{bmatrix} -1 & 3 & 0 \\ 0 & -1 & 0 \\ 0 & 0 & 0 \end{bmatrix}$$

Eigenspace corresponding to 2 has dimension 1.

$$\mathbf{A} - \mathbf{I} = \begin{bmatrix} 0 & 3 & 0 \\ 0 & 0 & 0 \\ 0 & 0 & 1 \end{bmatrix}$$

Eigenspace corresponding to 1 has dimension 1.

It is not possible to choose two linearly independent vectors from a space of dimension 1. Thus, it is not possible to find a set of three eigenvectors that is linearly independent. This matrix is not similar to a diagonal matrix.

b.

$$\mathbf{A} = \begin{bmatrix} 1 & 0 & 0 \\ 0 & 1 & -1 \\ 0 & 0 & 2 \end{bmatrix}$$

Eigenvalues: 1, 1, 2

$$\mathbf{A} - 2\mathbf{I} = \begin{bmatrix} -1 & 0 & 0 \\ 0 & -1 & -1 \\ 0 & 0 & 0 \end{bmatrix}$$

Eigenspace corresponding to 2 has dimension 1.

$$\mathbf{A} - \mathbf{I} = \begin{bmatrix} 0 & 0 & 0 \\ 0 & 0 & -1 \\ 0 & 0 & 1 \end{bmatrix} \Leftrightarrow \begin{bmatrix} 0 & 0 & 1 \\ 0 & 0 & 0 \\ 0 & 0 & 0 \end{bmatrix}$$

Eigenspace corresponding to 1 has dimension 2.

From the eigenspace corresponding to 1 choose two vectors $\mathbf{u}_1$ and $\mathbf{u}_2$ such that $\{\mathbf{u}_1, \mathbf{u}_2\}$ is a linearly independent set. For example, choose $\mathbf{u}_1 = (1, 0, 0)$ and

$\mathbf{u}_2 = (0, 1, 0)$. There are many possible choices. From the eigenspace corresponding to 2 choose an eigenvector, for example, $\mathbf{u}_3 = (0, 1, -1)$. The matrix $\mathbf{P}$ with these vectors as columns is nonsingular: $\mathbf{P} = \begin{bmatrix} 1 & 0 & 0 \\ 0 & 1 & 1 \\ 0 & 0 & -1 \end{bmatrix}$, and

$$\mathbf{P}^{-1}\mathbf{AP} = \begin{bmatrix} 1 & 0 & 0 \\ 0 & 1 & 1 \\ 0 & 0 & -1 \end{bmatrix} \begin{bmatrix} 1 & 0 & 0 \\ 0 & 1 & -1 \\ 0 & 0 & 2 \end{bmatrix} \begin{bmatrix} 1 & 0 & 0 \\ 0 & 1 & 1 \\ 0 & 0 & -1 \end{bmatrix} = \begin{bmatrix} 1 & 0 & 0 \\ 0 & 1 & 0 \\ 0 & 0 & 2 \end{bmatrix}$$

■

The following summary of the facts regarding the diagonalization of a matrix with multiple eigenvalues is given without proof. A more detailed treatment of this situation may be found in Lancaster (1969).

Theorem 4 Let T be a linear transformation from an n-dimensional space S into itself, and let $\mathbf{A}$ be the matrix of T relative to some basis, where $\mathbf{A}$ is $n \times n$. Assume the eigenvalues of T (and $\mathbf{A}$) are all real.

1. Let k be an eigenvalue of T with multiplicity m. The dimension d of the eigenspace corresponding to k satisfies the inequality $1 \leqslant d \leqslant m$.
2. Let $k_1, k_2, \ldots, k_r$ be the distinct eigenvalues of T and let $m_1, m_2, \ldots, m_r$ be the multiplicities of $k_1, k_2, \ldots, k_r$, respectively. Then

$$m_1 + m_2 + \cdots + m_r = n$$

3. The matrix $\mathbf{A}$ is similar to a diagonal matrix if and only if the eigenspace of $\mathbf{A}$ corresponding to k_i has dimension m_i for each $i = 1, 2, 3, \ldots, r$. □

Much of the discussion that follows assumes that the eigenvalues of the matrix $\mathbf{A}$ are real and that $\mathbf{A}$ is similar to a diagonal matrix. Large classes of matrices have these properties. In particular, all symmetric matrices do. Symmetric matrices are discussed in Section 6.2.

SUMMARY Let T be a linear transformation from W to W. The eigenvalues of T are the values of λ for which $T(\mathbf{x}) = \lambda\mathbf{x}$ has nonzero solutions. The nonzero vectors with this property for some λ are eigenvectors of T. Let the matrix of T relative to U be $\mathbf{A}$. The matrix of T relative to any other basis is similar to $\mathbf{A}$. The eigenvectors of $\mathbf{A}$ are coordinates relative to U of the eigenvectors of T.

For any eigenvalue λ, the eigenspace of T corresponding to λ is the null space of $T - \lambda I$. The eigenspace of $\mathbf{A}$ corresponding to λ is the null space of the matrix $\mathbf{A} - \lambda\mathbf{I}$.

The matrix of T is diagonal if U is a basis of eigenvectors. A basis of eigenvectors exists if for each eigenvector λ_i, the dimension of the eigenspace corresponding to λ_i is equal to the multiplicity of λ_i.

EXERCISES 6.1

1. Let T be defined by $T(x_1, x_2) = (4x_1 + 2x_2, -x_1 + x_2)$.
   a. Find the matrix of T relative to the standard basis.
   b. Calculate the eigenvalues of T.
   c. Let $\mathbf{v}_1 = (1, 0)$ and $\mathbf{v}_2 = (2, 1)$. Write the matrix of T relative to the basis $\{\mathbf{v}_1, \mathbf{v}_2\}$ and find its eigenvalues.

2. a. In Problem 1, the matrix of T relative to the standard basis is found to be $\begin{bmatrix} 4 & 2 \\ -1 & 1 \end{bmatrix}$, with eigenvalues 2 and 3. Find a basis for each of the eigenspaces of T.
   b. The matrix of T relative to the basis $U = \{\mathbf{v}_1, \mathbf{v}_2\}$, where $\mathbf{v}_1 = (1, 0)$, $\mathbf{v}_2 = (2, 1)$, is $\begin{bmatrix} 6 & 12 \\ -1 & -1 \end{bmatrix}$. Calculate an eigenvector corresponding to each of the eigenvalues of this matrix. Show that these eigenvectors are the coordinates relative to the basis U of the eigenvectors of T as found in **a**.

3. Let T be defined by $T(x_1, x_2, x_3) = (2x_1, 4x_2 + x_3, -5x_2 - 2x_3)$.
   a. Calculate the matrix of T relative to the standard basis.
   b. Find the eigenvalues of T.
   c. Let $\mathbf{u}_1 = (1, 0, 0)$, $\mathbf{u}_2 = (1, 1, 0)$, and $\mathbf{u}_3 = (1, 1, 1)$. Calculate the matrix of T relative to the basis $\{\mathbf{u}_1, \mathbf{u}_2, \mathbf{u}_3\}$. Find the eigenvalues of this matrix and compare with **b**.

4. Let T be a linear transformation from S to S. Let the basis of S be $U = \{\mathbf{u}_1, \mathbf{u}_2, \mathbf{u}_3\}$. Let the matrix of T relative to U be $\mathbf{A}$.
   a. If
   $$\mathbf{A}\begin{bmatrix} 1 \\ 2 \\ 1 \end{bmatrix} = \begin{bmatrix} -2 \\ -4 \\ -2 \end{bmatrix}$$
   what is an eigenvalue of T?
   b. Write an eigenvector of T.

5. Let T be a transformation on R^2 consisting of rotation of the plane through 45° in a counterclockwise direction about the origin. Then $T(1, 0) = (\frac{\sqrt{2}}{2}, \frac{\sqrt{2}}{2})$ and $T(0, 1) = (-\frac{\sqrt{2}}{2}, \frac{\sqrt{2}}{2})$. Is there any nonzero vector that is rotated into a multiple of itself? Write the matrix of T and show that this matrix has no real eigenvalues.

6. Let T be the transformation on R^2 corresponding to rotation of the plane through 180° about the origin. Is there any nonzero vector that is rotated into a multiple of itself? Check by writing the matrix of T and finding its eigenvalues and eigenvectors.

7. Show that the only rotations on R^2 with real eigenvalues are rotations through 0° or 180° (or some multiple of 180°).

8. Let P be projection of R^3 on the x_1x_2-plane: $P(x_1, x_2, x_3) = (x_1, x_2, 0)$. Find the eigenvalues of P and the corresponding eigenspaces. Describe the eigenspaces geometrically.

9. a. Let T be defined on P_2 by the equation $T(p) = p''$. Find the matrix of T, show that the only eigenvalue of T is 0, and find the dimension of the corresponding eigenspace. Interpret this result in the light of your knowledge of differentiation of polynomials.
   b. Let T be defined on P_2 by the equation $T(p) = p'' + p'$. Show that the only eigenvalue of T is 0 and find the dimension of the corresponding eigenspace.

10. Let T be defined on P_2 by the equation $T(p) = p' + 3p$. Write the matrix of T relative to the standard basis. Find the eigenvalues of T and the corresponding eigenvectors.

11. Recall that $M_{2\times 2}$ is the vector space consisting of 2×2 matrices and that a basis for this space is $\mathbf{E}_1 = \begin{bmatrix} 1 & 0 \\ 0 & 0 \end{bmatrix}$, $\mathbf{E}_2 = \begin{bmatrix} 0 & 1 \\ 0 & 0 \end{bmatrix}$, $\mathbf{E}_3 = \begin{bmatrix} 0 & 0 \\ 1 & 0 \end{bmatrix}$, and $\mathbf{E}_4 = \begin{bmatrix} 0 & 0 \\ 0 & 1 \end{bmatrix}$. For $\mathbf{X} = \begin{bmatrix} a & b \\ c & d \end{bmatrix}$, let
    $$T(\mathbf{X}) = \begin{bmatrix} a + kb & b \\ c + kd & d \end{bmatrix},\ k \text{ a nonzero scalar.}$$
    a. Find the matrix of T.
    b. Show that T has an eigenvector of multiplicity 4 and that the eigenspace corresponding to this eigenvector has dimension 2.
    c. Describe the vectors in this eigenspace.

12. Let $T(\mathbf{X}) = \begin{bmatrix} a + kc & b + kd \\ c & d \end{bmatrix}$, where $\mathbf{X}$ is defined as in Problem 11. Try to predict the eigenvalue and eigenspace corresponding to T. Check your prediction by calculation.

13. Let $T(\mathbf{X}) = \begin{bmatrix} 2a & 3b \\ 4c & 5d \end{bmatrix}$, where $\mathbf{X}$ is defined as in Problem 11. Find the eigenvalues and eigenvectors of T.

14. Let $T(\mathbf{X})$ be the matrix obtained from $\mathbf{X}$ by multiplying a row by a nonzero scalar. Describe the eigenvalues and eigenvectors of T.

15. Let $\mathbf{A} = \begin{bmatrix} a & b \\ c & d \end{bmatrix}$, where a, b, c, d are integers. For what conditions on a, b, c, d are the eigenvalues of $\mathbf{A}$ (i) real, (ii) equal, (iii) imaginary, (iv) integers?

16. The characteristic polynomial of T is $(\lambda - 1)^2(\lambda - 5)(\lambda + 1)^3$. What are the eigenvalues of T and what is the multiplicity of each eigenvalue? What is the size of the matrix of T?

17. In each case, write the characteristic polynomial of the matrix $\mathbf{A}$.

a. $\mathbf{A}$ has eigenvalues 0, 1, and 3, none of which is repeated.

b. $\mathbf{A}$ has eigenvalues 1 (of multiplicity 2) and 3 (of multiplicity 1).

c. $\mathbf{A}$ is similar to the matrix

$$\begin{bmatrix} 3 & 4 & 5 & 7 \\ 0 & -1 & 2 & 1 \\ 0 & 0 & 4 & -3 \\ 0 & 0 & 0 & 5 \end{bmatrix}$$

18. Show that

$$\mathbf{A} = \begin{bmatrix} 2 & 0 & 0 \\ 0 & 2 & 1 \\ 0 & 0 & 2 \end{bmatrix} \quad \text{and} \quad \mathbf{B} = \begin{bmatrix} 2 & 1 & 1 \\ 0 & 2 & 1 \\ 0 & 0 & 2 \end{bmatrix}$$

have the same eigenvalues. Find bases for the eigenspace of $\mathbf{A}$ and for the eigenspace of $\mathbf{B}$.

19. Let T be a linear transformation with matrix

$$\mathbf{A} = \begin{bmatrix} 0 & 0 & 1 \\ 1 & 0 & 0 \\ -3 & 1 & 3 \end{bmatrix}$$

Find the eigenvalues of T and the corresponding eigenvectors. Show that T cannot be represented by a diagonal matrix.

20. In each case, the transformation T has matrix $\mathbf{A}$. Is it possible to represent T by a diagonal matrix? If so, what basis should be used for this representation?

a. $\mathbf{A} = \begin{bmatrix} 6 & 4 & 4 \\ -7 & -2 & -1 \\ 7 & 4 & 3 \end{bmatrix}$

b. $\mathbf{A} = \begin{bmatrix} 5 & -1 & 2 \\ 0 & 1 & 0 \\ -4 & 2 & -1 \end{bmatrix}$

c. $\mathbf{A} = \begin{bmatrix} 6 & 7 & 7 \\ -7 & -8 & -7 \\ 7 & 7 & 6 \end{bmatrix}$

21. In each case, the transformation T has matrix $\mathbf{A}$. If possible, find a basis with respect to which the matrix of T is diagonal.

a. $\mathbf{A} = \begin{bmatrix} 5 & 0 & 2 \\ 0 & 1 & 0 \\ -4 & 0 & -1 \end{bmatrix}$

b. $\mathbf{A} = \begin{bmatrix} -1 & -1 & 2 & -10 \\ 4 & 3 & 0 & 14 \\ 0 & 0 & 5 & 9 \\ 0 & 0 & -1 & -1 \end{bmatrix}$

22. Let $\mathbf{A} = \begin{bmatrix} 7 & 4 \\ -2 & -2 \end{bmatrix}$. Choose $\mathbf{P}$ such that $\mathbf{P}^{-1}\mathbf{AP} = \begin{bmatrix} 6 & 0 \\ 0 & -1 \end{bmatrix}$. Is your choice of $\mathbf{P}$ unique? What other choices can be made?

23. a. If $\mathbf{D}$ and $\mathbf{F}$ are diagonal matrices of the same size and $\mathbf{F}^{-1}$ exists, show that $\mathbf{F}^{-1}\mathbf{DF} = \mathbf{D}$.

b. Show that if $\mathbf{P}^{-1}\mathbf{AP} = \mathbf{D}$, where $\mathbf{D}$ is diagonal, and $\mathbf{F}$ is a nonsingular diagonal matrix of the same size, then $(\mathbf{PF})^{-1}\mathbf{A}(\mathbf{PF}) = \mathbf{D}$.

24. The matrix

$$\mathbf{A} = \begin{bmatrix} 5 & 0 & 2 \\ 0 & 1 & 0 \\ -4 & 0 & -1 \end{bmatrix}$$

has eigenvalues 1, 1, and 3 and is similar to a diagonal matrix (see Problem 21). Discuss the choice of the eigenvector corresponding to 3. What freedom is there in the choice of this vector? What freedom is there in choosing the eigenvectors corresponding to 1?

25. Develop the proof of Theorem 3 for any finite n. The following steps are suggested.

a. Show that $(\mathbf{A} - \lambda_j\mathbf{I})\mathbf{U}_i = (\lambda_i - \lambda_j)\mathbf{U}_i$, and deduce that $\prod_{j=1}^{k} (\mathbf{A} - \lambda_j\mathbf{I})\mathbf{U}_i = \prod_{j=1}^{k} (\lambda_i - \lambda_j)\mathbf{U}_i$.

b. Assume $\sum_{i=1}^{k} c_i\mathbf{U}_i = \mathbf{0}$. Let r be any integer $1 \leqslant r \leqslant k$. Multiply both sides on the left by $\prod_{\substack{j=1\\ j\neq r}}^{k} (\mathbf{A} - \lambda_j\mathbf{I})$.

c. Simplify your answer in **b.** by noting that, for a fixed i,

$$\prod_{\substack{j=1\\ j\neq r}}^{k} (\mathbf{A} - \lambda_j\mathbf{I})c_i\mathbf{U}_i = \prod_{\substack{j=1\\ j\neq r}}^{k} (\lambda_i - \lambda_j)c_i\mathbf{U}_i$$

$$= \begin{cases} \mathbf{0} & \text{if } i \neq r \\ K_r c_r \mathbf{U}_r & \text{if } i = r, \text{ where } K_r \neq 0 \end{cases}$$

d. Hence, show that

$$\prod_{\substack{j=1\\ j\neq r}}^{k} (\mathbf{A} - \lambda_j\mathbf{I}) \sum_{i=1}^{k} c_i\mathbf{U}_i = \mathbf{0}$$

implies

$$c_r K_r \mathbf{U}_r = \mathbf{0}$$

e. Show that the result in **d.** implies $\{\mathbf{U}_1, \mathbf{U}_2, \ldots, \mathbf{U}_k\}$ is linearly independent.

26. Let $\mathbf{A}$ be a 3×3 matrix with eigenvalues a, b, b, $(a \neq b)$. Let $\{\mathbf{u}_1\}$ be a basis of the eigenspace corresponding to a, and $\{\mathbf{u}_2, \mathbf{u}_3\}$ a basis of the eigenspace corresponding to b. Show that the set $\{\mathbf{u}_1, \mathbf{u}_2, \mathbf{u}_3\}$ is linearly independent. (*Hint*: Set $c_1\mathbf{u}_1 + c_2\mathbf{u}_2 + c_3\mathbf{u}_3 = \mathbf{0}$. Multiply this equation on the left by $\mathbf{A} - a\mathbf{I}$, then use the linear independence of $\{\mathbf{u}_2, \mathbf{u}_3\}$.)

27. Let $\mathbf{A}$ be 4×4 with eigenvalues $a, a, b, b, (a \neq b)$. Let $\{\mathbf{u}_1, \mathbf{u}_2\}$ be a basis for the eigenspace corresponding to a, and $\{\mathbf{u}_3, \mathbf{u}_4\}$ be a basis for the eigenspace corresponding to b. Show that $\{\mathbf{u}_1, \mathbf{u}_2, \mathbf{u}_3, \mathbf{u}_4\}$ is linearly independent.

28. Let $\lambda_1, \lambda_2, \ldots, \lambda_k$ be distinct eigenvalues and S_i a basis for the eigenspace corresponding to λ_i. Show that the set $S_1 \cup S_2 \cup \cdots \cup S_k$ is a linearly independent set.

6.2 The Eigenvalues and Eigenvectors of a Symmetric Matrix

Symmetric matrices were defined in Chapter 1, Definition 10. Some simple properties that follow from the definition were listed in Theorem 6, Chapter 1. In this section, we study special properties of the eigenvalues and eigenvectors of a real symmetric matrix.

Example 6 Let $\mathbf{A} = \begin{bmatrix} 1 & 4 \\ 4 & 7 \end{bmatrix}$. The characteristic equation of $\mathbf{A}$ is $\lambda^2 - 8\lambda - 9 = 0$. Its eigenvalues are the real numbers 9 and -1. Let

$$\mathbf{B} = \begin{bmatrix} 3 & 1 & 1 \\ 1 & 0 & 2 \\ 1 & 2 & 0 \end{bmatrix}$$

Its characteristic equation is $(\lambda - 1)(\lambda - 4)(\lambda + 2) = 0$. It has three real eigenvalues: 1, 4, and -2. ■

If $\mathbf{A}$ is a real symmetric matrix, the eigenvalues of $\mathbf{A}$ are real. To prove this we need to use some properties of complex numbers.

Recall that a complex number has the form $a + bi$, where a and b are real and $i^2 = -1$. If $\alpha = a + bi$, the complex number $\bar{\alpha} = a - bi$ is called the conjugate of α. The product of any nonzero complex number and its conjugate is a positive real number: $\alpha\bar{\alpha} = (a + bi)(a - bi) = a^2 + b^2$. The conjugate of a real number is simply the real number itself, since $a + 0i$ and $a - 0i$ are the same. Conversely, any complex number that equals its conjugate is real.

Theorem 5 If $\mathbf{A}$ is a real symmetric matrix, the eigenvalues of $\mathbf{A}$ are real.

Proof Let k be an eigenvalue of $\mathbf{A}$ and $\mathbf{u} = (x_1, x_2, \ldots, x_n)$ its corresponding eigenvector. We know only that the numbers $k, x_1, x_2, \ldots, x_n$ are complex, and we want to show that k is real. One way to do this is to show that $k = \bar{k}$. Since k is an eigenvalue and $\mathbf{u}$ the corresponding eigenvector, we know that

$$\mathbf{AU} = k\mathbf{U}$$

where $\mathbf{U}$ is the $n \times 1$ array

$$\mathbf{U} = \begin{bmatrix} x_1 \\ x_2 \\ \vdots \\ x_n \end{bmatrix}$$

Also $\mathbf{U}^T = [x_1 \quad x_2 \quad \cdots \quad x_n]$. The array of conjugates is designated $\bar{\mathbf{U}}^T = [\bar{x}_1 \quad \bar{x}_2 \quad \cdots \quad \bar{x}_n]$. The product $\bar{\mathbf{U}}^T\mathbf{U} = \bar{x}_1 x_1 + \bar{x}_2 x_2 + \cdots + \bar{x}_n x_n$. Since $\mathbf{u} \neq \mathbf{0}$, $\bar{\mathbf{U}}^T\mathbf{U}$ is a positive real number, call it r.

Multiply both sides of the equation $\mathbf{AU} = k\mathbf{U}$ on the left by $\bar{\mathbf{U}}^T$:

$$\bar{\mathbf{U}}^T\mathbf{AU} = \bar{\mathbf{U}}^T k\mathbf{U} = k\mathbf{U}^T\mathbf{U} = kr$$

Take the transpose of $\bar{\mathbf{U}}^T\mathbf{AU}$ and replace each element in the product by its conjugate:

$$(\bar{\mathbf{U}}^T\mathbf{AU})^T = \mathbf{U}^T\mathbf{A}^T\bar{\mathbf{U}}$$

and the conjugate of this is $\bar{\mathbf{U}}^T\bar{\mathbf{A}}^T\mathbf{U}$. Since $\mathbf{A}$ is symmetric and the elements of $\mathbf{A}$ are real, $\bar{\mathbf{A}}^T = \mathbf{A}$. Thus, $\bar{\mathbf{U}}^T\bar{\mathbf{A}}^T\mathbf{U} = \bar{\mathbf{U}}^T\mathbf{AU}$. The transpose of kr is just kr, and its conjugate is $\bar{k}r$.

We now have two equations: $\bar{\mathbf{U}}^T\mathbf{AU} = kr$, and, from the conjugate transpose of this equation, $\bar{\mathbf{U}}^T\mathbf{AU} = \bar{k}r$. These imply that $kr = \bar{k}r$. Since $r \neq 0$, we have $\bar{k} = k$. A number that is equal to its conjugate must be real, thus k is real, and the eigenvalues of a real symmetric matrix are real. □

Now consider the eigenvectors of a real symmetric matrix. Example 7 continues Example 6.

Example 7

Let $\mathbf{A} = \begin{bmatrix} 1 & 4 \\ 4 & 7 \end{bmatrix}$. Its eigenvalues are 9 and -1. An eigenvector corresponding to 9 is $\mathbf{u}_1 = (1, 2)$. An eigenvector corresponding to -1 is $\mathbf{u}_2 = (-2, 1)$. The vectors $\mathbf{u}_1$ and $\mathbf{u}_2$ are orthogonal.

As a second example consider

$$\mathbf{B} = \begin{bmatrix} 3 & 1 & 1 \\ 1 & 0 & 2 \\ 1 & 2 & 0 \end{bmatrix}$$

This matrix has eigenvalues 1, 4, and -2. The eigenspace corresponding to 1 has basis $\{\mathbf{v}_1\}$, where $\mathbf{v}_1 = (-1, 1, 1)$. The eigenspace corresponding to 4 has basis $\{\mathbf{v}_2\}$, where $\mathbf{v}_2 = (2, 1, 1)$. The eigenspace corresponding to -2 has basis $\{\mathbf{v}_3\}$, where $\mathbf{v}_3 = (0, 1, -1)$. The three eigenvectors $\mathbf{v}_1, \mathbf{v}_2, \mathbf{v}_3$ are orthogonal in pairs; that is, $\mathbf{v}_1 \cdot \mathbf{v}_2 = 0$, $\mathbf{v}_1 \cdot \mathbf{v}_3 = 0$, and $\mathbf{v}_2 \cdot \mathbf{v}_3 = 0$. ■

The special property of the eigenvectors of symmetric matrices illustrated in Example 7 is stated below.

Theorem 6 If $\mathbf{A}$ is a symmetric matrix, eigenvectors corresponding to distinct eigenvalues are orthogonal.

Proof Let $k_1 \neq k_2$ be two distinct eigenvalues of $\mathbf{A}$, and let $\mathbf{u}_1$ and $\mathbf{u}_2$ be corresponding eigenvectors. We have two equations:

$\mathbf{AU}_1 = k_1\mathbf{U}_1$	$\mathbf{AU}_2 = k_2\mathbf{U}_2$
Multiply on the left by $\mathbf{U}_2^T$.	Multiply on the left by $\mathbf{U}_1^T$.
$\mathbf{U}_2^T\mathbf{AU}_1 = k_1\mathbf{U}_2^T\mathbf{U}_1$	$\mathbf{U}_1^T\mathbf{AU}_2 = k_2\mathbf{U}_1^T\mathbf{U}_2$
	Take the transpose of both sides.
	$(\mathbf{U}_1^T\mathbf{AU}_2)^T = (k_2\mathbf{U}_1^T\mathbf{U}_2)^T$
	$\mathbf{U}_2^T\mathbf{A}^T\mathbf{U}_1 = k_2\mathbf{U}_2^T\mathbf{U}_1$
	Since $\mathbf{A}$ is symmetric,
	$\mathbf{U}_2^T\mathbf{AU}_1 = k_2\mathbf{U}_2^T\mathbf{U}_1$

Both of these equations give a value for $\mathbf{U}_2^T\mathbf{AU}_1$, and these values must be the same. Hence, $k_1\mathbf{U}_2^T\mathbf{U}_1 = k_2\mathbf{U}_2^T\mathbf{U}_1$; that is, $(k_1 - k_2)\mathbf{U}_2^T\mathbf{U}_1 = \mathbf{0}$. But we assumed that $k_1 \neq k_2$, so $k_1 - k_2 \neq 0$. Therefore, $\mathbf{U}_2^T\mathbf{U}_1 = \mathbf{0}$. This means that $\mathbf{u}_1$ and $\mathbf{u}_2$ are orthogonal. □

The third special property of symmetric matrices concerns the rank of the matrix $\mathbf{A} - k\mathbf{I}$. If k is an eigenvalue of multiplicity m, the matrix $\mathbf{A} - k\mathbf{I}$ has rank $n - m$, so that its null space has dimension m; that is, if k is an eigenvalue of multiplicity m, its corresponding eigenspace has dimension m. This property is illustrated in Example 8.

Example 8 Let

$$\mathbf{A} = \begin{bmatrix} 7 & -2 & 1 \\ -2 & 10 & -2 \\ 1 & -2 & 7 \end{bmatrix}$$

The characteristic equation of $\mathbf{A}$ is $\lambda^3 - 24\lambda^2 + 180\lambda - 432 = 0$, and the eigenvalues are 6, 6, and 12. Corresponding to 12, we have the equations

$$\begin{bmatrix} 5 & 2 & -1 \\ 2 & 2 & 2 \\ -1 & 2 & 5 \end{bmatrix} \mathbf{X} = \mathbf{0}$$

from which an eigenvector is $\mathbf{u}_1 = (1, -2, 1)$. The equations corresponding to 6 are

$$\begin{bmatrix} -1 & 2 & -1 \\ 2 & -4 & 2 \\ -1 & 2 & -1 \end{bmatrix} \mathbf{X} = \mathbf{0}$$

The coefficient matrix has rank 1, so that its null space has dimension 2. Since the multiplicity of 6 is 2 and the dimension of the eigenspace corresponding to 6 is also 2, Theorem 4, part 3, assures us that **A** is similar to a diagonal matrix. A possible basis for the eigenspace corresponding to 6 is $\{\mathbf{u}_2, \mathbf{u}_3\}$, where $\mathbf{u}_2 = (2, 1, 0)$ and $\mathbf{u}_3 = (-1, 0, 1)$. The vectors $\{\mathbf{u}_1, \mathbf{u}_2, \mathbf{u}_3\}$ form a basis of R^3. If

$$\mathbf{P} = \begin{bmatrix} 1 & 2 & -1 \\ -2 & 1 & 0 \\ 1 & 0 & 1 \end{bmatrix}$$

then

$$\mathbf{P}^{-1}\mathbf{AP} = \begin{bmatrix} 12 & 0 & 0 \\ 0 & 6 & 0 \\ 0 & 0 & 6 \end{bmatrix}$$

■

The situation illustrated in Example 8 holds for every real symmetric matrix, as Theorem 7 asserts.

Theorem 7 If **A** is a symmetric matrix with eigenvalues $k_1, k_2, \ldots, k_r$ with multiplicities $m_1, m_2, \ldots, m_r$, the eigenspace corresponding to k_i has dimension m_i, $i = 1, 2, \ldots, r$. Every symmetric matrix is similar to a diagonal matrix.

Discussion of the Proof The argument to support the first part of the statement depends on a more thorough examination of the structure of the matrix $\mathbf{A} - \lambda\mathbf{I}$. Such an examination can be found in Lancaster (1969). The fact that a symmetric matrix is similar to a diagonal matrix is a direct consequence of Theorem 4. □

These three special properties of a real symmetric matrix **A** (Theorems 5, 6, and 7) guarantee that we can find a basis for R^n consisting of eigenvectors of **A**. Because of the orthogonality property stated in Theorem 6, we can do even better. We can find an orthonormal basis of eigenvectors (Definition 12, Chapter 4). The idea is to find an orthonormal basis for each of the eigenspaces of **A** and then combine these to form an orthonormal basis for R^n.

Example 9 Let

$$\mathbf{A} = \begin{bmatrix} 7 & -2 & 1 \\ -2 & 10 & -2 \\ 1 & -2 & 7 \end{bmatrix}$$

The eigenvalues of **A** are 6, 6, and 12. (See Example 8.) The eigenspace corresponding to 12 has dimension 1 and basis $\mathbf{u}_1 = (1, -2, 1)$. An orthonormal basis for this eigenspace is $\mathbf{v}_1 = (\frac{1}{\sqrt{6}}, -\frac{2}{\sqrt{6}}, \frac{1}{\sqrt{6}})$.

The eigenspace corresponding to 6 has dimension 2. A possible basis for this eigenspace is $\{\mathbf{u}_2, \mathbf{u}_3\}$, where $\mathbf{u}_2 = (2, 1, 0)$ and $\mathbf{u}_3 = (-1, 0, 1)$. This is not an orthonormal basis; it is not even an orthogonal basis, since $\mathbf{u}_2 \cdot \mathbf{u}_3 = -2$. Using the techniques of Section 4.5, we can construct an orthonormal basis as follows. Let $\mathbf{v}_2 = (\frac{2}{\sqrt{5}}, \frac{1}{\sqrt{5}}, 0)$; let $\mathbf{w}_3 = \mathbf{u}_3 - (\mathbf{u}_3 \cdot \mathbf{v}_2)\mathbf{v}_2 = (-\frac{1}{5}, \frac{2}{5}, 1)$; and let $\mathbf{v}_3 = \mathbf{w}_3/\|\mathbf{w}_3\| = (-\frac{1}{\sqrt{30}}, \frac{2}{\sqrt{30}}, \frac{5}{\sqrt{30}})$. The set $\{\mathbf{v}_2, \mathbf{v}_3\}$ is an orthonormal basis for the eigenspace corresponding to 6. The set $\{\mathbf{v}_1, \mathbf{v}_2, \mathbf{v}_3\}$ is an orthonormal basis for R^3 consisting of eigenvectors of **A**. ■

The Gram-Schmidt process for finding an orthonormal basis of R^n was discussed in Section 4.5. See also Section 4.6, Problem 9. In the following example, we use this process to find an orthonormal basis of R^4 made up of eigenvectors of a 4×4 matrix.

Example 10 Let

$$\mathbf{A} = \begin{bmatrix} 2 & -2 & 0 & 1 \\ -2 & 5 & 0 & -2 \\ 0 & 0 & 1 & 0 \\ 1 & -2 & 0 & 2 \end{bmatrix}$$

The eigenvalues of **A** are 7 and 1, where the eigenvalue 1 has multiplicity 3. The eigenspace corresponding to 7 has dimension 1 and basis $\mathbf{u}_1 = (1, -2, 0, 1)$. A unit vector in this space is $\mathbf{v}_1 = (\frac{1}{\sqrt{6}}, -\frac{2}{\sqrt{6}}, 0, \frac{1}{\sqrt{6}})$.

The eigenspace corresponding to 1 is the solution space of the system

$$\begin{bmatrix} 1 & -2 & 0 & 1 \\ -2 & 4 & 0 & -2 \\ 0 & 0 & 0 & 0 \\ 1 & -2 & 0 & 1 \end{bmatrix} \begin{bmatrix} x_1 \\ x_2 \\ x_3 \\ x_4 \end{bmatrix} = \mathbf{0}$$

The dimension of this space is 3, and a possible basis is

$$\mathbf{u}_2 = (1, 0, 0, -1), \qquad \mathbf{u}_3 = (0, 1, 0, 2), \quad \text{and} \quad \mathbf{u}_4 = (-2, 0, 1, 2)$$

We now use the Gram-Schmidt process to replace $\{\mathbf{u}_2, \mathbf{u}_3, \mathbf{u}_4\}$ by an orthonormal basis $\{\mathbf{v}_2, \mathbf{v}_3, \mathbf{v}_4\}$. The calculation goes as follows:

$$\mathbf{v}_2 = \frac{\mathbf{u}_2}{\|\mathbf{u}_2\|} = \frac{1}{\sqrt{2}}(1, 0, 0, -1)$$

$$\mathbf{w}_3 = \mathbf{u}_3 - \frac{-2}{\sqrt{2}}\mathbf{v}_2 = (1, 1, 0, 1)$$

$$\mathbf{v}_3 = \frac{1}{\sqrt{3}}(1, 1, 0, 1)$$

$$\mathbf{w}_4 = \mathbf{u}_4 - \frac{-4}{\sqrt{2}}\mathbf{v}_2 - \frac{0}{\sqrt{3}}\mathbf{v}_3 = (0, 0, 1, 0)$$

$$\mathbf{v}_4 = (0, 0, 1, 0)$$

The set $\{\mathbf{v}_1, \mathbf{v}_2, \mathbf{v}_3, \mathbf{v}_4\}$ is an orthonormal set.

Now, form the matrix $\mathbf{P}$ with columns $\mathbf{v}_1, \mathbf{v}_2, \mathbf{v}_3$, and $\mathbf{v}_4$. We obtain

$$\mathbf{P} = \begin{bmatrix} \frac{1}{\sqrt{6}} & \frac{1}{\sqrt{2}} & \frac{1}{\sqrt{3}} & 0 \\ -\frac{2}{\sqrt{6}} & 0 & \frac{1}{\sqrt{3}} & 0 \\ 0 & 0 & 0 & 1 \\ \frac{1}{\sqrt{6}} & -\frac{1}{\sqrt{2}} & \frac{1}{\sqrt{3}} & 0 \end{bmatrix}$$

Since $\mathbf{P}$ is orthogonal, $\mathbf{P}^T\mathbf{P} = \mathbf{I}$, so that $\mathbf{P}^{-1} = \mathbf{P}^T$. Because the columns of $\mathbf{P}$ are eigenvectors of $\mathbf{A}$, we have

$$\mathbf{P}^{-1}\mathbf{A}\mathbf{P} = \begin{bmatrix} 7 & 0 & 0 & 0 \\ 0 & 1 & 0 & 0 \\ 0 & 0 & 1 & 0 \\ 0 & 0 & 0 & 1 \end{bmatrix}$$

Because $\mathbf{P}^{-1} = \mathbf{P}^T$, we have also

$$\mathbf{P}^T\mathbf{A}\mathbf{P} = \begin{bmatrix} 7 & 0 & 0 & 0 \\ 0 & 1 & 0 & 0 \\ 0 & 0 & 1 & 0 \\ 0 & 0 & 0 & 1 \end{bmatrix}$$

The importance of this fact will be seen in Section 6.3 in the study of quadratic forms. ■

SUMMARY A symmetric matrix has the property $\mathbf{A}^T = \mathbf{A}$. The eigenvalues of a symmetric matrix are real. Eigenvectors corresponding to distinct eigenvalues are orthogonal. A basis of eigenvectors exists.

By choosing an orthonormal basis of eigenvectors in each eigenspace an orthonormal basis for R^n can be found consisting of eigenvectors of $\mathbf{A}$. The change-of-basis matrix $\mathbf{P}$ corresponding to an orthonormal basis in an orthogonal matrix.

Thus, for any symmetric matrix **A** there is an orthogonal matrix **P** such that

$$\mathbf{P}^{-1}\mathbf{AP} = \begin{bmatrix} \lambda_1 & 0 & \cdots & 0 \\ 0 & \lambda_2 & \cdots & 0 \\ \vdots & \vdots & & \vdots \\ 0 & 0 & \cdots & \lambda_n \end{bmatrix}$$

EXERCISES 6.2

1. If

$$\mathbf{A} = \begin{bmatrix} 1 & 2 & 1 \\ 2 & 0 & 1 \\ 1 & 1 & -3 \end{bmatrix} \quad \text{and} \quad \mathbf{B} = \begin{bmatrix} 1 & 4 & 2 \\ 4 & -1 & 0 \\ 2 & 0 & 3 \end{bmatrix}$$

show that **A** and **B** are symmetric. Calculate **A** + **B**. Is **A** + **B** symmetric? Calculate **AB**. Is **AB** symmetric?

2. Show, in general, that if **A** and **B** are symmetric and **A** + **B** is defined, then **A** + **B** is also symmetric but that **AB** is not necessarily symmetric.

3. a. Let $\mathbf{A} = \begin{bmatrix} 1 & 2 \\ 2 & -1 \end{bmatrix}$. Calculate $\mathbf{A}^3 - 3\mathbf{A}^2 + 4\mathbf{A} - 2\mathbf{I}$. Is this matrix symmetric?

b. Show that if **A** is symmetric, $p(\mathbf{A})$ is symmetric for any polynomial p.

4. Let $\mathbf{A} = \begin{bmatrix} 1 & 1 \\ 1 & 0 \end{bmatrix}$. Calculate $\mathbf{A}^{-1}$. Is $\mathbf{A}^{-1}$ symmetric?

5. Use the fact that $\mathbf{AA}^{-1} = \mathbf{I}$ to show that $(\mathbf{A}^{-1})^T = (\mathbf{A}^T)^{-1}$. From this show that if **A** is symmetric, then $\mathbf{A}^{-1}$ is symmetric.

6. Find the eigenvalues of each of the following matrices:

a. $\mathbf{A} = \begin{bmatrix} 1 & 2 \\ 2 & 1 \end{bmatrix}$ **b.** $\mathbf{A} = \begin{bmatrix} 1 & 3 \\ 3 & 2 \end{bmatrix}$

c. $\mathbf{A} = \begin{bmatrix} 1 & -5 \\ -5 & 1 \end{bmatrix}$ **d.** $\mathbf{A} = \begin{bmatrix} 8 & 2 \\ 2 & 1 \end{bmatrix}$

7. Find the characteristic equation of the matrix $\begin{bmatrix} a & b \\ b & d \end{bmatrix}$ and show that it has real roots for every choice of a, b, and d.

8. For each of the following matrices, find the eigenvalues.

a. $\mathbf{A} = \begin{bmatrix} 5 & 0 & 0 \\ 0 & 4 & 2 \\ 0 & 2 & 1 \end{bmatrix}$

b. $\mathbf{A} = \begin{bmatrix} 5 & 0 & -2 \\ 0 & 1 & 0 \\ -2 & 0 & 2 \end{bmatrix}$

c. $\mathbf{A} = \begin{bmatrix} 1 & 3 & 0 \\ 3 & 9 & 0 \\ 0 & 0 & 10 \end{bmatrix}$

9. In each case, find the eigenvalues.

a. $\mathbf{A} = \begin{bmatrix} 3 & 1 & 1 \\ 1 & 0 & 2 \\ 1 & 2 & 0 \end{bmatrix}$

b. $\mathbf{A} = \begin{bmatrix} 1 & -1 & -1 \\ -1 & 1 & 1 \\ -1 & 1 & 3 \end{bmatrix}$

c. $\mathbf{A} = \begin{bmatrix} 4 & 0 & -1 \\ 0 & 4 & -1 \\ -1 & -1 & 5 \end{bmatrix}$

10. For each of the following matrices, find the eigenspaces. Verify that eigenvectors corresponding to distinct eigenvalues are orthogonal.

a. $\mathbf{A} = \begin{bmatrix} 4 & 2 \\ 2 & 1 \end{bmatrix}$

b. $\mathbf{A} = \begin{bmatrix} 5 & -2 \\ -2 & 2 \end{bmatrix}$

c. $\mathbf{A} = \begin{bmatrix} 1 & 3 \\ 3 & 9 \end{bmatrix}$

d. $\mathbf{A} = \begin{bmatrix} 5 & -3 \\ -3 & -3 \end{bmatrix}$

11. For each of the following find the eigenvectors corresponding to each of the distinct eigenvalues. (Note that the eigenvalues were found in Problem 8.)

a. $\mathbf{A} = \begin{bmatrix} 5 & 0 & 0 \\ 0 & 4 & 2 \\ 0 & 2 & 1 \end{bmatrix}$

b. $\mathbf{A} = \begin{bmatrix} 5 & 0 & -2 \\ 0 & 1 & 0 \\ -2 & 0 & 2 \end{bmatrix}$

c. $\mathbf{A} = \begin{bmatrix} 1 & 3 & 0 \\ 3 & 9 & 0 \\ 0 & 0 & 10 \end{bmatrix}$

12. Let

$$\mathbf{A} = \begin{bmatrix} 6 & 4 & -5 \\ 4 & 6 & -5 \\ -5 & -5 & 15 \end{bmatrix}$$

Show that the eigenvalues of **A** are 2, 5, 20. Find a matrix **P** such that $\mathbf{P}^{-1}\mathbf{AP}$ is diagonal.

13. For the matrix in Problem 12, find an orthogonal matrix **P** such that $\mathbf{P}^{-1}\mathbf{AP}$ is diagonal.

14. a. For the matrix

$$\mathbf{A} = \begin{bmatrix} 5 & -1 & 0 \\ -1 & 5 & 0 \\ 0 & 0 & 4 \end{bmatrix}$$

find a matrix **P** such that

$$\mathbf{P}^{-1}\mathbf{AP} = \begin{bmatrix} 6 & 0 & 0 \\ 0 & 4 & 0 \\ 0 & 0 & 4 \end{bmatrix}$$

b. Is the choice of **P** unique? How must the first column be chosen? What restrictions are there on the choice of the second and third column?

c. Find an orthogonal matrix **P** such that $\mathbf{P}^{-1}\mathbf{AP}$ is diagonal.

15. Let

$$\mathbf{A} = \begin{bmatrix} 10 & -8 & -4 \\ -8 & 10 & 4 \\ -4 & 4 & 4 \end{bmatrix}$$

a. The eigenvalues of **A** are 2, 2, and 20. Find a matrix **P** such that $\mathbf{P}^{-1}\mathbf{AP}$ is diagonal.

b. Find an orthogonal matrix **P** such that $\mathbf{P}^{-1}\mathbf{AP}$ is diagonal.

16. a. Let $\mathbf{A} = \begin{bmatrix} 1 & 4 \\ 4 & 3 \end{bmatrix}$ and $\mathbf{U} = \begin{bmatrix} x_1 \\ x_2 \end{bmatrix}$. Calculate $\mathbf{U}^T\mathbf{AU}$.

b. Let $\mathbf{A} = \begin{bmatrix} a & b \\ b & d \end{bmatrix}$ and $\mathbf{U} = \begin{bmatrix} x_1 \\ x_2 \end{bmatrix}$. Calculate $\mathbf{U}^T\mathbf{AU}$.

c. Let $\mathbf{A} = \begin{bmatrix} 1 & 4 \\ 4 & 3 \end{bmatrix}$ and $\mathbf{U} = \begin{bmatrix} \alpha_1 \\ \alpha_2 \end{bmatrix}$, where $\alpha_1 = a_1 + ib_1$ and $\alpha_2 = a_2 + ib_2$. Calculate $\bar{\mathbf{U}}^T\mathbf{AU}$ and show that it is a real number as required in the proof of Theorem 5.

17. Show that the following matrices are skew-symmetric.

$$\begin{bmatrix} 0 & -1 & 3 \\ 1 & 0 & -2 \\ -3 & 2 & 0 \end{bmatrix}, \quad \begin{bmatrix} 0 & -5 \\ 5 & 0 \end{bmatrix}, \quad \begin{bmatrix} 0 & 2 \\ -2 & 0 \end{bmatrix}$$

18. Show that the eigenvalues of $\begin{bmatrix} 0 & a \\ -a & 0 \end{bmatrix}$ are complex numbers with real part 0.

***19.** If **A** is a square matrix, and $\mathbf{B} = (\frac{1}{2})(\mathbf{A} + \mathbf{A}^T)$ and $\mathbf{C} = (\frac{1}{2})(\mathbf{A} - \mathbf{A}^T)$, show that **B** is symmetric, **C** is skew-symmetric, and $\mathbf{B} + \mathbf{C} = \mathbf{A}$.

20. Let

$$\mathbf{A} = \begin{bmatrix} 1 & 3 & 5 \\ 2 & 4 & 2 \\ 3 & 1 & 1 \end{bmatrix}$$

Write **A** as the sum of a symmetric matrix and a skew-symmetric matrix.

21. Let $\mathbf{X} = \begin{bmatrix} a & b \\ c & d \end{bmatrix}$ and $T(\mathbf{X}) = \begin{bmatrix} a & c \\ b & d \end{bmatrix}$. T is a linear transformation from $M_{2\times 2}$ to $M_{2\times 2}$.

a. Find the matrix of T.

b. Find the eigenvalues and eigenvectors of T.

c. Describe the matrices in the eigenspace corresponding to $\lambda = 1$.

d. Describe the matrices in the eigenspace corresponding to $\lambda = -1$.

22. Use the information in Problem 21 to give an alternate proof of the fact that every 2×2 matrix is the sum of a symmetric matrix and a skew-symmetric matrix.

6.3 *Quadratic Forms*

A real quadratic form is a second-degree mathematical function with domain R^n and range a subset of the real numbers. Although a quadratic form is clearly not a linear transformation, matrix notation is convenient in representing it, and linear algebra is a useful tool in studying its properties.

Example 11 Let $\mathbf{x} = (x_1, x_2, x_3)$ be an element of R^3. The product

$$\begin{aligned} f(\mathbf{x}) &= \mathbf{X}^T \begin{bmatrix} 1 & 3 & -1 \\ 3 & 2 & 1 \\ -1 & 1 & 5 \end{bmatrix} \mathbf{X} \\ &= x_1^2 + 2x_2^2 + 5x_3^2 + 6x_1x_2 + 2x_2x_3 - 2x_1x_3 \end{aligned}$$

is a quadratic function from R^3 to the real numbers, usually called a quadratic form.

Any sum of second-degree terms in the three variables x_1, x_2, x_3 can be written as a matrix product of the form $\mathbf{X}^T\mathbf{A}\mathbf{X}$. The diagonal elements of the matrix $\mathbf{A}$ must be the coefficients of x_1^2, x_2^2, x_3^2. Since $x_1x_2 = x_2x_1$ for real numbers, these terms are usually combined. If the requirement is made that $\mathbf{A}$ be a symmetric matrix, then $a_{12} = a_{21} =$ half the coefficient of the combined terms x_1x_2 and x_2x_1. Let

$$f(\mathbf{x}) = x_1^2 - 4x_2^2 + 7x_3^2 - 4x_1x_2 + 8x_2x_3 - 12x_1x_3$$

As a matrix product with symmetric matrix $\mathbf{A}$, this is

$$f(\mathbf{x}) = [x_1 \quad x_2 \quad x_3] \begin{bmatrix} 1 & -2 & -6 \\ -2 & -4 & 4 \\ -6 & 4 & 7 \end{bmatrix} \begin{bmatrix} x_1 \\ x_2 \\ x_3 \end{bmatrix}$$

Notice that $a_{ij} =$ half the coefficient of x_ix_j if $i \neq j$. ■

Definition 4

Let $\mathbf{x} = (x_1, x_2, \ldots, x_n)$ be an element in R^n; let b_{ij}, $i,j = 1, 2, \ldots, n$ be real numbers. Let $\mathbf{A}$ be the symmetric matrix with $a_{ii} = b_{ii}$, $i = 1, 2, \ldots, n$ and $a_{ij} = \frac{1}{2}(b_{ij} + b_{ji})$, $i \neq j$, $i,j = 1, 2, \ldots, n$. An expression of the form

$$f(\mathbf{x}) = \sum_{i,j=1}^{n} b_{ij}x_ix_j = \mathbf{X}^T\mathbf{A}\mathbf{X}$$

Quadratic Form

is called a **quadratic form** in $x_1, x_2, \ldots, x_n$, or a quadratic form on R^n.

A quadratic form on R^n is a function from R^n to the real numbers. The n-tuple $\mathbf{x}$ represents both an element in the domain R^n and the coordinate n-tuple of $\mathbf{x}$

relative to the standard basis. The quadratic form could be written $[\mathbf{x}]_E^T\mathbf{A}[\mathbf{x}]_E$. We use the notation $\mathbf{X}$ rather than $[\mathbf{x}]_E$ unless a change of basis is being considered.

Matrix of f Relative to Standard Basis

Definition 5

For the quadratic form $f(\mathbf{x}) = \mathbf{X}^T\mathbf{A}\mathbf{X}$, the matrix $\mathbf{A}$ is called the **matrix of f relative to the standard basis.**

Our study of quadratic forms centers around two questions: What is the range of f? What is the preimage of a particular real number or of a set of real numbers? Each of these questions is easier to consider if the matrix of f is a diagonal matrix. So we begin by considering the effect on the representation of f when the basis in R^n is changed.

Example 12 Let $\mathbf{A} = \begin{bmatrix} 2 & -1 \\ -1 & 2 \end{bmatrix}$ and $f(\mathbf{x}) = \mathbf{X}^T\mathbf{A}\mathbf{X} = 2x_1^2 - 2x_1x_2 + 2x_2^2$. Introduce the new basis U in R^2 consisting of $\mathbf{u}_1 = (1, 1)$ and $\mathbf{u}_2 = (0, 2)$. The change-of-basis equation is

$$[\mathbf{x}]_E = \begin{bmatrix} 1 & 0 \\ 1 & 2 \end{bmatrix}[\mathbf{x}]_U$$

For simplicity we write

$$[\mathbf{x}]_E = \mathbf{X} \quad \text{and} \quad [\mathbf{x}]_U = \mathbf{Y} = \begin{bmatrix} y_1 \\ y_2 \end{bmatrix}$$

The change-of-basis equation is then $\mathbf{X} = \mathbf{C}\mathbf{Y}$, where $\mathbf{C} = \begin{bmatrix} 1 & 0 \\ 1 & 2 \end{bmatrix}$. Note that $\mathbf{X}^T = (\mathbf{C}\mathbf{Y})^T = \mathbf{Y}^T\mathbf{C}^T$. With this substitution, $\mathbf{X}^T\mathbf{A}\mathbf{X} = \mathbf{Y}^T\mathbf{C}^T\mathbf{A}\mathbf{C}\mathbf{Y} = \mathbf{Y}^T\mathbf{B}\mathbf{Y}$, where $\mathbf{B} = \mathbf{C}^T\mathbf{A}\mathbf{C}$. In this numerical case,

$$\mathbf{B} = \begin{bmatrix} 1 & 1 \\ 0 & 2 \end{bmatrix}\begin{bmatrix} 2 & -1 \\ -1 & 2 \end{bmatrix}\begin{bmatrix} 1 & 0 \\ 1 & 2 \end{bmatrix} = \begin{bmatrix} 2 & 2 \\ 2 & 8 \end{bmatrix}$$

Notice that $\mathbf{B}$ is a symmetric matrix so that $\mathbf{Y}^T\mathbf{B}\mathbf{Y}$ is a quadratic form. In fact,

$$f = 2y_1^2 + 4y_1y_2 + 8y_2^2.$$

The matrix of f relative to the basis U is $\mathbf{B} = \mathbf{C}^T\mathbf{A}\mathbf{C}$.

The change of basis does not change the range of the quadratic form. For example, if $\mathbf{x}_0 = (3, 1)$, $f(\mathbf{x}_0) = 14$. The corresponding value $\mathbf{y}_0$ is found by

$$\mathbf{Y}_0 = \mathbf{C}^{-1}\mathbf{X}_0 = \begin{bmatrix} 1 & 0 \\ -\frac{1}{2} & \frac{1}{2} \end{bmatrix}\begin{bmatrix} 3 \\ 1 \end{bmatrix} = \begin{bmatrix} 3 \\ -1 \end{bmatrix}$$

and

$$\mathbf{Y}_0^T\mathbf{B}\mathbf{Y}_0 = [3 \quad -1]\begin{bmatrix} 2 & 2 \\ 2 & 8 \end{bmatrix}\begin{bmatrix} 3 \\ -1 \end{bmatrix} = 14$$

■

Theorem 8 Let f be a quadratic form on R^n with matrix **A** relative to the standard basis. Let $U = \{\mathbf{u}_1, \mathbf{u}_2, \ldots, \mathbf{u}_n\}$ be a basis for R^n, and let **C** be the nonsingular matrix such that $[\mathbf{x}]_E = \mathbf{C}[\mathbf{x}]_U$. The matrix of f relative to the basis U is $\mathbf{C}^T\mathbf{AC}$. The range of f is unchanged by this change of basis.

Proof The matrix representation of f relative to the standard basis is $[\mathbf{x}]_E^T\mathbf{A}[\mathbf{x}]_E$. If we set $[\mathbf{x}]_E = \mathbf{C}[\mathbf{x}]_U$, we obtain:

$$f = [\mathbf{x}]_E^T\mathbf{A}[\mathbf{x}]_E = [\mathbf{x}]_U^T\mathbf{C}^T\mathbf{AC}[\mathbf{x}]_U = [\mathbf{x}]_U^T\mathbf{B}[\mathbf{x}]_U$$

where $\mathbf{B} = \mathbf{C}^T\mathbf{AC}$. The matrix **B** is symmetric, since $\mathbf{B}^T = (\mathbf{C}^T\mathbf{AC})^T = \mathbf{C}^T\mathbf{A}^T(\mathbf{C}^T)^T = \mathbf{C}^T\mathbf{AC} = \mathbf{B}$. The matrix of f relative to the basis U is $\mathbf{B} = \mathbf{C}^T\mathbf{AC}$.

To see that this change of basis does not affect the range of the form, consider any real number k in the range. Since k is in the range, there is some $\mathbf{x}_0$ in R^n such that $[\mathbf{x}_0]_E^T\mathbf{A}[\mathbf{x}_0]_E = k$. For this $\mathbf{x}_0$,

$$[\mathbf{x}_0]_U = \mathbf{C}^{-1}[\mathbf{x}_0]_E$$

and

$$\begin{aligned}[\mathbf{x}_0]_U^T\mathbf{B}[\mathbf{x}_0]_U &= [\mathbf{x}_0]_E^T(\mathbf{C}^{-1})^T\mathbf{B}\mathbf{C}^{-1}[\mathbf{x}_0]_E \\ &= [\mathbf{x}_0]_E^T\mathbf{A}[\mathbf{x}_0]_E = k\end{aligned}$$ □

A change of basis is useful if it produces a simpler representation of f. If the matrix of f is diagonal, there are no terms of the form x_ix_j in which $i \neq j$. In Theorem 7 we obtained a diagonal representation by using a basis of eigenvectors. However, we have a problem here. The matrix **B** described in Theorem 8 has the form $\mathbf{C}^T\mathbf{AC}$, which is not in general the same as $\mathbf{C}^{-1}\mathbf{AC}$. Thus the eigenvalues of **A** are not necessarily the same as the eigenvalues of **B**.

Example 13 The matrix **A** of Example 12 has characteristic equation $\lambda^2 - 4\lambda + 3 = 0$ and eigenvalues 3 and 1. The matrix **B** has characteristic equation $\lambda^2 - 10\lambda + 12 = 0$. The roots of this equation, though real, are definitely not 3 and 1. ■

Is there a basis of eigenvectors with respect to which **A** has a diagonal matrix? The special properties of symmetric matrices (Section 6.2) make it possible to find such a basis. In fact, since **A** is symmetric, there is an orthonormal basis of eigenvectors. For this orthonormal basis the change-of-basis matrix **P** is an orthogonal matrix, that is, $\mathbf{P}^T = \mathbf{P}^{-1}$. In this special case, then, $\mathbf{P}^T\mathbf{AP}$ is also $\mathbf{P}^{-1}\mathbf{AP}$ and is a diagonal matrix with the eigenvalues of **A** on the diagonal.

Example 14 Consider again $\mathbf{A} = \begin{bmatrix} 2 & -1 \\ -1 & 2 \end{bmatrix}$ as in Examples 12 and 13. The eigenvalues of **A** are 3 and 1 and corresponding eigenvectors are $(1, -1)$ and $(1, 1)$. An orthonormal basis of eigenvectors is $V = \{\mathbf{v}_1, \mathbf{v}_2\}$, where $\mathbf{v}_1 = (\frac{1}{\sqrt{2}}, -\frac{1}{\sqrt{2}})$ and $\mathbf{v}_2 = (\frac{1}{\sqrt{2}}, \frac{1}{\sqrt{2}})$. The matrix **P** is

$$\mathbf{P} = \begin{bmatrix} \frac{1}{\sqrt{2}} & \frac{1}{\sqrt{2}} \\ -\frac{1}{\sqrt{2}} & \frac{1}{\sqrt{2}} \end{bmatrix} \quad \text{and} \quad \mathbf{P}^T = \mathbf{P}^{-1} = \begin{bmatrix} \frac{1}{\sqrt{2}} & -\frac{1}{\sqrt{2}} \\ \frac{1}{\sqrt{2}} & \frac{1}{\sqrt{2}} \end{bmatrix}$$

so that $\mathbf{P}^T\mathbf{A}\mathbf{P} = \mathbf{P}^{-1}\mathbf{A}\mathbf{P} = \begin{bmatrix} 3 & 0 \\ 0 & 1 \end{bmatrix}$. ■

Theorem 9 Let f be a quadratic form with matrix **A**. Let $U = \{\mathbf{u}_1, \mathbf{u}_2, \ldots, \mathbf{u}_n\}$ be an orthonormal basis of eigenvectors of **A**. The matrix of f relative to U is diagonal and the diagonal elements are the eigenvalues of **A**.

Proof Since $[\mathbf{x}]_E = \mathbf{P}[\mathbf{x}]_U$ and the matrix **P** is orthogonal, the matrix of f relative to U is $\mathbf{P}^T\mathbf{A}\mathbf{P} = \mathbf{P}^{-1}\mathbf{A}\mathbf{P}$. This is a diagonal matrix with the eigenvalues of **A** on the diagonal. □

Every quadratic form has the property that $f(\mathbf{0}) = 0$. Are there other values of **x** for which $f(\mathbf{x}) = 0$? Is $f(\mathbf{x})$ always nonnegative? Is $f(\mathbf{x})$ always nonpositive? Such questions are easier to answer if the quadratic form has a diagonal matrix.

Example 15 Let

$$f(\mathbf{x}) = 3x_1^2 + x_2^2 + 2x_3^2 = \mathbf{X}^T \begin{bmatrix} 3 & 0 & 0 \\ 0 & 1 & 0 \\ 0 & 0 & 2 \end{bmatrix} \mathbf{X}$$

The range of f is all real numbers greater than or equal to 0. The only value of **x** that makes $f(\mathbf{x}) = 0$ is $\mathbf{x} = \mathbf{0}$; that is, the preimage of 0 is **0**.

Let

$$g(\mathbf{x}) = x_1^2 - x_2^2 + 4x_3^2 = \mathbf{X}^T \begin{bmatrix} 1 & 0 & 0 \\ 0 & -1 & 0 \\ 0 & 0 & 4 \end{bmatrix} \mathbf{X}$$

The range of g is all the real numbers, since $g(\mathbf{x}) = -k^2$ if $\mathbf{x} = (0, k, 0)$ and $g(\mathbf{x}) = k^2$ if $\mathbf{x} = (k, 0, 0)$. Notice that the diagonal matrix has both positive and negative elements.

Let

$$h(\mathbf{x}) = x_1^2 + 2x_2^2 = \mathbf{X}^T \begin{bmatrix} 1 & 0 & 0 \\ 0 & 2 & 0 \\ 0 & 0 & 0 \end{bmatrix} \mathbf{X}$$

In this case, $h(\mathbf{x}) \geqslant 0$ for every **x**, but $h(\mathbf{x}) = 0$ not only when $\mathbf{x} = \mathbf{0}$, but also for $\mathbf{x} = (0, 0, k)$. The preimage of 0 is the set $\{(0, 0, k), k \text{ real}\}$. Notice that one of the diagonal elements of the matrix is 0, and its nonzero diagonal elements are positive. ■

Quadratic forms are classified according to the nature of their range as follows:

Quadratic Forms Classified

Definition 6

Let f be a quadratic form from R^n to R, $f(\mathbf{x}) = \mathbf{X}^T\mathbf{A}\mathbf{X}$.

1. f is **positive definite** if and only if $f(\mathbf{x}) > 0$ for all $\mathbf{x} \neq \mathbf{0}$.
2. f is **positive semidefinite** if and only if $f(\mathbf{x}) \geqslant 0$ for all $\mathbf{x}$, and $f(\mathbf{x}) = 0$ for some $\mathbf{x} \neq \mathbf{0}$.
3. f is **indefinite** if and only if the range of f is R. In this case there exists an $\mathbf{x}$ such that $f(\mathbf{x}) > 0$ and there exists an $\mathbf{x}$ such that $f(\mathbf{x}) < 0$.
4. f is **negative semidefinite** if and only if $f(\mathbf{x}) \leqslant 0$ for all $\mathbf{x}$, and $f(\mathbf{x}) = 0$ for some $\mathbf{x} \neq \mathbf{0}$, that is, if and only if $-f$ is positive semidefinite.
5. f is **negative definite** if and only if $f(\mathbf{x}) < 0$ for all $\mathbf{x} \neq \mathbf{0}$, that is, if and only if $-f$ is positive definite.

In the diagonal representation of f described in Theorem 9, the diagonal elements are the eigenvalues of $\mathbf{A}$. Thus, the nature of the range of f can be predicted from the eigenvalues.

Theorem 10 Let f be a quadratic form from R^n to R with matrix $\mathbf{A}$.

1. f is positive definite if and only if the eigenvalues of $\mathbf{A}$ are all positive.
2. f is positive semidefinite if and only if the eigenvalues of $\mathbf{A}$ are all nonnegative, and at least one eigenvalue is 0.
3. f is indefinite if and only if there is at least one positive eigenvalue and at least one negative eigenvalue of $\mathbf{A}$.

Proof The matrix of a quadratic form relative to an orthonormal basis of eigenvectors is a diagonal matrix in which the diagonal elements are the eigenvalues of $\mathbf{A}$. □

The classification of quadratic forms (Definition 6) is independent of the basis in terms of which the form is represented. If the eigenvalues are known or easily found, Theorem 10 is easy to apply. Sometimes it is useful to have a way to classify quadratic forms without using eigenvalues. The number of positive and negative terms in any diagonal representation of a quadratic form can be determined by the following rule.

Gundelfinger's Rule

Let $f(\mathbf{x}) = \mathbf{X}^T\mathbf{A}\mathbf{X}$. Calculate the sequence $p_0, p_1, p_2, \ldots, p_r$ as follows:

$$p_0 = 1,\ p_1 = a_{11},\ p_2 = \det\begin{bmatrix} a_{11} & a_{12} \\ a_{21} & a_{22} \end{bmatrix},\ p_3 = \det\begin{bmatrix} a_{11} & a_{12} & a_{13} \\ a_{21} & a_{22} & a_{23} \\ a_{31} & a_{32} & a_{33} \end{bmatrix}, \ldots,$$

$$p_r = \det \begin{bmatrix} a_{11} & a_{12} & \cdots & a_{1r} \\ a_{21} & a_{22} & \cdots & a_{2r} \\ \vdots & \vdots & & \vdots \\ a_{r1} & a_{r2} & \cdots & a_{rr} \end{bmatrix}$$

Here, r is the rank of the $n \times n$ matrix **A**. Observe the signs in the sequence $p_0, p_1, \ldots, p_r$. A permanence occurs when a term is followed by a term of like sign. A variation occurs when a term is followed by a term of different sign. The number of positive coefficients in the diagonal form is precisely the number of permanences of sign, and the number of negative coefficients is precisely the number of variations of sign in the sequence $p_0, p_1, \ldots, p_r$. A zero term can be counted as either positive or negative but it must be counted. If any two consecutive terms of the sequence are zero, the matrix can be rearranged by renaming the variables so that the rule can be applied.

Example 16

Consider the matrix $\mathbf{B} = \begin{bmatrix} 3 & 1 & 1 \\ 1 & 0 & 2 \\ 1 & 2 & 0 \end{bmatrix}$. (Example 7) Here $p_0 = 1$, $p_1 = 3$, $p_2 = -1$, $p_3 = -8$. The sequence has one variation and two permanences. We conclude that the diagonal form has two positive coefficients and one negative coefficient. Thus, the quadratic form $3x_1^2 + 2x_1x_2 + 2x_1x_3 + 4x_2x_3$ is indefinite. The eigenvalues of **B** were found to be $1, 4, -2$, which leads to the same conclusion.

The matrix **A** of Example 8 is $\mathbf{A} = \begin{bmatrix} 7 & -2 & 1 \\ -2 & 10 & -2 \\ 1 & -2 & 7 \end{bmatrix}$, and its eigenvalues are 6, 6, and 12. The sequence of Gundelfinger's Rule is $p_0 = 1, p_1 = 7, p_2 = 66$, and $p_3 = 432$, which has three permanences and leads to the conclusion that the quadratic form with matrix **A** is positive definite.

In Example 11, the quadratic form has the matrix $\mathbf{C} = \begin{bmatrix} 1 & 3 & -1 \\ 3 & 2 & 1 \\ -1 & 1 & 5 \end{bmatrix}$. Here $p_0 = 1, p_1 = 1, p_2 = -7$, and $p_3 = -44$. Again, there is one variation in sign and the form is indefinite. You may wish to check this by finding the eigenvalues of **C**.

■

Gundelfinger's Rule is convenient to apply and is frequently used in applying a test for maxima and minima of functions of several variables.

Symmetric matrices and quadratic forms have many applications in a variety of areas, such as solutions of partial differential equations and error analysis. A few simple applications are included in Section 6.5

This section closes with a familiar geometric application.

Example 17

Let (x_1, x_2) be coordinates in the plane. What is the graph of $8x_1^2 + 4x_1x_2 + 5x_2^2 = 36$? Since the left-hand side of this equation is a quadratic form, the question can be rephrased as, What is the preimage of 36 under f, where $f(\mathbf{x}) = \mathbf{X}^T \begin{bmatrix} 8 & 2 \\ 2 & 5 \end{bmatrix} \mathbf{X}$? We expect it to be a conic, but because of the $x_1 x_2$ term we cannot immediately recognize whether it is an ellipse, a hyperbola, or a parabola. We change to an orthonormal basis of eigenvectors.

The matrix $\begin{bmatrix} 8 & 2 \\ 2 & 5 \end{bmatrix}$ has eigenvalues 9 and 4, with corresponding eigenvectors (2, 1) and $(-1, 2)$. An orthonormal basis is $\mathbf{v}_1 = (\frac{2}{\sqrt{5}}, \frac{1}{\sqrt{5}})$ and $\mathbf{v}_2 = (-\frac{1}{\sqrt{5}}, \frac{2}{\sqrt{5}})$. The coordinates of $\mathbf{x}$ relative to this basis are related to the coordinates relative to the standard basis by the equation $[\mathbf{x}]_E = \mathbf{P}[\mathbf{x}]_V$ in which

$$\mathbf{P} = \begin{bmatrix} \frac{2}{\sqrt{5}} & -\frac{1}{\sqrt{5}} \\ \frac{1}{\sqrt{5}} & \frac{2}{\sqrt{5}} \end{bmatrix}$$

Thanks to the fact that $\{\mathbf{v}_1, \mathbf{v}_2\}$ is an orthonormal basis, $\mathbf{P}^{-1}$ and $\mathbf{P}^T$ are the same.

Write $[\mathbf{x}]_E = \mathbf{X}$ and $[\mathbf{x}]_V = \begin{bmatrix} y_1 \\ y_2 \end{bmatrix} = \mathbf{Y}$. Then $\mathbf{X} = \mathbf{PY}$, and the quadratic form is

$$\mathbf{Y}^T\mathbf{P}^T\mathbf{APY} = \mathbf{Y}^T\mathbf{P}^{-1}\mathbf{APY} = \mathbf{Y}^T \begin{bmatrix} 9 & 0 \\ 0 & 4 \end{bmatrix} \mathbf{Y} = 9y_1^2 + 4y_2^2$$

In terms of the new basis, the original equation $f(\mathbf{x}) = 36$ becomes $9y_1^2 + 4y_2^2 = 36$. This equation is readily recognized as the equation of an ellipse. The coordinate axes for the y_1, y_2 system are the principal axes of the ellipse. Geometrically, the change of basis to an orthonormal system of eigenvectors has amounted to a rotation of axes so that the new axes are the principal axes of the ellipse (Figure 6.3).

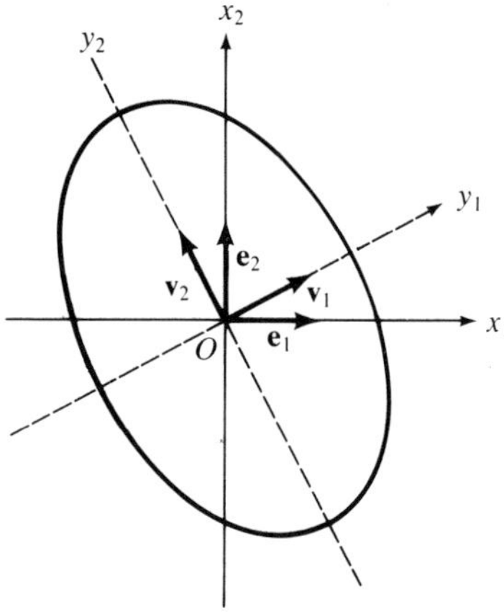

FIGURE 6.3 ■

Similar geometric questions arise in determining the preimage of a real number with respect to a quadratic form from R^3 to the real numbers.

Example 18 Let $f(\mathbf{x}) = 3x_1^2 + 2x_1x_2 + 2x_1x_3 + 4x_2x_3$. What is the preimage of 4? That is, what is the graph of the equation $3x_1^2 + 2x_1x_2 + 2x_1x_3 + 4x_2x_3 = 4$? The matrix of this form is

$$\mathbf{A} = \begin{bmatrix} 3 & 1 & 1 \\ 1 & 0 & 2 \\ 1 & 2 & 0 \end{bmatrix}$$

Its eigenvalues are 4, 1, −2, and an orthonormal basis of eigenvectors is $\{\mathbf{v}_1, \mathbf{v}_2, \mathbf{v}_3\}$, where $\mathbf{v}_1 = (\frac{2}{\sqrt{6}}, \frac{1}{\sqrt{6}}, \frac{1}{\sqrt{6}})$, $\mathbf{v}_2 = (-\frac{1}{\sqrt{3}}, \frac{1}{\sqrt{3}}, \frac{1}{\sqrt{3}})$, and $\mathbf{v}_3 = (0, \frac{1}{\sqrt{2}}, -\frac{1}{\sqrt{2}})$. Let $(\mathbf{x})_V = (y_1, y_2, y_3)$. The equation becomes

$$4y_1^2 + y_2^2 - 2y_3^2 = 4$$

This is an elliptic hyperboloid with elliptic cross sections in the $\mathbf{v}_1\mathbf{v}_2$ plane and with axis the $\mathbf{v}_3$-axis. See Figure 6.4.

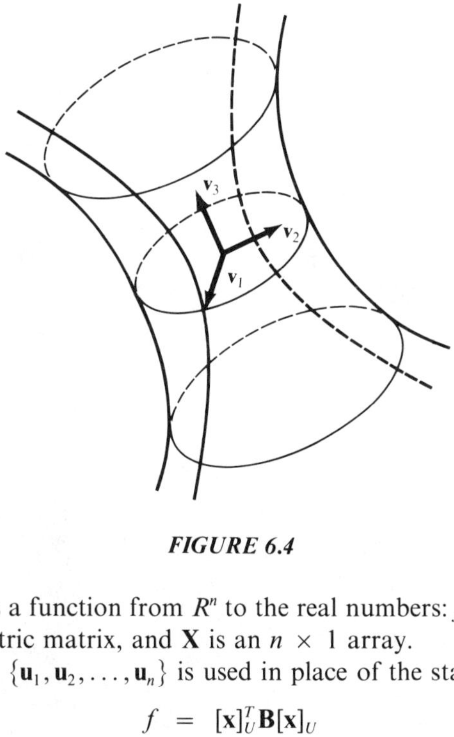

FIGURE 6.4 ■

SUMMARY A quadratic form is a function from R^n to the real numbers: $f = \mathbf{X}^T\mathbf{A}\mathbf{X}$, where $\mathbf{A}$ is an $n \times n$ symmetric matrix, and $\mathbf{X}$ is an $n \times 1$ array.

If the basis $U = \{\mathbf{u}_1, \mathbf{u}_2, \ldots, \mathbf{u}_n\}$ is used in place of the standard basis,

$$f = [\mathbf{x}]_U^T\mathbf{B}[\mathbf{x}]_U$$

where $\mathbf{B}$ is the symmetric matrix $\mathbf{C}^T\mathbf{A}\mathbf{C}$ and $\mathbf{C}$ is the change-of-basis matrix $[\mathbf{x}]_E = \mathbf{C}[\mathbf{x}]_U$.

If U is an orthonormal basis of eigenvectors of $\mathbf{A}$, the diagonal elements of the diagonal representation with respect to U are the eigenvalues of $\mathbf{A}$. The eigenvalues of $\mathbf{A}$ thus give a way of determining whether the range of the quadratic form is all real numbers, the positive real numbers, or the negative real numbers.

EXERCISES 6.3

1. Write the quadratic form corresponding to the matrix product $\mathbf{X}^T\mathbf{A}\mathbf{X}$ in each case.

   a. $\mathbf{A} = \begin{bmatrix} 1 & 2 \\ 2 & 1 \end{bmatrix}$ b. $\mathbf{A} = \begin{bmatrix} 8 & -5 \\ -5 & 2 \end{bmatrix}$

   c. $\mathbf{A} = \begin{bmatrix} 1 & 4 & 3 \\ 4 & 0 & -1 \\ 3 & -1 & 7 \end{bmatrix}$

2. In each case, write the quadratic form as a matrix product.

   a. $x_1^2 + 3x_2^2 - 6x_1x_2$
   b. $x_1^2 - 7x_1x_2$
   c. $x_1^2 + x_2^2 - 3x_3^2 + 2x_1x_2 - 4x_2x_3 + 6x_1x_3$
   d. $x_1^2 + 2x_2^2 + 3x_3^2 + 5x_1x_2 - 7x_2x_3 + x_1x_3$
   e. $2x_1x_2 + 6x_2x_3 - 4x_1x_3$

3. Find a basis that gives a diagonal matrix for the quadratic form

$$f(\mathbf{x}) = 3x_1^2 + 2x_1x_2 + 2x_1x_3 + 4x_2x_3$$

4. Let $f(\mathbf{x}) = 7x_1^2 - 4x_1x_2 + 2x_1x_3 + 10x_2^2 - 4x_2x_3 + 7x_3^2$. Find an equation for the change of basis that makes the quadratic form a diagonal form with the eigenvalues of **A** as coefficients.

5. Let $f(\mathbf{x}) = \mathbf{X}^T\mathbf{A}\mathbf{X}$, where **A** is the matrix $\begin{bmatrix} -1 & -2 & 1 \\ -2 & 2 & -2 \\ 1 & -2 & -1 \end{bmatrix}$. Find a matrix **C** such that $\mathbf{C}^T\mathbf{A}\mathbf{C}$ is a diagonal matrix with the eigenvalues of **A** on the diagonal.

6. Let $f(\mathbf{x}) = x_1^2 + 3x_2^2 - 7x_3^2$. Find an **x** such that $f(\mathbf{x}) > 0$. Find an **x** such that $f(\mathbf{x}) < 0$. Find **x** such that $f(\mathbf{x}) = 2$. Find **x** such that $f(\mathbf{x}) = -4$. Are your answers unique? Show that for any real number k there is an **x** such that $f(\mathbf{x}) = k$.

7. Let $f(\mathbf{x}) = 3x_1^2 + 2x_2^2 + 0x_3^2$ be a quadratic form from R^3 to R. Find **x** such that $f(\mathbf{x}) > 0$. Find $\mathbf{x} \neq \mathbf{0}$ such that $f(\mathbf{x}) = 0$. Is it possible to find **x** such that $f(\mathbf{x}) < 0$?

8. Let $f(\mathbf{x}) = x_1^2 + 2x_2^2 + 4x_3^2$. Find **x** such that $f(\mathbf{x}) = 7$. Find **x** such that $f(\mathbf{x}) = 6$. Is it possible to find $\mathbf{x} \neq \mathbf{0}$ such that $f(\mathbf{x}) = 0$?

9. Classify the following quadratic forms according to their range. In each case the domain is R^4.

   a. $3x_1^2 - 2x_2^2 + 3x_3^2 - 2x_4^2$ b. $3x_1^2 + 3x_3^2$
   c. $3x_1^2 - 2x_2^2 + 3x_3^2$ d. $-2x_2^2 - 2x_4^2$
   e. $x_1^2 + 2x_2^2 + 3x_3^2 + 2x_4^2$

10. Classify the following quadratic forms according to their range. In each case $f(\mathbf{x}) = \mathbf{X}^T\mathbf{A}\mathbf{X}$.

    a. **A** is diagonal with diagonal elements 3, 2, 1.
    b. **A** is diagonal with diagonal elements $-1, -1, -2, -4$.
    c. **A** is diagonal with diagonal elements 1, 2, 4, 0.
    d. **A** is a symmetric matrix with eigenvalues $-1, 4, 2$, and 3.
    e. **A** is a 3×3 matrix, one eigenvalue is 3, $\det \mathbf{A} = 0$, and the sum of the diagonal elements is 8.

11. Use Gundelfinger's Rule on the matrix of Problem 5. Does the result agree with the signs of the eigenvalues?

12. Write each equation as a matrix product. Then identify each of the graphs by rotating the axes so that the new axes correspond to eigenvectors of the matrix of the expression.

    a. $x^2 + 4xy + 4y^2 = 10$
    b. $2x^2 - 4xy + 5y^2 = 6$
    c. $4x^2 + 6xy - 4y^2 = 12$

13. Identify the graph of each of the following equations:

    a. $2x^2 + 3xy - 2y^2 = 25$
    b. $x^2 + 4xy + 4y^2 = 9$
    c. $8x^2 + 12xy + 13y^2 = 884$

14. The equation $4x^2 - 8xy - 2y^2 + 20x - 4y + 15 = 0$ has linear terms as well as quadratic terms. Using the quadratic terms alone, find a basis such that the new form has no product term. Let (u, v) be the coordinates relative to the new basis. Write the equation in terms of u and v.

15. In geometry books that discuss rotation of axes, the following statement is made: Let $Ax^2 + Bxy + Cy^2 = F$. The expression $B^2 - 4AC$ is invariant under rotation; that is, if $A'u^2 + B'uv + C'v^2 = F$ is the equation expressed in terms of coordinates with respect to the new

basis, then $B^2 - 4AC = B'^2 - 4A'C'$. Show this using the matrix form of change of coordinates.

16. Geometry books give the following rules for identifying $Ax^2 + Bxy + Cy^2 = F$:

a. If $B^2 - 4AC < 0$, the graph is an ellipse, a circle, a point, or there is no graph.

b. If $B^2 - 4AC = 0$, the graph is a parabola, two parallel lines, one line, or there is no graph.

c. If $B^2 - 4AC > 0$, the graph is a hyperbola or two intersecting lines.

Compare these rules with Gundelfinger's Rule.

17. Identify the surface represented by $7x^2 + 10y^2 + 7z^2 - 4xy + 2xz - 4yz = 36$.

6.4 Functions of a Square Matrix

Diagonalization leads to a natural way of dealing with functions of a square matrix. We begin by looking at polynomial functions $p(\mathbf{A})$ and the surprisingly simple way in which the eigenvalues of $\mathbf{A}$ are related to those of $p(\mathbf{A})$. For any square matrix $\mathbf{A}$, $\mathbf{A}^n$ is defined for positive integral n. If $p(x) = a_0 + a_1x + a_2x^2 + \cdots + a_nx^n$, the corresponding matrix polynomial is $p(\mathbf{A}) = a_0\mathbf{I} + a_1\mathbf{A} + a_2\mathbf{A}^2 + \cdots + a_n\mathbf{A}^n$ so that $p(\mathbf{A})$ is a square matrix of the same size as $\mathbf{A}$.

Theorem 11 Let $\mathbf{A}$ be an $n \times n$ matrix and p be a polynomial. If $\lambda_1, \lambda_2, \ldots, \lambda_n$ are the eigenvalues of $\mathbf{A}$, then $p(\lambda_1), p(\lambda_2), \ldots, p(\lambda_n)$ are eigenvalues of $p(\mathbf{A})$. The corresponding eigenvectors $\mathbf{v}_1, \mathbf{v}_2, \ldots, \mathbf{v}_n$ are also eigenvectors of the matrix $p(\mathbf{A})$.

Proof Since $\mathbf{AV}_i = \lambda_i\mathbf{V}_i$, then $\mathbf{A}^2\mathbf{V}_i = \mathbf{A}(\mathbf{AV}_i) = \mathbf{A}\lambda_i\mathbf{V}_i = \lambda_i\mathbf{AV}_i = \lambda_i^2\mathbf{V}_i$. The equation $\mathbf{A}^2\mathbf{V}_i = \lambda_i^2\mathbf{V}_i$ implies that λ_i^2 is an eigenvalue of $\mathbf{A}^2$ and that $\mathbf{v}_i$ is a corresponding eigenvector. An induction argument shows that for any positive integer n, $\mathbf{A}^n\mathbf{V}_i = \lambda_i^n\mathbf{V}_i$, so that λ_i^n is an eigenvalue of $\mathbf{A}^n$ and $\mathbf{v}_i$ is a corresponding eigenvector.

Now let $p(x) = a_0 + a_1x + \cdots + a_nx^n$ so that

$$p(\mathbf{A}) = a_0\mathbf{I} + a_1\mathbf{A} + \cdots + a_n\mathbf{A}^n$$

Consider

$$\begin{aligned} p(\mathbf{A})\mathbf{V}_i &= (a_0\mathbf{I} + a_1\mathbf{A} + a_2\mathbf{A}^2 + \cdots + a_n\mathbf{A}^n)\mathbf{V}_i \\ &= a_0\mathbf{IV}_i + a_1\mathbf{AV}_i + a_2\mathbf{A}^2\mathbf{V}_i + \cdots + a_n\mathbf{A}^n\mathbf{V}_i \\ &= a_0\mathbf{V}_i + a_1\lambda_i\mathbf{V}_i + a_2\lambda_i^2\mathbf{V}_i + \cdots + a_n\lambda_i^n\mathbf{V}_i \\ &= (a_0 + a_1\lambda_i + a_2\lambda_i^2 + \cdots + a_n\lambda_i^n)\mathbf{V}_i \\ &= p(\lambda_i)\mathbf{V}_i \end{aligned}$$

This equation says that $p(\lambda_i)$ is an eigenvalue of $p(\mathbf{A})$ and $\mathbf{v}_i$ is a corresponding eigenvector. □

Example 19 Let $\mathbf{A} = \begin{bmatrix} 1 & 2 \\ -1 & 4 \end{bmatrix}$. The eigenvalues of $\mathbf{A}$ are 3 and 2, and the corresponding eigenvectors are $\mathbf{v}_1 = (1, 1)$ and $\mathbf{v}_2 = (2, 1)$.

The matrix $\mathbf{A}^2 = \begin{bmatrix} -1 & 10 \\ -5 & 14 \end{bmatrix}$. The characteristic equation of $\mathbf{A}^2$ is $\lambda^2 - 13\lambda + 36 = 0$; the eigenvalues of $\mathbf{A}^2$ are 9 and 4 as Theorem 11 predicts. Also, the calculations $\mathbf{A}^2\begin{bmatrix} 1 \\ 1 \end{bmatrix} = \begin{bmatrix} 9 \\ 9 \end{bmatrix}$ and $\mathbf{A}^2\begin{bmatrix} 2 \\ 1 \end{bmatrix} = \begin{bmatrix} 8 \\ 4 \end{bmatrix}$ show that $\mathbf{v}_1$ and $\mathbf{v}_2$ are indeed eigenvectors of $\mathbf{A}^2$ corresponding to 9 and 4.

The eigenvalues of the matrix $p(\mathbf{A}) = \mathbf{I} - 2\mathbf{A} + 4\mathbf{A}^2 - \mathbf{A}^3$ are $1 - 2(3) + 4(3)^2 - 3^3 = 4$ and $1 - 2(2) + 4(2)^2 - 2^3 = 5$. An eigenvalue corresponding to 4 is (1, 1) and an eigenvector corresponding to 5 is (2, 1).

In this example, since the eigenvalues of $\mathbf{A}$ are distinct, $\mathbf{A}$ is similar to a diagonal matrix. For $\mathbf{P} = \begin{bmatrix} 1 & 2 \\ 1 & 1 \end{bmatrix}$ we have $\mathbf{P}^{-1}\mathbf{A}\mathbf{P} = \begin{bmatrix} 3 & 0 \\ 0 & 2 \end{bmatrix}$. Since the eigenvectors of $\mathbf{A}^2$ are the same as those of $\mathbf{A}$, the same matrix $\mathbf{P}$ will diagonalize $\mathbf{A}^2$ so that $\mathbf{P}^{-1}\mathbf{A}^2\mathbf{P} = \begin{bmatrix} 9 & 0 \\ 0 & 4 \end{bmatrix}$. The same reasoning applies to the matrix $p(\mathbf{A})$ so that for the same $\mathbf{P}$,

$$\mathbf{P}^{-1}(\mathbf{I} - 2\mathbf{A} + 4\mathbf{A}^2 - \mathbf{A}^3)\mathbf{P} = \begin{bmatrix} 4 & 0 \\ 0 & 5 \end{bmatrix}$$ ■

The product of the eigenvalues of $\mathbf{A}$ is $\det \mathbf{A}$. If a matrix $\mathbf{A}$ is invertible, its determinant is not 0 and none of its eigenvalues can be 0. Theorem 12 describes the eigenvalues and eigenvectors of $\mathbf{A}^{-1}$ if $\mathbf{A}^{-1}$ exists.

Theorem 12 If $\mathbf{A}$ is nonsingular and has eigenvalues $\lambda_1, \lambda_2, \ldots, \lambda_n$ and corresponding eigenvectors $\mathbf{v}_1, \mathbf{v}_2, \ldots, \mathbf{v}_n$, then $\mathbf{A}^{-1}$ has eigenvalues $1/\lambda_1, 1/\lambda_2, \ldots, 1/\lambda_n$ and corresponding eigenvectors $\mathbf{v}_1, \mathbf{v}_2, \ldots, \mathbf{v}_n$.

Proof The statement $\mathbf{A}\mathbf{V}_i = \lambda_i\mathbf{V}_i$ implies

$$\frac{1}{\lambda_i}\mathbf{V}_i = \mathbf{A}^{-1}\mathbf{V}_i$$

since $\mathbf{A}$ is nonsingular and none of its eigenvalues can be zero. From this it follows that $1/\lambda_i$ is an eigenvalue of $\mathbf{A}^{-1}$ and that $\mathbf{v}_i$ is a corresponding eigenvector. □

If the matrix $\mathbf{A}$ is similar to a diagonal matrix, then there is a matrix $\mathbf{P}$ whose columns are eigenvectors of $\mathbf{A}$ and such that $\mathbf{P}^{-1}\mathbf{A}\mathbf{P} = \mathbf{D}$. Since the eigenvectors of $p(\mathbf{A})$ and the eigenvectors of $\mathbf{A}^{-1}$ are the same as the eigenvectors of $\mathbf{A}$, the same matrix $\mathbf{P}$ will have the property that $\mathbf{P}^{-1}p(\mathbf{A})\mathbf{P}$ and $\mathbf{P}^{-1}\mathbf{A}^{-1}\mathbf{P}$ are diagonal matrices. In each case the diagonal elements will be the appropriate eigenvalues. Thus:

$$\mathbf{P}^{-1}p(\mathbf{A})\mathbf{P} = \begin{bmatrix} p(\lambda_1) & 0 & \cdots & 0 \\ 0 & p(\lambda_2) & \cdots & 0 \\ \vdots & \vdots & & \vdots \\ 0 & 0 & \cdots & p(\lambda_n) \end{bmatrix}$$

and

$$\mathbf{P}^{-1}\mathbf{A}^{-1}\mathbf{P} = \begin{bmatrix} \frac{1}{\lambda_1} & 0 & \cdots & 0 \\ 0 & \frac{1}{\lambda_2} & \cdots & 0 \\ \vdots & \vdots & & \vdots \\ 0 & 0 & \cdots & \frac{1}{\lambda_n} \end{bmatrix}$$

Once the eigenvalues and eigenvectors of **A** are known, these can be used to obtain expressions for $p(\mathbf{A})$ and for $\mathbf{A}^{-1}$ since

$$p(\mathbf{A}) = \mathbf{P}\begin{bmatrix} p(\lambda_1) & 0 & \cdots & 0 \\ 0 & p(\lambda_2) & \cdots & 0 \\ \vdots & \vdots & & \vdots \\ 0 & 0 & \cdots & p(\lambda_n) \end{bmatrix}\mathbf{P}^{-1}$$

and

$$\mathbf{A}^{-1} = \mathbf{P}\begin{bmatrix} \frac{1}{\lambda_1} & 0 & \cdots & 0 \\ 0 & \frac{1}{\lambda_2} & \cdots & 0 \\ \vdots & \vdots & & \vdots \\ 0 & 0 & \cdots & \frac{1}{\lambda_n} \end{bmatrix}\mathbf{P}^{-1}$$

Example 20 Let $\mathbf{A} = \begin{bmatrix} 1 & 2 \\ -1 & 4 \end{bmatrix}$; the eigenvalues are 3 and 2, and $\mathbf{P} = \begin{bmatrix} 1 & 2 \\ 1 & 1 \end{bmatrix}$. The eigenvalues of $\mathbf{A}^{-1}$ are $\frac{1}{3}$ and $\frac{1}{2}$, and

$$\begin{aligned} \mathbf{A}^{-1} &= \mathbf{P}\begin{bmatrix} \frac{1}{3} & 0 \\ 0 & \frac{1}{2} \end{bmatrix}\mathbf{P}^{-1} \\ &= \begin{bmatrix} 1 & 2 \\ 1 & 1 \end{bmatrix}\begin{bmatrix} \frac{1}{3} & 0 \\ 0 & \frac{1}{2} \end{bmatrix}\begin{bmatrix} -1 & 2 \\ 1 & -1 \end{bmatrix} \\ &= \begin{bmatrix} \frac{2}{3} & -\frac{1}{3} \\ \frac{1}{6} & \frac{1}{6} \end{bmatrix} \end{aligned}$$

■

The next two examples illustrate applications of this technique. In Section 3.6, in the study of the Leontief input-output model of economic behavior, the statement is made that $(\mathbf{1} - \mathbf{A})^{-1}$ can be approximated by a sum of the form $\mathbf{I} + \mathbf{A} + \mathbf{A}^2 + \cdots + \mathbf{A}^m$, provided $\mathbf{A}^{m+1}$ is almost the zero matrix when m is large enough. If **A** is similar to a diagonal matrix, $\mathbf{A}^{m+1} = \mathbf{P}\mathbf{D}^{m+1}\mathbf{P}^{-1}$, so $\mathbf{A}^{m+1}$ can be calculated when the eigenvalues of **A** are known.

Example 21 Let $\mathbf{A} = \begin{bmatrix} \frac{3}{8} & \frac{1}{8} \\ \frac{1}{4} & \frac{1}{4} \end{bmatrix}$. This matrix has eigenvalues $\frac{1}{2}$ and $\frac{1}{8}$ and eigenvectors (1, 1) and (1, −2). Thus

$$\mathbf{A}^{m+1} = \mathbf{P}\begin{bmatrix} (\frac{1}{2})^{m+1} & 0 \\ 0 & (\frac{1}{8})^{m+1} \end{bmatrix}\mathbf{P}^{-1}$$

where $\mathbf{P} = \begin{bmatrix} 1 & 1 \\ 1 & -2 \end{bmatrix}$. But $(\frac{1}{2})^{m+1}$ and $(\frac{1}{8})^{m+1}$ both approach zero as m becomes large. The matrix **P** does not depend on m. The matrix $\mathbf{A}^{m+1}$ approaches the zero matrix as m becomes large. ■

Given a matrix **A**, we sometimes need to find a matrix **C** such that $\mathbf{C}^2 = \mathbf{A}$. The matrix **C** in this case can be thought of as a square root of **A**. If **A** is similar to a diagonal matrix, we can identify a square root of **A** by using the expression $\mathbf{P}^{-1}\mathbf{AP} = \mathbf{D}$. Example 22 illustrates this.

Example 22 Find a matrix **C** with $\mathbf{C}^2 = \mathbf{A}$, if $\mathbf{A} = \begin{bmatrix} 26 & -10 \\ -10 & 26 \end{bmatrix}$.

Solution The eigenvalues of **A** are 36 and 16, and corresponding eigenvectors are (1, −1) and (1, 1). Then $\mathbf{P}^{-1}\mathbf{AP} = \begin{bmatrix} 36 & 0 \\ 0 & 16 \end{bmatrix}$. The matrix **C** will have the property that $\mathbf{C}^2 = \mathbf{A}$ if **C** has eigenvalues ± 6 and ± 4, and the same eigenvectors as **A**. There are four matrices with these properties.

$$\mathbf{C}_1 = \mathbf{P}\begin{bmatrix} 6 & 0 \\ 0 & 4 \end{bmatrix}\mathbf{P}^{-1} = \begin{bmatrix} 5 & -1 \\ -1 & 5 \end{bmatrix}$$

$$\mathbf{C}_2 = \mathbf{P}\begin{bmatrix} 6 & 0 \\ 0 & -4 \end{bmatrix}\mathbf{P}^{-1} = \begin{bmatrix} 1 & -5 \\ -5 & 1 \end{bmatrix}$$

$$\mathbf{C}_3 = \mathbf{P}\begin{bmatrix} -6 & 0 \\ 0 & 4 \end{bmatrix}\mathbf{P}^{-1} = \begin{bmatrix} -1 & 5 \\ 5 & -1 \end{bmatrix}$$

$$\mathbf{C}_4 = \mathbf{P}\begin{bmatrix} -6 & 0 \\ 0 & -4 \end{bmatrix}\mathbf{P}^{-1} = \begin{bmatrix} -5 & 1 \\ 1 & -5 \end{bmatrix}$$

■

Based on the analogy with polynomial functions and roots, it is not unreasonable to extend the definition of functions of a matrix to other functions like sin **A**, cos **A**, or exp **A**. This technique does prove consistent and useful. We consider here only matrices **A** that are similar to diagonal matrices. If $\mathbf{P}^{-1}\mathbf{AP} = \mathbf{D}$, where the diagonal elements of **D** are $d_1, d_2, \ldots, d_n$, the function $f(\mathbf{A})$ is defined to be the matrix $\mathbf{P}f(\mathbf{D})\mathbf{P}^{-1}$, where $f(\mathbf{D})$ is a diagonal matrix with diagonal elements $f(d_1), f(d_2), \ldots, f(d_n)$. For example, suppose

$$\mathbf{P}^{-1}\mathbf{AP} = \begin{bmatrix} d_1 & 0 \\ 0 & d_2 \end{bmatrix}$$

The following definitions are made:

$$\sin \mathbf{A} = \mathbf{P}\begin{bmatrix} \sin d_1 & 0 \\ 0 & \sin d_2 \end{bmatrix}\mathbf{P}^{-1}$$

$$\cos \mathbf{A} = \mathbf{P}\begin{bmatrix} \cos d_1 & 0 \\ 0 & \cos d_2 \end{bmatrix}\mathbf{P}^{-1}$$

$$\exp \mathbf{A} = e^{\mathbf{A}} = \mathbf{P}\begin{bmatrix} e^{d_1} & 0 \\ 0 & e^{d_2} \end{bmatrix}\mathbf{P}^{-1}$$

Definitions such as these are useful in the study of systems of differential equations. (See Section 6.5.) Example 23 illustrates some of the properties of $e^{\mathbf{A}}$ for a 2×2 matrix $\mathbf{A}$.

Example 23 Let $\mathbf{A} = \begin{bmatrix} 1 & 2 \\ -1 & 4 \end{bmatrix}$. The eigenvalues of $\mathbf{A}$ are 3 and 2, and $\mathbf{P}^{-1}\mathbf{A}\mathbf{P} = \begin{bmatrix} 3 & 0 \\ 0 & 2 \end{bmatrix}$ if $\mathbf{P} = \begin{bmatrix} 1 & 2 \\ 1 & 1 \end{bmatrix}$. According to the definition, $e^{\mathbf{A}} = \mathbf{P}\begin{bmatrix} e^3 & 0 \\ 0 & e^2 \end{bmatrix}\mathbf{P}^{-1}$; that is,

$$e^{\mathbf{A}} = \begin{bmatrix} -e^3 + 2e^2 & 2e^3 - 2e^2 \\ -e^3 + e^2 & 2e^3 - e^2 \end{bmatrix}$$

One property we associate with the function e^x is that $e^{2x} = (e^x)(e^x)$. This is easily verified for $e^{\mathbf{A}}$. Since $2\mathbf{A}$ has eigenvalues 6 and 4, $\mathbf{P}^{-1}2\mathbf{A}\mathbf{P} = \begin{bmatrix} 6 & 0 \\ 0 & 4 \end{bmatrix}$ and

$$e^{2\mathbf{A}} = \mathbf{P}\begin{bmatrix} e^6 & 0 \\ 0 & e^4 \end{bmatrix}\mathbf{P}^{-1}$$

But the product is

$$\begin{aligned} e^{\mathbf{A}}e^{\mathbf{A}} &= \left(\mathbf{P}\begin{bmatrix} e^3 & 0 \\ 0 & e^2 \end{bmatrix}\mathbf{P}^{-1}\right)\left(\mathbf{P}\begin{bmatrix} e^3 & 0 \\ 0 & e^2 \end{bmatrix}\mathbf{P}^{-1}\right) \\ &= \mathbf{P}\begin{bmatrix} e^3 & 0 \\ 0 & e^2 \end{bmatrix}\begin{bmatrix} e^3 & 0 \\ 0 & e^2 \end{bmatrix}\mathbf{P}^{-1} \\ &= \mathbf{P}\begin{bmatrix} e^6 & 0 \\ 0 & e^4 \end{bmatrix}\mathbf{P}^{-1} = e^{2\mathbf{A}} \end{aligned}$$

■

Perhaps the most characteristic property of the exponential function and the one that makes it useful in differential equations is the fact that the derivative of e^{at} with respect to t, written $D_t e^{at}$, is ae^{at}. Let t be a scalar. How shall we differentiate $e^{\mathbf{A}t}$? First, since t is a scalar, $\mathbf{A}t$ has eigenvalues $3t$ and $2t$, so

$$e^{\mathbf{A}t} = \mathbf{P}\begin{bmatrix} e^{3t} & 0 \\ 0 & e^{2t} \end{bmatrix}\mathbf{P}^{-1}$$

Since

$$D_t f(t) = \lim_{h \to 0} \frac{f(t+h) - f(t)}{h}$$

it is reasonable to define the derivative of a matrix $\mathbf{B}(t) = [b_{ij}(t)]$ in a similar way as:

$$D_t \mathbf{B}(t) = \lim_{h \to 0} \frac{\mathbf{B}(t+h) - \mathbf{B}(t)}{h}$$

These processes are done elementwise. The definition then says that the derivative of a matrix with elements that are functions of t is the matrix of derivatives taken elementwise. Thus,

$$D_t \begin{bmatrix} t^2 & 3t \\ 2 & t^3 \end{bmatrix} = \begin{bmatrix} 2t & 3 \\ 0 & 3t^2 \end{bmatrix}$$

With this definition,

$$D_t \begin{bmatrix} e^{3t} & 0 \\ 0 & e^{2t} \end{bmatrix} = \begin{bmatrix} 3e^{3t} & 0 \\ 0 & 2e^{2t} \end{bmatrix} = \begin{bmatrix} 3 & 0 \\ 0 & 2 \end{bmatrix} \begin{bmatrix} e^{3t} & 0 \\ 0 & e^{2t} \end{bmatrix}$$

Since the matrices $\mathbf{P}$ and $\mathbf{P}^{-1}$ do not involve t,

$$\begin{aligned} D_t e^{\mathbf{A}t} &= \mathbf{P} D_t \begin{bmatrix} e^{3t} & 0 \\ 0 & e^{2t} \end{bmatrix} \mathbf{P}^{-1} = \mathbf{P} \begin{bmatrix} 3 & 0 \\ 0 & 2 \end{bmatrix} \begin{bmatrix} e^{3t} & 0 \\ 0 & e^{2t} \end{bmatrix} \mathbf{P}^{-1} \\ &= \mathbf{P} \begin{bmatrix} 3 & 0 \\ 0 & 2 \end{bmatrix} \mathbf{P}^{-1}\mathbf{P} \begin{bmatrix} e^{3t} & 0 \\ 0 & e^{2t} \end{bmatrix} \mathbf{P}^{-1} \end{aligned}$$

where the matrix $\mathbf{P}^{-1}\mathbf{P}$ is inserted between the two diagonal matrices. But this is simply the product $\mathbf{A}e^{\mathbf{A}t}$.

It should be pointed out that not everything is simple in considering generalizations of functions to functions of matrices. Difficulties arise as soon as more than one matrix is involved. For example, in general, $e^{\mathbf{A}}e^{\mathbf{B}} \neq e^{\mathbf{A}+\mathbf{B}}$.

SUMMARY Let $\mathbf{A}$ be a square matrix with eigenvalues $\lambda_1, \lambda_2, \ldots, \lambda_n$ and corresponding eigenvectors $\mathbf{u}_1, \mathbf{u}_2, \ldots, \mathbf{u}_n$. Let $p(x)$ be any polynomial. The matrix $p(\mathbf{A})$ has eigenvalues $p(\lambda_1), p(\lambda_2), \ldots, p(\lambda_n)$ and corresponding eigenvectors $\mathbf{u}_1, \mathbf{u}_2, \ldots, \mathbf{u}_n$.

If $\mathbf{A}$ is similar to a diagonal matrix, $\mathbf{P}^{-1}\mathbf{A}\mathbf{P} = \mathbf{D}$, where $\mathbf{D}$ has diagonal elements $\lambda_1, \lambda_2, \ldots, \lambda_n$. This equation leads to the equations

$$\begin{aligned} \mathbf{A}^m &= \mathbf{P}\mathbf{D}^m\mathbf{P}^{-1} \\ \mathbf{A}^{-1} &= \mathbf{P}\mathbf{D}^{-1}\mathbf{P}^{-1} \end{aligned}$$

provided $\mathbf{A}^{-1}$ exists, which implies that no eigenvalue of $\mathbf{A}$ is 0. This technique can be extended to define other functions of $\mathbf{A}$. Let $f(\mathbf{D})$ be the diagonal matrix with diagonal elements $f(\lambda_i)$, $i = 1, 2, \ldots, n$. Then $f(\mathbf{A}) = \mathbf{P}f(\mathbf{D})\mathbf{P}^{-1}$.

EXERCISES 6.4

1. The eigenvalues of **A** are 3, -1, and 2.

a. Write the eigenvalues of $\mathbf{A}^2$, $\mathbf{A}^3$, and $\mathbf{A}^4$.

b. Write the eigenvalues of $\mathbf{A}^2 - 3\mathbf{A} + \mathbf{I}$.

c. Write the eigenvalues of $\mathbf{A}^3 - 4\mathbf{A}^2 + 2\mathbf{A} - 7\mathbf{I}$.

2. The eigenvalues of **A** are 4, 1, and -5.

a. Write the eigenvalues of $\mathbf{A} + 2\mathbf{I}$, $\mathbf{A} - \mathbf{I}$, $\mathbf{A} + 3\mathbf{I}$, and $\mathbf{A} - 3\mathbf{I}$.

b. For what values of k does the matrix $\mathbf{A} - k\mathbf{I}$ have one zero eigenvalue?

3. Let

$$\mathbf{A} = \begin{bmatrix} 8 & 7 & 7 \\ -5 & -6 & -9 \\ 5 & 7 & 10 \end{bmatrix}$$

The eigenvalues of **A** are 8, 3, and 1. Find a matrix **B** with eigenvalues of 6, 1, and -1.

4. The matrix **B** has the property that $\mathbf{B}^2 = \mathbf{A}$. If the eigenvalues of **A** are 9, 16, and 1, what are the possible eigenvalues of **B**?

5. The matrix **B** has the property that $\mathbf{B}^2 = \mathbf{A}$. The eigenvalues of **A** are 4, 1, and -5. Does **B** have real eigenvalues? Why?

6. Let

$$\mathbf{A} = \begin{bmatrix} 3 & -1 & -1 \\ -2 & 3 & 2 \\ 4 & -1 & -2 \end{bmatrix}$$

The characteristic function of **A** is $f(\lambda) = \lambda^3 - 4\lambda^2 + \lambda + 6$. Calculate $f(\mathbf{A})$.

7. Find the eigenvalues of the matrix

$$\mathbf{A} = \begin{bmatrix} 1 & 2 & 2 \\ 0 & 2 & 1 \\ -1 & 2 & 2 \end{bmatrix}$$

Write Adj **A**. Find the eigenvalues of Adj **A**.

8. Show that, in general, if **A** is nonsingular and k is an eigenvalue of **A**, then $(\det \mathbf{A})/k$ is an eigenvalue of Adj **A**.

9. Let $\mathbf{A} = \begin{bmatrix} 20 & 4 \\ 5 & 21 \end{bmatrix}$. The eigenvalues of **A** are 25 and 16. Write four matrices **B** such that $\mathbf{B}^2 = \mathbf{A}$.

10. Let $\mathbf{A} = \begin{bmatrix} 6 & 5 \\ 2 & 3 \end{bmatrix}$. Write a matrix **B** such that $\mathbf{B}^3 = \mathbf{A}$.

11. Let

$$\mathbf{A} = \begin{bmatrix} 3 & -1 & -1 \\ -2 & 3 & 2 \\ 4 & -1 & -2 \end{bmatrix}$$

The eigenvalues of **A** are 2, 3, and -1, and corresponding eigenvectors are $\mathbf{u}_1 = (1, 0, 1)$, $\mathbf{u}_2 = (1, -1, 1)$, and $\mathbf{u}_3 = (1, -3, 7)$. What are the eigenvalues of $\mathbf{A}^{-1}$? Use this information to calculate $\mathbf{A}^{-1}$.

12. Let $\mathbf{A} = \begin{bmatrix} 4 & 1 \\ 4 & 7 \end{bmatrix}$ and $\mathbf{B} = \begin{bmatrix} 2 & 4 \\ 3 & 6 \end{bmatrix}$. Calculate $\mathbf{A} + \mathbf{B}$. What are the eigenvalues of **A**, the eigenvalues of **B**, and the eigenvalues of $\mathbf{A} + \mathbf{B}$? This illustrates that the eigenvalues of $\mathbf{A} + \mathbf{B}$ are not related to the eigenvalues of **A** and of **B**.

13. In general, is there a relationship between the eigenvalues of **A**, the eigenvalues of **B**, and the eigenvalues of **AB**? Support your answer with an example.

14. Let

$$\mathbf{A} = \begin{bmatrix} 3 & -1 & -1 \\ -2 & 3 & 2 \\ 4 & -1 & -2 \end{bmatrix}$$

The eigenvalues of **A** are 2, 3, and -1. Let $p(x) = x^2 - 3x - 10$. Calculate $p(\mathbf{A})$. Show that $\det p(\mathbf{A}) = p(2)p(3)p(-1)$.

15. Let **A** have eigenvalues k_1, k_2, and k_3. Let $p(x) = (a_1 - x)(a_2 - x)$, so that

$$p(\mathbf{A}) = (a_1\mathbf{I} - \mathbf{A})(a_2\mathbf{I} - \mathbf{A})$$

a. Write $\det p(\mathbf{A})$. Use the eigenvalues of **A** to write $\det(a_1\mathbf{I} - \mathbf{A})$ as the product of three factors: $\det(a_1\mathbf{I} - \mathbf{A}) = (a_1 - k_1)(a_1 - k_2)(a_1 - k_3)$. And similarly for $\det(a_2\mathbf{I} - \mathbf{A})$.

b. Rearrange the factors in the product for $\det p(\mathbf{A})$ to obtain $\det p(\mathbf{A}) = p(k_1)p(k_2)p(k_3)$.

16. Let $g(x) = \lambda - p(x)$ so that $g(\mathbf{A}) = \lambda\mathbf{I} - p(\mathbf{A})$. Use Problem 15 to write $\det g(\mathbf{A})$ as a product. Use the fact that $\det g(\mathbf{A}) = \det[\lambda\mathbf{I} - p(\mathbf{A})]$ is the characteristic function of $p(\mathbf{A})$ to derive the result that the eigenvalues of $p(\mathbf{A})$ are exactly $p(k_1)$, $p(k_2)$, and $p(k_3)$. Here, $p(x)$, k_1, k_2, and k_3 are as in Problem 15.

17. A graph is a set of n vertices $p_1, p_2, \ldots, p_n$ connected by paths that go in a specific direction. The *adjacency matrix* for a graph is an $n \times n$ matrix $\mathbf{A}$ in which $a_{ij} = 1$ if there is a path from p_i to p_j, and $a_{ij} = 0$ otherwise. The matrix $\mathbf{A}^2$ gives the number of paths of length 2. If a graph has the property that for any two points p_i and p_j there is a unique path of length 2 from p_i to p_j, show that the number of vertices of the graph must be a square. [This includes a single path of length 2 from p_i to p_i. (*Hint:* Consider the eigenvalues of $\mathbf{A}^2$.)] (Suggested by Jim Lawrence.)

18. Let $u(t) = (f(t), g(t))$. The following argument presents the definition of the derivative of a pair with respect to t as $u'(t) = (f'(t), g'(t))$.

a. Write the pair $\dfrac{u(t+h) - u(t)}{h}$

b. Assuming that the limit of a pair is found by taking the limit of each element of the pair, find $$\lim_{h \to 0} \frac{u(t+h) - u(t)}{h}$$

19. Let $\mathbf{P}^{-1}\mathbf{AP} = \mathbf{D}$, and define $\sin \mathbf{A}t$ as on page 315. Show that $D_t \sin \mathbf{A}t = \mathbf{A} \cos \mathbf{A}t$.

20. With $\sin \mathbf{A}$ and $\cos \mathbf{A}$ as defined on page 315 show that $\sin^2 \mathbf{A} + \cos^2 \mathbf{A} = \mathbf{I}$.

21. Let $\mathbf{A} = \begin{bmatrix} 4 & 1 \\ 4 & 7 \end{bmatrix}$. Write the matrices $e^{\mathbf{A}}$, $\cos \mathbf{A}$, and $\sin \mathbf{A}$.

22. Find an example of matrices $\mathbf{A}$ and $\mathbf{B}$ such that $e^{\mathbf{A}} e^{\mathbf{B}} \neq e^{\mathbf{A}+\mathbf{B}}$.

Supplemental Topic

The Cayley-Hamilton Theorem

23. The Cayley-Hamilton Theorem states that every square matrix satisfies its characteristic equation. Thus, if $\mathbf{A}$ is a square matrix and $f(\lambda)$ is its characteristic polynomial, $f(\mathbf{A}) = \mathbf{0}$. Verify the Cayley-Hamilton Theorem if

$$\mathbf{A} = \begin{bmatrix} 8 & 7 & 7 \\ -5 & -6 & -9 \\ 5 & 7 & 10 \end{bmatrix}$$

The eigenvalues of $\mathbf{A}$ are 8, 3, 1.

24. **a.** Assume $\mathbf{A}$ is similar to a diagonal matrix, that is, $\mathbf{P}^{-1}\mathbf{AP} = \mathbf{D}$. Let $f(x) = x^2 - 7x + 4$. Show that $f(\mathbf{A})$ is similar to a diagonal matrix.

b. What are the diagonal elements of $\mathbf{P}^{-1} f(\mathbf{A})\mathbf{P}$?

c. If $\mathbf{A}$ is similar to a diagonal matrix and $f(x)$ is any polynomial, what are the diagonal elements of $\mathbf{P}^{-1} f(\mathbf{A})\mathbf{P}$?

25. Use the result of Problem 24 to prove the Cayley-Hamilton Theorem for the special case of matrices that are similar to diagonal matrices.

26. Let $\mathbf{A} = \begin{bmatrix} 1 & -1 & 0 \\ 0 & 1 & 0 \\ 0 & 1 & 2 \end{bmatrix}$. The characteristic polynomial of $\mathbf{A}$ is $f(\lambda) = \lambda^3 - 4\lambda^2 + 5\lambda - 2$. The matrix $\mathbf{A}$ is not similar to a diagonal matrix. Verify that in this case also $f(\mathbf{A}) = \mathbf{0}$.

27. Let

$$\mathbf{A} = \begin{bmatrix} 7 & -2 & 1 \\ -2 & 10 & -2 \\ 1 & -2 & 7 \end{bmatrix}. \text{ (See Example 8.)}$$

Verify the Cayley-Hamilton Theorem for this matrix.

28. Show that the matrix $\mathbf{A}$ in Problem 27 also satisfies the equation $g(\mathbf{A}) = \mathbf{0}$ where $g(\lambda) = \lambda^2 - 18\lambda + 72$.

29. **a.** For the matrix $\mathbf{A}$ in Problems 27 and 28, compare the characteristic polynomial $f(\lambda)$ and the polynomial $g(\lambda)$. (*Hint:* Factor the polynomials.)

b. Let $\mathbf{A} = \begin{bmatrix} 1 & -1 & 0 \\ 0 & 1 & 0 \\ 0 & 1 & 2 \end{bmatrix}$ (Problem 26) and

$\mathbf{B} = \begin{bmatrix} 1 & 0 & 0 \\ 0 & 1 & -1 \\ 0 & 0 & 2 \end{bmatrix}$. Verify the following statements: i. The characteristic polynomials of $\mathbf{A}$ and $\mathbf{B}$ are the same; ii. $\mathbf{A}$ is not similar to a diagonal matrix and $\mathbf{B}$ is similar to a diagonal matrix; iii. If $h(\lambda) = \lambda^2 - 3\lambda + 2$, verify that $h(\mathbf{A}) \neq \mathbf{0}$ and $h(\mathbf{B}) = \mathbf{0}$.

30. On the basis of your observations in Problem 29, make a conjecture about the polynomial of lowest degree satisfied by the matrix

$\mathbf{A} = \begin{bmatrix} 6 & 7 & 7 \\ -7 & -8 & -7 \\ 7 & 7 & 6 \end{bmatrix}$. Verify your conjecture.

31. The characteristic equation can be used to calculate the inverse of a matrix $\mathbf{A}$, if $\mathbf{A}^{-1}$ exists. Recall from Problem 23 that $\mathbf{A} = \begin{bmatrix} 8 & 7 & 7 \\ -5 & -6 & -9 \\ 5 & 7 & 10 \end{bmatrix}$ has the property that $\mathbf{A}^3 - 12\mathbf{A}^2 + 35\mathbf{A} - 24\mathbf{I} = \mathbf{0}$, or $\mathbf{A}^2 - 12\mathbf{A} + 35\mathbf{I} = 24\mathbf{A}^{-1}$. Use this property to calculate $\mathbf{A}^{-1}$.

32. For the matrix $\mathbf{A}$ of Problem 27, find $\mathbf{A}^{-1}$ using the characteristic equation and also using the equation of Problem 28.

33. Find $\mathbf{A}^{-1}$ for the matrix $\mathbf{A}$ defined in Problem 30.

For further discussion of the Cayley-Hamilton Theorem and its uses, see *Introduction to Differential Equations with Boundary Value Problems*, Third Edition, by Wm. R. Derrick and Stanley I. Grossman.

6.5 Applications: Dominant Eigenvalues, Maximum and Minimum, Structural Analysis, Differential Equations, Difference Equations

Dominant Eigenvalues

The discussion so far has been illustrated using matrices with integer entries and eigenvalues that are relatively easy to find. In practical situations, simplicity like this is rarely found. In many cases, numerical methods must be used to calculate the eigenvalues. As an example of these methods, we discuss one that is easy to use and will find the real eigenvalue of largest absolute value. Such an eigenvalue is called a *dominant eigenvalue*. Should there be more than one eigenvalue of largest absolute value, other methods must be used.

The technique is iterative in nature. Let $\mathbf{A}$ be a nonsingular matrix of order n with a dominant real eigenvalue λ. Select a vector $\mathbf{X}_0$ so that $\mathbf{AX}_0 \neq \mathbf{0}$ and calculate $\mathbf{Y}_1 = \mathbf{AX}_0$. Divide $\mathbf{Y}_1$ by the absolute value of its entry of largest absolute value to obtain $\mathbf{X}_1$. Compute $\mathbf{Y}_2 = \mathbf{AX}_1$; obtain $\mathbf{X}_2$ similarly by dividing $\mathbf{Y}_2$ by the absolute value of its entry of largest absolute value. Continue in this way. After $\mathbf{X}_{k-1}$ has been calculated, $\mathbf{Y}_k = \mathbf{AX}_{k-1}$. Then $\mathbf{X}_k$ is obtained from $\mathbf{Y}_k$ by dividing $\mathbf{Y}_k$ by the absolute value of its entry of greatest absolute value. Under suitable circumstances, $\mathbf{AX}_k$ is very nearly $\lambda\mathbf{X}_k$, so that as k becomes large, both λ and its corresponding eigenvector are generated. This technique for finding the dominant eigenvalue is called the *power method.*

Example 24 gives a simple case that illustrates the concepts involved. The program EIGEN in the appendix or a suitable matrix algebra package (for example, MAX) can be used to carry out the computations.

Example 24 Let $\mathbf{A} = \begin{bmatrix} 4 & 3 \\ 1 & 2 \end{bmatrix}$. The following sequence of computations shows the techniques described above applied to this matrix. Let $\mathbf{X}_0 = \begin{bmatrix} 1 \\ 1 \end{bmatrix}$.

Iteration	$\mathbf{AX}_k$	*Adjusted Vector*
1	$\mathbf{AX}_0 = \begin{bmatrix} 7 \\ 3 \end{bmatrix} = \mathbf{Y}_1$	$\mathbf{X}_1 = \begin{bmatrix} 1 \\ 0.42857 \end{bmatrix} = \frac{1}{7}\mathbf{Y}_1$
2	$\mathbf{AX}_1 = \begin{bmatrix} 5.28571 \\ 1.85714 \end{bmatrix}$	$\mathbf{X}_2 = \begin{bmatrix} 1 \\ 0.35135 \end{bmatrix}$
3	$\mathbf{AX}_2 = \begin{bmatrix} 5.05405 \\ 1.70270 \end{bmatrix}$	$\mathbf{X}_3 = \begin{bmatrix} 1 \\ 0.33690 \end{bmatrix}$
4	$\mathbf{AX}_3 = \begin{bmatrix} 5.01070 \\ 1.67380 \end{bmatrix}$	$\mathbf{X}_4 = \begin{bmatrix} 1 \\ 0.33404 \end{bmatrix}$
5	$\mathbf{AX}_4 = \begin{bmatrix} 5.00213 \\ 1.66809 \end{bmatrix}$	$\mathbf{X}_5 = \begin{bmatrix} 1 \\ 0.33348 \end{bmatrix}$
6	$\mathbf{AX}_5 = \begin{bmatrix} 5.00043 \\ 1.66695 \end{bmatrix}$	$\mathbf{X}_6 = \begin{bmatrix} 1 \\ 0.33336 \end{bmatrix}$
7	$\mathbf{AX}_6 = \begin{bmatrix} 5.00009 \\ 1.66672 \end{bmatrix}$	$\mathbf{X}_7 = \begin{bmatrix} 1 \\ 0.33334 \end{bmatrix}$
8	$\mathbf{AX}_7 = \begin{bmatrix} 5.00002 \\ 1.66668 \end{bmatrix}$	$\mathbf{X}_8 = \begin{bmatrix} 1 \\ 0.33333 \end{bmatrix}$
9	$\mathbf{AX}_8 = \begin{bmatrix} 5.00000 \\ 1.66667 \end{bmatrix}$	$\mathbf{X}_9 = \begin{bmatrix} 1 \\ 0.33333 \end{bmatrix}$

In nine iterations, then, we have found (correct to five decimal places) that

$$\mathbf{A}\begin{bmatrix} 1 \\ 0.33333 \end{bmatrix} = 5\begin{bmatrix} 1.00000 \\ 0.33333 \end{bmatrix}$$

Thus, 5 is the dominant eigenvalue and $(1, \frac{1}{3})$ an eigenvector for 5. This agrees with the results of a simple calculation: the eigenvalues of **A** are 5 and 1 with associated eigenvectors $(3, 1)$ and $(1, -1)$. ■

There are three underlying assumptions associated with the power method:

1. There is a dominant eigenvalue for **A**.
2. The eigenvectors of **A** form a linearly independent set.
3. The initial guess we make, when written as a linear combination of the eigenvectors, has a nonzero component in the direction of the eigenvector associated with the dominant eigenvalue.

In the previous example, the initial guess is $(1, 1) = \frac{1}{2}(3, 1) - \frac{1}{2}(1, -1)$; since $(3, 1)$ is an eigenvector associated with the dominant eigenvalue 5 and its component $\frac{1}{2}$ is nonzero, the power method yielded the dominant eigenvalue of 5. If we had chosen $(5, -5)$ as our initial guess, we could not have expected convergence to the dominant eigenvalue 5, since $0(3, 1) + 5(1, -1) = (5, -5)$, so that the component in the direction $(3, 1)$ is 0. In fact, if $\mathbf{X}_0 = \begin{bmatrix} 5 \\ -5 \end{bmatrix}$, $\mathbf{AX}_0 = \begin{bmatrix} 4 & 3 \\ 1 & 2 \end{bmatrix}\begin{bmatrix} 5 \\ -5 \end{bmatrix} =$

$\begin{bmatrix} 5 \\ -5 \end{bmatrix} = \mathbf{Y}_1$; $\mathbf{X}_1 = \begin{bmatrix} 1 \\ -1 \end{bmatrix}$. Now, $\mathbf{AX}_1 = \mathbf{X}_1$, and we immediately see that $\mathbf{X}_1$ is an eigenvector of $\mathbf{A}$ with associated eigenvalue 1 (which is not the dominant eigenvalue).

Example 25 Let

$$\mathbf{A} = \begin{bmatrix} 3 & -1 & -1 \\ -2 & 3 & 2 \\ 4 & -1 & -2 \end{bmatrix}$$

The eigenvalues of $\mathbf{A}$ are 2, 3, and -1 with associated eigenvectors $(1,0,1)$, $(-1,1,-1)$, and $(1,-3,7)$. This information, of course, is not known when the search for the dominant eigenvalue is applied. An initial choice for $\mathbf{X}_0$ could be $\begin{bmatrix} 1 \\ 2 \\ 3 \end{bmatrix}$. Is this a good choice in this particular problem? We write $(1,2,3)$ in terms of the eigenvectors of $\mathbf{A}$: $(1,2,3) = \frac{11}{3}(1,0,1) + 3(-1,1,-1) + \frac{1}{3}(1,-3,7)$. Thus, $(1,2,3)$ has a nonzero component in the direction of the eigenvector associated with the dominant eigenvalue. Indeed, after 25 iterations we find

$$\mathbf{Y}_{25} \approx \begin{bmatrix} -2.999855 \\ 3 \\ -2.999855 \end{bmatrix}$$

so we have approximately isolated 3 as the dominant eigenvalue with associated eigenvector $(-1,1,-1)$.

What if we were unlucky enough to choose $\mathbf{X}_0 = (5,3,-1)$? Then $(5,3,-1) = 6(1,0,1) + 0(-1,1,-1) - 1(1,-3,7)$. Remember: In general, you will not know the eigenvectors in advance. After 25 iterations, $\mathbf{Y}_{25} \approx \begin{bmatrix} 2.000884 \\ 0 \\ 2.000884 \end{bmatrix} \approx 2\begin{bmatrix} 1 \\ 0 \\ 1 \end{bmatrix}$. We have isolated the next dominant eigenvalue! These ideas are explored further in the exercises. ■

Maximum and Minimum

The classification of quadratic forms is used in identifying the nature of an extreme point of a function of several variables. Let $w = f(x,y,z)$ be a real-valued function of three independent variables. This function is not necessarily quadratic. We know from calculus that if f is continuous and has continuous derivatives, the points where f might have a maximum or minimum value can be located by solving the equations $f_x = 0, f_y = 0, f_z = 0$. The notation f_x means the partial derivative of the function f with respect to x. Points obtained by solving these equations are called critical points. After a critical point (x_0, y_0, z_0) has been found, it is still necessary to determine whether $f(x_0, y_0, z_0)$ is a maximum value, a minimum value, or neither. To do this, the Taylor expansion of the function f is written in powers of $(x - x_0)$, $(y - y_0)$, and $(z - z_0)$. This expansion begins with $f(x_0, y_0, z_0)$. The first-degree terms have coefficients $f_x(x_0, y_0, z_0)$, $f_y(x_0, y_0, z_0)$, and $f_z(x_0, y_0, z_0)$. Each of these three terms is zero because (x_0, y_0, z_0) is a critical point. The next group of terms in the Taylor expansion is of the second degree. For simplicity, write $u_1 = (x - x_0)$, $u_2 = (y - y_0)$, $u_3 = (z - z_0)$. The second-degree terms are

$$h(\mathbf{u}) = f_{xx}u_1^2 + f_{yy}u_2^2 + f_{zz}u_3^2 + 2f_{xy}u_1u_2 + 2f_{xz}u_1u_3 + 2f_{yz}u_2u_3$$

The coefficients in this expression are the second-order partial derivatives of f evaluated at the critical point. The second-degree terms, $h(\mathbf{u})$, give an approximation to the difference $f(x, y, z) - f(x_0, y_0, z_0)$. Under proper continuity conditions, the sign of the difference is determined by the sign of $h(\mathbf{u})$ as $\mathbf{u}$ takes values in R^3. If $h(\mathbf{u})$ is positive definite, then $f(x, y, z) - f(x_0, y_0, z_0) > 0$ in the neighborhood of the critical point, and the critical point is a relative minimum point for f. If $h(\mathbf{u})$ is negative definite, the critical point is a relative maximum point. If $h(\mathbf{u})$ is indefinite, then $f(x, y, z) - f(x_0, y_0, z_0)$ is positive for some (x, y, z) and negative for other (x, y, z). This means that $f(x_0, y_0, z_0)$ is neither a maximum nor a minimum. In this case, the critical point is called a saddle point. If $h(\mathbf{u})$ is semidefinite, the sign of the difference $f(x, y, z) - f(x_0, y_0, z_0)$ cannot be predicted from the sign of $h(\mathbf{u})$ and the test gives no information.

Example 26 Let $f(x, y, z) = 3xy - x^3 - y^3 - 3z^2$. Here $f_x = 3y - 3x^2$, $f_y = 3x - 3y^2$, and $f_z = -6z$. The critical points are $(0, 0, 0)$ and $(1, 1, 0)$. The partial derivatives of the second order are:

$$\begin{array}{lll} f_{xx} = -6x & f_{xy} = 3 & f_{xz} = 0 \\ f_{yx} = 3 & f_{yy} = -6y & f_{yz} = 0 \\ f_{zx} = 0 & f_{zy} = 0 & f_{zz} = -6 \end{array}$$

Consider the critical point $(0, 0, 0)$. The matrix of $h(\mathbf{u})$ at this point is found by evaluating the second partial derivatives at $(0, 0, 0)$. The matrix of $h(\mathbf{u}) = \mathbf{U}^T\mathbf{H}\mathbf{U}$ is

$$\mathbf{H} = \begin{bmatrix} 0 & 3 & 0 \\ 3 & 0 & 0 \\ 0 & 0 & -6 \end{bmatrix}$$

The characteristic equation of $\mathbf{H}$ is $\lambda^3 + 6\lambda^2 - 9\lambda - 54 = 0$, and the eigenvalues are 3, -6, and -3. The quadratic form $h(\mathbf{u})$ is indefinite and the critical point is a saddle point.

Now test f at the critical point $(1, 1, 0)$. The matrix $\mathbf{H}$ at this point is

$$\mathbf{H} = \begin{bmatrix} -6 & 3 & 0 \\ 3 & -6 & 0 \\ 0 & 0 & -6 \end{bmatrix}$$

If we apply Gundelfinger's Rule, we obtain the sequence $1, -6, 27, -162$. This has three variations in sign and no permanences. All the eigenvalues must be negative (they are -6, -3, and -9) and the form is negative definite. This means that f has a maximum at $(1, 1, 0)$. ■

Structural Analysis

An industrial problem in which quadratic forms play an important role was described to the authors by Mr. Kenneth Roger, structural engineer at the Airplane Production Company, Wichita, Kansas. The structural engineer must ensure that certain design criteria for aircraft are met. Mathematical models are compared with data collected in extensive flight testing. The behavior of the various structural variables is expressed in terms of departures from a mean or stability position. If there are n variables involved, the departure from the mean has the form

$$y = c_1 y_1 + c_2 y_2 + \cdots + c_n y_n$$

This is a linear combination of the values y_i, $i = 1, 2, \ldots, n$, each of which refers to a particular response. The magnitude of y is compared to a statistical measure called the standard deviation, σ_y, defined by

$$\sigma_y^2 = [c_1 \quad c_2 \quad \cdots \quad c_n] \begin{bmatrix} \sigma_{11} & \sigma_{12} & \cdots & \sigma_{1n} \\ \sigma_{21} & \sigma_{22} & \cdots & \sigma_{2n} \\ \vdots & \vdots & & \vdots \\ \sigma_{n1} & \sigma_{n2} & \cdots & \sigma_{nn} \end{bmatrix} \begin{bmatrix} c_1 \\ c_2 \\ \vdots \\ c_n \end{bmatrix}$$

$$= \sum_{i=1}^{n} \sum_{j=1}^{n} \sigma_{ij} c_i c_j$$

Here $[\sigma_{ij}]$ is the covariance matrix, $\operatorname{cov}(y_i, y_j)$, and is determined from the data collected.

The design specification in analysis of turbulence is

$$\left| \frac{y}{\sigma_y} \right| \leqslant U_\sigma$$

where U_σ is a given numerical constant. The quantity $\left| \dfrac{y}{\sigma_y} \right|$ depends on $c_1, c_2, \ldots, c_n$, as the following example shows.

Example 27 Suppose the critical stresses at Wing Station 175 are y_1 and y_2. The covariance matrix is found by experimental testing to be

$$\mathbf{B} = \begin{bmatrix} \sigma_{11} & \sigma_{12} \\ \sigma_{21} & \sigma_{22} \end{bmatrix} = \begin{bmatrix} 1.000 \times 10^{12} & 2.924 \times 10^{11} \\ 2.924 \times 10^{11} & 1.009 \times 10^{12} \end{bmatrix}$$

Thus,

$$\sigma_y^2 = c_1^2\sigma_{11} + 2c_1c_2\sigma_{12} + c_2^2\sigma_{22}$$
$$y^2 = c_1^2y_1^2 + 2c_1c_2y_1y_2 + c_2^2y_2^2$$

and the criterion $|y| \leqslant \sigma_y U_\sigma$ can be written $\sigma_y^2 U_\sigma^2 - y^2 \geqslant 0$. This inequality is then

$$c_1^2(U_\sigma^2\sigma_{11} - y_1^2) + 2c_1c_2(U_\sigma^2\sigma_{12} - y_1y_2) + c_2^2(U_\sigma^2\sigma_{22} - y_2^2) \geqslant 0$$

This is a quadratic form in c_1, c_2, in which the coefficients involve the elements of the covariance matrix (given), the number U_σ (given), and the variables y_1, y_2 (unknown). The designer would like to know the values of y_1, y_2 that make the inequality true for all choices of c_1, c_2. In other words, the designer wishes to know the values of y_1, y_2 that make the quadratic form positive definite. ■

In addition to its importance in relation to the structural integrity of our aircraft this problem is of interest because of the variety of linear algebra techniques involved in studying it.

First, we write the quadratic form in better notation:

$$y = c_1y_1 + c_2y_2 + \cdots + c_ny_n \quad \text{can be written as} \quad \mathbf{C}^T\mathbf{Y} \text{ or as } \mathbf{Y}^T\mathbf{C}$$

where

$$\mathbf{Y} = \begin{bmatrix} y_1 \\ y_2 \\ \vdots \\ y_n \end{bmatrix} \quad \text{and} \quad \mathbf{C} = \begin{bmatrix} c_1 \\ c_2 \\ \vdots \\ c_n \end{bmatrix}, \quad \text{so} \quad y^2 = \mathbf{C}^T\mathbf{Y}\mathbf{Y}^T\mathbf{C}$$

In the same notation, $\sigma^2 = \mathbf{C}^T[\sigma_{ij}]\mathbf{C}$. For simplicity, write $U_\sigma^2 = k$, and $[\sigma_{ij}] = \mathbf{B}$. The inequality becomes

$$k\mathbf{C}^T\mathbf{B}\mathbf{C} - \mathbf{C}^T\mathbf{Y}\mathbf{Y}^T\mathbf{C} \geqslant 0 \quad \text{or} \quad \mathbf{C}^T\{k\mathbf{B} - \mathbf{Y}\mathbf{Y}^T\}\mathbf{C} \geqslant 0$$

The left-hand side of this inequality is a quadratic form with matrix

$$\mathbf{A} = k\mathbf{B} - \mathbf{Y}\mathbf{Y}^T$$

Because of the special form of the matrix $\mathbf{A}$,

$$\det \mathbf{A} = k^{n-1}D[k - \mathbf{Y}^T\mathbf{B}^{-1}\mathbf{Y}]$$

where $D = \det \mathbf{B}$. Because $\mathbf{B}$ is a covariance matrix, $\det \mathbf{B} > 0$. The steps required to establish this are outlined in Problems 19 and 20.

Since $D > 0$, and $k = U_\sigma^2 > 0$, $\det \mathbf{A}$ is positive if $k - \mathbf{Y}^T\mathbf{B}^{-1}\mathbf{Y} > 0$. Thus, the design criterion is met as long as $\mathbf{Y}^T\mathbf{B}^{-1}\mathbf{Y} < k$, that is, as long as y is in the region bounded by $\mathbf{Y}^T\mathbf{B}^{-1}\mathbf{Y} = k$. Since $\mathbf{Y}^T\mathbf{B}^{-1}\mathbf{Y}$ is a quadratic form, the nature of this boundary can be identified by finding the eigenvalues of $\mathbf{B}^{-1}$ as Example 28 illustrates.

Example 28 The covariance matrix in Example 27 is

$$\mathbf{B} = \begin{bmatrix} 1.000 \times 10^{12} & 2.924 \times 10^{11} \\ 2.924 \times 10^{11} & 1.009 \times 10^{12} \end{bmatrix}$$

The characteristic equation is $\lambda^2 - 2.009 \times 10^{12}\lambda + 9.235 \times 10^{23} = 0$. The eigenvalues are 0.712×10^{12} and 1.297×10^{12}. The eigenvalues of the inverse of the covariance matrix are the reciprocals of these numbers. Thus, the diagonalized form of the equation $\mathbf{Y}^T\mathbf{B}^{-1}\mathbf{Y} = k$ is

$$\frac{v_1^2}{0.712 \times 10^{12}} + \frac{v_2^2}{1.297 \times 10^{12}} = U_\sigma^2$$

If we use the value $U_\sigma = 62$, this equation in normal form is

$$\frac{v_1^2}{(5.2318 \times 10^7)^2} + \frac{v_2^2}{(7.0607 \times 10^7)^2} = 1$$

Figure 6.5 shows a graph of the region in which the design criterion is satisfied.

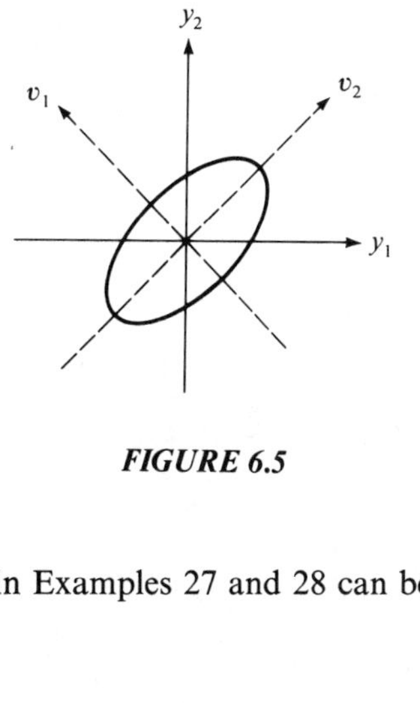

FIGURE 6.5 ■

The method discussed in Examples 27 and 28 can be extended to any number of responses.

Differential Equations

Linear algebra plays an important role in the solution of linear systems of differential equations. We will give some simple examples. Suppose a physical system is modeled by a set of functions $x_1(t), x_2(t), \ldots, x_n(t)$. Suppose that the rate of change of the quantities $x_i(t)$ depends only on the amounts of the various substances present. In mathematical terms, this is a system of equations

$$\frac{dx_i}{dt} = f_i(x_1, x_2, \ldots, x_n), \qquad i = 1, 2, \ldots, n$$

The study of such a system is sometimes approached by examining the system when the quantities x_i are changed by small amounts from a position of stability. Such investigations give rise to a system of equations with constant coefficients of the form

$$\frac{dx_i}{dt} = a_{i1}x_1 + a_{i2}x_2 + \cdots a_{in}x_n, \qquad i = 1, 2, \ldots, n$$

For example, if $n = 2$, we have

$$\frac{dx_1}{dt} = a_{11}x_1 + a_{12}x_2$$

$$\frac{dx_2}{dt} = a_{21}x_1 + a_{22}x_2$$

As we saw in Section 6.4, it is consistent to define the derivative of an n-tuple termwise. For convenience, we use Newton's dot notation for the derivative. Thus, if $x = (x_1(t), x_2(t))$, then $\dot{x} = (\dot{x}_1, \dot{x}_2)$. In matrix form the equation becomes

$$\dot{\mathbf{X}} = \begin{bmatrix} a_{11} & a_{12} \\ a_{21} & a_{22} \end{bmatrix} \mathbf{X}$$

Now suppose that there is a basis with respect to which **A** is diagonal:

$$\mathbf{P}^{-1}\mathbf{AP} = \begin{bmatrix} d_1 & 0 \\ 0 & d_2 \end{bmatrix}$$

Let $(x_1(t), x_2(t))$ be the coordinates of x with respect to the standard basis, and let $(y_1(t), y_2(t))$ be the coordinates of x with respect to the basis of eigenvectors. Then

$$\begin{bmatrix} x_1(t) \\ x_2(t) \end{bmatrix} = \mathbf{P}\begin{bmatrix} y_1(t) \\ y_2(t) \end{bmatrix} \quad \text{and} \quad \begin{bmatrix} \dot{x}_1(t) \\ \dot{x}_2(t) \end{bmatrix} = \mathbf{P}\begin{bmatrix} \dot{y}_1(t) \\ \dot{y}_2(t) \end{bmatrix}$$

The system of differential equations is

$$\mathbf{P}\begin{bmatrix} \dot{y}_1(t) \\ \dot{y}_2(t) \end{bmatrix} = \mathbf{AP}\begin{bmatrix} y_1(t) \\ y_2(t) \end{bmatrix}$$

so that

$$\begin{bmatrix} \dot{y}_1(t) \\ \dot{y}_2(t) \end{bmatrix} = \mathbf{P}^{-1}\mathbf{AP}\begin{bmatrix} y_1(t) \\ y_2(t) \end{bmatrix}$$

Since $\mathbf{P}^{-1}\mathbf{AP}$ is a diagonal matrix, this last equation can be written:

$$\dot{y}_1(t) = d_1 y_1(t) \quad \text{from which} \quad y_1(t) = c_1 e^{d_1 t}$$

and

$$\dot{y}_2(t) = d_2 y_2(t) \quad \text{from which} \quad y_2(t) = c_2 e^{d_2 t}$$

Here, c_1 is the value of y_1 at $t = 0$ and c_2 is the value of y_2 at $t = 0$. Let

$$\mathbf{Y}_0 = \begin{bmatrix} y_1(0) \\ y_2(0) \end{bmatrix} \quad \text{and} \quad \mathbf{Y} = \begin{bmatrix} y_1(t) \\ y_2(t) \end{bmatrix}$$

Then

$$\mathbf{Y} = \begin{bmatrix} e^{d_1 t} & 0 \\ 0 & e^{d_2 t} \end{bmatrix} \mathbf{Y}_0$$

To return to the original pair $(x_1(t), x_2(t))$, write the equation $\mathbf{X} = \mathbf{PY}$ in the form $\mathbf{Y} = \mathbf{P}^{-1}\mathbf{X}$. Also, $\mathbf{Y}_0 = \mathbf{P}^{-1}\mathbf{X}_0$, where $x_0 = (x_1(0), x_2(0))$. With these substitutions,

$$\mathbf{P}^{-1}\mathbf{X} = \begin{bmatrix} e^{d_1 t} & 0 \\ 0 & e^{d_2 t} \end{bmatrix} \mathbf{P}^{-1}\mathbf{X}_0$$

That is,

$$\mathbf{X} = \mathbf{P} \begin{bmatrix} e^{d_1 t} & 0 \\ 0 & e^{d_2 t} \end{bmatrix} \mathbf{P}^{-1}\mathbf{X}_0$$

The matrix

$$\mathbf{P} \begin{bmatrix} e^{d_1 t} & 0 \\ 0 & e^{d_2 t} \end{bmatrix} \mathbf{P}^{-1}$$

is exactly the matrix $e^{\mathbf{A}t}$, which was defined in Section 6.4. With this notation, the differential equation $\dot{\mathbf{X}} = \mathbf{AX}$, along with the condition at $t = 0$ that $\mathbf{X}(0) = \mathbf{X}_0$, has the solution $\mathbf{X} = e^{\mathbf{A}t}\mathbf{X}_0$.

Example 29 Let $x_1(t)$ and $x_2(t)$ be the amounts of two interacting chemicals present together at time t. Suppose they interact according to the equations

$$\begin{aligned} \dot{x}_1 &= -4x_1 - 2x_2 \\ \dot{x}_2 &= x_1 - x_2 \end{aligned}$$

If the initial quantities are (9, 3), find the amount present after t seconds.

In matrix form, we have $\dot{\mathbf{X}} = \mathbf{AX}$, where $\mathbf{A} = \begin{bmatrix} -4 & -2 \\ 1 & -1 \end{bmatrix}$. The eigenvalues of $\mathbf{A}$ are -3 and -2. Corresponding eigenvectors are $\mathbf{u}_1 = (2, -1)$ and $\mathbf{u}_2 = (1, -1)$. The solution of the system is $\mathbf{X} = e^{\mathbf{A}t}\begin{bmatrix} 9 \\ 3 \end{bmatrix}$.

To write this in a more familiar form we calculate

$$e^{\mathbf{A}t} = \mathbf{P} \begin{bmatrix} e^{-3t} & 0 \\ 0 & e^{-2t} \end{bmatrix} \mathbf{P}^{-1}$$

This gives

$$e^{\mathbf{A}t} = \begin{bmatrix} 2e^{-3t} - e^{-2t} & 2e^{-3t} - 2e^{-2t} \\ -e^{-3t} + e^{-2t} & -e^{-3t} + 2e^{-2t} \end{bmatrix}$$

Finally,

$$\begin{bmatrix} x_1(t) \\ x_2(t) \end{bmatrix} = e^{\mathbf{A}t}\begin{bmatrix} 9 \\ 3 \end{bmatrix} = \begin{bmatrix} 24e^{-3t} - 15e^{-2t} \\ -12e^{-3t} + 15e^{-2t} \end{bmatrix}$$ ■

A similar approach can be used to solve the linear differential equation with constant coefficients:

$$\frac{d^n x}{dt^n} = a_{n-1}\frac{d^{n-1}x}{dt^{n-1}} + a_{n-2}\frac{d^{n-2}x}{dt^{n-2}} + \cdots + a_1\frac{dx}{dt} + a_0 x$$

where all the coefficients a_i are constants. If, in addition, we have the n initial values $x(t_0) = c_0$, $\dot{x}(t_0) = c_1, \ldots, x^{(n-1)}(t_0) = c_{n-1}$, then this differential equation is called an *initial value problem*. The task is to find the solution of such a system subject to the initial constraints.

To reduce the above equation to a matrix equation, define the variables $x_i(t)$ as follows: $x_1(t) = x(t)$, $x_2(t) = \dot{x}_1(t)$, $x_3(t) = \dot{x}_2(t), \ldots, x_n(t) = \dot{x}_{n-1}(t)$. Then $\dot{x}_n(t) = d^n x/dt^n$, and we can rewrite the equation as

$$\dot{x}_n = a_0 x_1 + a_1 x_2 + \cdots + a_{n-1}x_n$$

Let

$$\mathbf{X}(t) = \begin{bmatrix} x_1(t) \\ x_2(t) \\ \vdots \\ x_n(t) \end{bmatrix}$$

so that

$$\dot{\mathbf{X}}(t) = \begin{bmatrix} \dot{x}_1(t) \\ \dot{x}_2(t) \\ \vdots \\ \dot{x}_n(t) \end{bmatrix} = \begin{bmatrix} x_2(t) \\ x_3(t) \\ \vdots \\ d^n x/dt^n \end{bmatrix}$$

Define the $n \times n$ matrix

$$\mathbf{A} = \begin{bmatrix} 0 & 1 & 0 & 0 & \cdots & 0 & 0 \\ 0 & 0 & 1 & 0 & \cdots & 0 & 0 \\ 0 & 0 & 0 & 1 & \cdots & 0 & 0 \\ \vdots & \vdots & \vdots & \vdots & & \vdots & \vdots \\ 0 & 0 & 0 & 0 & \cdots & 0 & 1 \\ a_0 & a_1 & a_2 & a_3 & \cdots & a_{n-2} & a_{n-1} \end{bmatrix}$$

Then the preceding differential equation becomes $\mathbf{AX}(t) = \dot{\mathbf{X}}(t)$. Define $\mathbf{C} = [c_i]_{n\times 1}$ to be the $n \times 1$ array of initial conditions. The initial value problem has as solution $\mathbf{X}(t) = e^{\mathbf{A}(t-t_0)}\mathbf{C}$, with $e^{\mathbf{A}}$ as defined in Section 6.4. If the equation is given with no initial conditions, then its solution is $\mathbf{X}(t) = e^{\mathbf{A}t}\mathbf{K}$, where $\mathbf{K}$ is an arbitrary $n \times 1$ vector of constants.

Example 30 Consider the electrical circuit shown in Figure 6.6, where

R = resistance, in ohms (Ω)
L = inductance, in henries (H)
C = capacitance, in farads (F)
i = current, in amperes (A)

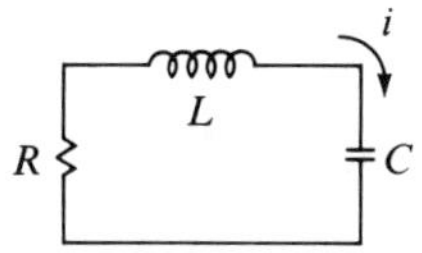

FIGURE 6.6

The differential equation describing the current is

$$\frac{d^2 i}{dt^2} + \frac{R}{L}\frac{di}{dt} + \frac{1}{LC}i = 0$$

which in matrix form is

$$\dot{\mathbf{X}} = \begin{bmatrix} 0 & 1 \\ \frac{-1}{LC} & -\frac{R}{L} \end{bmatrix} \mathbf{X}$$

Suppose that $R = 10^3$, $L = 10^{-3}$ H, and $C = 10^{-6}$ F. The matrix of the system is

$$\begin{bmatrix} 0 & 1 \\ -10^9 & -10^6 \end{bmatrix}$$

which has characteristic equation $x^2 + 10^6 x + 10^9 = 0$, and eigenvalues -0.999×10^6 and -0.001×10^6. The solution will be of the form

$$i = c_0 e^{-0.999 \times 10^6 t} + c_1 e^{-0.001 \times 10^6 t}$$

where the constants can be determined by initial conditions on i and di/dt. ■

For a more detailed discussion of matrix functions and matrix solutions of systems of differential equations, see *Introduction to Differential Equations with Boundary Value Problems*, Third Edition, by Wm. R. Derrick and Stanley I. Grossman.

Difference Equations

Let $x_0, x_1, x_2, \ldots$ be a sequence of numbers related by the equation $x_n = ax_{n-1} + bx_{n-2}$, for $n = 2, 3, 4, \ldots$, where a and b are fixed numbers. This system is a set of difference equations. The object is to determine the value of x_n in terms of a, b, and n. It is possible that for some choices of a and b, the value of x_n converges to a limiting value as n becomes large. Under what conditions might this happen?

The system can be written in matrix form by introducing the notation $y_n = x_{n-1}$ for all $n = 1, 2, \ldots$. Then we have

$$x_n = ax_{n-1} + by_{n-1}$$
$$y_n = x_{n-1}$$

that is,

$$\begin{bmatrix} x_n \\ y_n \end{bmatrix} = \begin{bmatrix} a & b \\ 1 & 0 \end{bmatrix} \begin{bmatrix} x_{n-1} \\ y_{n-1} \end{bmatrix}$$

If

$$\mathbf{A} = \begin{bmatrix} a & b \\ 1 & 0 \end{bmatrix} \quad \text{and} \quad \mathbf{W}_n = \begin{bmatrix} x_n \\ y_n \end{bmatrix}$$

the system of difference equations becomes the system of matrix equations $\mathbf{W}_n = \mathbf{A}^{n-1}\mathbf{W}_1$ for $n = 2, 3, \ldots$.

There are several options open to us now:

1. Attempt to find a closed-form expression for $\mathbf{A}^{n-1}$.
2. Compute $\mathbf{A}^{n-1}$ for a given $\mathbf{A}$ and n.
3. Diagonalize $\mathbf{A}$ (if possible) to find $\mathbf{A}^{n-1}$.

Option 3 is, by far, the most desirable. If there are matrices $\mathbf{P}$ and $\mathbf{D}$ such that $\mathbf{A} = \mathbf{PDP}^{-1}$, then $\mathbf{A}^k = \mathbf{PD}^k\mathbf{P}^{-1}$. The matrix $\mathbf{D}$ in this case is the matrix of eigenvalues $\begin{bmatrix} \lambda_1 & 0 \\ 0 & \lambda_2 \end{bmatrix}$ and the matrix $\mathbf{P}$ has as columns the corresponding eigenvectors. Thus

$$\mathbf{A}^{n-1} = \mathbf{P}\begin{bmatrix} \lambda_1^{n-1} & 0 \\ 0 & \lambda_2^{n-1} \end{bmatrix}\mathbf{P}^{-1} \quad \text{and} \quad \mathbf{W}_n = \mathbf{A}^{n-1}\mathbf{W}_1$$

The computation of $\mathbf{W}_n$ leads to

$$\begin{aligned} x_n &= d_1\lambda_1^{n-1} + d_2\lambda_2^{n-1} \\ y_n &= d_3\lambda_1^{n-1} + d_4\lambda_2^{n-1} \end{aligned}$$

where d_1, d_2, d_3, d_4 are fixed numbers involving the entries in $\mathbf{P}$, $\mathbf{P}^{-1}$, and $\mathbf{W}_1$.

In particular, if λ_1 and λ_2 have absolute values less than 1, the values of x_n and y_n approach zero as n becomes large.

Example 31

Let $a = -1, b = 2, x_0 = 3$, and $x_1 = 6$. Here $\mathbf{A} = \begin{bmatrix} -1 & 2 \\ 1 & 0 \end{bmatrix}$ with eigenvalues -2 and 1 and corresponding eigenvectors $(-2, 1)$ and $(1, 1)$. Hence

$$\mathbf{D} = \begin{bmatrix} -2 & 0 \\ 0 & 1 \end{bmatrix}, \quad \mathbf{P} = \begin{bmatrix} -2 & 1 \\ 1 & 1 \end{bmatrix}, \quad \text{and} \quad \mathbf{P}^{-1} = \begin{bmatrix} -\frac{1}{3} & \frac{1}{3} \\ \frac{1}{3} & \frac{2}{3} \end{bmatrix}$$

Thus,

$$\mathbf{A}^k = \frac{1}{3}\begin{bmatrix} (-1)^{k+2}2^{k+1} + 1 & (-1)^{k+1}2^{k+1} + 2 \\ (-1)^{k+1}2^k + 1 & (-1)^k 2^k + 2 \end{bmatrix}$$

Since $\mathbf{W}_n = \mathbf{A}^{n-1}\mathbf{W}_1$, this means

$$\mathbf{W}_n = \begin{bmatrix} (-1)^{n+1}2^n + 1 & (-1)^n 2^n + 2 \\ (-1)^n 2^{n-1} + 1 & (-1)^{n-1}2^{n-1} + 2 \end{bmatrix}\begin{bmatrix} 2 \\ 1 \end{bmatrix}$$

Finally,

$$\begin{aligned} x_n &= (-1)^{n+1}2^{n+1} + (-1)^n 2^n + 4 \\ &= (-1)^{n+1}2^n + 4 \end{aligned}$$

■

Example 32 As a final example we reach back 800 years into mathematical history. In 1202, Leonardo Fibonacci published what has become a very famous problem, not so much because it was such a difficult one, but because it has led to an abundant supply of elegant and surprising results. Simply stated, his problem was this: Suppose we have a pair of rabbits who during their first month are too young to reproduce but during their second month and every month thereafter do produce a new pair of rabbits. If each pair of their offspring do the same, and none of the rabbits dies, how many pairs of rabbits will there be at the beginning of every month? We have the following situation:

Beginning of:	**Pair of rabbits:**
First month	1 pair (our original)
Second month	1 pair (during this month, the pair produces a new pair)
Third month	2 pairs (original plus new pair)
Fourth month	3 pairs (original pair produces a new pair; previous new pair too young to reproduce)
Fifth month	5 pairs (original pair produces a new pair; second pair now produces their first pair)
Sixth month	8 pairs (original, first, and second pairs each produce a new pair)

and so on. The sequence so produced, $1, 1, 2, 3, 5, 8, 13, 21, \ldots$, is called the *Fibonacci Sequence*; each term $x_n = x_{n-1} + x_{n-2}$ for $n = 2, 3, \ldots$ (and $x_0 = 1$, $x_1 = 1$). We then have the set of matrix equations

$$\begin{bmatrix} x_n \\ y_n \end{bmatrix} = \begin{bmatrix} 1 & 1 \\ 1 & 0 \end{bmatrix} \begin{bmatrix} x_{n-1} \\ y_{n-1} \end{bmatrix} \qquad \text{for } n = 2, 3, 4, \ldots$$

As before, we seek a closed-form expression for x_n by diagonalizing the matrix $\mathbf{A} = \begin{bmatrix} 1 & 1 \\ 1 & 0 \end{bmatrix}$. The necessary algebra shows that the eigenvalues for $\mathbf{A}$ are $\lambda = (1 \pm \sqrt{5})/2$ and

$$\mathbf{P} = \frac{1}{2} \begin{bmatrix} 3 + \sqrt{5} & 3 - \sqrt{5} \\ 1 + \sqrt{5} & 1 - \sqrt{5} \end{bmatrix}$$

Thus, using the matrices $\mathbf{P}$ and $\mathbf{P}^{-1}$,

$$\mathbf{A}^k = \mathbf{P} \begin{bmatrix} \left(\dfrac{1 + \sqrt{5}}{2} \right)^k & 0 \\ 0 & \left(\dfrac{1 - \sqrt{5}}{2} \right)^k \end{bmatrix} \mathbf{P}^{-1}$$

But

$$\begin{bmatrix} x_n \\ y_n \end{bmatrix} = \mathbf{A}^{n-1} \begin{bmatrix} 1 \\ 1 \end{bmatrix}$$

so

$$\begin{bmatrix} x_n \\ y_n \end{bmatrix} = \mathbf{P}\begin{bmatrix} \left(\dfrac{1+\sqrt{5}}{2}\right)^{n-1} & 0 \\ 0 & \left(\dfrac{1-\sqrt{5}}{2}\right)^{n-1} \end{bmatrix}\mathbf{P}^{-1}\begin{bmatrix} 1 \\ 1 \end{bmatrix}$$

$$= \frac{1}{2\sqrt{5}}\begin{bmatrix} 3+\sqrt{5} & 3-\sqrt{5} \\ 1+\sqrt{5} & 1-\sqrt{5} \end{bmatrix}\begin{bmatrix} \left(\dfrac{1+\sqrt{5}}{2}\right)^{n-1} \\ -\left(\dfrac{1-\sqrt{5}}{2}\right)^{n-1} \end{bmatrix}$$

The computation along the bottom row seems more manageable, so we ignore the top entries and obtain a formula for y_n:

$$y_n = x_{n-1} = \frac{1}{\sqrt{5}}\left[\left(\frac{1+\sqrt{5}}{2}\right)^n - \left(\frac{1-\sqrt{5}}{2}\right)^n\right]$$

or

$$x_n = \frac{1}{\sqrt{5}}\left[\left(\frac{1+\sqrt{5}}{2}\right)^{n+1} - \left(\frac{1-\sqrt{5}}{2}\right)^{n+1}\right]$$

We would venture to say that this elegant closed-form expression for x_n is not the first thing a reasonable person would think of for the final answer! For example, is it obvious from this formula that all values of x_n are integers?

One result that follows easily from this expression for x_n is the long-known and admired property of the Fibonacci Sequence that

$$\lim_{n\to\infty} \frac{x_n}{x_{n-1}} = \frac{1+\sqrt{5}}{2}$$

This number was known to the Greeks as the *golden ratio*, because they felt that the most pleasing proportions for a rectangle were $(1 + \sqrt{5})/2:1$.

If we compute x_{n-1}/x_n and divide all terms by $[(1 + \sqrt{5})/2]^{n+1}$, we have

$$\frac{x_{n-1}}{x_n} = \frac{\left(\dfrac{1+\sqrt{5}}{2}\right)^n \Big/ \left(\dfrac{1+\sqrt{5}}{2}\right)^{n+1} - \left(\dfrac{1-\sqrt{5}}{2}\right)^n \Big/ \left(\dfrac{1+\sqrt{5}}{2}\right)^{n+1}}{1 - \left[\left(\dfrac{1-\sqrt{5}}{2}\right)^{n+1} \Big/ \left(\dfrac{1+\sqrt{5}}{2}\right)^{n+1}\right]}$$

$$= \frac{\left(\dfrac{2}{1+\sqrt{5}}\right) - 2\left(\dfrac{1-\sqrt{5}}{1+\sqrt{5}}\right)^n\left(\dfrac{1}{1+\sqrt{5}}\right)}{1 - \left(\dfrac{1-\sqrt{5}}{1+\sqrt{5}}\right)^{n+1}}$$

Since

$$\left| \frac{1 - \sqrt{5}}{1 + \sqrt{5}} \right| < 1$$

we know that

$$\lim_{n\to\infty} \left| \frac{1 - \sqrt{5}}{1 + \sqrt{5}} \right|^n = 0$$

Thus,

$$\lim_{n\to\infty} \frac{x_{n-1}}{x_n} = \frac{2}{1 + \sqrt{5}} \quad \text{or} \quad \lim_{n\to\infty} \frac{x_n}{x_{n-1}} = \frac{1 + \sqrt{5}}{2}$$

■

EXERCISES 6.5

1. Find the dominant eigenvalue and corresponding eigenvector for each of the following. Check your answer by calculating the eigenvalues directly.

   a. $\mathbf{A} = \begin{bmatrix} 11 & -7 \\ -7 & 1 \end{bmatrix}$

   b. $\mathbf{A} = \begin{bmatrix} 15.63 & -61.55 \\ -61.55 & 114.97 \end{bmatrix}$

2. Find the dominant eigenvalue and corresponding eigenvector in each case.

   a. $\mathbf{A} = \begin{bmatrix} 21 & -3 & 87 \\ -31 & 2 & 0 \\ 5 & -7 & 11 \end{bmatrix}$

   b. $\mathbf{A} = \begin{bmatrix} 65 & 2 & 9 & 14 \\ 11 & 23 & 9 & 43 \\ 11 & 8 & 25 & 17 \\ -8 & 9 & 13 & 9 \end{bmatrix}$

3. Let $\mathbf{A} = \begin{bmatrix} 6 & 4 & 4 \\ -7 & -2 & -1 \\ 7 & 4 & 3 \end{bmatrix}$ and $\mathbf{X}_0 = \begin{bmatrix} 1 \\ 1 \\ -2 \end{bmatrix}$.

   a. Use the power method with 10 iterations. What appears to be the dominant eigenvalue and associated eigenvector?

   b. Use 25 iterations to see if the convergence to your answer for **a.** continues.

   c. Which, if either, of the apparent dominant eigenvalues is the true dominant eigenvalue?

4. Find the dominant eigenvalue of the matrix

$$\mathbf{A} = \begin{bmatrix} 0.22 & 0.02 & 0.12 & 0.14 \\ 0.02 & 0.14 & 0.04 & -0.06 \\ 0.12 & 0.04 & 0.28 & 0.08 \\ 0.14 & -0.06 & 0.08 & 0.26 \end{bmatrix}$$

   What can you say about $\lim_{n\to\infty} \mathbf{A}^n$?

5. A sequence is defined by the condition $x_n = 3x_{n-1} - 2x_{n-2}$, where $x_0 = -1$ and $x_1 = 2$. Find the next five terms of the sequence, and express x_n in terms of n.

6. A sequence is defined by the condition $x_n = ax_{n-1} + bx_{n-2}$. What conditions on a and b will ensure that $\lim_{n\to\infty} x_n = 0$?

7. Find the solution of the following system of equations using the initial condition $(1, 0, 1)$:

$$\begin{aligned} \dot{x}_1 &= 6x_1 + 4x_2 + 4x_3 \\ \dot{x}_2 &= -7x_1 - 2x_2 - x_3 \\ \dot{x}_3 &= 7x_1 + 4x_2 + 3x_3 \end{aligned}$$

8. Find the solution of the differential equation

$$\frac{d^2x}{dt^2} + 4\frac{dx}{dt} + 3x = 0$$

9. For the differential equation

$$\frac{d^2x}{dt^2} + a\frac{dx}{dt} + bx = 0$$

   what conditions must be satisfied by a and b for the equation to have real eigenvalues? Under what conditions will x approach zero as t increases?

10. Solve the equation

$$\frac{d^4x}{dt^4} = 5\frac{d^2x}{dt^2} - 4x$$

   given that when $t = 1$, then $x = 1$, $dx/dt = 0$, $d^2x/dt^2 = -1$, and $d^3x/dt^3 = 0$.

TABLE 6.1 Heavy-weight, High-speed, Low-altitude Fuselage Station 694 ($U_\sigma = 62$)

Variables—Vert. Shear, Vert. Moment, Side Shear, Side Moment, Torsion.
Assume the origin has been adjusted so that the variables are deviations from the mean.

Covariance Matrix

8.621E 06	2.212E 09	0.000E − 01	0.000E − 01	0.000E − 01
2.212E 09	6.598E 11	0.000E − 01	0.000E − 01	0.000E − 01
0.000E − 01	0.000E − 01	2.720E 06	3.256E 09	1.154E 08
0.000E − 01	0.000E − 01	3.256E 09	4.106E 12	1.711E 11
0.000E − 01	0.000E − 01	1.154E 08	1.711E 11	1.051E 10

11. A chemical reaction involving three substances A, B, and C is governed by the equations $\dot{x}_1 = -4x_1$, $\dot{x}_2 = 4x_1 - 2x_2$, and $\dot{x}_3 = 2x_2$, where x_1, x_2, x_3 are the concentrations of A, B, and C, respectively, in suitable units. If the initial condition is $(100, 0, 0)$, find an expression for x_1, x_2, and x_3 at time t.

12. Let $f(x, y) = y^3 + x^2 - 6xy + 3x + 6y - 7$. Show that f has a relative minimum at $(\frac{27}{2}, 5)$ and a saddle point at $(\frac{3}{2}, 1)$.

13. Let $f(x, y) = x^4 + y^4 - 8x^2 - 2y^2 + 7$. Find the critical points from the equations $f_x = 0$ and $f_y = 0$, and test to see which gives maximum or minimum values.

14. Let $z = x^2y^2 - 6x^2 - 9y^2 + 5$. Verify that z has a maximum of $(0, 0)$.

15. Let $w = y^2z^2 - 2xyz - x^2 + y^2 - 2z^2$. Test for maximum or minimum at $(0, 0, 0)$.

16. Let $w = x^4 + 2xy + 2xz - 4yz - x^2 - 2y^2 - 4z^2 + 10$. Test for maximum or minimum at $(0, 0, 0)$.

17. The structure at Fuselage Station 694 has not yet been designed, but the critical stresses will be due to vertical moment and side moment. From the information supplied in Table 6.1, draw the region including all combinations of M_v and M_s that the designer must check.

18. Using the information in Table 6.1, find the shape of the design region assuming the critical stresses are vertical shear and vertical moment.

19. Let $\mathbf{A} = k\begin{bmatrix} b_{11} & b_{12} \\ b_{21} & b_{22} \end{bmatrix} - \begin{bmatrix} y_1 \\ y_2 \end{bmatrix}\begin{bmatrix} y_1 & y_2 \end{bmatrix}$.
Prove that $\det \mathbf{A} = k \det \mathbf{B}[k - \mathbf{Y}^T\mathbf{B}^{-1}\mathbf{Y}]$.

20. The following steps lead to the calculation of $\det \mathbf{A}$, where $\mathbf{A} = k\mathbf{B} - \mathbf{Y}\mathbf{Y}^T$.

a. Examine the special form of the matrix $\mathbf{A} = [kb_{ij} - y_iy_j]$. Use Theorem 7, Chapter 3, to write $\det \mathbf{A}$ as the sum of 2^n determinants in which each column is either $\begin{bmatrix} kb_{1j} \\ kb_{2j} \\ \vdots \\ kb_{nj} \end{bmatrix}$ or $\begin{bmatrix} y_1y_j \\ y_2y_j \\ \vdots \\ y_ny_j \end{bmatrix}$.
Write out the eight determinants that arise in the case $n = 3$.

b. Show that any determinant involving two or more columns of y's must be zero.

c. How many of the determinants in the sum can be different from zero?

d. Show that $\det \mathbf{A} = k^n \det \mathbf{B} - \sum_{j=1}^{n} k^{n-1} y_j \det \mathbf{B}_j$ where $\mathbf{B}_j$ is the matrix obtained from $\mathbf{B}$ by replacing the jth column with the column $\mathbf{Y}$.

e. Use Cramer's Rule (Section 3.3) to show that if $\mathbf{BX} = \mathbf{Y}$, that is, if $\mathbf{X} = \mathbf{B}^{-1}\mathbf{Y}$, then:

$$x_1 = \frac{\det \mathbf{B}_1}{\det \mathbf{B}}, \quad x_2 = \frac{\det \mathbf{B}_2}{\det \mathbf{B}}, \ldots, x_n = \frac{\det \mathbf{B}_n}{\det \mathbf{B}}$$

f. Use **e.** to show that $\sum_{i=1}^{n} y_i \dfrac{\det \mathbf{B}_i}{\det \mathbf{B}} = \mathbf{Y}^T\mathbf{B}^{-1}\mathbf{Y}$.

g. Use **d.** and **f.** to show that $\det \mathbf{A} = k^{n-1} \det \mathbf{B}[k - \mathbf{Y}^T\mathbf{B}^{-1}\mathbf{Y}]$.

Answers to Odd-Numbered Problems

EXERCISES 1.1

1. a. $(7, 0, -22)$ **b.** $(c_1 + 2c_2 + 4c_3, 0, -3c_1 + 4c_2 + c_3)$ **c.** second entry is zero

3. a. $\begin{bmatrix} 0 & -5 & 5 \\ 2 & -3 & 7 \end{bmatrix}$ **b.** $\begin{bmatrix} c_1 + 2c_2 + c_3 & -c_1 + c_2 & 2c_1 + c_2 + c_3 \\ 3c_1 - c_3 & c_1 + 3c_2 + c_3 & 4c_1 + 3c_2 + 2c_3 \end{bmatrix}$

5. a. $\mathbf{0} = -\mathbf{u}_1 + \mathbf{u}_2 + \mathbf{u}_3 + \mathbf{u}_4$ **b.** $\mathbf{u}_1 = \mathbf{u}_2 + \mathbf{u}_3 + \mathbf{u}_4$

7. a. $4((1, -1, 3) + (0, 1, 2)) = 4(1, 0, 5) = (4, 0, 20) = (4, -4, 12) + (0, 4, 8) = 4(1, -1, 3) + 4(0, 1, 2)$

b. $k(a_1 + b_1, a_2 + b_2, \ldots, a_n + b_n) = (k(a_1 + b_1), k(a_2 + b_2), \ldots, k(a_n + b_n)) = (ka_1 + kb_1, ka_2 + kb_2, \ldots, ka_n + kb_n) = (ka_1, ka_2, \ldots, ka_n) + (kb_1, kb_2, \ldots, kb_n) = k(a_1, a_2, \ldots, a_n) + k(b_1, b_2, \ldots, b_n)$

9. a. $\begin{bmatrix} -1 & 9 & 2 \\ 9 & 14 & 13 \end{bmatrix}$ **b.** $\begin{bmatrix} 2 & 2 & 1 \\ 2 & -3 & -1 \end{bmatrix}$ **c.** $\begin{bmatrix} -2 & -2 & -1 \\ -2 & 3 & 1 \end{bmatrix}$ **d.** 2×3

11. a. $a = 1, b = -2, c = -4, d = 3$

b. $\mathbf{u} = (a_1, a_2, \ldots, a_n)$, $(-1)\mathbf{u} = (-a_1, -a_2, \ldots, -a_n)$. Then $\mathbf{u} + (-1)\mathbf{u} = \mathbf{0}$

13. Let $\mathbf{A} = [a_{ij}]$, then $c_1\mathbf{A} = c_1[a_{ij}] = [c_1 a_{ij}]$ and $c_2\mathbf{A} = [c_2 a_{ij}]$. $c_1\mathbf{A} + c_2\mathbf{A} = [c_1 a_{ij}] + [c_2 a_{ij}] = [c_1 a_{ij} + c_2 a_{ij}] = [(c_1 + c_2)a_{ij}] = (c_1 + c_2)[a_{ij}] = (c_1 + c_2)\mathbf{A}$

15. $[a_{ij} + b_{ij}] + [c_{ij}] = [(a_{ij} + b_{ij}) + c_{ij}] = [a_{ij} + (b_{ij} + c_{ij})] = [a_{ij}] + [b_{ij} + c_{ij}]$

17. $(\mathbf{A} + \mathbf{B})^T = \begin{bmatrix} 2 & 6 \\ 3 & -1 \end{bmatrix}^T = \begin{bmatrix} 2 & 3 \\ 6 & -1 \end{bmatrix}$, and $\mathbf{A}^T + \mathbf{B}^T = \begin{bmatrix} -1 & 2 \\ 4 & -1 \end{bmatrix} + \begin{bmatrix} 3 & 1 \\ 2 & 0 \end{bmatrix} = \begin{bmatrix} 2 & 3 \\ 6 & -1 \end{bmatrix}$

19. $(k\mathbf{A})^T = [ka_{ij}]^T = [ka_{ji}] = k[a_{ji}] = k\mathbf{A}^T$

21. $40\begin{bmatrix} 15 & 40 & 10 \\ 1000 & 5000 & 3000 \end{bmatrix} + 60\begin{bmatrix} 20 & 70 & 15 \\ 1200 & 1000 & 500 \end{bmatrix}$ entry 1, 3; 1300 windshield wipers

EXERCISES 1.2

1. a. $\mathbf{u} \cdot \mathbf{v} = \mathbf{v} \cdot \mathbf{u} = 2$, $\mathbf{u} \cdot (\mathbf{v} + \mathbf{w}) = \mathbf{u} \cdot \mathbf{v} + \mathbf{u} \cdot \mathbf{w} = 9$

b. $\mathbf{u} \cdot \mathbf{v} = \mathbf{v} \cdot \mathbf{u} = -5$, $\mathbf{u} \cdot (\mathbf{v} + \mathbf{w}) = \mathbf{u} \cdot \mathbf{v} + \mathbf{u} \cdot \mathbf{w} = 2$

3. $\begin{bmatrix} \boxed{4} & 3 \\ 1 & 1 \\ 0 & 2 \\ 1 & 2 \end{bmatrix}$, $\begin{bmatrix} 9 & \boxed{9} \\ \boxed{13} & 19 \end{bmatrix}$

5. $\mathbf{U}\mathbf{V}^T = [a_1 \quad a_2 \quad a_3 \quad a_4]\begin{bmatrix} b_1 \\ b_2 \\ b_3 \\ b_4 \end{bmatrix} = [a_1 b_1 + a_2 b_2 + a_3 b_3 + a_4 b_4] = (a_1, a_2, a_3, a_4) \cdot (b_1, b_2, b_3, b_4) = \mathbf{u} \cdot \mathbf{v}$

7. $\mathbf{U}_1\mathbf{B} = [5 \quad 0 \quad 2]$, $\mathbf{U}_2\mathbf{B} = [5 \quad 7 \quad 1]$

9. a. $\mathbf{A}$ **b.** $\mathbf{A}\mathbf{A}^T$ **c.** $(\mathbf{B}^T + \mathbf{C}^T)\mathbf{A}^T$ **d.** $\mathbf{C}^T\mathbf{B}^T\mathbf{A}^T$ **e.** $\mathbf{A}^T\mathbf{B}^T\mathbf{A}$ **f.** $\mathbf{B}^T\mathbf{A} + \mathbf{A}^T\mathbf{B}$

11. Let $\mathbf{A}_1, \mathbf{A}_2, \ldots, \mathbf{A}_j$ be $n \times n$ symmetric matrices and $k_1, k_2, \ldots, k_j$ be reals. $(k_1\mathbf{A}_1 + k_2\mathbf{A}_2 + \cdots + k_j\mathbf{A}_j)^T = (k_1\mathbf{A}_1)^T + (k_2\mathbf{A}_2)^T + \cdots + (k_j\mathbf{A}_j)^T = k_1(\mathbf{A}_1^T) + k_2(\mathbf{A}_2^T) + \cdots + k_j(\mathbf{A}_j^T) = k_1\mathbf{A}_1 + k_2\mathbf{A}_2 + \cdots + k_j\mathbf{A}_j$, so $k_1\mathbf{A}_1 + k_2\mathbf{A}_2 + \cdots + k_j\mathbf{A}_j$ is symmetric.

13. $(\mathbf{A}^T\mathbf{B} + \mathbf{B}^T\mathbf{A})^T = (\mathbf{A}^T\mathbf{B})^T + (\mathbf{B}^T\mathbf{A})^T = \mathbf{B}^T(\mathbf{A}^T)^T + \mathbf{A}^T(\mathbf{B}^T)^T = \mathbf{B}^T\mathbf{A} + \mathbf{A}^T\mathbf{B} = \mathbf{A}^T\mathbf{B} + \mathbf{B}^T\mathbf{A}$, so $\mathbf{A}^T\mathbf{B} + \mathbf{B}^T\mathbf{A}$ is symmetric $(\mathbf{A}^T\mathbf{B} - \mathbf{B}^T\mathbf{A})^T = (\mathbf{A}^T\mathbf{B})^T - (\mathbf{B}^T\mathbf{A})^T = \mathbf{B}^T(\mathbf{A}^T)^T - \mathbf{A}^T(\mathbf{B}^T)^T = \mathbf{B}^T\mathbf{A} - \mathbf{A}^T\mathbf{B} = -(\mathbf{A}^T\mathbf{B} - \mathbf{B}^T\mathbf{A})$, so $\mathbf{A}^T\mathbf{B} - \mathbf{B}^T\mathbf{A}$ is skew-symmetric

15. Let $\mathbf{A} = [a_{ij}]_{m\times n}$ and $\mathbf{B} = [b_{ij}]_{n\times r}$. Then $(k\mathbf{A})(k'\mathbf{B}) = (k[a_{ij}]_{m\times n})(k'[b_{ij}]_{n\times r}) = [ka_{ij}]_{m\times n}[k'b_{ij}]_{n\times r} = \left[\sum_{j=1}^{n} ka_{ij}k'b_{jq}\right]_{m\times r} = \left[kk'\sum_{j=1}^{n} a_{ij}b_{jq}\right]_{m\times r} = kk'\left(\left[\sum_{j=1}^{n} a_{ij}b_{jq}\right]_{m\times r}\right) = (kk')(\mathbf{AB})$

17. a. $\begin{bmatrix} 3x + 5y \\ -x + 4y \end{bmatrix}$ **b.** $\begin{bmatrix} 3 & 4 \\ 2 & -1 \end{bmatrix}\begin{bmatrix} x \\ y \end{bmatrix}$

19. $\begin{bmatrix} 1 & 3 & -2 \\ 2 & -5 & 1 \\ 1 & 1 & -3 \end{bmatrix}\begin{bmatrix} x \\ y \\ z \end{bmatrix} = \begin{bmatrix} 7 \\ -1 \\ 0 \end{bmatrix}$

21. Suppose $\mathbf{u}_j = (u_{1j}, u_{2j}, \ldots, u_{mj})$, $1 \leqslant j \leqslant k$, then $c_1\mathbf{u}_1 + c_2\mathbf{u}_2 + \cdots + c_k\mathbf{u}_k = \begin{bmatrix} u_{11} & u_{12} & \cdots & u_{1k} \\ u_{21} & u_{22} & \cdots & u_{2k} \\ \vdots & \vdots & & \vdots \\ u_{m1} & u_{m2} & \cdots & u_{mk} \end{bmatrix}\begin{bmatrix} c_1 \\ c_2 \\ \vdots \\ c_k \end{bmatrix}$

23. $2x_1y_1 + 3x_1y_2 + x_1y_3 + x_2y_1 + 5x_2y_3$

25. $3x_1^2 + 2x_1x_2 + 2x_2^2$

27. $[x_1 \quad x_2]\begin{bmatrix} 1 & 3 \\ 3 & 4 \end{bmatrix}\begin{bmatrix} x_1 \\ x_2 \end{bmatrix}$

29. $5x^2 + 6xy + 5y^2 = [x \quad y]\begin{bmatrix} 5 & 3 \\ 3 & 5 \end{bmatrix}\begin{bmatrix} x \\ y \end{bmatrix}$. Set $\begin{bmatrix} x \\ y \end{bmatrix} = \begin{bmatrix} \frac{1}{\sqrt{2}} & \frac{-1}{\sqrt{2}} \\ \frac{1}{\sqrt{2}} & \frac{1}{\sqrt{2}} \end{bmatrix}\begin{bmatrix} x' \\ y' \end{bmatrix}$. $8x'^2 + 2y'^2 = 9$

31. b. $(\mathbf{CT})_{11}$ is the cost of outfitting an entry-level, type-1 lab.
$(\mathbf{CT})_{23}$ is the cost of outfitting a scientific type-3 lab.
$(\mathbf{CT})_{32}$ is the cost of outfitting a business type-2 lab.

c. $(\mathbf{PC})_{11}$ is the cost of outfitting Plan 1 (2 each entry-level, scientific, and business labs) with 1 monofloppy computer per lab.
$(\mathbf{PC})_{32}$ is the cost of outfitting Plan 3 with 1 monohard computer per lab.

d. $\mathbf{P}(\mathbf{CT})$ first finds the cost of each type lab (10 computers per lab) and then computes the total cost based on the various plans.
$(\mathbf{PC})\mathbf{T}$ first finds the cost of 1 computer per lab under the various plans and then computes the total cost based on the various types (10 computers per lab).

e. The $187,800 will purchase equipment for 6 type-2 labs (4 mono double floppy, 2 mono hard, 4 color double floppy); 4 of the labs will be entry-level and 1 each scientific and business.

EXERCISES 1.3

1. $\mathbf{0}_{3\times4}, \mathbf{0}_{2\times2}, \mathbf{0}_{m\times r}, \mathbf{0}_{m\times r}$

3. $\begin{bmatrix} 6 & 6 & 17 & 22 \\ 3 & 5 & 6 & 13 \\ 0 & -4 & 5 & -4 \end{bmatrix}, \begin{bmatrix} 6 & 6 & 17 & 22 \\ 3 & 5 & 6 & 13 \\ 0 & -4 & 5 & -4 \end{bmatrix}$; No, this problem is an example in which $\mathbf{AB} = \mathbf{AC}$ but $\mathbf{B} \neq \mathbf{C}$.

5. It is sufficient to show the linear combination of two $n \times n$ diagonal matrices is a diagonal matrix. Let $\mathbf{A}$ and $\mathbf{B}$ be $n \times n$ diagonal matrices and j and k be real numbers.

$$\mathbf{A} = \begin{bmatrix} a_1 & 0 & \cdots & 0 \\ 0 & a_2 & \cdots & 0 \\ \vdots & \vdots & & \vdots \\ 0 & 0 & \cdots & a_n \end{bmatrix} \qquad \mathbf{B} = \begin{bmatrix} b_1 & 0 & \cdots & 0 \\ 0 & b_2 & \cdots & 0 \\ \vdots & \vdots & & \vdots \\ 0 & 0 & \cdots & b_n \end{bmatrix}$$

$$j\mathbf{A} + k\mathbf{B} = \begin{bmatrix} ja_1 + kb_1 & 0 & \cdots & 0 \\ 0 & ja_2 + kb_2 & \cdots & 0 \\ \vdots & \vdots & & \vdots \\ 0 & 0 & \cdots & ja_n + kb_n \end{bmatrix}$$ is a diagonal matrix.

7. $$\mathbf{DA} = \begin{bmatrix} d_{11}a_{11} & d_{11}a_{12} & d_{11}a_{13} \\ d_{22}a_{21} & d_{22}a_{22} & d_{22}a_{23} \\ d_{33}a_{31} & d_{33}a_{32} & d_{33}a_{33} \end{bmatrix} \qquad \mathbf{AD} = \begin{bmatrix} a_{11}d_{11} & a_{12}d_{22} & a_{13}d_{33} \\ a_{21}d_{11} & a_{22}d_{22} & a_{23}d_{33} \\ a_{31}d_{11} & d_{32}d_{22} & a_{33}d_{33} \end{bmatrix}$$

a. is verified by inspection of **DA**
b. is verified by inspection of **AD**
c. ith column of **AD** is d_{ii} times ith column of **A**; jth row of **DA** is d_{jj} times jth row of **A**

9. $$\begin{bmatrix} 0 & 0 & 0 & 0 \\ 4 & 2 & 0 & 0 \\ 12 & 10 & 0 & 0 \\ 7 & 0 & 5 & -4 \end{bmatrix}$$

It is sufficient to show that the linear combination of two $n \times n$ lower triangular matrices is a lower triangular matrix. Let **A** and **B** be lower triangular matrices and j and k be real numbers.

$$\mathbf{A} = \begin{bmatrix} a_{11} & 0 & \cdots & 0 \\ a_{21} & a_{22} & \cdots & 0 \\ \vdots & \vdots & & \vdots \\ a_{n1} & a_{n2} & \cdots & a_{nn} \end{bmatrix} \qquad \mathbf{B} = \begin{bmatrix} b_{11} & 0 & \cdots & 0 \\ b_{21} & b_{22} & \cdots & 0 \\ \vdots & \vdots & & \vdots \\ b_{n1} & b_{n2} & \cdots & b_{nn} \end{bmatrix}$$

$$j\mathbf{A} + k\mathbf{B} = \begin{bmatrix} ja_{11} + kb_{11} & 0 & \cdots & 0 \\ ja_{21} + kb_{21} & ja_{22} + kb_{22} & \cdots & 0 \\ \vdots & \vdots & & \vdots \\ ja_{n1} + kb_{n1} & ja_{n2} + kb_{n2} & \cdots & ja_{nn} + kb_{nn} \end{bmatrix}$$

is a lower triangular matrix.

11. Let $\mathbf{C} = \mathbf{AB}$ where **A** and **B** are 3×3 lower triangular matrices. To show **C** is lower triangular, it suffices to show c_{12}, c_{13}, and c_{23} are all zero.

$$c_{12} = a_{11}b_{12} + a_{12}b_{22} + a_{13}b_{32} = a_{11}(0) + 0(b_{22}) + 0(b_{32}) = 0$$
$$c_{13} = a_{11}b_{13} + a_{12}b_{23} + a_{13}b_{33} = a_{11}(0) + 0(0) + 0(b_{33}) = 0$$
$$c_{23} = a_{21}b_{13} + a_{22}b_{23} + a_{23}b_{33} = a_{21}(0) + a_{22}(0) + 0(b_{33}) = 0$$

13. a. $\mathbf{e}_i \cdot \mathbf{e}_i = 0 \cdot 0 + 0 \cdot 0 + \cdots + \underset{i\text{th summand}}{1 \cdot 1} + \cdots + 0 \cdot 0 = 1$

b. Each summand is $0 \cdot 0$ except for the ith and jth, which are $1 \cdot 0$ or $0 \cdot 1$. In every case, if $i \neq j$, $\mathbf{e}_i \cdot \mathbf{e}_j = 0$.

15. a. $(5, -4, 3)$ **b.** (a_1, a_2, a_3) **c.** $3\mathbf{e}_1 - 2\mathbf{e}_2 - \mathbf{e}_3$

17. a. $\begin{bmatrix} 1 & 2 \\ 0 & 0 \\ 10 & 6 \end{bmatrix}$ **b.** $\begin{bmatrix} 1 & 2 & 2 \\ 3 & 6 & 1 \\ 8 & 16 & 1 \end{bmatrix}$ **c.** $\begin{bmatrix} 2 & 0 & 0 \\ 5 & 2 & 0 \\ 13 & 13 & 3 \end{bmatrix}$ **d.** $\begin{bmatrix} 6 & 7 & 7 & 9 \\ 1 & 2 & 3 & 4 \\ -2 & 4 & -2 & 2 \\ 7 & 9 & 10 & 13 \end{bmatrix}$ **e.** $\begin{bmatrix} 1 & 0 & 10 \\ 1 & 0 & 10 \\ 1 & 0 & 10 \\ 1 & 0 & 10 \end{bmatrix}$

19. a. $(\mathbf{A} - \mathbf{I})(\mathbf{A}^2 + \mathbf{A} + \mathbf{I}) = \mathbf{A}^3 + \mathbf{A}^2 + \mathbf{A} - \mathbf{A}^2 - \mathbf{A} - \mathbf{I} = \mathbf{A}^3 - \mathbf{I}$ **b.** $\mathbf{A}^3 + \mathbf{A}^2\mathbf{B} + \mathbf{AB}^2 - \mathbf{BA}^2 - \mathbf{BAB} - \mathbf{B}^3$

21. $\mathbf{P} = \begin{bmatrix} 0 & 1 & 1 \\ 0 & 0 & 1 \\ 0 & 0 & 0 \end{bmatrix}$, $\mathbf{P}^2 = \begin{bmatrix} 0 & 0 & 1 \\ 0 & 0 & 0 \\ 0 & 0 & 0 \end{bmatrix}$; 1 path of length 2. No paths of length 3. Total number of paths is 4.

23. $\mathbf{A}^2 = \begin{bmatrix} 1 & 2 & 1 \\ 0 & 1 & 2 \\ 0 & 0 & 1 \end{bmatrix}$, $\mathbf{A}^3 = \begin{bmatrix} 1 & 3 & 3 \\ 0 & 1 & 3 \\ 0 & 0 & 1 \end{bmatrix}$, $\mathbf{A}^n = \begin{bmatrix} 1 & n & \frac{1}{2}n(n-1) \\ 0 & 1 & n \\ 0 & 0 & 1 \end{bmatrix}$, for all $n \geqslant 1$.

25. $\begin{bmatrix} 1 & 0 & 0 \\ \frac{1}{2} & 0 & \frac{1}{2} \\ 0 & 0 & 1 \end{bmatrix}^2 = \begin{bmatrix} 1 & 0 & 0 \\ \frac{1}{2} & 0 & \frac{1}{2} \\ 0 & 0 & 1 \end{bmatrix}$

27. $a = b = c = 0$; or $a + b + c = 1$

31. a. $\begin{bmatrix} \begin{bmatrix} 1 & 2 \\ 3 & 4 \end{bmatrix}\begin{bmatrix} 4 & -1 \\ 2 & 0 \end{bmatrix} + \mathbf{0}_{2\times 2}\mathbf{0}_{2\times 2} & \begin{bmatrix} 1 & 2 \\ 3 & 4 \end{bmatrix}\mathbf{0}_{2\times 2} + \mathbf{0}_{2\times 2}\begin{bmatrix} -2 & 0 \\ -1 & 2 \end{bmatrix} \\ \mathbf{0}_{2\times 2}\begin{bmatrix} 4 & -1 \\ 2 & 0 \end{bmatrix} + \begin{bmatrix} 1 & 0 \\ 2 & 1 \end{bmatrix}\mathbf{0}_{2\times 2} & \mathbf{0}_{2\times 2}\mathbf{0}_{2\times 2} + \begin{bmatrix} 1 & 0 \\ 2 & 1 \end{bmatrix}\begin{bmatrix} -2 & 0 \\ 1 & 2 \end{bmatrix} \end{bmatrix} = \begin{bmatrix} 8 & -1 & 0 & 0 \\ 20 & -3 & 0 & 0 \\ 0 & 0 & -2 & 0 \\ 0 & 0 & -3 & 2 \end{bmatrix}$

b. $\begin{bmatrix} \begin{bmatrix} 3 & 1 \\ 5 & 2 \end{bmatrix}\begin{bmatrix} 2 & -1 \\ -5 & 3 \end{bmatrix} + \mathbf{0}_{2\times 2}\mathbf{0}_{2\times 2} & \begin{bmatrix} 3 & 1 \\ 5 & 2 \end{bmatrix}\mathbf{0}_{2\times 2} + \mathbf{0}_{2\times 2}\begin{bmatrix} 1 & -1 \\ 2 & 3 \end{bmatrix} \\ \mathbf{0}_{2\times 2}\begin{bmatrix} 2 & -1 \\ -5 & 3 \end{bmatrix} + \begin{bmatrix} 3 & 1 \\ 2 & 1 \end{bmatrix}\mathbf{0}_{2\times 2} & \mathbf{0}_{2\times 2}\mathbf{0}_{2\times 2} + \begin{bmatrix} 3 & 1 \\ 2 & 1 \end{bmatrix}\begin{bmatrix} 1 & -1 \\ -2 & 3 \end{bmatrix} \end{bmatrix} = \begin{bmatrix} 1 & 0 & 0 & 0 \\ 0 & 1 & 0 & 0 \\ 0 & 0 & 1 & 0 \\ 0 & 0 & 0 & 1 \end{bmatrix}$

33. a. $\left[\begin{array}{cc|ccc} 2 & 0 & 4 & 0 & 0 \\ 0 & 3 & 0 & 5 & 0 \\ \hline 0 & 0 & 0 & 0 & 6 \\ 0 & 0 & 0 & 1 & 0 \\ 0 & 0 & 0 & 0 & 1 \end{array}\right] \left[\begin{array}{ccc|cc} 1 & 0 & 0 & 0 & 0 \\ 0 & 2 & 0 & 0 & 0 \\ \hline 1 & 0 & 0 & 1 & 1 \\ 0 & 1 & 0 & -1 & 1 \\ 0 & 0 & 1 & 0 & 2 \end{array}\right] = \begin{bmatrix} 6 & 0 & 0 & 4 & 4 \\ 0 & 11 & 0 & -5 & 5 \\ 0 & 0 & 6 & 0 & 12 \\ 0 & 1 & 0 & -1 & 1 \\ 0 & 0 & 1 & 0 & 2 \end{bmatrix}$

b. $\begin{bmatrix} 17 & 0 & 19 & 0 \\ 0 & 17 & 0 & 19 \\ 24 & 0 & 26 & 0 \\ 0 & 24 & 0 & 26 \end{bmatrix}$

35. The partitioning in **A** and **B** should be the same.

EXERCISES 1.4

1. $\sqrt{11}, \sqrt{11}$; $(3, 1, 1), (1, 3, 1), (-3, 1, 1), (-3, -1, 1), (-1, 3, 1), (-1, -3, -1)$

3. a. $\pm\frac{1}{3}$ **b.** $k = \pm 1/(4\sqrt{3})$

5. $\sqrt{6}, 2\sqrt{3}, 3$

7. Let $\mathbf{u} = (a_1, a_2, \ldots, a_n)$, $\|\mathbf{u}\| = \sqrt{a_1^2 + a_2^2 + \cdots + a_n^2}$
If $\mathbf{u} = \mathbf{0}$, then $a_1 = a_2 = \cdots = a_n = 0$, so $\|\mathbf{u}\| = 0$.
If $\|\mathbf{u}\| = 0$, then $a_1^2 + a_2^2 + \cdots + a_n^2 = 0$. Thus $a_i = 0$, $i = 1, 2, \ldots, n$.

9. a. $\|k\mathbf{u}\| = \sqrt{(k\mathbf{u})\cdot(k\mathbf{u})} = \sqrt{k^2(\mathbf{u}\cdot\mathbf{u})} = |k|\sqrt{\mathbf{u}\cdot\mathbf{u}} = |k|\,\|\mathbf{u}\|$
b. $\|k\mathbf{u}\| = |k|\,\|\mathbf{u}\|$ by part (**a**). If $\mathbf{u} \neq \mathbf{0}$ then $\|\mathbf{u}\| \neq 0$.

Let $k = \dfrac{1}{\|\mathbf{u}\|}$, then $k > 0$, so $|k| = k$ and $\|k\mathbf{u}\| = |k|\,\|\mathbf{u}\| = \dfrac{1}{\|\mathbf{u}\|}\|\mathbf{u}\| = 1$

11.

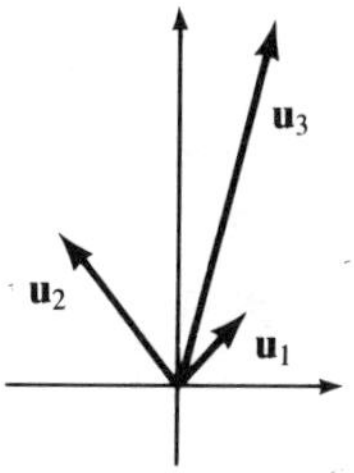

13.

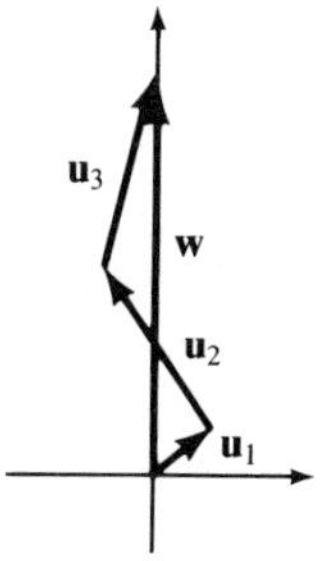

15. $\|\mathbf{u} - \mathbf{v}\|^2 = (\mathbf{u} - \mathbf{v}) \cdot (\mathbf{u} - \mathbf{v}) = \mathbf{u} \cdot \mathbf{u} - \mathbf{v} \cdot \mathbf{u} - \mathbf{u} \cdot \mathbf{v} + \mathbf{v} \cdot \mathbf{v} = \|\mathbf{u}\|^2 - 2\mathbf{u} \cdot \mathbf{v} + \|\mathbf{v}\|^2$

17. a. $\mathbf{u} \cdot \mathbf{v} = 15$, $\|\mathbf{u}\| = 3\sqrt{3}$, $\|\mathbf{v}\| = \sqrt{14}$, $15 < 3\sqrt{42}$

b. $\mathbf{u} \cdot \mathbf{v} = 5$, $\|\mathbf{u}\| = \sqrt{17}$, $\|\mathbf{v}\| = \sqrt{17}$, $5 < 17$

19. $|(k\mathbf{v}) \cdot \mathbf{v}| = |k|\mathbf{v} \cdot \mathbf{v} = |k|\sqrt{\mathbf{v} \cdot \mathbf{v}}\,\sqrt{\mathbf{v} \cdot \mathbf{v}} = \sqrt{(k\mathbf{v}) \cdot (k\mathbf{v})}\,\sqrt{\mathbf{v} \cdot \mathbf{v}} = \|k\mathbf{v}\|\,\|\mathbf{v}\|$

21.
$$\|\mathbf{u} + \mathbf{v}\| = \sqrt{(\mathbf{u} + \mathbf{v}) \cdot (\mathbf{u} + \mathbf{v})} = \sqrt{\mathbf{u} \cdot \mathbf{u} + 2\mathbf{u} \cdot \mathbf{v} + \mathbf{v} \cdot \mathbf{v}}$$
$$\leqslant \sqrt{\|\mathbf{u}\|^2 + 2|\mathbf{u} \cdot \mathbf{v}| + \|\mathbf{v}\|^2} \quad \text{(now use the Cauchy-Schwartz Inequality)}$$
$$\leqslant \sqrt{\|\mathbf{u}\|^2 + 2\|\mathbf{u}\|\,\|\mathbf{v}\| + \|\mathbf{v}\|^2}$$
$$= \sqrt{(\|\mathbf{u}\| + \|\mathbf{v}\|)^2} = |\,\|\mathbf{u}\| + \|\mathbf{v}\|\,|$$
$$= \|\mathbf{u}\| + \|\mathbf{v}\|$$

23. If the lengths of the diagonals are the same, $\|\mathbf{v} - \mathbf{u}\| = \|\mathbf{v} + \mathbf{u}\|$. Then $(\mathbf{v} - \mathbf{u}) \cdot (\mathbf{v} - \mathbf{u}) = (\mathbf{v} + \mathbf{u}) \cdot (\mathbf{v} + \mathbf{u})$. So $\mathbf{v} \cdot \mathbf{v} - 2\mathbf{u} \cdot \mathbf{v} + \mathbf{u} \cdot \mathbf{u} = \mathbf{v} \cdot \mathbf{v} + 2\mathbf{u} \cdot \mathbf{v} + \mathbf{u} \cdot \mathbf{u}$, or $-2\mathbf{u} \cdot \mathbf{v} = 2\mathbf{u} \cdot \mathbf{v}$, or $0 = \mathbf{u} \cdot \mathbf{v}$.

25. Side 1: $\frac{1}{2}\mathbf{v} + \frac{1}{2}\mathbf{w} = \frac{1}{2}(\mathbf{v} + \mathbf{w})$;
Side 2: $\frac{1}{2}\mathbf{w} - \frac{1}{2}(\mathbf{u} + \mathbf{v} + \mathbf{w}) = \frac{1}{2}(\mathbf{w} - \mathbf{u} - \mathbf{v} - \mathbf{w}) = -\frac{1}{2}(\mathbf{u} + \mathbf{v})$;
Side 3: $-\frac{1}{2}(\mathbf{u} + \mathbf{v} + \mathbf{w}) + \frac{1}{2}\mathbf{u} = \frac{1}{2}(-\mathbf{u} - \mathbf{v} - \mathbf{w} + \mathbf{u}) = -\frac{1}{2}(\mathbf{v} + \mathbf{w})$;
Side 4: $\frac{1}{2}\mathbf{u} + \frac{1}{2}\mathbf{v} = \frac{1}{2}(\mathbf{u} + \mathbf{v})$.
The figure is a parallelogram since both pairs of opposite sides are parallel since they are nonzero multiples of each other.

27. a. $(\mathbf{s} - \mathbf{t}) \cdot (\mathbf{s} - \mathbf{t}) = \mathbf{s} \cdot \mathbf{s} - 2\mathbf{s} \cdot \mathbf{t} + \mathbf{t} \cdot \mathbf{t} = 2 - 2\mathbf{s} \cdot \mathbf{t}$, since **s** and **t** are unit vectors.

b. Since $(\mathbf{s} - \mathbf{t}) \cdot (\mathbf{s} - \mathbf{t}) \geqslant 0$, $2 - 2\mathbf{s} \cdot \mathbf{t} \geqslant 0$—that is, $1 \geqslant \mathbf{s} \cdot \mathbf{t}$

29. a. Since $1 \geqslant \mathbf{s} \cdot \mathbf{t}$ (Problem 27b) and $\mathbf{s} \cdot \mathbf{t} \geqslant -1$ (Problem 28b), $-1 \leqslant \mathbf{s} \cdot \mathbf{t} \leqslant 1$

b. By the definition of **s** and **t** (Problem 27), $-1 \leqslant \dfrac{\mathbf{u} \cdot \mathbf{v}}{\|\mathbf{u}\|\,\|\mathbf{v}\|} \leqslant 1$ or $-\|\mathbf{u}\|\,\|\mathbf{v}\| \leqslant \mathbf{u} \cdot \mathbf{v} \leqslant \|\mathbf{u}\|\,\|\mathbf{v}\|$

c. $-\|\mathbf{u}\|\,\|\mathbf{v}\| \leqslant \mathbf{u} \cdot \mathbf{v} \leqslant \|\mathbf{u}\|\,\|\mathbf{v}\|$ written another way is $|\mathbf{u} \cdot \mathbf{v}| \leqslant \|\mathbf{u}\|\,\|\mathbf{v}\|$.

EXERCISES 1.5

1. a. $\frac{1}{2}$ **b.** $\frac{1}{3}$ **c.** $1/\sqrt{2}$ **d.** $7/(3\sqrt{6})$

3.

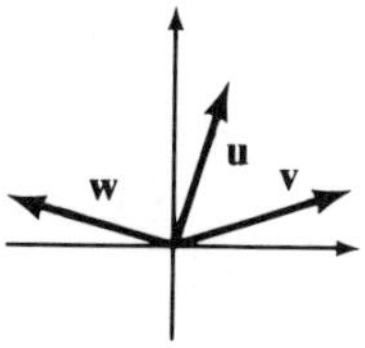

5. a. $x = 1 + 3k$, $y = 2 - k$

b. $x + 3y = 7$; $(1 + 3k) + 3(2 - k) = 1 + 3k + 6 - 3k = 7$

7. a. $x - y + 6z = -7$ **b.** $x - y + 6z = 0$

9. **a.** $2x + y - 7z = 0$ **b.** $2x + y - 7z = -27$
c. $\mathbf{x} - (1, -1, 4) = k(2, 1, -7)$

11. Plane 1 is parallel to plane 4; plane 1 is orthogonal to plane 2.

13. **a.** $\mathbf{v}_1 \cdot \mathbf{v}_2 = 0$, $\mathbf{v}_2 \cdot \mathbf{v}_3 = 0$, $\mathbf{v}_1 \cdot \mathbf{v}_3 = 0$ but $\|\mathbf{v}_1\| = \sqrt{3}$

b. $\begin{bmatrix} 3 & 0 & 0 \\ 0 & 6 & 0 \\ 0 & 0 & 2 \end{bmatrix}$ **c.** The squares of the lengths of $\mathbf{v}_1, \mathbf{v}_2, \mathbf{v}_3$

15. Let $U = \{\mathbf{u}_1, \mathbf{u}_2, \ldots, \mathbf{u}_n\}$ be an orthonormal set and $V = \{\mathbf{v}_1, \mathbf{v}_2, \ldots, \mathbf{v}_p\}$, $1 \leqslant p \leqslant n$ be a subset of U. For $i = 1, 2, \ldots, p$, $\mathbf{v}_i \cdot \mathbf{v}_i = \mathbf{u}_j \cdot \mathbf{u}_j = 1$ for some $j = 1, 2, \ldots, n$. For $i, j = 1, 2, \ldots, p$, $i \neq j$, $\mathbf{v}_i \cdot \mathbf{v}_j = \mathbf{u}_h \cdot \mathbf{u}_k = 0$ for some $h, k = 1, 2, \ldots, n$, $h \neq k$

17. **a.** $\mathbf{u} \cdot \mathbf{u} \times \mathbf{v} = a_1(a_2b_3 - a_3b_2) + a_2(a_3b_1 - a_1b_3) + a_3(a_1b_2 - a_2b_1) = 0$ **b.** $(3, -5, -2)$

19. Let $d = \sqrt{a^2 + b^2 + c^2}$. $\cos\alpha = a/d$, $\cos\beta = b/d$, $\cos\gamma = c/d$

21. dip = 22.6°, azimuth = 180°
dip = 50.2°, azimuth = 213.7°

23. If the parallelogram is a rectangle, the adjacent sides are perpendicular, so $\mathbf{a} \cdot \mathbf{b} = 0$. Then $\|\mathbf{a} + \mathbf{b}\| = \sqrt{(\mathbf{a} + \mathbf{b}) \cdot (\mathbf{a} + \mathbf{b})} = \sqrt{\mathbf{a} \cdot \mathbf{a} + 2\mathbf{a} \cdot \mathbf{b} + \mathbf{b} \cdot \mathbf{b}} = \sqrt{\mathbf{a} \cdot \mathbf{a} - 2\mathbf{a} \cdot \mathbf{b} + \mathbf{b} \cdot \mathbf{b}} = \sqrt{(\mathbf{a} - \mathbf{b}) \cdot (\mathbf{a} - \mathbf{b})} = \|\mathbf{a} - \mathbf{b}\|$. Thus the diagonals are equal. If $\|\mathbf{a} + \mathbf{b}\| = \|\mathbf{a} - \mathbf{b}\|$, then $\mathbf{a} \cdot \mathbf{a} + 2\mathbf{a} \cdot \mathbf{b} + \mathbf{b} \cdot \mathbf{b} = \mathbf{a} \cdot \mathbf{a} - 2\mathbf{a} \cdot \mathbf{b} + \mathbf{b} \cdot \mathbf{b}$. So $4\mathbf{a} \cdot \mathbf{b} = 0$ or $\mathbf{a} \cdot \mathbf{b} = 0$. Thus the adjacent sides are perpendicular.

25. Let $\mathbf{a}$, $\mathbf{b}$, $\mathbf{c}$, $\mathbf{d}$, T_1 and T_2 be as in the diagram. Then $\|\mathbf{a}\| + \|\mathbf{b}\| = \|\mathbf{c}\| + \|\mathbf{d}\| = \|\mathbf{u}\|$. The area of the parallelogram = area T_1 + area $T_2 = \frac{1}{2}(\|\mathbf{a}\| + \|\mathbf{c}\|)\|\mathbf{w}\| + \frac{1}{2}(\|\mathbf{b}\| + \|\mathbf{d}\|)\|\mathbf{w}\| = \frac{1}{2}(\|\mathbf{a}\| + \|\mathbf{b}\| + \|\mathbf{c}\| + \|\mathbf{d}\|)\|\mathbf{w}\| = \|\mathbf{u}\|\,\|\mathbf{w}\|$, where $\|\mathbf{w}\|$ is the distance between the bases of the trapezoids. But $\mathbf{w}$ is the projection of $\mathbf{v}$ orthogonal to $\mathbf{u}$. $\mathbf{w} = \mathbf{v} - \dfrac{\mathbf{u} \cdot \mathbf{v}}{\mathbf{u} \cdot \mathbf{u}}\mathbf{u}$, so

$$\mathbf{w} \cdot \mathbf{w} = \left(\mathbf{v} - \frac{\mathbf{u} \cdot \mathbf{v}}{\mathbf{u} \cdot \mathbf{u}}\mathbf{u}\right) \cdot \left(\mathbf{v} - \frac{\mathbf{u} \cdot \mathbf{v}}{\mathbf{u} \cdot \mathbf{u}}\mathbf{u}\right) = \mathbf{v} \cdot \mathbf{v} - 2\frac{\mathbf{u} \cdot \mathbf{v}}{\mathbf{u} \cdot \mathbf{u}}(\mathbf{u} \cdot \mathbf{v}) + \left(\frac{\mathbf{u} \cdot \mathbf{v}}{\mathbf{u} \cdot \mathbf{u}}\right)^2(\mathbf{u} \cdot \mathbf{u}) = \mathbf{v} \cdot \mathbf{v} - \frac{(\mathbf{u} \cdot \mathbf{v})^2}{\mathbf{u} \cdot \mathbf{u}} = \frac{\|\mathbf{v}\|^2\|\mathbf{u}\|^2 - (\mathbf{u} \cdot \mathbf{v})^2}{\|\mathbf{u}\|^2};$$

so $\|\mathbf{w}\| = \dfrac{\sqrt{\|\mathbf{v}\|^2\|\mathbf{u}\|^2 - (\mathbf{u} \cdot \mathbf{v})^2}}{\|\mathbf{u}\|}$. Thus, the area of the parallelogram is $\sqrt{\|\mathbf{v}\|^2\|\mathbf{u}\|^2 - (\mathbf{u} \cdot \mathbf{v})^2}$.

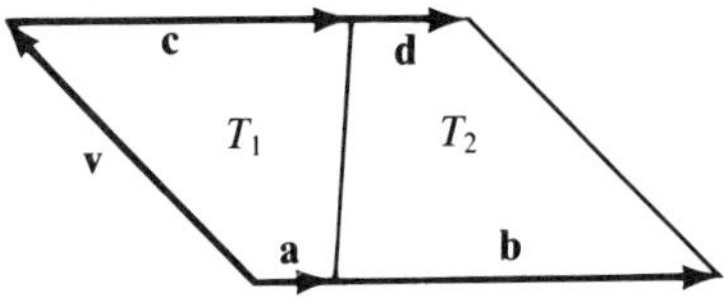

EXERCISES 1.6

1. (Answers to programs vary both in style and language used. Typical programs can be written in Pascal as shown.)

```
Program PrintTranspose(Input, Output);

Const
  RowMax = 5Ø;
  ColMax = 5Ø;

Type
  Matrix = Array [1..RowMax, 1..ColMax] of Real;

Var
  CurrentRowSize, RowCounter: 1..RowMax;
  CurrentColSize, ColCounter: 1..ColMax;
  A, AT: Matrix;

Procedure PRINTMATRIX (Var X: Matrix; R, C: Integer);

Var
  RowCt, ColCt: Integer;
```

```
Begin
  Writeln;
  For RowCt := 1 to R Do
    Begin
      For ColCt := 1 to C Do
        Write(X[RowCt, ColCt] :8:2);
      Writeln
    End
End;

Begin { MAIN }
  Writeln;
  Write('Enter the number of    rows in your matrix: ');
  Readln(CurrentRowSize);
  Write('Enter the number of columns in your matrix: ');
  Readln(CurrentColSize);

  Writeln;
  Writeln('Enter each value in the matrix when prompted: ');
  Writeln;
  For RowCounter := 1 to CurrentRowSize Do
     For ColCounter := 1 to CurrentColSize Do
        Begin
          Write('Row: ', RowCounter :Ø, ' Column: ',
                ColCounter :Ø, '  ');
          Readln(A[RowCounter, ColCounter])
        End;

  Writeln;
  Writeln('Matrix entry routine complete.');
  Writeln;
  Writeln('YOUR MATRIX WAS ENTERED AS:');

  PrintMatrix(A, CurrentRowSize, CurrentColSize);

  For ColCounter := 1 to CurrentColSize Do
    For RowCounter := 1 to CurrentRowSize Do
      AT[ColCounter, RowCounter] := A[RowCounter, ColCounter];

  Writeln;
  Writeln('ITS TRANSPOSE IS:');

  PrintMatrix(AT, CurrentColSize, CurrentRowSize)

End.
```

3.
```
Program FindMatrixProduct(Input, Output);

Const
  RowMax = 5Ø;
  ColMax = 5Ø;

Type
  Matrix = Array [1..RowMax, 1..ColMax] of Real;

Var
  CurrentRowSize, RowCounter: Integer;
  CurrentColSize, ColCounter: Integer;
  ProductRowSize: Integer;
  ProductColSize: Integer;
  A, AT, Product: Matrix;
```

```
{*************************************************************************}
Procedure PRINTMATRIX(Var X: Matrix; R, C: Integer);

Var
  RowCt, ColCt: Integer;

Begin
  Writeln;
  For RowCt := 1 to R Do
    Begin
      For ColCt := 1 to C Do
        Write(X[RowCt, ColCt] :8:2);
      Writeln
    End
End;
{*************************************************************************}
Procedure MULTIPLYMATRICES(Var A, B, P: Matrix;
                               RowA, ColA, RowB, Col B: Integer;
                           Var RowP, ColP: Integer);

Var
  Row, Col, Inner: Integer;
  Sum: Real;

Begin
  If ColA <> RowB Then Writeln('Matrix product cannot be found...')
  Else
    Begin
      RowP := RowA;
      ColP := ColB;
      For Row := 1 to RowA Do
        For Col := 1 to ColB Do
          Begin
            Sum := Ø.Ø;
            For Inner := 1 to ColA Do
              Sum := Sum + A[Row,Inner] * B[Inner,Col];
            P[Row, Col] := Sum
          End;  { FOR COL }
       Writeln
     End  { ELSE }
End;
{*************************************************************************}
Begin { MAIN }
  Writeln;
  Write('Enter the number of    rows in your matrix: ');
  Readln(CurrentRowSize);
  Write('Enter the number of columns in your matrix: ');
  Readln(CurrentColSize);

  Writeln;
  Writeln('Enter each value in the matrix when prompted: ');
  Writeln;
  For RowCounter := 1 to CurrentRowSize Do
     For ColCounter := 1 to CurrentColSize Do
        Begin
          Write('Row: ', RowCounter :Ø, ' Column: ', ColCounter :Ø, '  ');
          Readln(A[RowCounter, ColCounter])
        End;
```

```
  Writeln;
  Writeln('Matrix entry routine complete.');
  Writeln;
  Writeln('YOUR MATRIX WAS ENTERED AS:');
  PrintMatrix(A, CurrentRowSize, CurrentColSize);
  For ColCounter := 1 to CurrentColSize Do
    For RowCounter := 1 to CurrentRowSize Do
      AT[ColCounter, RowCounter] := A[RowCounter, ColCounter];
  Writeln;
  Writeln('ITS TRANSPOSE IS:');
  PrintMatrix(AT, CurrentColSize, CurrentRowSize);
  MultiplyMatrices(A, AT, Product, CurrentRowSize, CurrentColSize,
                   CurrentColSize, CurrentRowSize, ProductRowSize,
                   ProductColSize);
  Writeln('The product of A and A transpose is:');
  Writeln;
  PrintMatrix(Product, ProductRowSize, ProductColSize);
  MultiplyMatrices(AT, A, Product, CurrentColSize, CurrentRowSize;
                   CurrentRowSize, CurrentColSize, ProductRowSize,
                   ProductColSize);
  Writeln('The product of A transpose and A is:');
  Writeln:
  PrintMatrix(Product, ProductRowSize, ProductColSize)
End.
```

5. Examples verifying the statements in Theorem 6 are:

1. $\begin{bmatrix} 1 & 3 \\ 3 & 2 \end{bmatrix} + \begin{bmatrix} 3 & -4 \\ -4 & 1 \end{bmatrix} = \begin{bmatrix} 4 & -1 \\ -1 & 3 \end{bmatrix}$; **2.** $\begin{bmatrix} 1 & 3 \\ 3 & 2 \end{bmatrix}^T = \begin{bmatrix} 1 & 3 \\ 3 & 2 \end{bmatrix}$;

3. $\begin{bmatrix} 2 & 3 & 0 \\ 1 & -2 & 1 \end{bmatrix} \begin{bmatrix} 2 & 1 \\ 3 & -2 \\ 0 & 1 \end{bmatrix} = \begin{bmatrix} 13 & -4 \\ -4 & 5 \end{bmatrix}$; **4.** $\begin{bmatrix} 0 & 1 \\ -1 & 0 \end{bmatrix} + \begin{bmatrix} 0 & -7 \\ 7 & 0 \end{bmatrix} = \begin{bmatrix} 0 & -6 \\ 6 & 0 \end{bmatrix}$;

5. $\begin{bmatrix} 0 & 1 \\ -1 & 0 \end{bmatrix}^T = \begin{bmatrix} 0 & -1 \\ 1 & 0 \end{bmatrix}$.

7. $\mathbf{T}^{20} \approx \begin{bmatrix} 0.28 & 0.28 & 0.28 \\ 0.23 & 0.23 & 0.23 \\ 0.47 & 0.47 & 0.47 \end{bmatrix}$; all columns approach $\begin{bmatrix} 0.28 \\ 0.23 \\ 0.47 \end{bmatrix}$

9. a. $\mathbf{A} = \begin{bmatrix} 0 & 1 & 1 & 0 & 1 \\ 0 & 0 & 1 & 1 & 0 \\ 1 & 0 & 0 & 0 & 1 \\ 1 & 1 & 1 & 0 & 1 \\ 0 & 0 & 0 & 0 & 0 \end{bmatrix}$

b. After one step, F_3 and F_4 have heard it; after two steps, F_1, F_2, and F_5 have heard it; yes.
c. 3

11. a. $\begin{bmatrix} 0 & 1 & 1 & 0 & 1 \\ 0 & 0 & 1 & 1 & 0 \\ 0 & 0 & 0 & 1 & 0 \\ 0 & 1 & 0 & 0 & 1 \\ 1 & 0 & 0 & 0 & 0 \end{bmatrix}$ **b.** $\begin{bmatrix} 1 & 1 & 2 & 2 & 1 \\ 0 & 1 & 1 & 2 & 1 \\ 0 & 1 & 0 & 1 & 1 \\ 1 & 1 & 1 & 1 & 1 \\ 1 & 1 & 1 & 0 & 1 \end{bmatrix}$ **c.** Legislator 1

13. a. $(-2, 4)$ **b.** $(9, -1)$ **c.** $(1, 4)$ **d.** $(-10, -3)$ **e.** $(\sqrt{2}, 0)$

15. b. Rescale by factor of 2 in positive x-direction only.
c. Rescale by factor of 2 in positive x-direction and rescale by factor of 3 in positive y-direction.
d. Reflect (x, y) in x-axis to $(x, -y)$.
e. Reflect (x, y) in y-axis to $(-x, y)$.
f. Reflect (x, y) in line $y = x$ to (y, x).
g. Shear by 3 in x-direction; that is, (x, y) moves to $(x + 3y, y)$.
h. Shear by 2 in y-direction; that is, (x, y) moves to $(x, 2x + y)$.
i. Shear by both 3 in x-direction and 2 in y-direction, so (x, y) moves to $(x + 3y, 2x + y)$.
j. Rotate $+30°$ about origin.
k. Rotate $+270°$ about origin.

17. $\begin{bmatrix} \frac{1}{2} & -\frac{1}{2}\sqrt{3} \\ \frac{1}{2}\sqrt{3} & \frac{1}{2} \end{bmatrix}\begin{bmatrix} 2 & 0 \\ 0 & 4 \end{bmatrix} = \begin{bmatrix} 1 & -2\sqrt{3} \\ \sqrt{3} & 2 \end{bmatrix}$

The line joining $(2, 0)$ and $(0, 4)$ rotates into the line joining $(1, \sqrt{3})$ and $(-2\sqrt{3}, 2)$.

19. $\begin{bmatrix} 1 & 0 \\ 2 & 1 \end{bmatrix}\begin{bmatrix} x \\ -x + 1 \end{bmatrix} = \begin{bmatrix} x \\ x + 1 \end{bmatrix}$. The line is changed to $y = x + 1$.

21. $\begin{bmatrix} 1 & 3 \\ 3 & 1 \end{bmatrix}$

23. $\begin{bmatrix} -\frac{1}{2}\sqrt{2} & \frac{1}{2}\sqrt{2} \\ -\frac{1}{2}\sqrt{2} & -\frac{1}{2}\sqrt{2} \end{bmatrix}\begin{bmatrix} 1 & 0 \\ 3 & 1 \end{bmatrix}$

EXERCISES 2.1

1. b. $\begin{bmatrix} 1 & 2 & 1 \\ 1 & 0 & -1 \\ 4 & 1 & 1 \end{bmatrix}\begin{bmatrix} x_1 \\ x_2 \\ x_3 \end{bmatrix} = \begin{bmatrix} 7 \\ 3 \\ 10 \end{bmatrix}$

3. b. $\begin{bmatrix} 2 & 4 & 1 & 3 \\ -1 & 2 & 5 & 6 \end{bmatrix}\begin{bmatrix} x_1 \\ x_2 \\ x_3 \\ x_4 \end{bmatrix} = \begin{bmatrix} 4 \\ 9 \end{bmatrix}$

5. a. Add -2 times equation 1 to equation 2. Add equation 1 to equation 3.
b. $\left[\begin{array}{rrr|r} 1 & -1 & 1 & 3 \\ 2 & 3 & -4 & 9 \\ -1 & 3 & 8 & 1 \end{array}\right]$, $\left[\begin{array}{rrr|r} 1 & -1 & 1 & 3 \\ 0 & 5 & -6 & 3 \\ 0 & 2 & 9 & 4 \end{array}\right]$

7. $\left[\begin{array}{rrr|r} 1 & 2 & -1 & 6 \\ 0 & 5 & 5 & 5 \\ 0 & -8 & 2 & -18 \end{array}\right]$; $\begin{aligned} x_1 + 2x_2 - x_3 &= 6 \\ 5x_2 + 5x_3 &= 5 \\ -8x_2 + 2x_3 &= -18 \end{aligned}$

9. $x_1 - x_2 = 3$, $5x_1 + x_2 = 1$; $x_1 = \frac{2}{3}$, $x_2 = -\frac{7}{3}$
11. Infinitely many pairs $(k, -k)$, where k is any real number.
13. a. If and only if all the diagonal elements are nonzero.
b. If and only if all the diagonal elements are nonzero.

15. $\left[\begin{array}{rrr|r} 1 & 1 & 2 & 1 \\ 1 & 0 & -1 & 1 \\ 2 & 3 & 5 & 4 \end{array}\right]$ $x = 0$, $y = 3$, $z = -1$; intersect at the point $(0, 3, -1)$

17. No. The planes have no points in common.
19. Oldest \$90,000; second \$60,000; youngest \$70,000
21. a. $r_1 + r_2 = 40$, $r_1 + 20 = r_3$, $r_2 + r_3 = r_4$
b. From the first two equations $r_2 + r_3 = 60$, so $r_4 = 60$.
c. $r_1 = -20 + k$, $x_2 = 60 - k$, $r_3 = k$, $r_4 = 60$

EXERCISES 2.2

1. a. $\begin{bmatrix} 1 & 0 \\ 0 & 1 \\ 0 & 0 \end{bmatrix}$ $r = 2$ **b.** $\begin{bmatrix} 1 & 0 & -4 \\ 0 & 1 & 11 \end{bmatrix}$ $r = 2$

c. $\begin{bmatrix} 1 & 0 & 0 \\ 0 & 1 & 0 \\ 0 & 0 & 1 \end{bmatrix}$ $r = 3$ **d.** $\begin{bmatrix} 1 & 0 & 1 \\ 0 & 1 & -1 \\ 0 & 0 & 0 \end{bmatrix}$ $r = 2$

3. a. 0, 0 **b.** 2, 3, n

5. 3, 2, 2, 4, the smaller of m and n. Rank is less than or equal to the number of rows and less than or equal to the number of columns.

7. a. $\begin{bmatrix} 1 & 0 & -4 \\ 0 & 0 & 0 \\ 0 & 0 & 0 \end{bmatrix}, \begin{bmatrix} 0 & 0 & 0 \\ 0 & 1 & 2 \\ 0 & 0 & 0 \end{bmatrix}$ **b.** $\mathbf{A} = \begin{bmatrix} 1 & 2 & 3 \\ 0 & 4 & 5 \\ 0 & 0 & 6 \end{bmatrix}, \mathbf{B} = \begin{bmatrix} -1 & -2 & -3 \\ 0 & -4 & -5 \\ 0 & 0 & -6 \end{bmatrix}$

c. $\begin{bmatrix} 1 & 2 & 3 \\ 2 & 3 & 4 \\ 1 & 2 & 1 \end{bmatrix}, \begin{bmatrix} 1 & 2 & 3 \\ -2 & -3 & -4 \\ -1 & -2 & -1 \end{bmatrix}$

9. a. $(1, 1, 0, -1)$ **b.** $\{(-2 - 3k - 3j, 2 + k + j, k, j), j, k \text{ real numbers}\}$

11. $\mathbf{E}_1\mathbf{A} = \begin{bmatrix} a_{11} & a_{12} & \cdots & a_{1n} \\ a_{31} & a_{32} & \cdots & a_{3n} \\ a_{21} & a_{22} & \cdots & a_{2n} \end{bmatrix}$ interchanges rows 2 and 3.

$\mathbf{E}_2\mathbf{A} = \begin{bmatrix} a_{11} & a_{12} & \cdots & a_{1n} \\ ka_{21} & ka_{22} & \cdots & ka_{2n} \\ a_{31} & a_{32} & \cdots & a_{3n} \end{bmatrix}$ multiplies row 2 by k.

$\mathbf{E}_3\mathbf{A} = \begin{bmatrix} a_{11} & a_{12} & \cdots & a_{1n} \\ a_{21} & a_{22} & \cdots & a_{2n} \\ ka_{11} + a_{31} & ka_{12} + a_{32} & \cdots & ka_{1n} + a_{3n} \end{bmatrix}$ adds k times row 1 to row 3.

13. $\mathbf{A}_1 = \begin{bmatrix} 1 & 2 & 1 \\ 0 & 3 & 1 \\ 1 & 2 & 4 \end{bmatrix}$ $\mathbf{A}_2 = \begin{bmatrix} 1 & 2 & 1 \\ 0 & 3 & 1 \\ 0 & 0 & 3 \end{bmatrix}$ $\mathbf{A}_3 = \begin{bmatrix} 1 & 2 & 1 \\ 0 & 3 & 1 \\ 0 & 0 & 1 \end{bmatrix}$ $\mathbf{A}_4 = \begin{bmatrix} 1 & 2 & 0 \\ 0 & 3 & 1 \\ 0 & 0 & 1 \end{bmatrix}$

$\mathbf{A}_5 = \begin{bmatrix} 1 & 2 & 0 \\ 0 & 3 & 0 \\ 0 & 0 & 1 \end{bmatrix}$ $\mathbf{A}_6 = \begin{bmatrix} 1 & 2 & 0 \\ 0 & 1 & 0 \\ 0 & 0 & 1 \end{bmatrix}$ $\mathbf{A}_7 = \begin{bmatrix} 1 & 0 & 0 \\ 0 & 1 & 0 \\ 0 & 0 & 1 \end{bmatrix}$

15. $[\mathbf{C}_1 \ \mathbf{C}_2 \ \mathbf{C}_3] = \begin{bmatrix} 1 & 3 & 1 \\ 0 & -5 & -1 \\ 0 & 1 & 5 \end{bmatrix}$ $\mathbf{D} = \begin{bmatrix} 1 & 1 & 3 \\ -1 & 0 & -5 \\ 5 & 0 & 1 \end{bmatrix} = [\mathbf{C}_3 \ \mathbf{C}_1 \ \mathbf{C}_2]$

17. a. 2, 3, no solution. **b.** 2, 2, $k_1\begin{bmatrix} -2 \\ 1 \\ 0 \\ 0 \end{bmatrix} + k_2\begin{bmatrix} 0 \\ 0 \\ -1 \\ 1 \end{bmatrix}$ **c.** 3, 3, $\begin{bmatrix} 3 \\ 0 \\ 5 \\ 7 \\ 0 \end{bmatrix} + k_1\begin{bmatrix} -2 \\ 1 \\ 0 \\ 0 \\ 0 \end{bmatrix} + k_2\begin{bmatrix} -4 \\ 0 \\ -2 \\ -3 \\ 1 \end{bmatrix}$

19. a. Solution exists, not unique, one unknown is arbitrary. $r = r_a = 3, n = 4$
b. Solution exists, not unique, two unknowns arbitrary. $r = r_a = 2, n = 4$
c. No solution; $r = 2, r_a = 3$. **d.** Unique solution; $r = r_a = n = 4$.

21. a. Solution, not unique, 1 arbitrary unknown **b.** No solution
c. Solution, not unique, 1 arbitrary unknown **d.** Unique solution

23. a. Inconsistent; $r = 2, r_a = 3, n = 3$ **b.** $(\frac{33}{2}, -\frac{19}{2})$; $r = 2, r_a = 2, n = 2$ **c.** $(2, 1, -1)$; $r = 3, r_a = 3, n = 3$
d. $\{(\frac{4}{3}, \frac{1}{3}, \frac{4}{3}, 0) + k(1, 0, 2, 1), k \text{ a real number}\}$; $r = 3, r_a = 3, n = 4$

25. a. Consistent
b. Inconsistent

c. Need to know the rank of $[\mathbf{A}|\mathbf{B}]$
d. Need to know the rank of **A**
e. Need to know the rank of **A**

27. a. **B** is obtained from **A** by adding k times row 1 to row 3 of **A**. Row 1 of **B** is the same as row 1 of **A**. The matrix $\begin{bmatrix} 1 & 0 & 0 \\ 0 & 1 & 0 \\ -k & 0 & 1 \end{bmatrix}$ **B** has k times the first row of **B** subtracted from the third row. This yields matrix **A**.
b. Add k times row 1 to row 3. Add $-k$ times row 1 to row 3.

29. a. $\mathbf{B}_1 = \begin{bmatrix} 1 & 0 & 0 \\ 3 & 1 & 0 \\ 0 & 0 & 1 \end{bmatrix}, \quad \mathbf{B}_2 = \begin{bmatrix} 1 & 0 & 0 \\ 0 & 1 & 0 \\ -2 & 0 & 1 \end{bmatrix}, \quad \mathbf{B}_3 = \begin{bmatrix} 1 & 0 & 0 \\ 0 & 1 & 0 \\ 0 & -2 & 1 \end{bmatrix}$
b. $\mathbf{L} = \mathbf{B}_1\mathbf{B}_2\mathbf{B}_3 = \begin{bmatrix} 1 & 0 & 0 \\ 3 & 1 & 0 \\ -2 & -2 & 1 \end{bmatrix}$
c. Lower triangular

31. a. $\begin{bmatrix} 1 & 0 \\ 2 & 1 \end{bmatrix}\begin{bmatrix} 2 & 3 \\ 0 & -1 \end{bmatrix}$
b. $\begin{bmatrix} 1 & 0 & 0 \\ 2 & 1 & 0 \\ -1 & -\frac{1}{3} & 1 \end{bmatrix}\begin{bmatrix} 3 & 5 & 4 \\ 0 & -3 & -9 \\ 0 & 0 & 5 \end{bmatrix}$

33. a. $\begin{bmatrix} 1 & 0 & 0 \\ 3 & 1 & 0 \\ 2 & 0 & 1 \end{bmatrix}\begin{bmatrix} 2 & 1 & 4 \\ 0 & 2 & -10 \\ 0 & 0 & -5 \end{bmatrix}$
b. After the steps $\begin{bmatrix} 1 & 0 & 0 \\ -2 & 1 & 0 \\ 0 & 0 & 1 \end{bmatrix}\begin{bmatrix} 2 & 1 & 4 \\ 4 & 2 & 3 \\ 6 & 5 & 2 \end{bmatrix} = \begin{bmatrix} 2 & 1 & 4 \\ 0 & 0 & -5 \\ 6 & 5 & 2 \end{bmatrix}$ and $\begin{bmatrix} 1 & 0 & 0 \\ 0 & 1 & 0 \\ -3 & 0 & 1 \end{bmatrix}\begin{bmatrix} 2 & 1 & 4 \\ 0 & 0 & -5 \\ 6 & 5 & 2 \end{bmatrix} = \begin{bmatrix} 2 & 1 & 4 \\ 0 & 0 & -5 \\ 0 & 2 & -10 \end{bmatrix}$, an interchange of rows 2 and 3 is needed to complete the process.
c. Because the resulting matrix would no longer be lower triangular.

35.

$$\begin{array}{rcr|r|r} d_1 & = & 5 & 13 & -4 \\ 3d_1 + d_2 & = & 7 & 10 & -1 \\ -2d_1 - 2d_2 + d_3 & = & 0 & 14 & -2 \\ x_1 + 2x_2 + 4x_3 & = & 5 & 13 & -4 \\ -5x_2 - 8x_3 & = & -8 & -29 & 11 \\ -6x_3 & = & -6 & -18 & 12 \end{array} \qquad \begin{array}{rcr|r|r} d_1 & = & 5 & 13 & -4 \\ d_2 & = & -8 & -29 & 11 \\ d_3 & = & -6 & -18 & 12 \\ x_1 & = & 1 & -1 & 2 \\ x_2 & = & 0 & 1 & 1 \\ x_3 & = & 1 & 3 & -2 \end{array}$$

Would be useful if the **LU** factorization is already known or if there are many sets of equations with the same matrix **A**.

EXERCISES 2.3

1. a. $\{k(-17, -4, 9), k$ a real number$\}$; nontrivial solutions
b. $\{(0, 0, 0)\}$ only the trivial solution
c. $\{k(1, -1, 1), k$ a real number$\}$; nontrivial solutions
d. $\{k_1(-2, 1, 0) + k_2(1, 0, 1), k_1, k_2$ real numbers$\}$; nontrivial solutions

3. a. Yes, no **b.** No
c. No. The equations are consistent if $r = r_a$, inconsistent if $r < r_a$.

5. a. $r = 3, n = 3$, none; **b.** $r = 2, n = 3$, one; **c.** $r = 2, n = 4$, two; **d.** $r = 2, n = 3$, one.

7. **a.** $\{(-3k_1 - 2k_2, 2k_1, k_2),\ k_1, k_2$ real numbers$\}$, coincident planes
b. $\{(1 - 3k_1 - 2k_2, 2k_1, k_2),\ k_1, k_2$ real numbers$\}$; coincident planes
c. No solution; parallel nonintersecting planes

9. **a.** Same lines, consistent
b. Inconsistent, lines are parallel
c. Consistent, three lines all through $(0, 0)$
d. Consistent, three lines all through $(1, 1)$
e. Inconsistent; lines intersect by pairs in three points

11. If $\mathbf{X}_1$ and $\mathbf{X}_2$ are solutions of $\mathbf{AX} = \mathbf{B}$, then $\mathbf{AX}_1 = \mathbf{B}$ and $\mathbf{AX}_2 = \mathbf{B}$. $\mathbf{AX}_3 = \mathbf{A}(\mathbf{X}_1 - \mathbf{X}_2) = \mathbf{AX}_1 - \mathbf{AX}_2 = \mathbf{B} - \mathbf{B} = \mathbf{0}$. Thus $\mathbf{X}_3$ is a solution of $\mathbf{AX} = \mathbf{0}$.

13. $a = b = c = 1$; $P = KWQH$

15. $a = 2 - k,\ b = -1 + k,\ c = d = k$; $F = K\mu^{2-k}\rho^{-1+k}V^kL^k$

17. Let $\mathbf{x} = k(a_2b_3 - a_3b_2, a_3b_1 - a_1b_3, a_1b_2 - a_2b_1)$ with k real. Substitution shows that $\mathbf{x}$ is a solution of the system. If $(a_1, a_2, a_3) \neq k(b_1, b_2, b_3)$ for any k, then $(a_2b_3 - a_3b_2, a_3b_1 - a_1b_3, a_1b_2 - a_2b_1) \neq (0, 0, 0)$ and for each value of k, $\mathbf{x}$ is a distinct vector with direction $(a_2b_3 - a_3b_2, a_3b_1 - a_1b_3, a_1b_2 - a_2b_1)$.

EXERCISES 2.4

1. **a.** linearly dependent **b.** linearly independent **c.** linearly independent **d.** linearly independent

3. When $\begin{bmatrix} 1 & 0 & 4 & 1 \\ 0 & 1 & -2 & -2 \\ 0 & 0 & 3 & 4 \\ 0 & 0 & 0 & 5 \end{bmatrix}$ is obtained, or at the preceding step since the next step can be done by inspection.

5. Let $\mathbf{A}$ be the 4×5 matrix with columns the 5 4-tuples and let $\mathbf{X}$ be the 5×1 matrix of unknowns x_1, x_2, x_3, x_4, and x_5. The equation $\mathbf{AX} = \mathbf{0}$ has nontrivial solution if the rank of $\mathbf{A}$ is less than the number of unknowns, 5. Since the rank of $\mathbf{A}$ is $\leqslant 4$, $\mathbf{AX} = \mathbf{0}$ has a nontrivial solution. Thus, the 5 4-tuples are linearly dependent. Any set of 3 pairs is linearly dependent. Any set of $n + 1$ n-tuples is linearly dependent.

7. $a = -1,\ b = 0$

9. The matrix $\mathbf{M}$ (Theorem 3) is 3×4, so has rank at most 3, which is less than 4.

11. The set $\{\mathbf{u}_1, \mathbf{u}_2, \ldots, \mathbf{u}_k\}$ is linearly dependent, $c_1\mathbf{u}_1 + c_2\mathbf{u}_2 + \cdots + c_k\mathbf{u}_k = \mathbf{0}$, where $c_i \neq 0$ for some i. The set $\{\mathbf{u}_1, \mathbf{u}_2, \ldots, \mathbf{u}_k, \mathbf{u}_{k+1}, \ldots, \mathbf{u}_m\}$ is linearly dependent since $c_1\mathbf{u}_1 + c_2\mathbf{u}_2 + \cdots + c_k\mathbf{u}_k + 0\mathbf{u}_{k+1} + \cdots + 0\mathbf{u}_m = \mathbf{0}$, where $c_i \neq 0$ for some i.

13. **a.** The plane $x_1 - x_2 + x_3 = 0$; $\{(-1, 0, 1), (0, 1, 1)\}$
b. The line through $(0, 0, 0)$ with the direction of $(-1, 2, 3)$; $x_1 + 2x_2 - x_3 = 0$ and $x_1 - x_2 + x_3 = 0$

15. 0

17. **a.** r
b. The kth leading column has the kth element 1 and other elements 0. The elements x_{i_k} have coefficients 1. The elements x_{j_k} can be assigned arbitrarily.
c. The $n - r$ rows j_k have a 1 in the kth position and the remaining elements 0
d. $n - r$
e. Dimension of the solution set is $n - r$

EXERCISES 2.5

1. Unique solution: $(-2, 9, -11, 5)$

3. Infinitely many solutions: $\{(8 - k_1 + k_2, k_1, 6 - k_1 + 4k_2, k_2),\ k_1, k_2$ real$\}$

5. Infinitely many solutions: $\{(-2.25 + 0.25k_2, k_1, -0.25 + 0.25k_2, k_2, 0),\ k_1, k_2$ real$\}$

7. No solution

9. Infinitely many solutions: $\{(k, -1 - k, k),\ k$ real$\}$

11. No solution

13. Unique solution: $(1, 1, 0, 0, 1)$

15. **a.** $8KClO_3 + C_{12}H_{22}O_{11} \rightarrow 12CO_2 + 11H_2O + 8KCl$
b. $3CH_2O + 16Ag(NH_3)_2NO_3 + 18NaOH \rightarrow 3NaNCO_3 + 16Ag + 30NH_3 + 15NaNO_3 + 15H_2O$

17. Unique solution: $x_1 = x_3 = 142.86$, $x_4 = x_6 = 131.25$, $x_7 = x_9 = 107.14$, $x_2 = 140.18$, $x_5 = 125.00$, $x_8 = 97.32$

19. **a.** $\begin{bmatrix} x \\ y \end{bmatrix}' = \begin{bmatrix} 0 & -1 \\ 2 & 0 \end{bmatrix}\begin{bmatrix} x \\ y \end{bmatrix} + \begin{bmatrix} 1 \\ -\frac{1}{2} \end{bmatrix}$
b. $(0,0) \rightarrow (1, -\frac{1}{2}) \rightarrow (\frac{3}{2}, \frac{3}{2}) \rightarrow (-\frac{1}{2}, \frac{5}{2}) \rightarrow (-\frac{3}{2}, -\frac{3}{2}) \rightarrow (\frac{5}{2}, -\frac{3}{2}) \rightarrow (\frac{9}{2}, \frac{9}{2}) \rightarrow \cdots$ no
c. The points are moving in an outward spiral getting farther from $(\frac{1}{2}, \frac{1}{2})$ at each step.
d. $(1,2) \rightarrow (-1, \frac{3}{2}) \rightarrow (-\frac{1}{2}, -\frac{5}{2}) \rightarrow (\frac{7}{2}, -\frac{3}{2}) \rightarrow (\frac{5}{2}, \frac{13}{2}) \rightarrow (-\frac{11}{2}, \frac{9}{2}) \rightarrow \cdots$ no

21. **a.** $x_1 = \frac{116}{19}$, $x_2 = \frac{146}{19}$, $x_3 = \frac{108}{19}$, which, using six-place decimal numbers is $x_1 = 6.105263$, $x_2 = 7.684211$, $x_3 = 5.684211$.
b. $\begin{bmatrix} x_1 \\ x_2 \\ x_3 \end{bmatrix}' = \begin{bmatrix} 0 & \frac{1}{3} & -\frac{2}{3} \\ 0 & 0 & 1 \\ \frac{1}{4} & -\frac{1}{2} & 0 \end{bmatrix}\begin{bmatrix} x_1 \\ x_2 \\ x_3 \end{bmatrix} + \begin{bmatrix} \frac{22}{3} \\ 2 \\ 8 \end{bmatrix}$. Using $x_1 = 1$, $x_2 = 2$, and $x_3 = 3$ as our initial guess, convergence is quite slow (80 iterations) to the decimal values in **a**.

EXERCISES 3.1

1. **a.** No inverse; **A** is not square.
b. Inverse exists; triangular rank 3.
c. No inverse; two identical rows.

3. **C**

5. **a.** $\begin{bmatrix} 2 & -1 \\ -1 & 1 \end{bmatrix}$ **b.** $\begin{bmatrix} 2 & -2 & 1 \\ -1 & 3 & -2 \\ 0 & -1 & 1 \end{bmatrix}$ **c.** No inverse **d.** $\begin{bmatrix} 1 & -\frac{1}{2} & \frac{1}{2} \\ 0 & \frac{1}{4} & \frac{5}{4} \\ 0 & 0 & -1 \end{bmatrix}$

7. **a.** $\begin{bmatrix} -7 \\ 4 \end{bmatrix}$ **b.** $\begin{bmatrix} 1 \\ 0 \end{bmatrix}$ **c.** $\begin{bmatrix} -5 \\ 3 \end{bmatrix}$ **d.** $\begin{bmatrix} 0 \\ 1 \end{bmatrix}$

9. $-1, 3$

11. Let **A** be a triangular matrix. If each diagonal element is not zero, the matrix is row-equivalent to **I** and has rank n so that $\mathbf{A}^{-1}$ exists (Theorem 1). If some diagonal element is zero, the column containing that element is not a leading column so that rank $(\mathbf{A}) < n$ and $\mathbf{A}^{-1}$ does not exist.

13. $\begin{bmatrix} 8 & -3 \\ -2 & 2 \end{bmatrix}, \begin{bmatrix} 8 & 7 \\ 10 & 10 \end{bmatrix}$

15. **a.** **BC** **b.** **AB, CA**

17. **a.** $\mathbf{I} + \mathbf{B}^{-1}\mathbf{A}^{-1}$ **b.** $\mathbf{BA}^{-1} - \mathbf{AB}^{-1}$ **c.** **A**

19. **a.** $\begin{bmatrix} -2 & 1 & 0 & 0 \\ \frac{3}{2} & -\frac{1}{2} & 0 & 0 \\ 0 & 0 & 1 & 0 \\ 0 & 0 & -2 & 1 \end{bmatrix}$ **b.** $\begin{bmatrix} 1 & -1 & 0 & 0 & 0 \\ 0 & 1 & 0 & 0 & 0 \\ 0 & 0 & 1 & 2 & -\frac{7}{4} \\ 0 & 0 & 0 & -1 & \frac{1}{2} \\ 0 & 0 & 0 & 0 & \frac{1}{4} \end{bmatrix}$

21. **a.** $\mathbf{A}^{-1} = \begin{bmatrix} -3 & 2 \\ 2 & -1 \end{bmatrix}$, $\mathbf{B}^{-1} = \begin{bmatrix} \frac{2}{3} & -\frac{1}{3} \\ \frac{1}{3} & \frac{1}{3} \end{bmatrix}$
b. $\mathbf{AB} = \begin{bmatrix} -1 & 5 \\ -1 & 8 \end{bmatrix}$, $(\mathbf{AB})^{-1} = \mathbf{B}^{-1}\mathbf{A}^{-1} = \begin{bmatrix} -\frac{8}{3} & \frac{5}{3} \\ -\frac{1}{3} & \frac{1}{3} \end{bmatrix}$, $\mathbf{A}^{-1}\mathbf{B}^{-1} = \begin{bmatrix} -\frac{4}{3} & \frac{5}{3} \\ 1 & -1 \end{bmatrix}$
c. $\mathbf{A} + \mathbf{B} = \begin{bmatrix} 2 & 3 \\ 1 & 5 \end{bmatrix}$; $(\mathbf{A} + \mathbf{B})^{-1} = (\frac{1}{7})\begin{bmatrix} 5 & -3 \\ -1 & 2 \end{bmatrix}$; $\mathbf{A}^{-1} + \mathbf{B}^{-1} = (\frac{1}{3})\begin{bmatrix} -7 & 5 \\ 7 & -2 \end{bmatrix}$

23. **a.** $\mathbf{A}^T = \begin{bmatrix} 1 & -1 \\ -2 & 3 \end{bmatrix}$, $\mathbf{A}^{-1} = \begin{bmatrix} 3 & 2 \\ 1 & 1 \end{bmatrix}$, $(\mathbf{A}^T)^{-1} = \begin{bmatrix} 3 & 1 \\ 2 & 1 \end{bmatrix}$; $(\mathbf{A}^{-1})^T = (\mathbf{A}^T)^{-1}$
b. $\mathbf{AA}^{-1} = \mathbf{I}$ so that $(\mathbf{AA}^{-1})^T = \mathbf{I}$. This means that $(\mathbf{A}^{-1})^T\mathbf{A}^T = \mathbf{I}$ and $(\mathbf{A}^T)^{-1} = (\mathbf{A}^{-1})^T$, since the inverse of a matrix is unique (Theorem 1).

25. $\mathbf{AA}^T = \begin{bmatrix} \mathbf{A}_1 \\ \mathbf{A}_2 \\ \mathbf{A}_3 \end{bmatrix} [\mathbf{A}_1^T \quad \mathbf{A}_2^T \quad \mathbf{A}_3^T] = \begin{bmatrix} \mathbf{A}_1 \cdot \mathbf{A}_1 & \mathbf{A}_1 \cdot \mathbf{A}_2 & \mathbf{A}_1 \cdot \mathbf{A}_3 \\ \mathbf{A}_2 \cdot \mathbf{A}_1 & \mathbf{A}_2 \cdot \mathbf{A}_2 & \mathbf{A}_2 \cdot \mathbf{A}_3 \\ \mathbf{A}_3 \cdot \mathbf{A}_1 & \mathbf{A}_3 \cdot \mathbf{A}_2 & \mathbf{A}_3 \cdot \mathbf{A}_3 \end{bmatrix}$. $\mathbf{AA}^T = \mathbf{I}$ if and only if $\mathbf{A}_i \cdot \mathbf{A}_i = 1$, $i = 1, 2, 3$, and $\mathbf{A}_i \cdot \mathbf{A}_j = 0$, $i, j = 1, 2, 3$, $i \neq j$, if and only if $\{\mathbf{A}_1, \mathbf{A}_2, \mathbf{A}_3\}$ is an orthonormal set.

27. $\mathbf{X} = \mathbf{A}^{-1}\mathbf{CA} - \mathbf{B}$

29. a. $\mathbf{A}^2 = \begin{bmatrix} 7 & 0 \\ 0 & 7 \end{bmatrix}$, $\mathbf{B}^2 = \begin{bmatrix} 4 & 3 \\ 9 & 7 \end{bmatrix}$, $\mathbf{A}^2\mathbf{B}^2 = \begin{bmatrix} 28 & 21 \\ 63 & 49 \end{bmatrix}$, $(\mathbf{AB})^2 = \begin{bmatrix} 93 & 70 \\ -10 & -7 \end{bmatrix}$

b. In general matrix multiplication is not commutative.

EXERCISES 3.2

1. a. -7 **b.** -20 **c.** 26

3. a. -12 **b.** -12 **c.** 4

5. a. -52 **b.** -156

7. -9; no value of x makes $\det \mathbf{A} = 0$.

9. a. 0, 0, 0

b. If two rows (or columns) of $\mathbf{A}$ are proportional, obtain matrix $\mathbf{B}$ by replacing the row (column) by $1/k$ times the original row (column). Then $\det \mathbf{A} = k \det \mathbf{B}$ (Theorem 4, part 2) and $\mathbf{B}$ has two identical rows (columns). Form $\mathbf{C}$ by interchanging these rows (columns). Then $\det \mathbf{B} = -\det \mathbf{C}$ (Theorem 4, part 1); but $\mathbf{B} = \mathbf{C}$. Thus, $\det \mathbf{B} = 0$ and so $\det \mathbf{A} = 0$.

11. Yes—in the definition all the terms can be made identical if one uses the same arrangement of columns.

No—for example, $\mathbf{A} = \begin{bmatrix} 1 & 0 \\ 0 & 1 \end{bmatrix}$, $\mathbf{B} = \begin{bmatrix} 2 & 1 \\ 1 & 1 \end{bmatrix}$.

13. a. $k\mathbf{u}_1, k\mathbf{u}_2, \ldots, k\mathbf{u}_n$

b. n

c. $\det(k\mathbf{A}) = k^n \det \mathbf{A}$

15. -18

17. $\det \mathbf{A} = af + bf - ce - de$, $\det \begin{bmatrix} a & c \\ e & f \end{bmatrix} + \det \begin{bmatrix} b & d \\ e & f \end{bmatrix} = af - ce + bf - de = \det \mathbf{A}$.

19. $\mathbf{u}_i = (b_{i1}, b_{i2}, \ldots, b_{in})$ and $\mathbf{v}_i = (c_{i1}, c_{i2}, \ldots, c_{in})$. By Definition 3, $\det \mathbf{A} = \Sigma\,(-1)^k a_{1j_1} a_{2j_2} \cdots (b_{ij_i} + c_{ij_i}) \cdots a_{nj_n}$. Each term in this summation is the sum of two terms, so that $\det \mathbf{A} = \Sigma\,(-1)^k a_{1j_1} a_{2j_2} \cdots b_{ij_i} \cdots a_{nj_n} + \Sigma\,(-1)^k a_{1j_1} a_{2j_2} \cdots c_{ij_i} \cdots a_{nj_n} = \det \mathbf{B} + \det \mathbf{C}$ by Definition 3.

21. a. $\det \begin{bmatrix} a & c \\ e & g \end{bmatrix} + \det \begin{bmatrix} b & d \\ e & g \end{bmatrix}$ **b.** $\det \begin{bmatrix} a & c \\ e & g \end{bmatrix} + \det \begin{bmatrix} b & d \\ e & g \end{bmatrix} + \det \begin{bmatrix} a & c \\ f & h \end{bmatrix} + \det \begin{bmatrix} b & d \\ f & h \end{bmatrix}$

23. $-\lambda^3 + (\det[a_{11}] + \det[a_{22}] + \det[a_{33}])\lambda^2 -$

$$\left(\det \begin{bmatrix} a_{11} & a_{12} \\ a_{21} & a_{22} \end{bmatrix} + \det \begin{bmatrix} a_{11} & a_{13} \\ a_{31} & a_{33} \end{bmatrix} + \det \begin{bmatrix} a_{22} & a_{23} \\ a_{32} & a_{33} \end{bmatrix}\right)\lambda + \det \begin{bmatrix} a_{11} & a_{12} & a_{13} \\ a_{21} & a_{22} & a_{23} \\ a_{31} & a_{32} & a_{33} \end{bmatrix}$$

25. Det $\mathbf{A} = 0$. **a.** No **b.** No **c.** No **d.** Yes

27. If the $m \times m$ submatrix has nonzero determinant, the submatrix has rank m and the row reduced form of the submatrix has m leading columns. These same columns will be leading columns in $\mathbf{A}$. So rank of $\mathbf{A}$ is at least m, since $\mathbf{A}$ is $m \times n$ with $m < n$ the rank of $\mathbf{A}$ must be m.

29.
$$\begin{bmatrix} 1 & x_1 & x_1^2 & x_1^3 \\ 1 & x_2 & x_2^2 & x_2^3 \\ 1 & x_3 & x_3^2 & x_3^3 \end{bmatrix} \Leftrightarrow \begin{bmatrix} 1 & x_1 & x_1^2 & x_1^3 \\ 0 & x_2 - x_1 & x_2^2 - x_1^2 & x_2^3 - x_1^3 \\ 0 & x_3 - x_1 & x_3^2 - x_1^2 & x_3^3 - x_1^3 \end{bmatrix} \quad \text{since } x_2 \neq x_1 \text{ and } x_3 \neq x_1$$

$$\Leftrightarrow \begin{bmatrix} 1 & x_1 & x_1^2 & x_1^3 \\ 0 & 1 & x_2 + x_1 & x_2^2 + x_1x_2 + x_1^2 \\ 0 & 1 & x_3 + x_1 & x_3^2 + x_1x_3 + x_1^2 \end{bmatrix}$$

$$\Leftrightarrow \begin{bmatrix} 1 & x_1 & x_1^2 & x_1^3 \\ 0 & 1 & x_2 + x_1 & x_2^2 + x_1x_2 + x_1^2 \\ 0 & 0 & x_3 - x_2 & x_3^2 - x_2^2 + x_1x_3 - x_1x_2 \end{bmatrix}$$

which has rank 3 since $x_2 \neq x_3$.

EXERCISES 3.3

1. a. $\mathbf{A}_{11} = \begin{bmatrix} 1 & 5 \\ 1 & 3 \end{bmatrix}$, $\mathbf{A}_{12} = \begin{bmatrix} 0 & 5 \\ 1 & 3 \end{bmatrix}$, $\mathbf{A}_{13} = \begin{bmatrix} 0 & 1 \\ 1 & 1 \end{bmatrix}$

$\gamma_{11} = -2, \gamma_{12} = 5, \gamma_{13} = -1$

$\det \mathbf{A} = 1(-2) + 2(5) + 3(-1) = 5$

b. $\det \mathbf{A} = 0(-3) + 1(0) + 5(1) = 5$

3. a. $\begin{bmatrix} (-1)^{1+1} & (-1)^{1+2} \\ (-1)^{2+1} & (-1)^{2+2} \end{bmatrix} = \begin{bmatrix} + & - \\ - & + \end{bmatrix}$

b. $\begin{bmatrix} (-1)^{1+1} & (-1)^{1+2} & (-1)^{1+3} \\ (-1)^{2+1} & (-1)^{2+2} & (-1)^{2+3} \\ (-1)^{3+1} & (-1)^{3+2} & (-1)^{3+3} \end{bmatrix} = \begin{bmatrix} + & - & + \\ - & + & - \\ + & - & + \end{bmatrix}$

c. $\begin{bmatrix} + & - & + & - \\ - & + & - & + \\ + & - & + & - \\ - & + & - & + \end{bmatrix}$, $\begin{bmatrix} + & - & + & - & + \\ - & + & - & + & - \\ + & - & + & - & + \\ - & + & - & + & - \\ + & - & + & - & + \end{bmatrix}$

5. a. -31 **b.** 0 **c.** 52

7. a. -24 **b.** -20

9. a. $\begin{bmatrix} 1 & -4 \\ -5 & 2 \end{bmatrix}$, $\begin{bmatrix} -18 & 0 \\ 0 & -18 \end{bmatrix}$ **b.** $\begin{bmatrix} 1 & 2 & -1 \\ -2 & 0 & 2 \\ 1 & -2 & 3 \end{bmatrix}$, $\begin{bmatrix} 4 & 0 & 0 \\ 0 & 4 & 0 \\ 0 & 0 & 4 \end{bmatrix}$

c. $\begin{bmatrix} -1 & 0 & 0 & 1 \\ 1 & 0 & 0 & -1 \\ 0 & 0 & 0 & 0 \\ 0 & 0 & 0 & 0 \end{bmatrix}$, $\begin{bmatrix} 0 & 0 & 0 & 0 \\ 0 & 0 & 0 & 0 \\ 0 & 0 & 0 & 0 \\ 0 & 0 & 0 & 0 \end{bmatrix}$

11. a. $\operatorname{Adj}\mathbf{A} = \begin{bmatrix} 3 & -2 \\ 1 & 1 \end{bmatrix}$, $\mathbf{A}(\operatorname{Adj}\mathbf{A}) = \begin{bmatrix} 5 & 0 \\ 0 & 5 \end{bmatrix}$ **b.** $\begin{bmatrix} 1 & -5 & -14 \\ 2 & -10 & 3 \\ -7 & 4 & 5 \end{bmatrix}$, $\begin{bmatrix} -31 & 0 & 0 \\ 0 & -31 & 0 \\ 0 & 0 & -31 \end{bmatrix}$

c. $\begin{bmatrix} 1 & -2 & 1 \\ 1 & 1 & -2 \\ 0 & 0 & 1 \end{bmatrix}$, $\begin{bmatrix} 1 & 0 & 0 \\ 0 & 1 & 0 \\ 0 & 0 & 1 \end{bmatrix}$

13. $\operatorname{Adj}\mathbf{A} = \begin{bmatrix} -2 & -3 & 7 \\ 5 & 0 & -5 \\ -1 & 1 & 1 \end{bmatrix}$, $\operatorname{Adj}(\operatorname{Adj}\mathbf{A}) = \begin{bmatrix} 5 & 10 & 15 \\ 0 & 5 & 25 \\ 5 & 5 & 15 \end{bmatrix} = (\det \mathbf{A})\mathbf{A}$

15. a. $\begin{bmatrix} 1 & -4 \\ -5 & 2 \end{bmatrix}$, $\mathbf{A}^{-1} = \begin{bmatrix} -\frac{1}{18} & \frac{2}{9} \\ \frac{5}{18} & -\frac{1}{9} \end{bmatrix}$

b. $\begin{bmatrix} 1 & 2 & -1 \\ -2 & 0 & 2 \\ 1 & -2 & 3 \end{bmatrix}$, $\mathbf{A}^{-1} = \begin{bmatrix} \frac{1}{4} & \frac{1}{2} & -\frac{1}{4} \\ -\frac{1}{2} & 0 & \frac{1}{2} \\ \frac{1}{4} & -\frac{1}{2} & \frac{3}{4} \end{bmatrix}$

c. $\begin{bmatrix} -1 & 0 & 0 & 1 \\ 1 & 0 & 0 & -1 \\ 0 & 0 & 0 & 0 \\ 0 & 0 & 0 & 0 \end{bmatrix}$; no inverse since $\det \mathbf{A} = 0$

17. If $\det \mathbf{A} = 0$, $\mathbf{A}(\operatorname{Adj}\mathbf{A}) = (\det \mathbf{A})\mathbf{I} = \mathbf{0}$. If $\det \mathbf{A} \neq 0$, $\operatorname{Adj}\mathbf{A} = (\det \mathbf{A})\mathbf{A}^{-1}$, so $\det(\operatorname{Adj}\mathbf{A}) = \det((\det \mathbf{A})\mathbf{A}^{-1}) = (\det \mathbf{A})^n \det \mathbf{A}^{-1} = (\det \mathbf{A})^n \dfrac{1}{\det \mathbf{A}} = (\det \mathbf{A})^{n-1} \neq 0$

19. $x_1 = -\frac{23}{5}$, $x_2 = 6$, $x_3 = -\frac{4}{5}$

21. No. Yes—an infinite number of solutions
23. 0. (*Hint*: Add column 2 to column 3.)
25. $t^4 - 3t^2$
27. To row 1 add the sum of all the other rows. The resulting matrix has all zeros in row 1 and hence has determinant 0.
29.

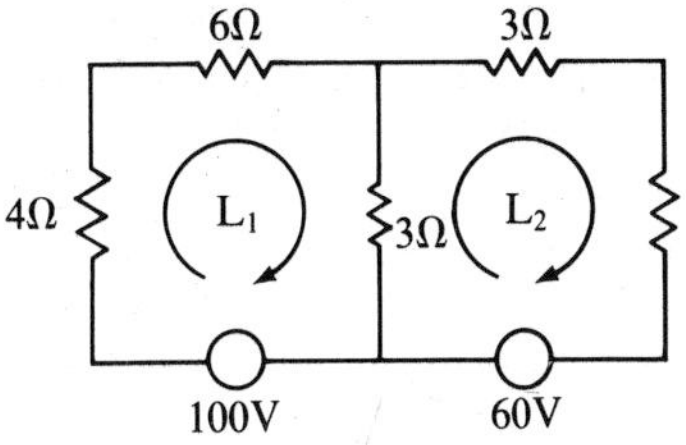

$100 = 13L_1 - 3L_2$

$60 = 13L_2 - 3L_1$

$L_1 = 9.25,\ L_2 = 6.75$

EXERCISES 3.4

1. a. $6, -2, \begin{bmatrix} 7 & 2 \\ -1 & -2 \end{bmatrix}, -12$

b. $0, -2, \begin{bmatrix} 2 & 2 \\ -6 & -6 \end{bmatrix}, 0$

c. $-2, 24, \begin{bmatrix} 6 & 3 & 9 \\ 0 & 4 & -4 \\ 6 & 6 & 4 \end{bmatrix}, -48$

3. a. Singular, determinant is zero
b. Singular, determinant is zero
c. Nonsingular, determinant is nonzero
d. Nonsingular, determinant is nonzero

5. 6

7. Determinant of coefficient matrix is 0; thus, the system has an infinite number of solutions: $(2t, -2t, t)$.

9. a. If **A** and **B** are nonsingular, then $\det \mathbf{A} \neq 0$ and $\det \mathbf{B} \neq 0$, so $\det(\mathbf{AB}) = \det \mathbf{A} \det \mathbf{B} \neq 0$ and $\det(\mathbf{BA}) = \det \mathbf{B} \det \mathbf{A} \neq 0$. Thus **AB** and **BA** are nonsingular.
b. If **A** is nonsingular, $\mathbf{A}^{-1}$ exists. Then $\mathbf{B} = \mathbf{A}^{-1}\mathbf{AB} = \mathbf{A}^{-1}\mathbf{0} = \mathbf{0}$, a contradiction.

11. a. $\mathbf{AB} = \begin{bmatrix} 16 & 5 \\ 22 & 7 \end{bmatrix}$, $\operatorname{Adj}(\mathbf{AB}) = \begin{bmatrix} 7 & -5 \\ -22 & 16 \end{bmatrix}$, $\operatorname{Adj}\mathbf{A} = \begin{bmatrix} 3 & -2 \\ -1 & 1 \end{bmatrix}$, $\operatorname{Adj}\mathbf{B} = \begin{bmatrix} 2 & -1 \\ -6 & 4 \end{bmatrix}$, $\begin{bmatrix} 7 & -5 \\ -22 & 16 \end{bmatrix} = \begin{bmatrix} 2 & -1 \\ -6 & 4 \end{bmatrix}\begin{bmatrix} 3 & -2 \\ -1 & 1 \end{bmatrix}$

b. Since **A**, **B**, and **AB** are nonsingular, $\mathbf{A}^{-1}$, $\mathbf{B}^{-1}$, and $(\mathbf{AB})^{-1} = \mathbf{B}^{-1}\mathbf{A}^{-1}$ exist.

$$\begin{aligned} \operatorname{Adj}(\mathbf{AB}) &= (\mathbf{AB})^{-1} \det(\mathbf{AB})\mathbf{I} \\ &= \mathbf{B}^{-1}\mathbf{A}^{-1} \det \mathbf{A} \det \mathbf{B}\mathbf{I} \\ &= \mathbf{B}^{-1} \det \mathbf{B}\mathbf{I}\mathbf{A}^{-1} \det \mathbf{A}\mathbf{I} \\ &= (\operatorname{Adj}\mathbf{B})(\operatorname{Adj}\mathbf{A}) \end{aligned}$$

13. $\begin{bmatrix} 1 & 1 & 1 \\ 0 & 0 & 1 \\ 4 & 2 & 1 \end{bmatrix}\begin{bmatrix} a \\ b \\ c \end{bmatrix} = \begin{bmatrix} 1 \\ 0 \\ 4 \end{bmatrix}$ has a unique solution, since the determinant of the matrix is nonzero.

15. The points are collinear.

17. a. Not similar, since they are not the same size.
b. Not similar, since they have different determinants.
c. Not similar, since they have different determinants.

19. a. If **A** is similar to **B**, there exists a nonsingular matrix **C** so that $\mathbf{A} = \mathbf{C}^{-1}\mathbf{BC}$; then $\mathbf{B} = (\mathbf{C}^{-1})^{-1}\mathbf{AC}^{-1}$ and $\mathbf{C}^{-1}$ is nonsingular, so **B** is similar to **A**.
b. $\mathbf{A} = \mathbf{I}^{-1}\mathbf{AI}$, so **A** is similar to **A**.
c. If **A** is similar to **B**, there exists a nonsingular matrix **D** so that $\mathbf{A} = \mathbf{D}^{-1}\mathbf{BD}$, and if **B** is similar to **C**, there exists a nonsingular matrix **E** so that $\mathbf{B} = \mathbf{E}^{-1}\mathbf{CE}$. Then $\mathbf{A} = \mathbf{D}^{-1}\mathbf{BD} = \mathbf{D}^{-1}\mathbf{E}^{-1}\mathbf{CED} = (\mathbf{ED})^{-1}\mathbf{C}(\mathbf{ED})$, so **A** is similar to **C**.

21. $(\mathbf{C}^{-1}\mathbf{AC})^n = (\mathbf{C}^{-1}\mathbf{AC})(\mathbf{C}^{-1}\mathbf{AC})\cdots(\mathbf{C}^{-1}\mathbf{AC}) = \mathbf{C}^{-1}\mathbf{A}^n\mathbf{C}$ as in Problem 20. If $\mathbf{B} = \mathbf{C}^{-1}\mathbf{AC}$, then $\mathbf{B}^n = (\mathbf{C}^{-1}\mathbf{AC})^n = \mathbf{C}^{-1}\mathbf{A}^n\mathbf{C}$, so $\mathbf{B}^n$ is similar to $\mathbf{A}^n$.

23. $\mathbf{B} = \mathbf{C}^{-1}\mathbf{AC}$ and $p(x) = a_nx^n + a_{n-1}x^{n-1} + \cdots + a_1x + a_0$.

$$\begin{aligned} p(\mathbf{B}) &= a_n\mathbf{B}^n + a_{n-1}\mathbf{B}^{n-1} + \cdots + a_1\mathbf{B} + a_0\mathbf{I} \\ &= a_n(\mathbf{C}^{-1}\mathbf{AC})^n + a_{n-1}(\mathbf{C}^{-1}\mathbf{AC})^{n-1} + \cdots + a_1\mathbf{C}^{-1}\mathbf{AC} + a_0\mathbf{C}^{-1}\mathbf{IC} \\ &= a_n\mathbf{C}^{-1}\mathbf{A}^n\mathbf{C} + a_{n-1}\mathbf{C}^{-1}\mathbf{A}^{n-1}\mathbf{C} + \cdots + a_1\mathbf{C}^{-1}\mathbf{AC} + a_0\mathbf{C}^{-1}\mathbf{IC} \\ &= \mathbf{C}^{-1}(a_n\mathbf{A}^n + a_{n-1}\mathbf{A}^{n-1} + \cdots + a_1\mathbf{A} + a_0\mathbf{I})\mathbf{C} = \mathbf{C}^{-1}p(\mathbf{A})\mathbf{C} \end{aligned}$$

EXERCISES 3.5

1. a. 2, 3 **b.** 3, 1 **c.** $\frac{1}{2}(5+\sqrt{5}), \frac{1}{2}(5-\sqrt{5})$ **d.** 4, 2

3. a. $\lambda = 2$: $\{k(1,0), k \neq 0\}$, $\lambda = 3$: $\{k(1,1), k \neq 0\}$,
b. $\lambda = 3$: $\{k(1,1), k \neq 0\}$, $\lambda = 1$: $\{k(1,-1), k \neq 0\}$,
c. $\lambda = \frac{1}{2}(5+\sqrt{5})$: $\{k(-1+\sqrt{5},2), k \neq 0\}$,
$\lambda = \frac{1}{2}(5-\sqrt{5})$: $\{k(-1-\sqrt{5},2), k \neq 0\}$,
d. $\lambda = 4$: $\{k(1,0,1), k \neq 0\}$,
$\lambda = 2$: $\{k_1(1,0,-2) + k_2(0,1,0), k_1, k_2 \neq 0\}$.

5. a. (i) 0, 8; 2 distinct eigenvalues
(ii) -1, -1, 6; 2 distinct eigenvalues
(iii) 0, 1, 8; 3 distinct eigenvalues
(iv) 1, 1, 2, 2; 2 distinct eigenvalues
b. (i) $\lambda = 0$: $\{k(-2,1), k \neq 0\}$, rank 1; $\lambda = 8$: $\{k(2,3), k \neq 0\}$, rank 1
(ii) $\lambda = -1$: $\{k_1(-1,1,0) + k_2(-1,0,1), k_1, k_2$ not both $0\}$, rank 1; $\lambda = 6$: $\{k(1,-1,1), k \neq 0\}$, rank 2
(iii) $\lambda = 0$: $\{k(-2,-1,1), k \neq 0\}$, rank 2; $\lambda = 1$, $\{k(-1,1,0), k \neq 0\}$, rank 2; $\lambda = 8$, $\{k(2,-3,3), k \neq 0\}$, rank 2
(iv) $\lambda = 1$, $\{k(1,-2,0,0), k \neq 0\}$, rank 3; $\lambda = 2$, $\{k(2,-22,-3,1), k \neq 0\}$, rank 3

7. a. $\{k(1,-3,1), k$ nonzero real$\}$; rank is 2.
b. $\{k_1(0,1,0) + k_2(1,0,-2), k_1$ and k_2 not both zero$\}$; rank is 1.

9. 2, 2, 3; 2, 2, 3. The matrices in this problem have the same eigenvalues but they are not similar. The matrix $\begin{bmatrix} 2 & 1 & 0 \\ 0 & 2 & 0 \\ 0 & 0 & 3 \end{bmatrix}$ is not similar to a diagonal matrix because the eigenvectors corresponding to 2 are $\{k(1,0,0), k \neq 0\}$.

11. $\begin{bmatrix} 2 & 0 & -1 \\ 6 & -4 & -6 \\ 0 & 0 & 1 \end{bmatrix}$

13. No, λ is an eigenvalue of $\mathbf{A}$ if $\det(\mathbf{A} - \lambda\mathbf{I}) = 0$. If the rank of $\mathbf{A} - 3\mathbf{I}$ is n then $\det(\mathbf{A} - 3\mathbf{I}) \neq 0$, so 3 is not an eigenvalue of $\mathbf{A}$.

15. 0 is an eigenvalue; the matrix $\begin{bmatrix} 2 & 2 & 1 \\ 2 & 5 & 3 \\ 1 & 2 & 3 \end{bmatrix}$.

17. $\begin{bmatrix} 0 & 2 \\ 2 & 0 \end{bmatrix}$

19. (0, 0, 0); no; there is an error in finding the eigenvalue; if λ is an eigenvalue, $(\mathbf{A} - \lambda\mathbf{I})\mathbf{X} = \mathbf{0}$ has a nontrivial solution.

21. a. $\mathbf{A}^2 - 2\mathbf{A} - 3\mathbf{I} = \mathbf{0}$, $\mathbf{A}^2 - 2\mathbf{A} = 3\mathbf{I}$, $\frac{1}{3}(\mathbf{A} - 2\mathbf{I})\mathbf{A} = \mathbf{I}$, $\mathbf{A}^{-1}$ exists and equals $\frac{1}{3}(\mathbf{A} - 2\mathbf{I})$ (Theorem 1)
b. $\mathbf{B}^3 - 4\mathbf{B}^2 + 5\mathbf{B} - 2\mathbf{I} = \mathbf{0}$ implies $\frac{1}{2}(\mathbf{B}^2 - 4\mathbf{B} + 5\mathbf{I})\mathbf{B} = \mathbf{I}$

23. $$\begin{bmatrix} 0 & 1 & 1 \\ -1 & -2 & -1 \\ 1 & 1 & 1 \end{bmatrix}\begin{bmatrix} 1 & 0 & 0 \\ 0 & 4 & 0 \\ 0 & 0 & 36 \end{bmatrix}\begin{bmatrix} -1 & 0 & 1 \\ 0 & -1 & -1 \\ 1 & 1 & 1 \end{bmatrix} = \begin{bmatrix} 36 & 32 & 32 \\ -35 & -28 & -29 \\ 35 & 32 & 33 \end{bmatrix}$$

25. $$\begin{aligned} \mathbf{C}^{-1}f(\mathbf{A})\mathbf{C} &= \mathbf{C}^{-1}(\mathbf{A}^n + c_1\mathbf{A}^{n-1} + \cdots + c_n\mathbf{I})\mathbf{C} \\ &= \mathbf{C}^{-1}\mathbf{A}^n\mathbf{C} + \mathbf{C}^{-1}(c_1\mathbf{A}^{n-1})\mathbf{C} + \cdots + \mathbf{C}^{-1}(c_n\mathbf{I})\mathbf{C} \\ &= \mathbf{D}^n + c_1\mathbf{C}^{-1}\mathbf{A}^{n-1}\mathbf{C} + \cdots + c_n\mathbf{C}^{-1}(\mathbf{I})\mathbf{C} \text{ (by Problem 24)} \\ &= \mathbf{D}^n + c_1\mathbf{D}^{n-1} + \cdots + c_n\mathbf{I} \end{aligned}$$

27. The product of the eigenvalues is $\det \mathbf{A}$, so $\det \mathbf{A} = 0$ if and only if an eigenvalue is 0.

29. $x_1^{(1)} = 0.9x_1 + 0.4x_2$. The eigenvalues of $\begin{bmatrix} 0.9 & 0.4 \\ 0.2 & 0.7 \end{bmatrix}$ are 1.1 and 0.5.

$x_2^{(1)} = 0.2x_1 + 0.7x_2$. An eigenvector corresponding to 1.1 is $x_1 = 2x_2$.

The distribution will tend toward the stable distribution of Example 20, but population increases.

EXERCISES 3.6

1. a. -45 **b.** $39337/250 = 157.348$ **c.** -264.391809

3. a. -8 **b.** -5764423434

5. a. $$\mathbf{A}^{-1} = \begin{bmatrix} \frac{3}{8} & \frac{1}{4} & -\frac{3}{8} & -\frac{1}{8} & \frac{1}{4} \\ -\frac{1}{8} & \frac{1}{4} & \frac{1}{8} & \frac{3}{8} & \frac{1}{4} \\ 0 & 0 & 1 & 0 & 0 \\ \frac{1}{4} & \frac{1}{2} & -\frac{1}{4} & \frac{1}{4} & -\frac{1}{2} \\ -\frac{1}{4} & \frac{1}{2} & \frac{1}{4} & -\frac{1}{4} & -\frac{1}{2} \end{bmatrix}$$

b. $$\mathbf{B}^{-1} = (1/5764423434)\mathbf{D}, \text{ where } \mathbf{D} = \begin{bmatrix} 58508529 & -3942024 & 14889543 & -3065655 & 34092471 \\ 35951844 & -33998718 & -19469202 & -33990168 & -34239366 \\ 46151772 & -60845514 & -16463520 & 35352480 & -25778886 \\ 27887472 & -2410356 & 28468014 & 33826104 & -31244178 \\ 58748335 & -4797004 & -71008297 & 3461033 & -8673091 \end{bmatrix}$$

7. Let a_n, b_n, and c_n be the number of students in sections A, B, and C, respectively, during the nth week of instruction. According to the problem,

$$\begin{aligned} a_{n+1} &= (\tfrac{3}{4})a_n - (\tfrac{1}{6})a_n + (\tfrac{1}{6})b_n + (\tfrac{1}{8})c_n \\ b_{n+1} &= (\tfrac{2}{3})b_n + (\tfrac{1}{6})a_n - (\tfrac{1}{6})b_n + (\tfrac{1}{4})c_n \\ c_{n+1} &= (\tfrac{1}{4})a_n + (\tfrac{1}{3})b_n + c_n - (\tfrac{1}{8})c_n - (\tfrac{1}{4})c_n \end{aligned}$$

Then $\mathbf{T} = \begin{bmatrix} \frac{7}{12} & \frac{1}{6} & \frac{1}{8} \\ \frac{1}{6} & \frac{1}{2} & \frac{1}{4} \\ \frac{1}{4} & \frac{1}{3} & \frac{5}{8} \end{bmatrix}$

Yes. $\mathbf{T}^k$ approaches $\begin{bmatrix} 0.25 & 0.25 & 0.25 \\ 0.31 & 0.31 & 0.31 \\ 0.44 & 0.44 & 0.44 \end{bmatrix}$, so 25 students in section A, 31 in B, and 44 in C.

9. $$\mathbf{T}^{10} = \begin{bmatrix} 0.603 & 0.603 & 0.603 \\ 0.245 & 0.245 & 0.245 \\ 0.150 & 0.150 & 0.150 \end{bmatrix}$$

This suggests $\mathbf{T}^k y = (0.603, 0.245, 0.150)$ is an equilibrium vector for $\mathbf{T}$.

The characteristic matrix is $\mathbf{T} - x\mathbf{I}_3 = \begin{bmatrix} \frac{1}{2} - x & \frac{4}{5} & \frac{7}{10} \\ \frac{3}{10} & \frac{1}{5} - x & \frac{1}{10} \\ \frac{1}{5} & 0 & \frac{1}{5} - x \end{bmatrix}$

The characteristic equation is $50x^3 - 45x^2 - 7x + 2 = 0$, or $(x - 1)(50x^2 + 5x - 2) = 0$. Thus, the eigenvalues are $x = 1$ (and $(-1 \pm \sqrt{17})/20$). Row-reducing the matrix

$$\begin{bmatrix} -0.5 & 0.8 & 0.7 \\ 0.3 & -0.8 & 0.1 \\ 0.2 & 0.0 & -0.8 \end{bmatrix} \quad \text{to} \quad \begin{bmatrix} 1 & 0 & -4 \\ 0 & 1 & -1.625 \\ 0 & 0 & 0 \end{bmatrix}$$

gives the eigenvector corresponding to $x = 1$ as $(4, 1.625, 1)$. Then $s = 6.625$, so the desired steady state vector is $(\frac{32}{53}, \frac{13}{53}, \frac{8}{53})$.

11. Let $\mathbf{T} = \begin{bmatrix} u & w \\ 1-u & 1-w \end{bmatrix}$. Then $\mathbf{Tx} = \lambda\mathbf{x}$ gives the equations $ux_1 + wx_2 = \lambda x_1$ and $(1-u)x_1 + (1-w)x_2 = \lambda x_2$, assuming $\mathbf{x} = (x_1, x_2)$. Simplifying and adding the equations gives $(1-\lambda)x_1 + (1-\lambda)x_2 = 0$. Since $\lambda \neq 1$, $1 - \lambda \neq 0$, so $x_1 + x_2 = 0$.

13. $$\mathbf{A} = \begin{bmatrix} 0.25 & 0.21 & 0.12 & 0.00 & 0.00 \\ 0.00 & 0.13 & 0.00 & 0.00 & 0.00 \\ 0.02 & 0.09 & 0.35 & 0.03 & 0.00 \\ 0.05 & 0.03 & 0.01 & 0.08 & 0.14 \\ 0.07 & 0.10 & 0.02 & 0.04 & 0.10 \end{bmatrix}, \mathbf{D} = \begin{bmatrix} 100 \\ 100 \\ 100 \\ 100 \\ 100 \end{bmatrix}, (\mathbf{I} - \mathbf{A})^{-1}\mathbf{D} = \begin{bmatrix} 194.72 \\ 114.94 \\ 182.51 \\ 146.58 \\ 141.72 \end{bmatrix}$$

15. $$\begin{bmatrix} h_3 \\ h_5 \\ h_8 \\ v_3 \\ v_5 \\ v_8 \end{bmatrix} = \begin{bmatrix} 1.720 & 3.095 & -0.751 & -0.941 & 0.553 & -0.313 \\ 3.095 & 61.430 & -10.107 & -49.771 & 9.179 & -5.195 \\ -0.751 & -10.107 & 11.810 & 10.140 & -8.405 & 15.458 \\ -0.941 & -49.771 & 10.140 & 46.479 & -9.175 & 1.376 \\ 0.553 & 9.179 & -8.405 & -9.175 & 27.316 & 51.886 \\ -0.313 & -5.195 & 15.457 & 1.376 & 51.886 & 227.269 \end{bmatrix}^{-1} \begin{bmatrix} 0.6 \\ -0.6 \\ 0.4 \\ -0.5 \\ 0.2 \\ -0.1 \end{bmatrix}. \text{ Therefore } \begin{bmatrix} h_3 \\ h_5 \\ h_8 \\ v_3 \\ v_5 \\ v_8 \end{bmatrix} = \begin{bmatrix} 1.38064 \\ -0.70032 \\ 1.41244 \\ -0.82856 \\ 1.02399 \\ -0.34377 \end{bmatrix}$$

17. Let $\mathbf{A} = \begin{bmatrix} 0.2 & 0.4 & 0.5 \\ 0.5 & 0.4 & 0.1 \\ 0.3 & 0.2 & 0.4 \end{bmatrix}$ and $\mathbf{B} = \begin{bmatrix} 0.4 & 0 & 0 \\ 0 & 0.3 & 0 \\ 0 & 0 & 0.3 \end{bmatrix} \begin{bmatrix} 120 & 180 & 75 \\ 120 & 180 & 75 \\ 120 & 180 & 75 \end{bmatrix} = \begin{bmatrix} 48 & 72 & 30.0 \\ 36 & 54 & 22.5 \\ 36 & 54 & 22.5 \end{bmatrix}$.

The solutions are the columns of the matrix $\mathbf{A}^{-1}\mathbf{B}$:

$$\begin{bmatrix} 24 & 36 & 15 \\ 48 & 72 & 30 \\ 48 & 72 & 30 \end{bmatrix}$$

19. **a.** 40% of the newborn chicks die before reaching 1 year old.
b. $\mathbf{x}_2 = (85, 18, 26, 29, 20)$, $\mathbf{x}_4 = (35, 6, 10, 12, 5)$
(Entries are expressed using the greatest integer function.)
c. In 10 years there will be no more adult birds if this trend is not reversed.

EXERCISES 4.1

1. **a.** $(0,0)$ **b.** $(0,0,0,0)$ **c.** $\begin{bmatrix} 0 & 0 & 0 \\ 0 & 0 & 0 \end{bmatrix}$ **d.** $f(x) = 0$

3. **a.** $(a,a,-a) + (b,b,-b) = (a+b, a+b, -(a+b))$ and $k(a,a,-a) = (ka, ka, -(ka))$ are in the set.
b. $(0,0,0)$ is not in the set.
c. Yes

5. $$\begin{bmatrix} d_1 & a_1 & a_2 \\ a_1 & d_2 & a_3 \\ a_2 & a_3 & d_3 \end{bmatrix} + \begin{bmatrix} e_1 & b_1 & b_2 \\ b_1 & e_2 & b_3 \\ b_2 & b_3 & e_3 \end{bmatrix} = \begin{bmatrix} d_1+e_1 & a_1+b_1 & a_2+b_2 \\ a_1+b_1 & d_2+e_2 & a_3+b_3 \\ a_2+b_2 & a_3+b_3 & d_3+e_3 \end{bmatrix} \text{ and } k\begin{bmatrix} d_1 & a_1 & a_2 \\ a_1 & d_2 & a_3 \\ a_2 & a_3 & d_3 \end{bmatrix} = \begin{bmatrix} kd_1 & ka_1 & ka_2 \\ ka_1 & kd_2 & ka_3 \\ ka_2 & ka_3 & kd_3 \end{bmatrix}$$
are both 3×3 symmetric matrices, so S is a subspace of $M_{3\times3}$.

7. **a.** Yes, P_2 is a subset of P_3 and P_2 is a vector space, so P_2 is a subspace of P_3.
b. No, $M_{3\times2}$ is not a subset of $M_{3\times3}$.

9. **a.** Yes
b. No, the set has no zero and it is not closed with respect to scalar multiplication.

11. **a.** This statement is true because S is closed with respect to scalar multiplication.
b. Let $u \neq 0$ belong to the subspace. Then $2u, 3u, 4u, \ldots$ are all distinct and belong to the subspace so the subspace contains an infinite set of vectors. No.

13. **a.** $\mathbf{0} + \mathbf{0} = \mathbf{0}$ and $k\mathbf{0} = \mathbf{0}$, so the set is closed with respect to addition and scalar multiplication.
b. $\mathbf{0}$; yes

15. Let **u** and **v** be in $S \cap T$. Then **u** and **v** are in S and **u** and **v** are in T; **u** + **v** and k**u** are in S and in T and hence in $S \cap T$, which implies $S \cap T$ is a subspace.

17. **a.** $S = \{(x_1, 0, 0)\}$, $T = \{(0, 0, x_3)\}$
b. $S = \{(x_1, x_2, 0)\}$, $T = \{(0, x_2, x_3)\}$, $S \cap T = \{(0, x_2, 0)\}$
c. $S = \{(x_1, 0, 0)\}$, $T = \{(x_1, 0, x_3)\}$

19. **a.** Call the correspondence $\leftrightarrow$. Define $(x_1, x_2, 0) \leftrightarrow (x_1, x_2)$.
b. Let $\mathbf{u}_1 = (a_1, a_2, 0)$, $\mathbf{u}_2 = (b_1, b_2, 0)$. Then $\mathbf{v}_1 = (a_1, a_2)$, $\mathbf{v}_2 = (b_1, b_2)$.
$\mathbf{u}_1 + \mathbf{u}_2 = (a_1 + b_1, a_2 + b_2, 0) \leftrightarrow (a_1 + b_1, a_2 + b_2) = \mathbf{v}_1 + \mathbf{v}_2$
c. $k(a_1, a_2, 0) = (ka_1, ka_2, 0)$. Since $(a_1, a_2, 0) \leftrightarrow (a_1, a_2)$ and $(ka_1, ka_2, 0) \leftrightarrow (ka_1, ka_2)$; $\leftrightarrow$ is preserved under scalar multiplication.

21. Set up the correspondence $a_1 + a_2x + a_3x^2 \leftrightarrow (a_1, a_2, a_3)$

23. Suppose $A + (-A) = 0$ and $A + (-A') = 0$, then $-A = -A + 0 = -A + [A + (-A')] = [-A + A] + (-A') = 0 + (-A') = -A'$, so $-A = -A'$.

EXERCISES 4.2

1. No, yes, no

3. **a.** The x_1x_2 plane
b. $\mathbf{e}_1 = (\frac{1}{5})\mathbf{u}_1 + (\frac{3}{5})\mathbf{u}_2$, $\mathbf{e}_2 = (\frac{1}{5})\mathbf{u}_1 - (\frac{2}{5})\mathbf{u}_2$

5. **a.** $c_1 = -d_1 = d_2$, $c_2 = -2d_1$
b. The intersection of the two spaces consists of those linear combinations $d_1\mathbf{v}_1 + d_2\mathbf{v}_2$ with $d_1 = -d_2$.

7. **a.** Vectors of the form $a_0 + a_1x + a_2x^2$, where $a_0 + 2a_1 + 3a_2 = 0$

b. $$\left[\begin{array}{rr|r} 1 & 2 & 4 \\ 1 & -1 & 1 \\ -1 & 0 & -3 \end{array}\right] \Leftrightarrow \left[\begin{array}{rr|r} 1 & 0 & 3 \\ 0 & 1 & 1 \\ 0 & 0 & -\frac{1}{2} \end{array}\right];\ \text{no solution}$$

c. $$\left[\begin{array}{rrr|c} 1 & 2 & 4 & a \\ 1 & -1 & 1 & b \\ -1 & 0 & -3 & c \end{array}\right] \Leftrightarrow \left[\begin{array}{rrr|c} 1 & 0 & 0 & a + 2b + 2c \\ 0 & 1 & 0 & (2a + b + 3c)/3 \\ 0 & 0 & 1 & (-a - 2b - 3c)/3 \end{array}\right]$$ has a solution for any choice of a, b, c, so $a + bx + cx^2$ is in $\operatorname{lin}\{p_1, p_2, p_3\}$.

9. **a.** $a_1 + 2a_2 + a_1x - a_2x^2$
b. $5c_1 + 2c_2 + (2c_1 + c_2)x + c_1x^2$
c. Equating coefficients in **a.** and **b.**: $a_1 + 2a_2 = 5c_1 + 2c_2$, $a_1 = 2c_1 + c_2$, $-a_2 = c_1$. Eliminating c_1 and c_2 yields $3a_2 = a_1$
d. Eliminating a_1 and a_2 from the three equations in **c.**, yields $5c_1 = -c_2$.

11. **a.** $p_1 - 13p_2 + 5p_3 + 12p_4 = 0$
b. Let p_1, p_2, p_3, p_4 be four vectors in P_2. To show that the set is linearly dependent, it is sufficient to show that

$$\mathbf{A}\begin{bmatrix} a \\ b \\ c \\ d \end{bmatrix} = \begin{bmatrix} 0 \\ 0 \\ 0 \\ 0 \end{bmatrix}$$

has a nontrivial solution, where the columns of **A** are the coefficients of p_1, p_2, p_3, p_4; rank $\mathbf{A} \leqslant 3$, rank $\mathbf{A}$ = rank $[\mathbf{A}|\mathbf{0}]$, and the number of unknowns is 4. Thus, there are nontrivial solutions of the system, so the vectors are linearly dependent.

13. **a.** Suppose $a_1\mathbf{A}_1 + a_2\mathbf{A}_2 + a_3\mathbf{A}_3 = \mathbf{0}$. Then $\begin{bmatrix} a_1 & a_2 & a_3 \\ 0 & 0 & 0 \end{bmatrix} = \mathbf{0}$, so $a_1 = a_2 = a_3 = 0$.
b. Clearly $\operatorname{lin}\{\mathbf{A}_1, \mathbf{A}_2, \mathbf{A}_3\}$ is a subset of $M_{2\times 3}$, but $\begin{bmatrix} 0 & 0 & 0 \\ 1 & 0 & 0 \end{bmatrix}$ is in $M_{2\times 3}$ and not in $\operatorname{lin}\{\mathbf{A}_1, \mathbf{A}_2, \mathbf{A}_3\}$.

15. a. $\begin{bmatrix} 1 & 0 \\ 0 & 1 \end{bmatrix} - \begin{bmatrix} 1 & 0 \\ 1 & 1 \end{bmatrix} - \begin{bmatrix} 1 & 1 \\ 0 & 1 \end{bmatrix} + \begin{bmatrix} 1 & 1 \\ 1 & 1 \end{bmatrix} = \mathbf{0}$, thus not linearly independent.

b. $\begin{bmatrix} a_1 & a_2 \\ a_3 & a_4 \end{bmatrix} = \mathbf{0}$ only if $a_1 = a_2 = a_3 = a_4 = 0$, so linearly independent.

c. $\begin{bmatrix} a_1 - a_2 + a_3 - a_4 & a_1 + a_2 + a_3 - a_4 \\ a_3 - a_4 & a_3 + a_4 \end{bmatrix} = \mathbf{0}$ only if $a_1 = a_2 = a_3 = a_4 = 0$, so linearly independent.

d. $\begin{bmatrix} a_1 & a_2 \\ a_3 & a_4 \end{bmatrix} = \mathbf{0}$ only if $a_1 = a_2 = a_3 = a_4 = 0$, so linearly independent.

e. $\begin{bmatrix} 0 & 1 \\ 1 & 0 \end{bmatrix} + \begin{bmatrix} 1 & 0 \\ 0 & 1 \end{bmatrix} - \begin{bmatrix} 1 & 1 \\ 1 & 1 \end{bmatrix} = \mathbf{0}$, so not linearly independent.

17. Since the set is linearly dependent, there are scalars, not all zero, such that $a_1\mathbf{u}_1 + a_2\mathbf{u}_2 + \cdots + a_n\mathbf{u}_n \neq \mathbf{0}$. If $a_i \neq 0$, then $\mathbf{u}_i = -(a_1/a_i)\mathbf{u}_1 + -(a_2/a_i)\mathbf{u}_2 + \cdots + -(a_n/a_i)\mathbf{u}_n$ (there is no $\mathbf{u}_i$ term in the sum on the right).

19. $\mathbf{M}$ is $n \times n$. $\operatorname{Det}\mathbf{M} \neq 0$ implies that the rank of $\mathbf{M}$ is n. Thus the set is linearly independent.

21. P_n is isomorphic to R^{n+1} (Problem 21, Section 4.1). More than $n + 1$ vectors in R^{n+1} are linearly dependent. Thus, more than $n + 1$ vectors in P_n are linearly dependent.

23. $\begin{bmatrix} a & b \\ b & c \end{bmatrix} = a\begin{bmatrix} 1 & 0 \\ 0 & 0 \end{bmatrix} + b\begin{bmatrix} 0 & 1 \\ 1 & 0 \end{bmatrix} + c\begin{bmatrix} 0 & 0 \\ 0 & 1 \end{bmatrix}$

25. Since $\{i_1, i_2, \ldots, i_k\}$ is a subset of $\{1, 2, \ldots, n\}$, $\{\mathbf{u}_{i_1}, \mathbf{u}_{i_2}, \ldots, \mathbf{u}_{i_k}\}$ is a subset of $\{\mathbf{u}_1, \mathbf{u}_2, \ldots, \mathbf{u}_n\}$. Thus, any linear combination of $\mathbf{u}_{i_1}, \mathbf{u}_{i_2}, \ldots, \mathbf{u}_{i_k}$ is also a linear combination of $\mathbf{u}_1, \mathbf{u}_2, \ldots, \mathbf{u}_n$. So $\operatorname{lin}\{\mathbf{u}_{i_1}, \mathbf{u}_{i_2}, \ldots, \mathbf{u}_{i_k}\} \subseteq \operatorname{lin}\{\mathbf{u}_1, \mathbf{u}_2, \ldots, \mathbf{u}_n\}$.

EXERCISES 4.3

1. a. $c_1 = 1$, $c_2 = 2$, $c_3 = 1$; no, $c_1 = 2 - k$, $c_2 = 1 + k$, $c_3 = k$

b. $\begin{bmatrix} 1 & 2 & -1 \\ 0 & 1 & -1 \\ 1 & 0 & 1 \end{bmatrix}\begin{bmatrix} c_1 \\ c_2 \\ c_3 \end{bmatrix} = \begin{bmatrix} a \\ b \\ c \end{bmatrix}$; rank is 2.

c. No

3. a. $c_1 = 1$, $c_2 = -2$, $c_3 = 1$; yes **b.** Yes; yes **c.** No; $(2, 1, 1, -1)$ is not in the space spanned by $\{\mathbf{v}_1, \mathbf{v}_2, \mathbf{v}_3\}$.

5. a. $(\mathbf{v})_U = (-\frac{1}{3}, \frac{2}{3}, 0)$ **b.** $\mathbf{v} = \mathbf{u}_1 + \mathbf{u}_2 + 2\mathbf{u}_3 = (5, 7, 7)$, $\mathbf{w} = -2\mathbf{u}_1 + 4\mathbf{u}_2 - \mathbf{u}_3 = (5, 4, -2)$

7. $(\mathbf{x})_U = (c_1, c_2, c_3)$, $(\mathbf{y})_U = (d_1, d_2, d_3)$
$\mathbf{x} = c_1\mathbf{u}_1 + c_2\mathbf{u}_2 + c_3\mathbf{u}_3$, $\mathbf{y} = d_1\mathbf{u}_1 + d_2\mathbf{u}_2 + d_3\mathbf{u}_3$
$\mathbf{x} + \mathbf{y} = (c_1 + d_1)\mathbf{u}_1 + (c_2 + d_2)\mathbf{u}_2 + (c_3 + d_3)\mathbf{u}_3$
$(\mathbf{x} + \mathbf{y})_U = (c_1 + d_1, c_2 + d_2, c_3 + d_3) = (\mathbf{x})_U + (\mathbf{y})_U$.
This shows that if $\mathbf{z} = \mathbf{x} + \mathbf{y}$, $(\mathbf{z})_U = (\mathbf{x})_U + (\mathbf{y})_U$. Now suppose $(\mathbf{z})_U = (\mathbf{x})_U + (\mathbf{y})_U$. Since $(\mathbf{x})_U + (\mathbf{y})_U = (\mathbf{x} + \mathbf{y})_U$ and coordinates are unique, $\mathbf{z} = \mathbf{x} + \mathbf{y}$.

9. It is necessary to show that E spans P_2 and E is linearly independent. Let $p = a + bx + cx^2$ be in P_2. Then $p = a(1) + b(x) + c(x^2)$, so E spans P_2. If $c_1(1) + c_2(x) + c_3(x^2) = 0$ then $c_1 = c_2 = c_3 = 0$ so E is linearly independent. The dimension of P_2 is 3. $(3 - 4x + x^2)_E = (3, -4, 1)$. If $(p)_E = (2, 0, 1)$, then $p = 2 + x^2$.

11. a. $c_1 = -6$, $c_2 = \frac{5}{2}$, $c_3 = \frac{1}{2}$
b. $(a_0 + a_1 - a_2, \frac{1}{2}(a_1 + a_2), \frac{1}{2}(-a_1 + a_2))$

13. Let m_0, m_1, m_2 be the coordinates of p relative to the basis $\{p_1, p_2, p_3\}$. Then

$$\begin{bmatrix} a_0 & b_0 & c_0 \\ a_1 & b_1 & c_1 \\ a_2 & b_2 & c_2 \end{bmatrix}\begin{bmatrix} m_0 \\ m_1 \\ m_2 \end{bmatrix} = \begin{bmatrix} d_0 \\ d_1 \\ d_2 \end{bmatrix}$$

must be solved. Thus

$$\begin{bmatrix} m_0 \\ m_1 \\ m_2 \end{bmatrix} = \begin{bmatrix} a_0 & b_0 & c_0 \\ a_1 & b_1 & c_1 \\ a_2 & b_2 & c_2 \end{bmatrix}^{-1}\begin{bmatrix} d_0 \\ d_1 \\ d_2 \end{bmatrix}$$

15. $b_1\mathbf{B}_1 + b_2\mathbf{B}_2 + b_3\mathbf{B}_3 + b_4\mathbf{B}_4 = \begin{bmatrix} b_1 + b_2 + b_3 + b_4 & b_4 \\ b_2 + b_3 + b_4 & b_3 + b_4 \end{bmatrix} = \mathbf{0}$ only if $b_1 = b_2 = b_3 = b_4 = 0$. So $\{\mathbf{B}_1, \mathbf{B}_2, \mathbf{B}_3, \mathbf{B}_4\}$ is a linearly independent subset of $M_{2\times2}$ which, by Problem 14, has dimension 4. Thus $\{\mathbf{B}_1, \mathbf{B}_2, \mathbf{B}_3, \mathbf{B}_4\}$ is a basis for $M_{2\times2}$. **A** has coordinate vector $(-2, -1, 2, 3)$.

17. $U = \{\mathbf{u}_1, \mathbf{u}_2, \ldots, \mathbf{u}_n\}$ is a linearly independent set. It is a basis if it spans R^n. The equation $c_1\mathbf{u}_1 + c_2\mathbf{u}_2 + \cdots + c_n\mathbf{u}_n = \mathbf{x}$ in matrix form is $\mathbf{M}\begin{bmatrix} c_1 \\ c_2 \\ \vdots \\ c_n \end{bmatrix} = \mathbf{X}$. This has a solution for every $\mathbf{x}$ since $\mathbf{M}$ is $n \times n$ and has rank n.

19. Show $8 \leftrightarrow 9$. Let **A** be an $n \times n$ matrix.

$8 \to 9$: If the n columns of **A** are linearly independent, then by Theorem 7 the columns of **A** are a basis of R^n, which has dimension n.

$9 \to 8$: If the columns of **A** are a basis for R^n, then the columns are linearly independent.

21. $$\begin{bmatrix} 1 & 1 & 2 & 3 & 2 & 1 \\ -1 & 0 & 1 & 0 & 2 & 1 \\ 1 & 1 & 2 & 3 & 2 & 1 \\ 0 & 0 & 1 & 1 & 2 & 1 \end{bmatrix} \Leftrightarrow \begin{bmatrix} 1 & 0 & 0 & 1 & 0 & 0 \\ 0 & 1 & 0 & 0 & -2 & -1 \\ 0 & 0 & 1 & 1 & 2 & 1 \\ 0 & 0 & 0 & 0 & 0 & 0 \end{bmatrix}$$. The leading columns are first, second, and third.

A basis can be $\{\mathbf{u}_5, \mathbf{u}_2, \mathbf{u}_4\}$. Rank is unchanged.

EXERCISES 4.4

1. a. $(1, 1, -1)$; dimension 1
b. $(1, 1, -1)$; dimension 1
c. $(-1, 1, 0)$; $(-2, 0, 1)$, dimension 2

3. a. $(1, 0, 1)$, $(0, 1, 1)$; dimension 2
b. $(1, 0, 1)$, $(0, 1, 1)$; dimension 2
c. $(1, 1, 2)$; dimension 1

5. a. Null space is the line determined by the vector $(1, 1, -1)$; row space is the plane determined by the vectors $(1, 0, 1)$ and $(0, 1, 1)$.
b. Null space is the line determined by the vector $(1, 1, -1)$; row space is the plane determined by the vectors $(1, 0, 1)$ and $(0, 1, 1)$.
c. Null space is the plane determined by the vectors $(-1, 1, 0)$ and $(-2, 0, 1)$.
Row space is the line determined by the vector $(1, 1, 2)$.

7. Basis for null space: $\mathbf{n}_1 = (1, -3, 0, 1)$, $\mathbf{n}_2 = (-2, 0, 1, 0)$; basis for row space: $\mathbf{r}_1 = (1, 0, 2, -1)$, $\mathbf{r}_2 = (0, 1, 0, 3)$; $(6, -7, 3, -3) = (2, -1, 4, -5) + (4, -6, -1, 2)$ with $(2, -1, 4, -5) = 2\mathbf{r}_1 - \mathbf{r}_2$ in the row space and $(4, -6, -1, 2) = 2\mathbf{n}_1 - \mathbf{n}_2$ in the null space.

9. a. 2 **b.** 1
c. If $\mathbf{x}$ is in the null space of **B**, $(1, 1, 0, 0) \cdot \mathbf{x} = 0$ and $(0, 1, 2, 3) \cdot \mathbf{x} = 0$, so $\mathbf{x}$ is in the null space of **A**.

11. The null space of $\begin{bmatrix} 1 & 1 & 0 & 0 \\ 0 & 1 & 2 & 3 \\ 0 & 0 & 1 & 2 \end{bmatrix}$.

13. a. 1 **b.** 2

15. Null space of $\mathbf{A} - \lambda\mathbf{I}$ has dimension greater than zero if and only if $\det(\mathbf{A} - \lambda\mathbf{I}) = 0$

17. Every linear combination of $(1, 1, 0, 0)$ and $(0, 1, 2, 3)$ is also a linear combination of $(1, 1, 0, 0)$, $(0, 1, 2, 3)$, and $(0, 0, 1, 2)$.

19. The row space of **B** is the same as the null space of **A** since the rows of **B** are $\mathbf{u}_1, \mathbf{u}_2, \mathbf{u}_3$. The null space of **B** is the set of vectors perpendicular to the row space of **B**, that is, the set of vectors perpendicular to the null space of **A**, that is, the row space of **A** (Theorem 11).

21. 2

23. **a.** Column 3 = (1) column 1; column 5 = (3) column 1 + (−1) column 2 + (−1) column 4
b. It remains to show that columns 1, 2, and 4 are linearly independent.

$$\begin{bmatrix} 1 & 1 & 1 \\ 1 & -1 & 3 \\ 1 & 1 & 2 \\ 1 & 1 & 3 \end{bmatrix} \Leftrightarrow \begin{bmatrix} 1 & 0 & 0 \\ 0 & 1 & 0 \\ 0 & 0 & 1 \\ 0 & 0 & 0 \end{bmatrix} \text{ has rank 3}$$

c. Columns 1, 2, 4 span a space in which each vector is $(c_1, c_2, c_3, 0)$. The columns of **A** are not in this space.

25. **a.** $(1, 0, -1, 1)$, $(0, 1, 1, 4)$
b. $(1, -1, 1, 0)$, $(-1, -4, 0, 1)$
c. $\mathbf{u} = (1, 2, 1, 9)$, $\mathbf{n} = (3, 2, 2, -1)$

EXERCISES 4.5

1. **a.** $(3, 6) = 4(1, 1) + (-1, 2)$; $[\mathbf{x}]_U = \begin{bmatrix} 4 \\ 1 \end{bmatrix}$

b. $[\mathbf{x}]_U = (\frac{1}{3})\begin{bmatrix} 2a_1 + a_2 \\ -a_1 + a_2 \end{bmatrix}$ **c.** $[\mathbf{x}]_U = (\frac{1}{3})\begin{bmatrix} 2 & 1 \\ -1 & 1 \end{bmatrix}[\mathbf{x}]_E$

d. $(7, -5)$, $\begin{bmatrix} 7 \\ -5 \end{bmatrix}$ **e.** $\begin{bmatrix} a - b \\ a + 2b \end{bmatrix}$ **f.** $\mathbf{A} = \begin{bmatrix} 1 & -1 \\ 1 & 2 \end{bmatrix}$

3. **a.** $(p)_U = (-\frac{3}{2}, 3, \frac{5}{2})$ **b.** $[p]_E = \begin{bmatrix} 1 & 0 & 1 \\ 0 & 1 & 0 \\ 1 & 0 & -1 \end{bmatrix}[p]_U$

5. **b.** $\begin{bmatrix} \frac{1}{2} & 0 & 1 \\ \frac{1}{2} & 0 & 0 \\ \frac{1}{2} & 1 & 1 \end{bmatrix}$

7. $(1, 0, 0, -1)$; no. These are solutions of $x_1 + 2x_3 + x_4 = 0$. This is a three-dimensional subspace with basis $\{(0, 1, 0, 0), (-2, 0, 1, 0), (-1, 0, 0, 1)\}$.

9. *a*, *c*, *d*

11. **a.** Let $\mathbf{P} = [\mathbf{u}_1 \ \ \mathbf{u}_2 \ \ \mathbf{u}_3]$. Then $\mathbf{P}\mathbf{P}^T = \mathbf{I}_3$.
b. $[\mathbf{x}]_U = \mathbf{P}^T[\mathbf{x}]_E$, $[\mathbf{x}]_E = \mathbf{P}[\mathbf{x}]_U$

15. $\left\{(\frac{1}{3}, \frac{2}{3}, \frac{2}{3}), \left(\frac{4}{3\sqrt{2}}, -\frac{1}{3\sqrt{2}}, -\frac{1}{3\sqrt{2}}\right)\right\}$

17. If **A** and **B** are orthogonal, $\mathbf{A}^T\mathbf{A} = \mathbf{I}$ and $\mathbf{B}^T\mathbf{B} = \mathbf{I}$; $(\mathbf{AB})(\mathbf{AB})^T = \mathbf{ABB}^T\mathbf{A}^T = \mathbf{I}$, so **AB** is orthogonal.

19. $\mathbf{PP}^T = \begin{bmatrix} 1 & 0 & 0 \\ 0 & a & b \\ 0 & c & d \end{bmatrix}\begin{bmatrix} 1 & 0 & 0 \\ 0 & a & c \\ 0 & b & d \end{bmatrix} = \begin{bmatrix} 1 & 0 & 0 \\ 0 & a^2 + b^2 & ac + bd \\ 0 & ac + bd & c^2 + d^2 \end{bmatrix} = \begin{bmatrix} 1 & 0 & 0 \\ 0 & 1 & 0 \\ 0 & 0 & 1 \end{bmatrix}$, since

$$\begin{bmatrix} a & b \\ c & d \end{bmatrix}\begin{bmatrix} a & c \\ b & d \end{bmatrix} = \begin{bmatrix} a^2 + b^2 & ac + bd \\ ac + bd & c^2 + d^2 \end{bmatrix} = \begin{bmatrix} 1 & 0 \\ 0 & 1 \end{bmatrix}.$$

21. Each vector is a unit vector and $\mathbf{u}_i \cdot \mathbf{u}_j = 0$, $\mathbf{v}_i \cdot \mathbf{v}_j = 0$ for $i \neq j$, and $\mathbf{u}_i \cdot \mathbf{v}_j = 0$ for all i, j.

23. **a.** $\int_{-1}^{1} x\,dx = 0$ **b.** $\int_{-1}^{1} x^2\,dx = [x^3/3]_{-1}^{1} = \frac{2}{3} \neq 0$ **c.** $\int_{-1}^{1} x^3\,dx = 0$

25. Standard basis is $1, x, x^2, x^3$. Orthonormal basis is $u_1 = \frac{1}{\sqrt{2}}$, $u_2 = (\frac{\sqrt{3}}{\sqrt{2}})x$, $u_3 = (\frac{\sqrt{5}}{2\sqrt{2}})(3x^2 - 1)$, $u_4 = (\frac{\sqrt{7}}{2\sqrt{2}})(5x^3 - 3x)$.

29. $c_0 = p \cdot q_0 = \int_{-1}^{1} (p)(\frac{1}{\sqrt{2}})\,dx$

$c_1 = p \cdot q_1 = (\frac{\sqrt{3}}{\sqrt{2}})\int_{-1}^{1} (p)(x)\,dx$

$c_2 = p \cdot q_2 = (\frac{\sqrt{5}}{2\sqrt{2}})\int_{-1}^{1} (p)(3x^2 - 1)\,dx$

$c_3 = p \cdot q_3 = (\frac{\sqrt{7}}{2\sqrt{2}})\int_{-1}^{1} (p)(5x^3 - 3x)\,dx$

EXERCISES 4.6

1. 64; $1 \cdot (1 + 0) = 1 \cdot 1 = 1$; $1 \cdot 1 + 1 \cdot 0 = 1 + 0 = 1$, and so on.

3. $\mathbf{0} = (0, 0)$, $\mathbf{u} = (1, 0)$, $\mathbf{v} = (0, 1)$, $\mathbf{w} = (1, 1)$
$\mathbf{u} + \mathbf{v} = \mathbf{w}$; $\mathbf{u} + \mathbf{w} = (1 + 1, 0 + 1) = (0, 1) = \mathbf{v}$; $\mathbf{v} + \mathbf{w} = \mathbf{u}$; $\mathbf{w} + \mathbf{w} = \mathbf{0}$, $\mathbf{u} + \mathbf{u} = \mathbf{0}$; $\mathbf{v} + \mathbf{v} = \mathbf{0}$

5. 24

7. $2^{12} = 4{,}096$

9. $(0.408^+, -0.816^-, 0.000, -0.408^+)$, $(0.577^+, 0.577^+, 0.000, -0.577^-)$, $(0.707^+, 0.000, 0.000, 0.707^+)$, $(0.000, 0.000, 1.000, 0.000)$.

11. a. $\begin{bmatrix} 5 \\ 6 \\ 1 \end{bmatrix}, \begin{bmatrix} 50 \\ 60 \\ 10 \end{bmatrix}, \begin{bmatrix} 2.5 \\ 3.0 \\ 0.5 \end{bmatrix}, \begin{bmatrix} 0.25 \\ 0.30 \\ 0.05 \end{bmatrix}$

b. $\begin{bmatrix} -100 \\ 5 \\ 1 \end{bmatrix}, \begin{bmatrix} -1000 \\ 50 \\ 10 \end{bmatrix}, \begin{bmatrix} -50.0 \\ 2.5 \\ 0.5 \end{bmatrix}, \begin{bmatrix} -5.00 \\ 0.25 \\ 0.05 \end{bmatrix}$

c. $\begin{bmatrix} 1000 \\ -5000 \\ 1 \end{bmatrix}, \begin{bmatrix} 10000 \\ -50000 \\ 10 \end{bmatrix}, \begin{bmatrix} 500.0 \\ -2500.0 \\ 0.5 \end{bmatrix}, \begin{bmatrix} 50.00 \\ -250.00 \\ 0.05 \end{bmatrix}$

d. $\begin{bmatrix} 255000 \\ -562000 \\ 1 \end{bmatrix}, \begin{bmatrix} 2550000 \\ -5620000 \\ 10 \end{bmatrix}, \begin{bmatrix} 127500.0 \\ -281000.0 \\ 0.5 \end{bmatrix}, \begin{bmatrix} 12750.00 \\ -28100.00 \\ 0.05 \end{bmatrix}$

13. a. $\begin{bmatrix} 0 & -1 & 0 \\ 1 & 0 & 0 \\ 0 & 0 & 1 \end{bmatrix}$ **b.** $\begin{bmatrix} 1 & 0 & 2 \\ 0 & 1 & -3 \\ 0 & 0 & 1 \end{bmatrix}$

c. $\begin{bmatrix} 0 & -1 & 1 \\ 1 & 0 & -1 \\ 0 & 0 & 1 \end{bmatrix}$ **d.** $\begin{bmatrix} 1 & 2 & 0 \\ 0 & 1 & 0 \\ 0 & 0 & 1 \end{bmatrix}$

e. $\begin{bmatrix} 1 & 2 & -5 \\ 0 & 1 & 0 \\ 0 & 0 & 1 \end{bmatrix}$

f. $\begin{bmatrix} 1 & 0 & 0 \\ 3 & 1 & 0 \\ 0 & 0 & 1 \end{bmatrix}\begin{bmatrix} -1 & 0 & 0 \\ 0 & 1 & 0 \\ 0 & 0 & 1 \end{bmatrix} = \begin{bmatrix} -1 & 0 & 0 \\ -3 & 1 & 0 \\ 0 & 0 & 1 \end{bmatrix}$

15. $\begin{bmatrix} 1 & 0 & 2 \\ 0 & 1 & -3 \\ 0 & 0 & 1 \end{bmatrix}\begin{bmatrix} x \\ 3x - 4 \\ 1 \end{bmatrix} = \begin{bmatrix} x + 2 \\ 3x - 7 \\ 1 \end{bmatrix}$

Let $x' = x + 2$ and $y' = 3x - 7$, so that $y' = 3x' - 13$.

17. $\mathbf{M} = \mathbf{M}_Y\mathbf{M}_R\mathbf{M}_P = \begin{bmatrix} 0.9229 & 0.2536 & -0.2870 \\ -0.1872 & 0.9506 & 0.2430 \\ 0.3332 & -0.1700 & 0.9212 \end{bmatrix}$ where $\mathbf{M}_Y, \mathbf{M}_R, \mathbf{M}_P$ are as in Example 52.

19. $\mathbf{M} = \begin{bmatrix} 0.35 & 0.93 & 0.13 \\ -0.61 & 0.13 & 0.78 \\ 0.71 & -0.35 & 0.61 \end{bmatrix}$, $\mathbf{M}_R = \begin{bmatrix} 1 & 0.00 & 0.00 \\ 0 & 0.87 & 0.50 \\ 0 & -0.50 & 0.87 \end{bmatrix}$, $\mathbf{M}_P = \begin{bmatrix} 0.71 & 0 & -0.71 \\ 0.00 & 1 & 0.00 \\ 0.71 & 0 & 0.71 \end{bmatrix}$, and

$\mathbf{M}_Y = \mathbf{M}\mathbf{M}_R^{-1}\mathbf{M}_P^{-1} = \begin{bmatrix} 0.49 & 0.87 & * \\ -0.86 & 0.50 & * \\ * & * & 0.99 \end{bmatrix}$ where $*$ is a number essentially zero. Thus, the yaw was 60°.

21. For yaw followed by pitch, $\mathbf{M} = \begin{bmatrix} ac & ad & -b \\ -d & c & 0 \\ bc & bd & a \end{bmatrix}$; For pitch followed by yaw, $\mathbf{M} = \begin{bmatrix} ac & d & -bc \\ -ad & c & bd \\ b & 0 & a \end{bmatrix}$; where $a = \cos P$, $b = \sin P$, $c = \cos Y$ and $d = \sin Y$.

EXERCISES 5.1

1. a. $\begin{bmatrix} 0 \\ 5 \\ 1 \end{bmatrix}, \begin{bmatrix} 4 \\ 7 \\ 19 \end{bmatrix}$ **b.** $\mathbf{w} = (9, -11)$; $T(\mathbf{W}) = \begin{bmatrix} -20 \\ -15 \\ -91 \end{bmatrix}$ **c.** $\begin{bmatrix} -20 \\ -15 \\ -91 \end{bmatrix} = 4\begin{bmatrix} 0 \\ 5 \\ 1 \end{bmatrix} - 5\begin{bmatrix} 4 \\ 7 \\ 19 \end{bmatrix}$

3. $S(0,0) = (0^2, 0 \cdot 0) = (0,0)$, $S(2,2) = (4,4)$, $S(1,1) = (1,1)$; $S(2,2) \neq 2S(1,1)$

5.
$$\begin{aligned} \mathbf{x} = (a_1, a_2, a_3);\ T(\mathbf{x}) &= T(a_1(1,0,0) + a_2(0,1,0) + a_3(0,0,1)) \\ &= a_1T(1,0,0) + a_2T(0,1,0) + a_3T(0,0,1) \\ &= a_1(1,2,3) + a_2(2,4,6) + a_3(3,6,9) \\ &= (a_1 + 2a_2 + 3a_3)(1,2,3) \end{aligned}$$

7. $(13, 18)$; $(1, -2)$, $(5a + b, 6a + 2b)$; $T(\mathbf{X}) = \begin{bmatrix} 5 & 1 \\ 6 & 2 \end{bmatrix}\mathbf{X}$

9. a. $2 - x^2$

b. Let $p = p_0 + p_1x + p_2x^2$ and $q = q_0 + q_1x + q_2x^2$
$$\begin{aligned} T(ap + bq) &= T(ap_0 + ap_1x + ap_2x^2 + bq_0 + bq_1x + bq_2x^2) \\ &= T(ap_0 + bq_0 + (ap_1 + bq_1)x + (ap_2 + bq_2)x^2) \\ &= ap_0 + bq_0 + (ap_1 + bq_1)(x+1) + (ap_2 + bq_2)(x+1)^2 \\ &= a(p_0 + p_1(x+1) + p_2(x+1)^2) + b(q_0 + q_1(x+1) + q_2(x+1)^2) \\ &= aT(p) + bT(q) \end{aligned}$$

11.
$$\begin{aligned} T((a\mathbf{u}) + (b\mathbf{v})) &= T(a\mathbf{u}) + T(b\mathbf{v}) && \text{by (1)} \\ &= aT(\mathbf{u}) + bT(\mathbf{v}) && \text{by (2) used twice} \end{aligned}$$

13. $T(0) = T(0 + 0x + 0x^2) = 1 + 0x + 0x^2 + 0x^3 = 1 \neq 0$; thus, T is not a linear transformation.

15. a. $\begin{bmatrix} 1 \\ 4 \end{bmatrix}, \begin{bmatrix} 3 \\ 0 \end{bmatrix}, \begin{bmatrix} 4 \\ 4 \end{bmatrix}, \begin{bmatrix} 5 \\ 6 \end{bmatrix}, \begin{bmatrix} -1 \\ 8 \end{bmatrix}, \begin{bmatrix} -1 \\ 6 \end{bmatrix}, \begin{bmatrix} 9 \\ 6 \end{bmatrix}$

b. $\begin{bmatrix} a \\ 4a \end{bmatrix}, \begin{bmatrix} 3b \\ 0 \end{bmatrix}, \begin{bmatrix} a + 3b \\ 4a \end{bmatrix}, T\left(\begin{bmatrix} a \\ 0 \\ 0 \end{bmatrix}\right) + T\left(\begin{bmatrix} 0 \\ b \\ 0 \end{bmatrix}\right) = T\left(\begin{bmatrix} a \\ b \\ 0 \end{bmatrix}\right)$

17. $\begin{bmatrix} 1 \\ 4 \\ 2 \end{bmatrix}, \begin{bmatrix} 3 \\ 1 \\ 5 \end{bmatrix}, \begin{bmatrix} 2 \\ 6 \\ 3 \end{bmatrix}$

19. $T(\mathbf{x}) = (4x_1 + x_2 - x_3, x_1 + x_2 + x_3)$

$T(\mathbf{X}) = \begin{bmatrix} 4 & 1 & -1 \\ 1 & 1 & 1 \end{bmatrix}\mathbf{X}$

21. $(1,0)$; $(0,-1)$; $T(\mathbf{X}) = \begin{bmatrix} 1 & 0 \\ 0 & -1 \end{bmatrix}\mathbf{X}$

23. $Z(\mathbf{X}) = \mathbf{0}$ for every $\mathbf{X}$, so $Z(a\mathbf{U} + b\mathbf{V}) = \mathbf{0} = a\mathbf{0} + b\mathbf{0} = aZ(\mathbf{U}) + bZ(\mathbf{V})$

$I(\mathbf{X}) = \mathbf{X}$ for every $\mathbf{X}$, so $I(a\mathbf{U} + b\mathbf{V}) = a\mathbf{U} + b\mathbf{V} = aI(\mathbf{U}) + bI(\mathbf{V})$.

25. a. Yes **b.** No **c.** Yes

d. Yes; $T\left(a\begin{bmatrix} x_1 & x_2 \\ x_3 & x_4 \end{bmatrix} + b\begin{bmatrix} y_1 & y_2 \\ y_3 & y_4 \end{bmatrix}\right) = T\left(\begin{bmatrix} ax_1 + by_1 & ax_2 + by_2 \\ ax_3 + by_3 & ax_4 + by_4 \end{bmatrix}\right) = \begin{bmatrix} ax_1 + by_1 & 0 \\ 0 & ax_4 + by_4 \end{bmatrix} =$

$a\begin{bmatrix} x_1 & 0 \\ 0 & x_4 \end{bmatrix} + b\begin{bmatrix} y_1 & 0 \\ 0 & y_4 \end{bmatrix} = aT\left(\begin{bmatrix} x_1 & x_2 \\ x_3 & x_4 \end{bmatrix}\right) + bT\left(\begin{bmatrix} y_1 & y_2 \\ y_3 & y_4 \end{bmatrix}\right)$

e. No; $T\left(\begin{bmatrix} 1 & 1 \\ 1 & 1 \end{bmatrix} + \begin{bmatrix} 1 & 1 \\ 1 & 1 \end{bmatrix}\right) = \begin{bmatrix} 4 & 0 \\ 0 & 4 \end{bmatrix}$, but $T\left(\begin{bmatrix} 1 & 1 \\ 1 & 1 \end{bmatrix}\right) + T\left(\begin{bmatrix} 1 & 1 \\ 1 & 1 \end{bmatrix}\right) = \begin{bmatrix} 2 & 0 \\ 0 & 2 \end{bmatrix}$

EXERCISES 5.2

1. a. $\mathbf{u}_1 + 2\mathbf{u}_2 - \mathbf{u}_3$; $\mathbf{u}_1 + \mathbf{u}_2$; $3\mathbf{u}_2 + \mathbf{u}_3$

b. $T(\mathbf{w}) = 3T(\mathbf{u}_1) - 4T(\mathbf{u}_2) + T(\mathbf{u}_3) = -\mathbf{u}_1 + 5\mathbf{u}_2 - 2\mathbf{u}_3$

c. $\left[\begin{array}{rrr|r} 1 & 1 & 0 & -1 \\ 2 & 1 & 3 & 3 \\ -1 & 0 & 1 & 0 \end{array}\right] \Leftrightarrow \left[\begin{array}{rrr|r} 1 & 0 & 0 & 1 \\ 0 & 1 & 0 & -2 \\ 0 & 0 & 1 & 1 \end{array}\right]$. Thus, $\mathbf{w} = \mathbf{u}_1 - 2\mathbf{u}_2 + \mathbf{u}_3$

d. $\mathbf{A}$ is nonsingular; thus, the preimage of $\mathbf{0}$ is only $\mathbf{0}$.

3. $\dfrac{(x_1, x_2)\cdot(1,3)}{(1,3)\cdot(1,3)}(1,3) = \dfrac{x_1 + 3x_2}{1+9}(1,3) = \left(\dfrac{x_1+3x_2}{10}, \dfrac{3x_1+9x_2}{10}\right)$; $\begin{bmatrix} 0.1 & 0.3 \\ 0.3 & 0.9 \end{bmatrix}\mathbf{X}$; line through $(0,0)$ and $(1,3)$; preimage of $k_1(1,3)$ is the set of all vectors in R^2 with endpoints on the line perpendicular to $k(1,3)$ and passing through $k_1(1,3)$.

5. a. $(1,1)$, $(0,1)$, $\begin{bmatrix} 1 & 0 \\ 1 & 1 \end{bmatrix}$ **b.** $(0,0)$

7. a. $\mathbf{A} \Leftrightarrow \begin{bmatrix} 1 & 0 & 4 \\ 0 & 1 & 1 \\ 0 & 0 & 0 \end{bmatrix}$. Thus, the range of T is a two-dimensional subspace of R^3; a basis is $\{(1,0,1), (-1,1,0)\}$.

b. R^3

c. Two-dimensional subspace; $\{(1,2,3), (1,2,2)\}$

d. R^3

e. R^3

9. a. All of R^2

b. $(0, \frac{1}{3}, 0) + k(-3,-1,6)$, $(\frac{1}{4}, -\frac{1}{12}, 0) + k(-3,-1,6)$, $k(-3,-1,6)$, $(\frac{3}{2}, -\frac{5}{6}, 0) + k(-3,-1,6)$

c. The one-dimensional subspace of R^3 with basis $\{(-3,-1,6)\}$

11. a. r **b.** $n = r$ **c.** $n = r$

13. The coordinates of the zero vector relative to any basis are 0. $Z(\mathbf{u}_i) = 0$ for each i.

15. $p(x) = -1 + 2x + 3x^2$

17. $p(x) = -1 + 2x + 3x^2$

19. a. $\begin{bmatrix} 1 & x_1 & x_1^2 \\ 1 & x_2 & x_2^2 \\ 1 & x_3 & x_3^2 \end{bmatrix}$ **c.** Since rank of $\mathbf{A} = 3$, $\mathbf{AX} = \mathbf{Y}$ has a unique solution.

21. a. $\begin{bmatrix} 1 & x_1 & x_1^2 \\ 1 & x_2 & x_2^2 \\ 1 & x_3 & x_3^2 \\ 1 & x_4 & x_4^2 \end{bmatrix}$

b. Rank r of the matrix of T is the dimension of the range, so $r \leqslant 3$. Range is a proper subset of R^4.

23. a. $D(ap + bq) = aD(p) + bD(q)$ by properties of derivative.

b. $D(1) = 0$, $D(x) = 1$, $D(x^2) = 2x, \ldots, D(x^n) = nx^{n-1}$

$$\begin{bmatrix} 0 & 1 & 0 & \cdots & 0 \\ 0 & 0 & 2 & \cdots & 0 \\ \vdots & \vdots & \vdots & & \vdots \\ 0 & 0 & 0 & \cdots & n \end{bmatrix}$$

25. a. $(ap + bq)'' - 3(ap + bq)' + 4(ap + bq) = ap'' - 3ap' + 4ap + bq'' - 3bq' + 4bq = a(p'' - 3p' + 4p) + b(q'' - 3q' + 4q)$

b. $\begin{bmatrix} 4 & -3 & 2 \\ 0 & 4 & -6 \\ 0 & 0 & 4 \end{bmatrix}$ **c.** $22 - 22x + 4x^2$ **d.** Zero polynomial **e.** $(\frac{5}{32}) - (\frac{5}{8})x - (\frac{3}{4})x^2$

27. a. $\begin{bmatrix} 1 & 0 & 0 & 0 \\ 0 & \frac{1}{2} & \frac{1}{2} & 0 \\ 0 & \frac{1}{2} & \frac{1}{2} & 0 \\ 0 & 0 & 0 & 1 \end{bmatrix}$

b. 1

c. $\begin{bmatrix} 0 & b \\ -b & 0 \end{bmatrix}$, where b is any real number

d. $\begin{bmatrix} a & b \\ c & d \end{bmatrix} = \begin{bmatrix} a & (b+c)/2 \\ (b+c)/2 & d \end{bmatrix} + \begin{bmatrix} 0 & (b-c)/2 \\ -(b-c)/2 & 0 \end{bmatrix}$

EXERCISES 5.3

1. a. $\begin{bmatrix} 6 & 8 \\ 9 & 13 \end{bmatrix}$ **b.** $\begin{bmatrix} 3 & 6 \\ 7 & 16 \end{bmatrix}$ **c.** No

3. Let $\mathbf{A}$ be the matrix of S and $\mathbf{B}$ be the matrix of T. Then $T \circ S(a\mathbf{u} + b\mathbf{v}) = \mathbf{BA}(a\mathbf{U} + b\mathbf{V}) = \mathbf{BA}(a\mathbf{U}) + \mathbf{BA}(b\mathbf{V}) = a\mathbf{BA}(\mathbf{U}) + b\mathbf{BA}(\mathbf{V}) = aT \circ S(\mathbf{u}) + bT \circ S(\mathbf{v})$.

5. $c \neq \frac{1}{2}$

7. $\begin{bmatrix} 1 & 0 \\ -1 & 0 \end{bmatrix}$; yes

9. a. Domain $T_1 = R^3$, domain $T_2 = R^2$; both ranges are R^2; T_1 and T_2 do not have a common domain.
b. Both domains are R^3; range $T_1 = R^2$, range $T_3 = R^3$; T_1 and T_3 do not have a common range.

11. $S(\mathbf{X}) = \begin{bmatrix} -2 & -1 \\ -4 & -5 \end{bmatrix}\mathbf{X}$

13. Properties 2, 3, 6, 7, 8, and 9 follow from properties of the matrices associated with the linear transformations.
1. If P and S are linear transformations from R^3 to R^2, so is $P + S$.
4. $(P + Z)(\mathbf{x}) = (\mathbf{A} + \mathbf{0}_{2\times 3})\mathbf{X} = \mathbf{AX} = P(\mathbf{x})$, so Z is the additive identity.
5. $(P + (-P))(\mathbf{x}) = (\mathbf{A} + (-1)\mathbf{A})\mathbf{X} = \mathbf{0}_{2\times 3}\mathbf{X} = Z(\mathbf{x})$
10. $(I \circ P)(\mathbf{x}) = \mathbf{I}_{2\times 2}\mathbf{AX} = \mathbf{AX} = P(\mathbf{x})$, so I is the multiplicative identity.

15. $P_1 + P_2$ is the identity transformation; matrix of P_1 is $\begin{bmatrix} 0 & 0 & 0 \\ 0 & 0 & 0 \\ 0 & 0 & 1 \end{bmatrix}$, matrix of P_2 is $\begin{bmatrix} 1 & 0 & 0 \\ 0 & 1 & 0 \\ 0 & 0 & 0 \end{bmatrix}$; matrix of $P_1 + P_2$ is $\mathbf{I}$.

17. $R_1(x_1, x_2) = (x_1, -x_2)$, $R_2(x_1, x_2) = (-x_1, x_2)$. $(R_1 + R_2)(x_1, x_2) = (0, 0)$, so $R_1 + R_2 = Z$. $R_1 \circ R_2(x_1, x_2) = R_1(-x_1, x_2) = (-x_1, -x_2)$, so $R_1 \circ R_2 = -I$, reflection through the origin.

19. a. $\{(k, -k, 0), k \text{ real}\}$
b. $\{(j + k, -j, -3k), j, k \text{ real}\}$
c. $\begin{bmatrix} 1 & 1 & 0 \\ 2 & 2 & 1 \\ 3 & 3 & 1 \end{bmatrix}\begin{bmatrix} j+k \\ -j \\ -3k \end{bmatrix} = \begin{bmatrix} k \\ -k \\ 0 \end{bmatrix}$

21. a. $\begin{bmatrix} 1 & 3 \\ 1 & -2 \end{bmatrix}$ **b.** $\begin{bmatrix} 6 & 0 \\ 0 & 1 \end{bmatrix}$

23. Let T be a linear transformation on a vector space W with bases U and V. If $\mathbf{A}$ and $\mathbf{B}$ are the matrices of T relative to bases U and V, respectively, then by theorem 8, $\mathbf{A}$ is similar to $\mathbf{B}$. But similar matrices have the same determinants.

25. a. $\mathbf{P}^T\begin{bmatrix} -\frac{5}{2} & \frac{3}{2} \\ \frac{3}{2} & \frac{3}{2} \end{bmatrix}\mathbf{P} = \begin{bmatrix} 2 & 0 \\ 0 & -3 \end{bmatrix} = \mathbf{B}$
b. $\begin{bmatrix} -2 & -2 \\ -2 & 1 \end{bmatrix}$
c. -3 with eigenvector $(2, 1)$, 2 with eigenvector $(1, -2)$
d. The basis V consists of eigenvectors of $\mathbf{C}$ of length 1
e. 2 with eigenvector $(1, 3)$, -3 with eigenvector $(3, -1)$
f. $(1, 3) = \sqrt{10}(1/\sqrt{10}, 3/\sqrt{10}) = \sqrt{10}(\mathbf{v}_1)_U$
$(3, -1) = \sqrt{10}(3/\sqrt{10}, -1/\sqrt{10}) = \sqrt{10}(\mathbf{v}_2)_U$

27. **a.** $\begin{bmatrix} 1 & 1 & 1 \\ 1 & -1 & 1 \\ 0 & 0 & 1 \end{bmatrix}$ **b.** $\begin{bmatrix} \frac{5}{2} & -\frac{1}{2} & \frac{5}{2} \\ \frac{1}{2} & \frac{3}{2} & \frac{1}{2} \\ 0 & 0 & 2 \end{bmatrix}$

c. $T(1 + x) = 3 + 2x = (\frac{5}{2})\mathbf{u}_1 + (\frac{1}{2})\mathbf{u}_2$
$T(1 - x) = 1 - 2x = (-\frac{1}{2})\mathbf{u}_1 + (\frac{3}{2})\mathbf{u}_2$
$T(1 + x + x^2) = (\frac{5}{2})\mathbf{u}_1 + (\frac{1}{2})\mathbf{u}_2 + 2\mathbf{u}_3$

29. $\begin{bmatrix} 1 & 0 & 0 \\ 4 & -2 & 2 \\ 2 & -4 & 2 \end{bmatrix}$

31. **b.** 0 **c.** $(2, 4, 3, 1, -1, 0)$

d. $T_{1,2,5}\left(\begin{bmatrix} 2 & 4 & 3 \\ 1 & -1 & 0 \end{bmatrix}\right) = \begin{bmatrix} 1 & 0 & 0 & 5 & 0 & 0 \\ 0 & 1 & 0 & 0 & 5 & 0 \\ 0 & 0 & 1 & 0 & 0 & 5 \\ 0 & 0 & 0 & 1 & 0 & 0 \\ 0 & 0 & 0 & 0 & 1 & 0 \\ 0 & 0 & 0 & 0 & 0 & 1 \end{bmatrix}\begin{bmatrix} 2 \\ 4 \\ 3 \\ 1 \\ -1 \\ 0 \end{bmatrix} = \begin{bmatrix} 7 \\ -1 \\ 3 \\ 1 \\ -1 \\ 0 \end{bmatrix} \Leftrightarrow \begin{bmatrix} 7 & -1 & 3 \\ 1 & -1 & 0 \end{bmatrix}$

33. **a.** $T = (T_{1,2,-1}) \circ (R_{2,1/3}) \circ (T_{2,1,-2}) \circ (S_{1,2})$

b. The matrix of $T_{1,2,-1}$ is $\begin{bmatrix} \mathbf{I} & -\mathbf{I} \\ \mathbf{0} & \mathbf{I} \end{bmatrix}$; the matrix of $R_{2,1/3}$ is $\begin{bmatrix} \mathbf{I} & \mathbf{0} \\ \mathbf{0} & (\frac{1}{3})\mathbf{I} \end{bmatrix}$; the matrix of $T_{2,1,-2}$ is $\begin{bmatrix} \mathbf{I} & \mathbf{0} \\ -2\mathbf{I} & \mathbf{I} \end{bmatrix}$; the matrix of $S_{1,2}$ is $\begin{bmatrix} \mathbf{0} & \mathbf{I} \\ \mathbf{I} & \mathbf{0} \end{bmatrix}$; the matrix of T is $(\frac{1}{3})\begin{bmatrix} -\mathbf{I} & 5\mathbf{I} \\ \mathbf{I} & -2\mathbf{I} \end{bmatrix}$.

c. $(\frac{1}{3})\begin{bmatrix} -\mathbf{I} & 5\mathbf{I} \\ \mathbf{I} & -2\mathbf{I} \end{bmatrix}\begin{bmatrix} 2 \\ 5 \\ 1 \\ 1 \end{bmatrix} = \begin{bmatrix} 1 \\ 0 \\ 0 \\ 1 \end{bmatrix}$

EXERCISES 5.4

1. $10y = 36 - 9x$

3. $3.8 - 1.6x + 0.25x^2$. The points are $(0, 3.8)$, $(1, 2.45)$, $(2, 1.6)$, $(3, 1.25)$

5. $1 - x + 2x^2$. The work is identical. In this case $\mathbf{A}$ is square, $(\mathbf{A}^T\mathbf{A})^{-1} = \mathbf{A}^{-1}(\mathbf{A}^T)^{-1}$ so that $(\mathbf{A}^T\mathbf{A})^{-1}\mathbf{A}^T[p] = \mathbf{A}^{-1}[p]$.

7. $\begin{bmatrix} 1 + 1 + 1 & x_1 + x_2 + x_3 \\ x_1 + x_2 + x_3 & x_1^2 + x_2^2 + x_3^2 \end{bmatrix}$

9. $\mathbf{AA}^T = \begin{bmatrix} 1 + 1 + \cdots + 1 & x_1 + x_2 + \cdots + x_n \\ x_1 + x_2 + \cdots + x_n & x_1^2 + x_2^2 + \cdots + x_n^2 \end{bmatrix}$; $\det \mathbf{AA}^T = \sum \det \begin{bmatrix} 1 & x_j \\ x_i & x_j^2 \end{bmatrix}$, $i,j = 1, 2, \ldots, n$

The only nonzero determinants in this sum occur when $i \neq j$. For fixed i,j $\det \begin{bmatrix} 1 & x_i \\ x_j & x_i^2 \end{bmatrix} + \det \begin{bmatrix} 1 & x_j \\ x_i & x_j^2 \end{bmatrix} =$ $x_i^2 - 2x_ix_j + x_j^2 = (x_i - x_j)^2$. Thus $\det \mathbf{AA}^T = \sum (x_i - x_j)^2$, $i,j = 1, 2, \ldots, n$, $i < j$.

11. Let $\mathbf{X} = \begin{bmatrix} 1 \\ 0 \\ 0 \\ 1 \end{bmatrix}$, $\mathbf{P} = \begin{bmatrix} \frac{\sqrt{2}}{2} & 0 & \frac{\sqrt{2}}{2} & 0 \\ 0 & 1 & 0 & 0 \\ -\frac{\sqrt{2}}{2} & 0 & \frac{\sqrt{2}}{2} & 0 \\ 0 & 0 & 0 & 1 \end{bmatrix}$, and $\mathbf{R} = \begin{bmatrix} 1 & 0 & 0 & 0 \\ 0 & \frac{\sqrt{2}}{2} & -\frac{\sqrt{2}}{2} & 0 \\ 0 & \frac{\sqrt{2}}{2} & \frac{\sqrt{2}}{2} & 0 \\ 0 & 0 & 0 & 1 \end{bmatrix}$. Then $\mathbf{PRX} = \begin{bmatrix} \frac{\sqrt{2}}{2} \\ 0 \\ -\frac{\sqrt{2}}{2} \\ 1 \end{bmatrix}$

and $\mathbf{RPX} = \begin{bmatrix} \frac{\sqrt{2}}{2} \\ \frac{1}{2} \\ -\frac{1}{2} \\ 1 \end{bmatrix}$.

13. a. $\begin{bmatrix} 1 & 0 & 0 & 3 \\ 0 & 1 & 0 & 2 \\ 0 & 0 & 1 & 0 \\ 0 & 0 & 0 & 1 \end{bmatrix} \begin{bmatrix} \frac{\sqrt{2}}{2} & -\frac{\sqrt{2}}{2} & 0 & 0 \\ \frac{\sqrt{2}}{2} & \frac{\sqrt{2}}{2} & 0 & 0 \\ 0 & 0 & 1 & 0 \\ 0 & 0 & 0 & 1 \end{bmatrix} \begin{bmatrix} 1 \\ 0 \\ 0 \\ 1 \end{bmatrix} = \begin{bmatrix} 3 + \frac{\sqrt{2}}{2} \\ 2 + \frac{\sqrt{2}}{2} \\ 0 \\ 1 \end{bmatrix}$

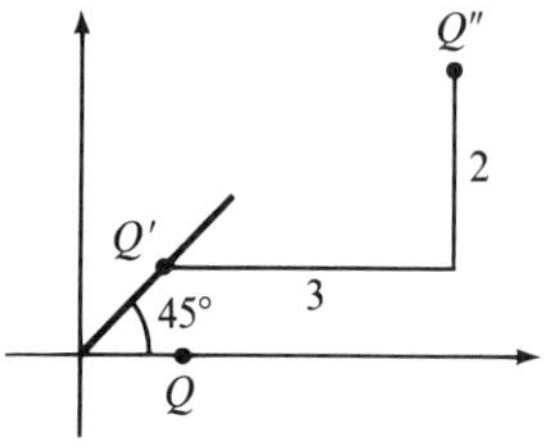

Let $Q = (1, 0, 0)$. Then $Q' = (\frac{\sqrt{2}}{2}, \frac{\sqrt{2}}{2}, 0)$ is the location of the point after the yaw of 45° and $Q'' = (\frac{\sqrt{2}}{2} + 3, \frac{\sqrt{2}}{2} + 2, 0)$ is the location of the point following the translation.

b. $\begin{bmatrix} \frac{\sqrt{2}}{2} & -\frac{\sqrt{2}}{2} & 0 & 0 \\ \frac{\sqrt{2}}{2} & \frac{\sqrt{2}}{2} & 0 & 0 \\ 0 & 0 & 1 & 0 \\ 0 & 0 & 0 & 1 \end{bmatrix} \begin{bmatrix} 1 & 0 & 0 & 3 \\ 0 & 1 & 0 & 2 \\ 0 & 0 & 1 & 0 \\ 0 & 0 & 0 & 1 \end{bmatrix} \begin{bmatrix} 1 \\ 0 \\ 0 \\ 1 \end{bmatrix} = \begin{bmatrix} \sqrt{2} \\ 3\sqrt{2} \\ 0 \\ 1 \end{bmatrix}$

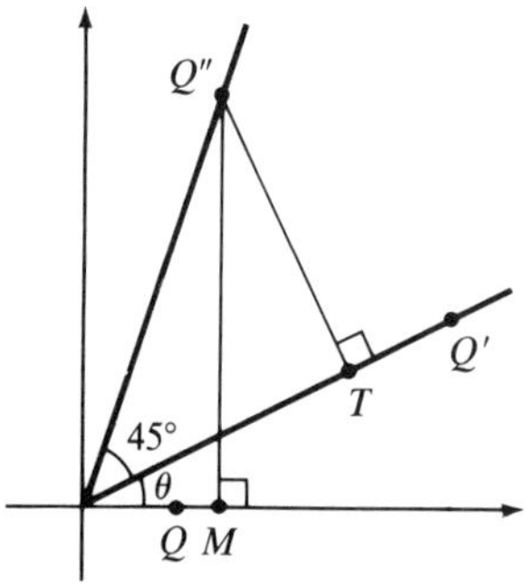

If $Q = (1, 0, 0)$, the translation of Q is $Q' = (4, 2, 0)$. Let Q'' be the position of Q' after a yaw of 45°. We need to find the coordinates of Q''. $OM = OQ'' \cos(\theta + 45°)$, $Q''M = OQ'' \sin(\theta + 45°)$, $OQ' = OQ'' = 2\sqrt{5}$, $\sin\theta = \frac{\sqrt{5}}{5}$, $\cos\theta = \frac{2\sqrt{5}}{5}$, $\cos(\theta + 45°) = \frac{\sqrt{10}}{10}$ and $\sin(\theta + 45°) = \frac{3\sqrt{10}}{10}$. Thus $OM = \sqrt{2}$ and $Q''M = 3\sqrt{2}$. So $Q'' = (\sqrt{2}, 3\sqrt{2}, 0)$.

15.
```
 1Ø  DIM MATCODE(2Ø,2Ø), B(2Ø,5Ø), C(2Ø,5Ø)
 2Ø  REM
 3Ø  REM  *****  PROGRAM FOR CODING/DECODING MESSAGES
 4Ø  REM
 5Ø  PRINT : INPUT "ORDER OF CODING/DECODING MATRIX";SIZEMAT
 6Ø  PRINT
 7Ø  REM
 8Ø  REM  *****  PUT ENTRIES OF CODING/DECODING MATRIX
 9Ø  REM  *****  IN DATA LINES STARTING AT LINE 1ØØØ
1ØØ  REM
11Ø  FOR ROW = 1 TO SIZEMAT
12Ø     FOR COL = 1 TO SIZEMAT
13Ø        READ MATCODE(ROW,COL)
14Ø     NEXT COL
15Ø  NEXT ROW
16Ø  PRINT : PRINT "ENTER MESSAGE (UPPER CASE LETTERS ONLY!):"
17Ø  INPUT MESG$
18Ø  REM
19Ø  REM  *****  GET LENGTH OF MESSAGE
2ØØ  REM
21Ø  LENMESG = LEN(MESG$)
22Ø  REM
23Ø  REM  *****  NCOL = NUMBER OF COLUMNS IN MESSAGE MATRIX
24Ø  REM
```

```
250  NCOL = INT(LENMESG/SIZEMAT)
260  IF NCOL = LENMESG/SIZEMAT THEN 400
270  REM
280  REM  *****  ONE MORE COLUMN NEEDED IF LENMESG ISN'T AN
290  REM  *****  INTEGER MULTIPLE OF ORDER OF CODING MATRIX
300  REM
310  NCOL = NCOL + 1
320  REM
330  REM  *****  INSERT EXTRA BLANKS AT END OF MESSAGE
340  REM
350  FOR COUNT = LENMESG + 1 TO NCOL * SIZEMAT
360     MESG$ = MESG$ + " "
370  NEXT COUNT
380  REM
390  REM  *****  FORM MESSAGE MATRIX IN COLUMNS
395  REM
400  FOR COL = 1 TO NCOL
410     FOR ROW = 1 TO SIZEMAT
420        B(ROW, COL) = ASC(MID$(MESG$, ROW + (COL - 1) * SIZEMAT, 1))
425        IF B(ROW, COL) = 32 THEN B(ROW, COL) = 64
430     NEXT ROW
440  NEXT COL
450  REM
460  REM  *****  MULTIPLY MESSAGE MATRIX BY CODING/DECODING MATRIX
470  REM
480  FOR ROW = 1 TO SIZEMAT
490     FOR COL = 1 TO NCOL
500        C(ROW, COL) = 0
510        FOR INNER = 1 TO SIZEMAT
520           C(ROW, COL) = C(ROW, COL) + MATCODE(ROW, INNER) * B(INNER, COL)
530        NEXT INNER
540        REM
550        REM  *****  CONVERT C(ROW, COL) TO SCALE 64 - 90
560        REM  *****  CHR$(64) WILL BE USED TO REPRESENT 'space'
570        GOSUB 850
580     NEXT COL
590  NEXT ROW
600  REM
610  REM  *****  CONVERT MESSAGE TO ALPHA FORMAT, 20 CHARACTERS PER LINE
620  REM
630  NUMCHAR = 0
640  FOR COL = 1 TO NCOL
650     FOR ROW = 1 TO SIZEMAT
655        IF C(ROW, COL) = 64 THEN C(ROW, COL) = 32  'CHANGE TO SPACE
660        PRINT CHR$( C(ROW, COL) );
670        NUMCHAR = NUMCHAR + 1
680        IF NUMCHAR MOD 20 = 0 THEN PRINT
690     NEXT ROW
700  NEXT COL
710  GOTO 2000
800  REM
810  REM  *****  DATA IN LINES 1000 -
820  REM
850  REM *****  SUBROUTINE TO CONVERT CHARACTERS TO SCALE 64 - 90
```

```
860  REM
870  IF C(ROW, COL) > 90 THEN 900
880  IF C(ROW, COL) < 64 THEN 910
890  RETURN
900  C(ROW, COL) = C(ROW, COL) - 27 : GOTO 870
910  C(ROW, COL) = C(ROW, COL) + 27 : GOTO 880
960  REM
970  REM  *****  ENTRIES OF CODING MATRIX FOLLOW
980  REM
1000 DATA 1, 2, -1, 3
1010 DATA -1, -1, 1, 2
1020 DATA 1, 2, 0, 7
1030 DATA 0, 1, 1, 10
1040 REM
1050 REM  *****  ENTRIES OF CORRESPONDING DECODING MATRIX FOLLOW
1055 REM
1060 DATA -2, -5, -2, 3
1070 DATA 1, 6, 5, -5
1080 DATA -1, 4, 5, -4
1090 DATA 0, -1, -1, 1
2000 END
```

17. AGENT DOUBLE O SEVEN DUE FROM CAIRO SEVEN PM YOUR TIME

19. a. $y = -x - \frac{1}{2}$ **b.** $y = -(\frac{1}{4}) - (\frac{1}{2})x + ce^x + (\frac{2}{3})xe^x$

c. $y = (-\frac{5}{9})\sin 2x - (\frac{1}{3})x\cos 2x$

d. $y = c_1 \sin 2x + c_2 \cos 2x + c_3 x \sin 2x + (-\frac{11}{16})x \operatorname{cox} 2x + 2c_4 x^2 \sin 2x + (\frac{1}{8})x^2 \sin 2x$

EXERCISES 6.1

1. a. $\begin{bmatrix} 4 & 2 \\ -1 & 1 \end{bmatrix}$ **b.** 2, 3 **c.** $\begin{bmatrix} 6 & 12 \\ -1 & -1 \end{bmatrix}$; 2, 3

3. a. $\begin{bmatrix} 2 & 0 & 0 \\ 0 & 4 & 1 \\ 0 & -5 & -2 \end{bmatrix}$ **b.** $-1, 2, 3$ **c.** $\begin{bmatrix} 2 & -2 & -3 \\ 0 & 9 & 12 \\ 0 & -5 & -7 \end{bmatrix}$; eigenvalues are $-1, 2, 3$.

5. No. $\mathbf{A} = \begin{bmatrix} \frac{\sqrt{2}}{2} & -\frac{\sqrt{2}}{2} \\ \frac{\sqrt{2}}{2} & \frac{\sqrt{2}}{2} \end{bmatrix}$

$\det(\mathbf{A} - \lambda\mathbf{I}) = \lambda^2 - \sqrt{2}\lambda + 1 = 0$ has roots $\lambda = (\frac{\sqrt{2}}{2})(1 \pm i)$.

7. $\det\begin{bmatrix} \cos\theta - \lambda & \sin\theta \\ -\sin\theta & \cos\theta - \lambda \end{bmatrix} = (\cos\theta - \lambda)^2 + \sin^2\theta = 1 - 2\lambda\cos\theta + \lambda^2 = 0$; $\lambda = \dfrac{2\cos\theta \pm \sqrt{4\cos^2\theta - 4}}{2}$ is real if and only if $\cos^2\theta = 1$ if and only if $\theta = k180°$, k an integer.

9. a. $\begin{bmatrix} 0 & 0 & 2 \\ 0 & 0 & 0 \\ 0 & 0 & 0 \end{bmatrix}$; $\det(\mathbf{A} - \lambda\mathbf{I}) = \lambda^3$; eigenvalue is 0. $\mathbf{A} - 0\mathbf{I}$ has rank 1; eigenspace has basis $\{1, x\}$. The second derivative of any constant or first-degree polynomial is zero.

b. $\begin{bmatrix} 0 & 1 & 2 \\ 0 & 0 & 2 \\ 0 & 0 & 0 \end{bmatrix}$; eigenvalue 0; $\mathbf{A} - 0\mathbf{I}$ has rank 2; eigenspace has dimension one.

11. a. $\mathbf{A} = \begin{bmatrix} 1 & k & 0 & 0 \\ 0 & 1 & 0 & 0 \\ 0 & 0 & 1 & k \\ 0 & 0 & 0 & 1 \end{bmatrix}$

b. $\det(\mathbf{A} - \lambda\mathbf{I}) = (1 - \lambda)^4 = 0$ has $\lambda = 1$ as a root with multiplicity 4; $\mathbf{A} - \mathbf{I} = \begin{bmatrix} 0 & k & 0 & 0 \\ 0 & 0 & 0 & 0 \\ 0 & 0 & 0 & k \\ 0 & 0 & 0 & 0 \end{bmatrix}$

c. The vectors must have second and fourth coordinates zero.

13. Eigenvalue 2, eigenvector $(1, 0, 0, 0)$; eigenvalue 3, eigenvector $(0, 1, 0, 0)$; eigenvalue 4, eigenvector $(0, 0, 1, 0)$; eigenvalue 5, eigenvector $(0, 0, 0, 1)$

15. a. $(a - d)^2 + 4bc \geqslant 0$ **b.** $(a - d)^2 + 4bc = 0$ **c.** $(a - d)^2 + 4bc < 0$
d. $(a - d)^2 + 4bc$ must be a square and $(a + d) \pm \sqrt{(a - d)^2 + 4bc}$ must be divisible by 2.

17. a. $\lambda(\lambda - 1)(\lambda - 3)$ **b.** $(\lambda - 1)^2(\lambda - 3)$ **c.** $(\lambda - 3)(\lambda + 1)(\lambda - 4)(\lambda - 5)$

19. Eigenvalue 1, multiplicity 3; eigenvector $(1, 1, 1)$. **A** is similar to a diagonal matrix if and only if the eigenspace of $\lambda = 1$ has dimension 3; however, the dimension of this space is 1.

21. a. Basis $\{(0, 1, 0), (-1, 0, 2), (1, 0, -1)\}$ **b.** Eigenvalues are $1, 1, 2, 2$; eigenspace of $\lambda = 2$ has dimension 1.

23. a. By Problem 9, Section 1.3, multiplication of diagonal matrices is commutative, so $\mathbf{DF} = \mathbf{FD}$. Thus, if $\mathbf{F}^{-1}$ exists, then $\mathbf{F}^{-1}\mathbf{DF} = \mathbf{D}$.
b. $(\mathbf{PF})^{-1}\mathbf{A}(\mathbf{PF}) = \mathbf{F}^{-1}\mathbf{P}^{-1}\mathbf{APF} = \mathbf{F}^{-1}\mathbf{DF} = \mathbf{D}$

25. a. By definition, $\mathbf{AU}_i = \lambda_i \mathbf{U}_i$, $i = 1, 2, \ldots, k$. So $(\mathbf{A} - \lambda_j \mathbf{I})\mathbf{U}_i = \mathbf{AU}_i - \lambda_j \mathbf{IU}_i = \lambda_i \mathbf{U}_i - \lambda_j \mathbf{U}_i = (\lambda_i - \lambda_j)\mathbf{U}_i$. Thus $\prod_{j=1}^{k} (\mathbf{A} - \lambda_j \mathbf{I})\mathbf{U}_i = \prod_{j=1}^{k} (\lambda_i - \lambda_j)\mathbf{U}_i$.

b. Assume $\sum_{i=1}^{k} c_i \mathbf{U}_i = \mathbf{0}$ (1). Let r be an integer, $1 \leqslant r \leqslant k$. Multiply both sides of equation (1) on the left by $\prod_{\substack{j=1 \\ j \neq r}}^{k} (\mathbf{A} - \lambda_j \mathbf{I})$. We obtain $\prod_{\substack{j=1 \\ j \neq r}}^{k} (\mathbf{A} - \lambda_j \mathbf{I}) \sum_{i=1}^{k} c_i \mathbf{U}_i = \mathbf{0}$. (2)

c. For any fixed i, $1 \leqslant i \leqslant k$, in equation (2) we have $\prod_{\substack{j=1 \\ j \neq r}}^{k} (\mathbf{A} - \lambda_j \mathbf{I})c_i \mathbf{U}_i = \prod_{\substack{j=1 \\ j \neq r}}^{k} (\lambda_i - \lambda_j)c_i \mathbf{U}_i =$

$$\begin{cases} \mathbf{0} & \text{if } i \neq r \\ K_r c_r \mathbf{U}_r & \text{if } i = r, \text{ where } K_r = \prod_{\substack{j=1 \\ j \neq r}}^{k} (\lambda_r - \lambda_j) \neq 0 \end{cases}$$

d. By (c) for any fixed r, $1 \leqslant r \leqslant k$, $\prod_{\substack{j=1 \\ j \neq r}}^{k} (\mathbf{A} - \lambda_j \mathbf{I}) \sum_{i=1}^{k} c_i \mathbf{U}_i = K_r c_r \mathbf{U}_r = \mathbf{0}$. By (b) and (c), since $K_r \neq 0$ and $\mathbf{U}_r \neq \mathbf{0}$, $c_r = 0$.

e. In (b), r was any fixed integer, $1 \leqslant r \leqslant k$ and by (d) $c_r = 0$. Thus, $\sum_{i=1}^{k} c_i \mathbf{U}_i = \mathbf{0}$ implies $c_r = 0$, $1 \leqslant r \leqslant k$. Hence $\{\mathbf{U}_1, \mathbf{U}_2, \ldots, \mathbf{U}_k\}$ is linearly independent.

27. Set $c_1\mathbf{u}_1 + c_2\mathbf{u}_2 + c_3\mathbf{u}_3 + c_4\mathbf{u}_4 = \mathbf{0}$. Multiply by $\mathbf{A} - a\mathbf{I}$. We have $\mathbf{0} + \mathbf{0} + c_3(b - a)\mathbf{u}_3 + c_4(b - a)\mathbf{u}_4 = \mathbf{0}$. Since $b - a \neq 0$ and $\{\mathbf{u}_3, \mathbf{u}_4\}$ is linearly independent, $c_3 = 0$ and $c_4 = 0$. Now multiply by $\mathbf{A} - b\mathbf{I}$. $c_1(a - b)\mathbf{u}_1 + c_2(a - b)\mathbf{u}_2 = \mathbf{0}$, which implies $c_1 = 0$ and $c_2 = 0$. Hence $\{\mathbf{u}_1, \mathbf{u}_2, \mathbf{u}_3, \mathbf{u}_4\}$ is linearly independent.

EXERCISES 6.2

1. $\mathbf{A} = \mathbf{A}^T$, $\mathbf{B} = \mathbf{B}^T$

$\mathbf{A} + \mathbf{B} = \begin{bmatrix} 2 & 6 & 3 \\ 6 & -1 & 1 \\ 3 & 1 & 0 \end{bmatrix}$; $\mathbf{A} + \mathbf{B}$ is symmetric

$\mathbf{AB} = \begin{bmatrix} 11 & 2 & 5 \\ 4 & 8 & 7 \\ -1 & 3 & -7 \end{bmatrix}$; **AB** is not symmetric

3. a. $\begin{bmatrix} -8 & 18 \\ 18 & -26 \end{bmatrix}$, yes

b. If **A** is symmetric $\mathbf{A} = \mathbf{A}^T$. Since $(\mathbf{A}^2)^T = \mathbf{A}^T\mathbf{A}^T = \mathbf{AA}$, $(\mathbf{A}^2)^T = \mathbf{A}^2$ and $\mathbf{A}^2$ is symmetric. By induction we can show that $\mathbf{A}^n$ is symmetric for any n. Clearly, $k\mathbf{A}$ and **I** are symmetric. By (2), the sum of symmetric matrices is symmetric. Thus $p(\mathbf{A})$ is symmetric.

5. $(\mathbf{A}^T)(\mathbf{A}^{-1})^T = (\mathbf{A}^{-1}\mathbf{A})^T = \mathbf{I}^T = \mathbf{I}$. Thus, $(\mathbf{A}^T)^{-1} = (\mathbf{A}^{-1})^T$. $(\mathbf{A}^{-1})^T = (\mathbf{A}^T)^{-1} = \mathbf{A}^{-1}$. Thus, $\mathbf{A}^{-1}$ is symmetric.

7. $\lambda^2 - (a + d)\lambda + (ad - b^2) = 0$. λ is real if $(a + d)^2 - 4(ad - b^2) \geqslant 0$; that is, $(a - d)^2 + 4b^2 \geqslant 0$ for all a, b, d.

9. a. $-2, 1, 4$ **b.** $0, 1, 4$ **c.** $3, 4, 6$

11. a. $\lambda = 0$, eigenvector $(0, -1, 2)$; $\lambda = 5$, eigenvectors $(1, 0, 0)$ and $(0, 2, 1)$

b. $\lambda = 1$, eigenvectors $(0, 1, 0)$ and $(1, 0, 2)$; $\lambda = 6$, eigenvector $(2, 0, -1)$

c. $\lambda = 0$, eigenvector $(-3, 1, 0)$; $\lambda = 10$, eigenvectors $(0, 0, 1)$ and $(1, 3, 0)$

13. $\begin{bmatrix} \frac{1}{\sqrt{6}} & \frac{1}{\sqrt{3}} & \frac{1}{\sqrt{2}} \\ \frac{1}{\sqrt{6}} & \frac{1}{\sqrt{3}} & -\frac{1}{\sqrt{2}} \\ -\frac{2}{\sqrt{6}} & \frac{1}{\sqrt{3}} & 0 \end{bmatrix}$

15. a. $\begin{bmatrix} 1 & 1 & -2 \\ 1 & 0 & 2 \\ 0 & 2 & 1 \end{bmatrix}$ **b.** $\begin{bmatrix} \frac{1}{\sqrt{2}} & -\frac{2}{3} & \frac{1}{3\sqrt{2}} \\ \frac{1}{\sqrt{2}} & \frac{2}{3} & -\frac{1}{3\sqrt{2}} \\ 0 & \frac{1}{3} & \frac{4}{3\sqrt{2}} \end{bmatrix}$

17. $\mathbf{A}^T = \begin{bmatrix} 0 & 1 & -3 \\ -1 & 0 & 2 \\ 3 & -2 & 0 \end{bmatrix} = -\mathbf{A}$, $\mathbf{A}^T = \begin{bmatrix} 0 & 5 \\ -5 & 0 \end{bmatrix} = -\mathbf{A}$, $\mathbf{A}^T = \begin{bmatrix} 0 & -2 \\ 2 & 0 \end{bmatrix} = -\mathbf{A}$

19. $\mathbf{B}^T = \frac{1}{2}(\mathbf{A}^T + \mathbf{A}) = \mathbf{B}$
$\mathbf{C}^T = \frac{1}{2}(\mathbf{A}^T - \mathbf{A}) = -\mathbf{C}$

21. a. $\begin{bmatrix} 1 & 0 & 0 & 0 \\ 0 & 0 & 1 & 0 \\ 0 & 1 & 0 & 0 \\ 0 & 0 & 0 & 1 \end{bmatrix}$

b. Eigenvalue 1, multiplicity 3, eigenvectors $(0, 1, 1, 0)$, $(1, 0, 0, 0)$, and $(0, 0, 0, 1)$
Eigenvalue -1, multiplicity 1, eigenvector $(0, 1, -1, 0)$

c. The matrices are symmetric.

d. The matrices are skew-symmetric.

EXERCISES 6.3

1. a. $x_1^2 + 4x_1x_2 + x_2^2$ **b.** $8x_1^2 - 10x_1x_2 + 2x_2^2$ **c.** $x_1^2 + 8x_1x_2 + 6x_1x_3 - 2x_2x_3 + 7x_3^2$

3. $\{(\frac{2}{\sqrt{6}}, \cdot\frac{1}{\sqrt{6}}, \frac{1}{\sqrt{6}}), (-\frac{1}{\sqrt{3}}, \frac{1}{\sqrt{3}}, \frac{1}{\sqrt{3}}), (0, -\frac{1}{\sqrt{2}}, \frac{1}{\sqrt{2}})\}$

5. $\mathbf{C} = \begin{bmatrix} \frac{1}{\sqrt{6}} & \frac{2}{\sqrt{5}} & -\frac{1}{\sqrt{30}} \\ -\frac{2}{\sqrt{6}} & \frac{1}{\sqrt{5}} & \frac{2}{\sqrt{30}} \\ \frac{1}{\sqrt{6}} & 0 & \frac{5}{\sqrt{30}} \end{bmatrix}$

7. $(1, 1, 1)$; $(0, 0, 2)$; no

9. a. Indefinite **b.** Positive semidefinite **c.** Indefinite **d.** Negative semidefinite **e.** Positive definite

11. $p_0 = 1$, $p_1 = -1$, $p_2 = -6$, $p_3 = 16$. One sign permanence, thus, one positive coefficient in the diagonal form of **A**. Two sign changes, thus, two negative coefficients in the diagonal form of **A**. Yes

13. a. The matrix is $\begin{bmatrix} 2 & \frac{3}{2} \\ \frac{3}{2} & -2 \end{bmatrix}$, which has eigenvalues $\frac{5}{2}$ and $-\frac{5}{2}$. The change of basis results in $\frac{5}{2}u^2 - \frac{5}{2}v^2 = 25$, which is the equation of a hyperbola.
b. $5v^2 = 9$; two parallel lines
c. $4u^2 + 17v^2 = 834$; an ellipse

15. $F = [x \;\; y]\begin{bmatrix} A & B/2 \\ B/2 & C \end{bmatrix}\begin{bmatrix} x \\ y \end{bmatrix}$ and $F = [u \;\; v]\begin{bmatrix} A' & B'/2 \\ B'/2 & C' \end{bmatrix}\begin{bmatrix} u \\ v \end{bmatrix}$. The matrices are similar, so their determinants are equal. Thus $AC - B^2/4 = A'C' - B'^2/4$. Therefore, $4AC - B^2 = 4A'C' - B'^2$.

17. The matrix of the equation is $\begin{bmatrix} 7 & -2 & 1 \\ -2 & 10 & -2 \\ 1 & -2 & 7 \end{bmatrix}$, which has eigenvalues 6, 6, and 12. A change in basis gives $6u^2 + 6v^2 + 12w^2 = 36$, which is an ellipsoid with circular trace in the u, v-plane.

EXERCISES 6.4

1. a. $9, 1, 4; 27, -1, 8; 81, 1, 16$ **b.** $1, 5, -1$ **c.** $-10, -14, -11$

3. $\mathbf{A} - 2\mathbf{I}$

5. No; if the eigenvalues of $\mathbf{B}$ are real, then their squares are eigenvalues of $\mathbf{A} = \mathbf{B}^2$, but -5 is not the square of a real number.

7. $1, 2, 2; \begin{bmatrix} 2 & 0 & -2 \\ -4 & 4 & -1 \\ 2 & -4 & 2 \end{bmatrix}; 2, 2, 4$

9. $\mathbf{P}^{-1}\mathbf{AP} = \begin{bmatrix} 25 & 0 \\ 0 & 16 \end{bmatrix}, \mathbf{P} = \begin{bmatrix} 4 & 1 \\ 5 & -1 \end{bmatrix}, \mathbf{B}_1 = \mathbf{P}\begin{bmatrix} 5 & 0 \\ 0 & 4 \end{bmatrix}\mathbf{P}^{-1} = \begin{bmatrix} \frac{40}{9} & \frac{4}{9} \\ \frac{5}{9} & \frac{41}{9} \end{bmatrix}; \mathbf{B}_2 = \mathbf{P}\begin{bmatrix} 5 & 0 \\ 0 & -4 \end{bmatrix}\mathbf{P}^{-1} = \begin{bmatrix} 0 & 4 \\ 5 & 1 \end{bmatrix};$

$\mathbf{B}_3 = \mathbf{P}\begin{bmatrix} -5 & 0 \\ 0 & 4 \end{bmatrix}\mathbf{P}^{-1} = \begin{bmatrix} 0 & -4 \\ -5 & -1 \end{bmatrix}; \mathbf{B}_4 = \mathbf{P}\begin{bmatrix} -5 & 0 \\ 0 & -4 \end{bmatrix}\mathbf{P}^{-1} = \begin{bmatrix} -\frac{40}{9} & -\frac{4}{9} \\ -\frac{5}{9} & -\frac{41}{9} \end{bmatrix}$

11. $\frac{1}{2}, \frac{1}{3}, -1; \mathbf{A}^{-1} = \begin{bmatrix} 1 & 1 & 1 \\ 0 & -1 & -3 \\ 1 & 1 & 7 \end{bmatrix}\begin{bmatrix} \frac{1}{2} & 0 & 0 \\ 0 & \frac{1}{3} & 0 \\ 0 & 0 & -1 \end{bmatrix}\begin{bmatrix} \frac{2}{3} & 1 & \frac{1}{3} \\ \frac{1}{2} & -1 & -\frac{1}{2} \\ -\frac{1}{6} & 0 & \frac{1}{6} \end{bmatrix} = \begin{bmatrix} \frac{2}{3} & \frac{1}{6} & -\frac{1}{6} \\ -\frac{2}{3} & \frac{1}{3} & \frac{2}{3} \\ \frac{5}{3} & \frac{1}{6} & -\frac{7}{6} \end{bmatrix}$

13. No; $\mathbf{A} = \begin{bmatrix} 4 & 1 \\ 4 & 7 \end{bmatrix}, \lambda = 3, 8; \mathbf{B} = \begin{bmatrix} 3 & 2 \\ -2 & -2 \end{bmatrix}, \lambda = 2, -1; \mathbf{AB} = \begin{bmatrix} 10 & 6 \\ -2 & -6 \end{bmatrix}, \lambda = 2 \pm 2\sqrt{13}$

15. a. $\det p(\mathbf{A}) = \det(a_1\mathbf{I} - \mathbf{A})\det(a_2\mathbf{I} - \mathbf{A}); \mathbf{P}^{-1}\mathbf{AP} = \begin{bmatrix} k_1 & 0 & 0 \\ 0 & k_2 & 0 \\ 0 & 0 & k_3 \end{bmatrix} = \mathbf{D}; a_1\mathbf{I} - \mathbf{A} = \mathbf{P}(a_1\mathbf{I} - \mathbf{A})\mathbf{P}^{-1} = a_1\mathbf{I} - \mathbf{D};$

$\det(a_1\mathbf{I} - \mathbf{A}) = \det(a_1\mathbf{I} - \mathbf{D}) = (a_1 - k_1)(a_1 - k_2)(a_1 - k_3)$

b. $\det p(\mathbf{A}) = (a_1 - k_1)(a_1 - k_2)(a_1 - k_3)(a_2 - k_1)(a_2 - k_2)(a_2 - k_3) = p(k_1)p(k_2)p(k_3)$

17. The property that there is a unique path of length 2 from p_i to p_j for all i and j implies that $\mathbf{A}^2$ is an $n \times n$ matrix in which every entry is 1. The eigenvalues of $\mathbf{A}^2$ are $n, 0, 0, \ldots, 0$. The eigenvalues of $\mathbf{A}$ must be $\pm\sqrt{n}, 0, 0, \ldots, 0$. Since the entries of $\mathbf{A}$ are integers, and there is only one nonzero eigenvalue, that eigenvalue must be an integer, since it is the sum of the diagonal elements. If $\pm\sqrt{n}$ is an integer, n is a square.

19. $\sin \mathbf{A}t = \mathbf{P}\sin \mathbf{D}t\mathbf{P}^{-1}; D_t \sin \mathbf{A}t = \mathbf{PD}\cos \mathbf{D}t\mathbf{P}^{-1} = \mathbf{PDP}^{-1}\mathbf{P}\cos \mathbf{D}t\mathbf{P}^{-1} = \mathbf{A}\cos \mathbf{A}t$

$e^{\mathbf{A}} = \begin{bmatrix} (e^8 + 4e^3)/5 & (e^8 - e^3)/5 \\ (4e^8 - 4e^3)/5 & (4e^8 + e^3)/5 \end{bmatrix}$

21. $\cos \mathbf{A} = \begin{bmatrix} (\cos 8 + 4\cos 3)/5 & (\cos 8 - \cos 3)/5 \\ (4\cos 8 - 4\cos 3)/5 & (4\cos 8 + \cos 3)/5 \end{bmatrix}$

$\sin \mathbf{A} = \begin{bmatrix} (\sin 8 + 4\sin 3)/5 & (\sin 8 - \sin 3)/5 \\ (4\sin 8 - 4\sin 3)/5 & (4\sin 8 + \sin 3)/5 \end{bmatrix}$

23. $\mathbf{A}^2 = \begin{bmatrix} 64 & 63 & 63 \\ -55 & -62 & -71 \\ 55 & 63 & 72 \end{bmatrix}$, $\mathbf{A}^3 = \begin{bmatrix} 512 & 511 & 511 \\ -485 & -510 & -537 \\ 485 & 511 & 538 \end{bmatrix}$

$\mathbf{A}^3 - 12\mathbf{A}^2 + 35\mathbf{A} - 24\mathbf{I} = \mathbf{0}$

25. If $f(\lambda)$ is the characteristic polynomial of $\mathbf{A}$, $f(\lambda_i) = 0$, $i = 1, 2, \ldots, n$. Since $\mathbf{A}$ is similar to a diagonal matrix $\mathbf{D}$ with diagonal elements the eigenvalues of $\mathbf{A}$, $\mathbf{P}^{-1}f(\mathbf{A})\mathbf{P} = \mathbf{0}$. Thus $f(\mathbf{A}) = \mathbf{0}$.

29. **a.** $f(\lambda) = (\lambda - 12)(\lambda - 6)^2$. $g(\lambda) = (\lambda - 12)(\lambda - 6)$. They have the same factors with $\lambda - 6$ repeated in $f(\lambda)$.

b. **i.** The characteristic polynomials are $f(\lambda) = (\lambda - 1)^2(\lambda - 2)$ in both cases.

ii. The eigenvectors corresponding to $\lambda = 1$ in matrix $\mathbf{A}$ are solutions of $\begin{bmatrix} 0 & -1 & 0 \\ 0 & 0 & 0 \\ 0 & 1 & 1 \end{bmatrix}\begin{bmatrix} x_1 \\ x_2 \\ x_3 \end{bmatrix} = \begin{bmatrix} 0 \\ 0 \\ 0 \end{bmatrix}$, that is $\{k(1,0,0),\ k \text{ real}\}$. $\mathbf{A}$ is not similar to a diagonal matrix. The eigenvectors corresponding to $\lambda = 1$ in matrix $\mathbf{B}$ are solutions of $\begin{bmatrix} 0 & 0 & 0 \\ 0 & 0 & -1 \\ 0 & 0 & 1 \end{bmatrix}\begin{bmatrix} x_1 \\ x_2 \\ x_3 \end{bmatrix} = \begin{bmatrix} 0 \\ 0 \\ 0 \end{bmatrix}$, that is, $\{k_1(1,0,0) + k_2(0,1,1),\ k_1, k_2 \text{ real numbers}\}$. $\mathbf{B}$ is similar to a diagonal matrix.

31. $\mathbf{A}^{-1} = (\frac{1}{24})(\mathbf{A}^2 - 12\mathbf{A} + 35\mathbf{I}) = (\frac{1}{24})\begin{bmatrix} 3 & -21 & -21 \\ 5 & 45 & 37 \\ -5 & -21 & -13 \end{bmatrix}$

33. $\mathbf{A}^2 - 5\mathbf{A} - 6\mathbf{I} = \mathbf{0}$. $\mathbf{A}^{-1} = (\frac{1}{6})(\mathbf{A} - 5\mathbf{I}) = (\frac{1}{6})\begin{bmatrix} 1 & 7 & 7 \\ -7 & -13 & -7 \\ 7 & 7 & 1 \end{bmatrix}$

EXERCISES 6.5

1. **a.** Dominant eigenvalue is 14.6022 with associated eigenvector $(1.0000, -0.5146)$.

b. Dominant eigenvalue is 144.3909 with associated eigenvector $(-0.4780, 1.0000)$.

3. **a.** 2, $(1, -2, 1)$

b. It now appears the dominant eigenvalue is 6 with eigenvector $(1, -1, 1)$.

c. 6 is the dominant eigenvalue, 2 is also an eigenvalue. This problem illustrates two limitations of the power method. The eigenvalues of $\mathbf{A}$ are 6, 2, and -1 with associated eigenvectors $(1, -1, 1)$, $(1, -2, 1)$ and $(0, -1, 1)$. Also, $(1, 1, -2) = 0(1, -1, 1) + 1(1, -2, 1) - 3(0, -1, 1)$. Thus assumption (c) of the power method is not satisfied and we should not expect to obtain 6 as the dominant eigenvalue. Part **a** of the problem illustrates this. But what happens during the next 15 iterations to cause the apparent convergence to 6? Recall the process: At each step $\mathbf{X}_i$ is obtained from $\mathbf{Y}_i$ by division and, in most cases, the results are rounded off. The cumulative effect of many small round-off errors eventually yields an $\mathbf{X}_i$ with nonzero component in the direction of $(1, -1, 1)$. From this point on, the power method converges to the actual dominant eigenvalue, 6.

5. $x_0 = -1$, $x_1 = 2$, $x_2 = 8$, $x_3 = 20$, $x_4 = 44$, $x_5 = 92$, $x_6 = 188, \cdots$

$\mathbf{W}_n = \begin{bmatrix} x_n \\ y_n \end{bmatrix} = \begin{bmatrix} 3 & -2 \\ 1 & 0 \end{bmatrix}\begin{bmatrix} x_{n-1} \\ y_{n-1} \end{bmatrix}$; let $\mathbf{A} = \begin{bmatrix} 3 & -2 \\ 1 & 0 \end{bmatrix}$; $\mathbf{A}$ has eigenvalues 1, 2 and eigenvectors $\begin{bmatrix} 1 \\ 1 \end{bmatrix}, \begin{bmatrix} 2 \\ 1 \end{bmatrix}$;

$\mathbf{A}^k = \begin{bmatrix} 1 & 2 \\ 1 & 1 \end{bmatrix}\begin{bmatrix} 1 & 0 \\ 0 & 2^k \end{bmatrix}\begin{bmatrix} -1 & 2 \\ 1 & -1 \end{bmatrix} = \begin{bmatrix} -1 + 2^{k+1} & 2 - 2^{k+1} \\ -1 + 2^k & 2 - 2^k \end{bmatrix}$; $\mathbf{W}_n = \mathbf{A}^{n-1}\begin{bmatrix} 2 \\ -1 \end{bmatrix}$; therefore,

$x_n = -4 + 3 \cdot 2^n$, $n = 0, 1, 2, \ldots$.

7. The solution is $\mathbf{X} = e^{\mathbf{A}t}\mathbf{X}_0$, where $\mathbf{A} = \begin{bmatrix} 6 & 4 & 4 \\ -7 & -2 & -1 \\ 7 & 4 & 3 \end{bmatrix}$, and $\mathbf{X}_0 = \begin{bmatrix} 1 \\ 0 \\ 1 \end{bmatrix}$. Then

$e^{\mathbf{A}t} = \begin{bmatrix} 0 & 1 & 1 \\ -1 & -2 & -1 \\ 1 & 1 & 1 \end{bmatrix}\begin{bmatrix} e^{-t} & 0 & 0 \\ 0 & e^{2t} & 0 \\ 0 & 0 & e^{6t} \end{bmatrix}\begin{bmatrix} -1 & 0 & 1 \\ 0 & -1 & -1 \\ 1 & 1 & 1 \end{bmatrix}$, since $\mathbf{A}$ has eigenvectors $\begin{bmatrix} 0 \\ -1 \\ 1 \end{bmatrix}, \begin{bmatrix} 1 \\ -2 \\ 1 \end{bmatrix}, \begin{bmatrix} 1 \\ -1 \\ 1 \end{bmatrix}$. Thus,

$$e^{\mathbf{A}t} = \begin{bmatrix} e^{6t} & -e^{2t} + e^{6t} & -e^{2t} + e^{6t} \\ e^{-t} - e^{6t} & 2e^{2t} - e^{6t} & -e^{-t} + 2e^{2t} - e^{6t} \\ -e^{-t} + e^{6t} & -e^{2t} + e^{6t} & e^{-t} - e^{2t} + e^{6t} \end{bmatrix}. \text{ Finally, } \mathbf{X} = \begin{bmatrix} x_1(t) \\ x_2(t) \\ x_3(t) \end{bmatrix} = \begin{bmatrix} -e^{2t} + 2e^{6t} \\ 2e^{2t} - 2e^{6t} \\ -e^{2t} + 2e^{6t} \end{bmatrix}.$$

9. The eigenvalues are $\frac{1}{2}(-a \pm \sqrt{a^2 - 4b})$. To ensure real eigenvalues, $a^2 > 4b$. The solution approaches zero as t increases if $a > 0$.

11. The solution is $\mathbf{X} = e^{\mathbf{A}t}\mathbf{X}_0$, where $\mathbf{A} = \begin{bmatrix} -4 & 0 & 0 \\ 4 & -2 & 0 \\ 0 & 2 & 0 \end{bmatrix}$, and $\mathbf{X}_0 = \begin{bmatrix} 100 \\ 0 \\ 0 \end{bmatrix}$. $\mathbf{A}$ has eigenvalues -4, -2, and 0 with corresponding eigenvectors $\begin{bmatrix} 1 \\ -2 \\ 1 \end{bmatrix}$, $\begin{bmatrix} 0 \\ 1 \\ -1 \end{bmatrix}$, and $\begin{bmatrix} 0 \\ 0 \\ 1 \end{bmatrix}$. Then $e^{\mathbf{A}t} = \begin{bmatrix} 1 & 0 & 0 \\ -2 & 1 & 0 \\ 1 & -1 & 1 \end{bmatrix} \begin{bmatrix} e^{-4t} & 0 & 0 \\ 0 & e^{-2t} & 0 \\ 0 & 0 & 1 \end{bmatrix} \begin{bmatrix} 1 & 0 & 0 \\ 2 & 1 & 0 \\ 1 & 1 & 1 \end{bmatrix} =$

$$\begin{bmatrix} e^{-4t} & 0 & 0 \\ -2e^{-4t} + 2e^{-2t} & 2e^{-2t} & 0 \\ e^{-4t} - 2e^{-2t} + 1 & -e^{2t} + 1 & 1 \end{bmatrix}. \text{ Thus, } \mathbf{X} = \begin{bmatrix} x_1(t) \\ x_2(t) \\ x_3(t) \end{bmatrix} = \begin{bmatrix} 100e^{-4t} \\ 200(e^{-2t} - e^{-4t}) \\ 100(e^{-4t} - 2e^{-2t} + 1) \end{bmatrix}.$$

13. $f_x = 4x^3 - 16x = 4x(x - 2)(x + 2) = 0$; $x = 0, 2, -2$; $f_y = 4y^3 - 4y = 4y(y - 1)(y + 1) = 0$; $y = 0, 1, -1$.

Thus, the matrix is $\begin{bmatrix} 12x^2 - 16 & 0 \\ 0 & 12y^2 - 4 \end{bmatrix}$.

Point	*Matrix*	*Sequence*	*Eigenvalues*	*f*
(0, 0)	$\begin{bmatrix} -16 & 0 \\ 0 & -4 \end{bmatrix}$	1, −16, 64	2 neg	max
(0, ±1)	$\begin{bmatrix} -16 & 0 \\ 0 & 8 \end{bmatrix}$	1, −16, −128	1 pos, 1 neg	neither
(±2, 0)	$\begin{bmatrix} 32 & 0 \\ 0 & -4 \end{bmatrix}$	1, 32, −128	1 pos, 1 neg	neither
(±2, 1) (±2, −1)	$\begin{bmatrix} 32 & 0 \\ 0 & 8 \end{bmatrix}$	1, 32, 256	2 pos	min

15. The matrix is $\begin{bmatrix} -2 & -2z & -2y \\ -2z & 2z^2 + 2 & 4yz - 2x \\ -2y & 4yz - 2x & 2y^2 - 4 \end{bmatrix}$. Evaluated at (0, 0, 0), this is $\begin{bmatrix} -2 & 0 & 0 \\ 0 & 2 & 0 \\ 0 & 0 & -4 \end{bmatrix}$, which has a sequence 1, −2, −4, 16; an indefinite form. Thus, the function has neither maximum nor minimum at (0, 0, 0).

17. The covariance matrix is $\begin{bmatrix} 6.598 \times 10^{11} & 0 \\ 0 & 4.106 \times 10^{12} \end{bmatrix}$. If x_1 is vertical moment and x_2 is side moment, the equation of the gust design surface is

$$\frac{x_1^2}{(5.036 \times 10^7)^2} + \frac{x_2^2}{(1.256 \times 10^8)^2} = 1$$

19. $\det \mathbf{A} = \det \begin{bmatrix} kb_{11} - y_1^2 & kb_{12} - y_1y_2 \\ kb_{21} - y_2y_1 & kb_{22} - y_2^2 \end{bmatrix} = k^2 \det \mathbf{B} - ky_2 \det \begin{bmatrix} b_{11} & y_1 \\ b_{21} & y_2 \end{bmatrix} - ky_1 \det \begin{bmatrix} y_1 & b_{12} \\ y_2 & b_{22} \end{bmatrix} + 0$, by Theorem 7, Chapter 3. Note that $y_2 \det \begin{bmatrix} b_{11} & y_1 \\ b_{21} & y_2 \end{bmatrix} + y_1 \det \begin{bmatrix} y_1 & b_{12} \\ y_2 & b_{22} \end{bmatrix} = [y_1 \;\; y_2] \begin{bmatrix} b_{22} & -b_{12} \\ -b_{21} & b_{11} \end{bmatrix} \begin{bmatrix} y_1 \\ y_2 \end{bmatrix} =$ $(\det \mathbf{B})\mathbf{Y}^T\mathbf{B}^{-1}\mathbf{Y}$. Thus, $\det \mathbf{A} = k \det \mathbf{B}[k - \mathbf{Y}^T\mathbf{B}^{-1}\mathbf{Y}]$.

References

A number of elementary texts are available that treat the basic topics of linear algebra with a variety of emphases. For a complete yet readable treatment of elementary topics and also of more advanced topics in linear algebra and matrix analysis, the following books are suggested:

Faddeeva, V, N. *Computational methods of linear algebra.* New York: Dover, 1959.

Forsythe, G., and Moler, C. B. *Computer solution of linear algebraic systems.* Englewood Cliffs, N.J.: Prentice-Hall, 1967.

Gantmacher, F. R. *The theory of matrices.* New York: Chelsea, 1959.

Lancaster, P. *Theory of matrices.* New York: Academic Press, 1969.

The following books emphasize computational methods and applications:

Noble, B. *Applications of undergraduate mathematics in engineering.* New York: Macmillan, 1967.

Noble, B. *Applied linear algebra.* Englewood Cliffs, N.J.: Prentice-Hall, 1969.

Rice, J. R. *Matrix computations and mathematical software.* New York: McGraw-Hill, 1981.

For a slightly more advanced treatment of some topics touched on in this book see:

Derrick, William R., and Stanley I. Grossman. *Introduction to differential equations with boundary value problems*, 3rd edition. St. Paul, MN: West, 1987.

Strang, Gilbert. *Linear algebra and its applications*, 2nd Edition. New York: Academic Press, 1976.

An excellent source for interesting and elementary supplementary material related to linear algebra is almost any issue of the *Two-Year College Mathematics Journal*, published by the Mathematical Association of America.

A number of units discussing applications of undergraduate mathematics are available from the Consortium for Mathematics and its Applications (COMAP). Units related to linear algebra are numbers 207, 208, 209, 313, 336, 337, 339, 345, 346, 484, 526, 558, 568, and 569. Some of these are also described in the UMAP *Journal of Undergraduate Mathematics and its Applications*, again published by COMAP. A complete catalog of these materials can be obtained from COMAP Inc. 60 Lowell St., Arlington, MA, 02174.

Appendix Programs in BASIC

Find Powers and Sums of Powers of a Square Matrix

```
1ØØ REM ****************************************************************************
1Ø5 REM *   MATRIX POWER PROGRAM
11Ø REM *          SOURCE: LINEAR ALGEBRA WITH APPLICATIONS,
115 REM *                  BY AGNEW & KNAPP, 3RD EDITION, 1988
12Ø REM *    A  IS THE GIVEN MATRIX, READ FROM DATA LINES OR INPUT FROM
13Ø REM *       KEYBOARD
14Ø REM *    B  IS SUM OF ALL MATRIX POWERS
15Ø REM *    T  IS CURRENT POWER OF  A
16Ø REM *    D  RECORDS A COPY OF T
17Ø REM *    N  IS ORDER OF  A
18Ø REM *    Z  IS CHOICE OF INPUT ROUTINE DESIRED FOR  A
19Ø REM *    M  HIGHEST DESIRED POWER OF  A
2ØØ REM *    F  ALL OR FINAL RESULTS ONLY OPTION
21Ø REM ****************************************************************************
22Ø DIM A(1Ø,1Ø), B(1Ø,1Ø), T(1Ø,1Ø), D(1Ø,1Ø)
23Ø REM ****************************************************************************
24Ø REM *    PRINT INITIAL MENU TO USER'S SCREEN
25Ø REM ****************************************************************************
26Ø I$ = "#########.### "          ' Image string to be used in print routine
27Ø CLS : PRINT : PRINT : PRINT : KEY OFF
28Ø INPUT "      WHAT IS THE ORDER OF THE GIVEN MATRIX";N : PRINT
29Ø IF (N <= Ø) or (INT(N) <> N) THEN 28Ø
3ØØ PRINT "DO YOU WISH TO READ THE ENTRIES OF THE GIVEN MATRIX FROM"
31Ø PRINT "DATA LINES (BEGINNING AT LINE 125Ø) OR FROM THE KEYBOARD?"
32Ø PRINT : PRINT
33Ø PRINT "ENTER YOUR CHOICE:     DATA LINES  (1)"
34Ø INPUT "                    KEYBOARD INPUT  (2)     ";Z
35Ø IF Z<>1 and Z<>2 THEN 3ØØ
36Ø PRINT : INPUT "WHAT IS THE HIGHEST DESIRED POWER";M : PRINT
37Ø IF (M <= Ø) OR (INT(M) <> M) THEN 36Ø
38Ø PRINT "      DO YOU WISH ALL THE INTERMEDIATE RESULTS"
39Ø INPUT "PRINTED (1) OR JUST THE FINAL RESULTS ONLY (2)";F : PRINT
4ØØ REM ****************************************************************************
41Ø IF Z=1 THEN GOSUB 93Ø          ' Read matrix from data lines subroutine
42Ø IF Z=2 THEN GOSUB 1Ø2Ø         ' Read matrix from keyboard subroutine
43Ø REM ****************************************************************************
44Ø CLS: PRINT "THE MATRIX  A  JUST READ INTO MEMORY: " : PRINT : PRINT
```

```
45Ø REM ***********************************************************************
46Ø GOSUB 13ØØ                          ' Matrix print subroutine
47Ø GOSUB 116Ø                          ' Any errors to correct?
48Ø REM ***********************************************************************
49Ø If M = 1 THEN 161Ø
5ØØ REM ***********************************************************************
51Ø GOSUB 84Ø                           ' Initialize matrices  B  and  D
52Ø REM ***********************************************************************
53Ø FOR P = 2 TO M                      ' Start main processing loop
54Ø    GOSUB 62Ø
55Ø    IF F = 2 then 57Ø
56Ø    GOSUB 141Ø
57Ø    GOSUB 74Ø
58Ø NEXT P
59Ø REM ***********************************************************************
6ØØ GOTO 152Ø                           ' Finish processing
61Ø REM ***********************************************************************
62Ø REM *    SUBROUTINE TO MULTIPLY  A  BY THE LAST POWER OF  A
63Ø REM ***********************************************************************
64Ø FOR R = 1 TO N
65Ø    FOR C = 1 TO N
66Ø       LET T(R,C) = Ø
67Ø       FOR K = 1 TO N
68Ø          T(R,C) = T(R,C) + D(R,K) * A(K,C)
69Ø       NEXT K
7ØØ    NEXT C
71Ø NEXT R
72Ø RETURN
73Ø REM ***********************************************************************
74Ø REM *    SUBROUTINE TO ACCUMULATE THE POWERS OF  A
75Ø REM ***********************************************************************
76Ø FOR R = 1 TO N
77Ø    FOR C = 1 TO N
78Ø       D(R,C) = T(R,C)
79Ø       B(R,C) = B(R,C) + T(R,C)
8ØØ    NEXT C
81Ø NEXT R
82Ø RETURN
83Ø REM ***********************************************************************
84Ø REM *    SUBROUTINE TO INITIALIZE MATRICES  B  AND  D
85Ø REM ***********************************************************************
86Ø FOR R = 1 TO N
87Ø    FOR C = 1 TO N
88Ø       B(R,C) = A(R,C) : D(R,C) = A(R,C)
89Ø    NEXT C
9ØØ NEXT R
91Ø RETURN
92Ø REM ***********************************************************************
93Ø REM *    SUBROUTINE TO READ THE INITIAL MATRIX  A  FROM DATA LINES
94Ø REM ***********************************************************************
95Ø FOR R = 1 TO N
96Ø    FOR C = 1 TO N
97Ø       READ A(R,C)
98Ø    NEXT C
```

```
 99Ø NEXT R
1ØØØ RETURN
1Ø1Ø REM **********************************************************************
1Ø2Ø REM *    SUBROUTINE TO READ THE INITIAL MATRIX  A
1Ø3Ø REM *    INTERACTIVELY FROM THE KEYBOARD
1Ø4Ø REM **********************************************************************
1Ø5Ø FOR R = 1 TO N
1Ø6Ø    FOR C = 1 TO N
1Ø7Ø       PRINT "ENTER MATRIX VALUE IN ROW ";R;" COLUMN ";C;":";
1Ø8Ø       INPUT A(R,C)
1Ø9Ø    NEXT C
11ØØ    PRINT
111Ø NEXT R
112Ø REM **********************************************************************
113Ø REM *   SUBROUTINE TO ALTER ENTRIES IN MATRIX -- EDITING ROUTINES
114Ø REM **********************************************************************
115Ø GOSUB 13ØØ
116Ø PRINT : INPUT "ARE ALL ENTRIES CORRECT (Y/N)";Q$
117Ø IF Q$<>"y" AND Q$<>"Y" AND Q$<>"n" AND Q$<>"N" THEN 116Ø
118Ø IF Q$="y" OR Q$="Y" THEN 128Ø
119Ø PRINT : INPUT "ENTRY TO BE ALTERED IS IN ROW";R
12ØØ IF (R > N) OR (R < 1) THEN 119Ø
121Ø INPUT "ENTRY TO BE ALTERED IS IN COLUMN";C
122Ø IF (C > N) OR (C < 1) THEN 121Ø
123Ø PRINT : PRINT "ENTRY IN THAT POSITION CURRENTLY IS ";A(R,C)
124Ø PRINT "NEW VALUE FOR MATRIX IN ROW ";R;" COLUMN ";C;" IS ";
125Ø INPUT A(R,C)
126Ø PRINT : PRINT "MATRIX NOW IS:" : GOSUB 13ØØ
127Ø GOTO 116Ø
128Ø RETURN
129Ø REM **********************************************************************
13ØØ REM *   SUBROUTINE TO PRINT OUT MATRIX  A  AS READ
131Ø REM **********************************************************************
132Ø PRINT "THE MATRIX CURRENTLY IS: " : PRINT
133Ø FOR R = 1 TO N
134Ø    FOR C = 1 TO N
135Ø       PRINT USING I$;A(R,C);
136Ø    NEXT C
137Ø    PRINT
138Ø NEXT R
139Ø RETURN
14ØØ REM **********************************************************************
141Ø REM *   SUBROUTINE TO PRINT CURRENT POWER OF  A
142Ø REM **********************************************************************
143Ø PRINT : PRINT "POWER OF  A: ";P : PRINT
144Ø FOR R = 1 TO N
145Ø    FOR C = 1 TO N
146Ø       PRINT USING I$;T(R,C);
147Ø    NEXT C
148Ø    PRINT
149Ø NEXT R
15ØØ RETURN
151Ø REM **********************************************************************
152Ø REM *   FINAL PRINTOUT OF THE PROGRAM
```

```
153Ø REM ***********************************************************************
154Ø PRINT : PRINT "SUM OF ALL POWERS IS: " : PRINT
155Ø FOR R = 1 TO N
156Ø    FOR C = 1 TO N
157Ø       PRINT USING I$;B(R,C);
158Ø    NEXT C
159Ø    PRINT
16ØØ NEXT R
161Ø PRINT : PRINT "PROGRAM COMPLETE."
162Ø REM ***********************************************************************
163Ø REM *   DATA LINES HERE
164Ø REM ***********************************************************************
165Ø DATA 1, -1,2,-1,Ø,2,Ø,1,1
166Ø END
```

GAUSS—Solves Systems of Linear Equations

```
1ØØ REM ***********************************************************************
11Ø REM *   GAUSS -- A PROGRAM TO SOLVE  M  LINEAR EQUATIONS IN
12Ø REM *   N  UNKNOWNS.  LINES 22ØØ-- RESERVED FOR DATA; 1ST
13Ø REM *   DATA MUST BE VALUES OF  M  AND  N  RESPECTIVELY.
14Ø REM *   SOURCE: LINEAR ALGEBRA WITH APPLICATIONS BY AGNEW &
15Ø REM *           KNAPP, BROOKS/COLE, THIRD EDITION, 1988
16Ø REM *
17Ø REM *   A  IS MATRIX OF COEFFICIENTS; MAXIMUM DIMENSION  5Ø x 5Ø
18Ø REM *   X  IS COLUMN OF UNKNOWNS; MAX UNKNOWNS IS 5Ø
19Ø REM ***********************************************************************
2ØØ DIM A(5Ø,51), X(5Ø)
21Ø CLS : KEY OFF
22Ø PRINT "THIS PROGRAM, CALLED GAUSS, SOLVES SYSTEMS OF LINEAR EQUATIONS."
23Ø PRINT
24Ø PRINT "DO YOU WISH TO READ THE ENTRIES OF THE GIVEN MATRIX FROM"
25Ø PRINT "DATA LINES (BEGINNING AT LINE 22ØØ) OR FROM THE KEYBOARD?"
26Ø PRINT : PRINT
27Ø PRINT "ENTER YOUR CHOICE:     DATA LINES  (1)"
28Ø INPUT "                       KEYBOARD INPUT  (2)     ";Z
29Ø IF Z<>1 AND Z<>2 THEN 27Ø
3ØØ IF Z = 1 THEN GOSUB 129Ø ELSE GOSUB 147Ø
31Ø REM ***********************************************************************
32Ø REM *    BEGIN MAIN LOOP OF GAUSS
33Ø REM ***********************************************************************
34Ø PRINT : PRINT "SOLVING SYSTEM...ONE MOMENT, PLEASE"
35Ø Z = Ø
36Ø FOR RØ = 1 TO N
37Ø    GOSUB 57Ø
38Ø    IF S = Ø THEN 43Ø
39Ø    GOSUB 68Ø
4ØØ    GOSUB 76Ø
41Ø    GOSUB 85Ø
42Ø    Z = Z + 1
43Ø NEXT RØ
44Ø REM ***********************************************************************
45Ø REM *    END OF MAIN LOOP OF GAUSS
```

```
46Ø REM ***************************************************************************
47Ø GOSUB 94Ø
48Ø IF Z = M THEN 113Ø
49Ø RØ = N+1
5ØØ GOSUB 57Ø
51Ø IF S <> Ø THEN 124Ø
52Ø IF Z = N THEN 114Ø
53Ø GOTO 12ØØ
54Ø REM ***************************************************************************
55Ø REM *    COLUMN SEARCH SUBROUTINE
56Ø REM ***************************************************************************
57Ø IF M = 1 THEN 63Ø
58Ø FOR J = Z+1 TO M
59Ø    IF A(J,RØ) = Ø THEN 62Ø
6ØØ    S = J
61Ø    RETURN
62Ø NEXT J
63Ø S = Ø
64Ø RETURN
65Ø REM ***************************************************************************
66Ø REM *    ROW INTERCHANGE SUBROUTINE
67Ø REM ***************************************************************************
68Ø IF Z+1 = S THEN RETURN
69Ø FOR K = 1 TO N+1
7ØØ    T = A(S,K) : A(S,K) = A(Z+1,K) : A(Z+1,K) = T
71Ø NEXT K
72Ø RETURN
73Ø REM ***************************************************************************
74Ø REM *    ROW DIVISION SUBROUTINE
75Ø REM ***************************************************************************
76Ø T = A(Z+1,RØ)
77Ø IF T = 1, THEN RETURN
78Ø FOR K = 1 TO N+1
79Ø    A(Z+1,K) = A(Z+1,K)/T
8ØØ NEXT K
81Ø RETURN
82Ø REM ***************************************************************************
83Ø REM *    USE ROW  Z+1  TO CLEAR REMAINING ROWS
84Ø REM ***************************************************************************
85Ø FOR J = Z + 2 TO M
86Ø    T = A(J,RØ)
87Ø    IF T = Ø THEN 91Ø
88Ø    FOR K = 1 TO N+1
89Ø       A(J,K) = A(J,K) - A(Z+1,K) * T
9ØØ    NEXT K
91Ø NEXT J
92Ø RETURN
93Ø REM ***************************************************************************
94Ø REM *    BEGIN BACKPASS ROUTINE
95Ø REM ***************************************************************************
96Ø FOR C = N TO 2 STEP -1
97Ø    FOR R = M TO 1 STEP -1
98Ø       IF A(R,C) = Ø THEN 1ØØØ
99Ø       S = R : GOTO 1Ø1Ø
```

```
1ØØØ     NEXT R
1Ø1Ø     FOR W = S-1 TO 1 STEP -1
1Ø2Ø        T = A(W,C) : IF T = Ø THEN 1Ø6Ø
1Ø3Ø        FOR K = 1 TO N+1
1Ø4Ø           A(W,K) = A(W,K) - A(S,K) * T
1Ø5Ø        NEXT K
1Ø6Ø     NEXT W
1Ø7Ø NEXT C
1Ø8Ø RETURN
1Ø9Ø REM ************************************************************************
11ØØ REM *    START SOLUTION PRINT ROUTINE
111Ø REM ************************************************************************
112Ø REM
113Ø IF M < N THEN 12ØØ
114Ø PRINT : PRINT "THE UNIQUE SOLUTION IS: " : PRINT
115Ø FOR R = 1 TO N
116Ø     PRINT "X(";R;") = ";
117Ø     PRINT USING "#####.###";A(R,N+1)
118Ø NEXT R
119Ø GOTO 226Ø
12ØØ PRINT : PRINT "THERE ARE INFINITELY MANY SOLUTIONS."
121Ø PRINT : PRINT "          THE ROW-REDUCED MATRIX IS:"
122Ø GOSUB 2Ø9Ø
123Ø GOTO 226Ø
124Ø PRINT : PRINT "     THERE IS NO SOLUTION."
125Ø PRINT : PRINT "THE ROW-REDUCED MATRIX IS:"
126Ø GOSUB 2Ø9Ø
127Ø GOTO 226Ø
128Ø REM ************************************************************************
129Ø REM *    READ VALUES OF  M  AND  N  FROM DATA LINES
13ØØ REM *    AND  ELIMINATE ILLEGAL VALUES OF  M  AND  N
131Ø REM ************************************************************************
132Ø READ M,N
133Ø GOSUB 169Ø
134Ø FOR R = 1 TO M
135Ø     FOR C = 1 TO N+1
136Ø        READ A(R,C)
137Ø     NEXT C
138Ø NEXT R
139Ø PRINT
1395 REM ************************************************************************
14ØØ REM *    START SYSTEM PRINT AND CORRECTION ROUTINES
141Ø REM ************************************************************************
142Ø INPUT "DO YOU WISH TO SEE THE SYSTEM PRINTED AT THIS TIME (Y OR N)";Q$
143Ø IF (Q$ = "N") OR (Q$ = "n") THEN RETURN
144Ø IF (Q$ = "Y") OR (Q$ = "y") THEN GOSUB 2Ø9Ø : RETURN
145Ø GOTO 139Ø
146Ø REM ************************************************************************
147Ø REM *    READ VALUES OF MATRIX  A  INTERACTIVELY FROM KEYBOARD
148Ø REM ************************************************************************
149Ø CLS
15ØØ INPUT "NUMBER OF EQUATIONS: ";M
151Ø INPUT " NUMBER OF UNKNOWNS: ";N
152Ø REM ************************************************************************
```

```
153Ø REM *    ELIMINATE ABSURD VALUES OF  M  AND  N
154Ø REM ***************************************************************************
155Ø GOSUB 169Ø
156Ø PRINT : PRINT
157Ø FOR R = 1 TO M
158Ø    FOR C = 1 TO N+1
159Ø       PRINT "ROW: ";R;" COL: ";C;" < Ø. >"; : INPUT A(R,C)
16ØØ    NEXT C
161Ø PRINT
162Ø NEXT R
163Ø REM ***************************************************************************
164Ø REM *    CORRECT MATRIX IF NECESSARY
165Ø REM ***************************************************************************
166Ø GOSUB 179Ø
167Ø RETURN
168Ø REM ***************************************************************************
169Ø REM *    DETECT INCORRECT VALUES OF  M  AND  N
17ØØ REM ***************************************************************************
171Ø IF (M < 1) OR (INT(M) <> M) OR (M > 5Ø) THEN 174Ø
172Ø IF (N < 1) OR (INT(N) <> N) OR (N > 5Ø) THEN 176Ø
173Ø RETURN
174Ø PRINT : PRINT "ILLEGAL VALUE OF  M  DETECTED....M = ";M
175Ø GOTO 226Ø
176Ø PRINT : PRINT "ILLEGAL VALUE OF  N  DETECTED....N = ";N
177Ø GOTO 226Ø
178Ø REM ***************************************************************************
179Ø REM *    CORRECT ANY ERRORS IN MATRIX READ FROM KEYBOARD
18ØØ REM ***************************************************************************
181Ø PRINT : PRINT "DO YOU WISH THE AUGMENTED MATRIX OF THE SYSTEM"
182Ø INPUT "PRINTED (Y OR N)";Q$
183Ø IF (Q$ = "Y") OR (Q$ = "y") THEN GOSUB 2Ø9Ø : GOTO 186Ø
184Ø IF (Q$ = "N") OR (Q$ = "n") THEN 186Ø
185Ø GOTO 181Ø
186Ø PRINT : PRINT "ARE THERE ERRORS IN THIS SYSTEM (YES OR NO)";
187Ø INPUT A$ : IF (A$ = "NO") OR (A$ = "no") THEN RETURN
188Ø IF (A$ = "YES") OR (A$ = "yes") THEN 19ØØ
189Ø GOTO 186Ø
19ØØ PRINT : PRINT "ENTER THE ROW AND COLUMN NUMBER WHEN PROMPTED..."
191Ø PRINT : INPUT "ROW: ";R
192Ø IF (R < 1) OR (R > M) THEN 191Ø
193Ø PRINT : INPUT "COL: ";C
194Ø IF (C < 1) OR (C > N+1) THEN 193Ø
195Ø PRINT "CURRENT VALUE IN ROW ";R;" COL ";C;" IS ";A(R,C) : PRINT
196Ø INPUT "CHANGE THIS TO: ";TØ
197Ø PRINT : PRINT "VALUE IN ROW ";R;" COL ";C;" IS ";A(R,C);" AND WILL ";
198Ø PRINT "BE CHANGED TO ";TØ
199Ø PRINT : INPUT "IS THIS OK (Y OR N)";Q$
2ØØØ IF (Q$ = "N") OR (Q$ = "n") THEN 181Ø
2Ø1Ø IF (Q$ = "Y") OR (Q$ = "y") THEN 2Ø3Ø
2Ø2Ø GOTO 199Ø
2Ø3Ø A(R,C) = TØ
2Ø4Ø PRINT : INPUT "ANY MORE CHANGES (YES OR NO)";A$
2Ø5Ø IF (A$ = "NO") OR (A$ = "no") THEN GOSUB 139Ø : RETURN
2Ø6Ø IF (A$ = "YES") OR (A$ = "yes") THEN 181Ø
```

```
2070 GOTO 2040
2080 REM ******************************************************************************
2090 REM *    SUBROUTINE TO PRINT MATRIX CURRENTLY IN MEMORY
2100 REM ******************************************************************************
2110 PRINT
2120 FOR ROW = 1 TO M
2130    FOR COL = 1 TO N+1
2140       PRINT USING " ####.###";A(ROW,COL);
2150    NEXT COL
2160 PRINT
2170 NEXT ROW
2180 RETURN
2190 REM ******************************************************************************
2200 REM *    DATA BEGINS HERE
2210 REM ******************************************************************************
2220 DATA  3, 3
2230 DATA  1, 1, -1,  1
2240 DATA  1, 1,  1,  0
2250 DATA -1, 0, -1, -1
2260 KEY ON : END
```

Find the Determinant of a Square Matrix

```
100 REM ******************************************************************************
110 REM *    FIND THE DETERMINANT OF A MATRIX.
120 REM *    THE SIZE OF THE MATRIX IS READ FROM THE FIRST
130 REM *    DATA LINE, AND THE ENTRIES OF THE MATRIX ARE READ FROM THE
140 REM *    REMAINING DATA LINES.
145 REM *       SOURCE: LINEAR ALGEBRA WITH APPLICATIONS, 3rd EDITION
150 REM *                BY AGNEW & KNAPP, BROOKS/COLE, 1988
160 REM ******************************************************************************
170 DIM A(25,25)
180 READ N
190 IF N < 2 THEN 880
200 REM ******************************************************************************
210 REM *    READ THE ENTRIES OF THE MATRIX
220 REM ******************************************************************************
230 FOR J = 1 TO N
240    FOR K = 1 TO N
250       READ A(J,K)
260    NEXT K
270 NEXT J
280 REM ******************************************************************************
290 REM *    IF THE MATRIX IS 2x2, THE DETERMINANT IS EASY
300 REM ******************************************************************************
310 IF N = 2 THEN 850
320 REM ******************************************************************************
330 REM *    OTHERWISE, FIND THE DETERMINANT BY ROW REDUCTION TO A
340 REM *    TRIANGULAR FORM, COUNTING THE NUMBER OF ROW OPERATIONS
350 REM *    PERFORMED
360 REM ******************************************************************************
370 P = 1 : W = 0
```

```
38Ø REM ***********************************************************************
39Ø REM *    BEGIN THE REDUCTION OF THE MATRIX TO TRIANGULAR FORM
4ØØ REM ***********************************************************************
41Ø FOR C = 1 TO N
42Ø    GOSUB 54Ø
43Ø    IF S = Ø THEN 48Ø
44Ø    GOSUB 65Ø
45Ø    P = A(C,C) * P
46Ø NEXT C
47Ø GOTO 81Ø
48Ø PRINT : PRINT
49Ø PRINT "THE DETERMINANT IS ZERO."
5ØØ GOTO 88Ø
51Ø REM ***********************************************************************
52Ø REM *    BEGIN COLUMN SEARCH ROUTINE
53Ø REM ***********************************************************************
54Ø FOR J = C TO N
55Ø    IF A(J,C) = Ø THEN 58Ø
56Ø    S = J
57Ø    RETURN
58Ø NEXT J
59Ø S = Ø
6ØØ RETURN
61Ø REM ***********************************************************************
62Ø REM *    SUBROUTINES: ROW INTERCHANGE, INCREMENT ROW INTERCHANGE
63Ø REM *    COUNTER (W), AND ROW CLEAR
64Ø REM ***********************************************************************
65Ø IF C = S THEN 7ØØ
66Ø W = W+1
67Ø FOR K = 1 TO N
68Ø    T(K) = A(S,K) : A(S,K) = A(C,K) : A(C,K) = T(K)
69Ø NEXT K
7ØØ FOR J = C+1 TO N
71Ø    T = A(J,C)
72Ø    IF T = Ø THEN 76Ø
73Ø    FOR K = 1 TO N
74Ø       A(J,K) = A(J,K) - A(C,K) * T / A(C,C)
75Ø    NEXT K
76Ø NEXT J
77Ø RETURN
78Ø REM ***********************************************************************
79Ø REM *    PRINT THE DETERMINANT AS COMPUTED
8ØØ REM ***********************************************************************
81Ø PRINT : PRINT "THE DETERMINANT OF A IS ";
83Ø IF W MOD 2 = Ø THEN PRINT P ELSE PRINT -P
84Ø GOTO 88Ø
85Ø PRINT A(1,1)*A(2,2) - A(1,2)*A(2,1)
86Ø DATA 3
87Ø DATA 4,2,4,3,5,Ø,7,1,8
88Ø END
```

Find the Inverse of a Square Matrix

```
1ØØ REM **********************************************************************
11Ø REM *    FIND THE INVERSE OF A MATRIX. THE SIZE OF THE MATRIX AND
12Ø REM *    ITS ENTRIES ARE READ FROM DATA LINES BEGINNING AT LINE 1ØØØ
13Ø REM *    SOURCE:  LINEAR ALGEBRA WITH APPLICATIONS, 3RD EDITION
135 REM *             BY AGNEW & KNAPP, BROOKS/COLE, 1988
14Ø REM **********************************************************************
15Ø DIM A(25,5Ø)
16Ø READ N
17Ø IF N < 2 THEN 1Ø7Ø
18Ø REM **********************************************************************
19Ø REM *    READ THE SIZE OF THE MATRIX AND ITS ENTRIES
2ØØ REM **********************************************************************
21Ø FOR J=1 TO N
22Ø    FOR K=1 TO N
23Ø       READ A(J,K)
24Ø    NEXT K
25Ø NEXT J
26Ø REM **********************************************************************
27Ø REM *    AUGMENT THE MATRIX WITH AN  N × N  IDENTITY MATRIX
28Ø REM **********************************************************************
29Ø FOR J=1 TO N
3ØØ    FOR K=N+1 TO 2*N
31Ø       IF J = K-N THEN 34Ø
32Ø       A(J,K) = Ø
33Ø       GOTO 35Ø
34Ø       A(J,K) = 1
35Ø    NEXT K
36Ø NEXT J
37Ø REM **********************************************************************
38Ø REM *    BEGIN ROW OPERATION (A LA GAUSS) TO TRANSFORM THE GIVEN
39Ø REM *    MATRIX TO AN IDENTITY MATRIX.
4ØØ REM **********************************************************************
41Ø Z = Ø
42Ø FOR R = 1 TO N
43Ø    GOSUB 68Ø
44Ø    IF S=Ø THEN 63Ø
45Ø    GOSUB 76Ø
46Ø    GOSUB 82Ø
47Ø    GOSUB 89Ø
48Ø    Z = Z+1
49Ø NEXT R
5ØØ REM **********************************************************************
51Ø REM *    PRINT THE INVERSE OF THE GIVEN MATRIX, IF IT EXISTS
52Ø REM **********************************************************************
53Ø PRINT : PRINT
54Ø PRINT "A INVERSE IS: ":PRINT
55Ø IMG$ = " ######.####"
56Ø FOR J = 1 TO N
57Ø    FOR K = N+1 TO 2*N
58Ø       PRINT USING IMG$;A(J,K);
59Ø    NEXT K
6ØØ    PRINT
```

```
 61Ø NEXT J
 62Ø GOTO 1Ø7Ø
 63Ø PRINT "A IS NOT INVERTIBLE."
 64Ø GOTO 1Ø7Ø
 65Ø REM ***********************************************************************
 66Ø REM *    BEGIN ROW REDUCTION SUBROUTINES
 67Ø REM ***********************************************************************
 68Ø FOR J = Z+1 TO N
 69Ø    IF A(J,R) = Ø THEN 72Ø
 7ØØ    S = J
 71Ø    RETURN
 72Ø NEXT J
 73Ø S = Ø
 74Ø RETURN
 75Ø REM ***********************************************************************
 76Ø IF Z+1 = S THEN 8ØØ
 77Ø FOR K=1 TO 2*N
 78Ø    T(K)=A(S,K) : A(S,K) = A(Z+1,K) : A(Z+1,K) = T(K)
 79Ø NEXT K
 8ØØ RETURN
 81Ø REM ***********************************************************************
 82Ø LET T = A(Z+1,R)
 83Ø IF T=1 THEN RETURN
 84Ø FOR K=1 TO 2*N
 85Ø    A(Z+1,K) = A(Z+1,K) / T
 86Ø NEXT K
 87Ø RETURN
 88Ø REM ***********************************************************************
 89Ø FOR J = 1 TO N
 9ØØ    IF J = Z+1 THEN 96Ø
 91Ø    T = A(J,R)
 92Ø    IF T = Ø THEN 96Ø
 93Ø    FOR K = 1 TO 2*N
 94Ø       A(J,K) = A(J,K) - A(Z+1,K) * T
 95Ø    NEXT K
 96Ø NEXT J
 97Ø RETURN
 98Ø REM ***********************************************************************
 99Ø REM *    DATA HERE --- FIRST DATA ENTRY IS THE SIZE OF THE MATRIX
1ØØØ REM ***********************************************************************
1Ø1Ø DATA 3
1Ø2Ø DATA  3, -5, 7
1Ø3Ø DATA  Ø,  4, 2
1Ø4Ø DATA -1,  8, 4
1Ø7Ø END
```

EIGEN—Find the Dominant Eigenvalue of a Square Matrix

```
 1Ø REM ***********************************************************************
 2Ø REM *    FIND THE DOMINATE EIGENVALUE OF A MATRIX
 3Ø REM *    SOURCE: LINEAR ALGEBRA WITH APPLICATIONS, 3RD EDITION
 35 REM *            BY AGNEW AND KNAPP, BROOKS/COLE, 1988
```

```
 4Ø REM ***********************************************************************
 5Ø DIM A(1Ø,1Ø), X(1Ø,1), Y(1Ø,1)
 6Ø REM ***********************************************************************
 7Ø REM *    INPUT THE SIZE OF THE MATRIX AND READ IT FROM DATA LINES
 8Ø REM *    AT LINE  65Ø
 9Ø REM ***********************************************************************
1ØØ PRINT : INPUT "WHAT IS THE SIZE OF A"; N: PRINT
11Ø FOR J = 1 TO N
12Ø    FOR K = 1 TO N
13Ø       READ A(J,K)
14Ø    NEXT K
15Ø NEXT J
16Ø REM ***********************************************************************
17Ø REM *    READ INITIAL COLUMN VECTOR  X  AND PRINT IT
18Ø REM ***********************************************************************
19Ø FOR J = 1 TO N
2ØØ    READ X(J,1)
21Ø NEXT J
22Ø PRINT "THE INITIAL VECTOR IS;"
23Ø FOR J = 1 TO N
24Ø    PRINT X(J,1)
25Ø NEXT J
26Ø REM ***********************************************************************
27Ø REM *    START 25 ITERATIONS TO FIND EIGENVECTOR FOR  A
28Ø REM ***********************************************************************
29Ø FOR I = 1 TO 25
3ØØ    FOR J = 1 TO N
31Ø       Y(J,1) = Ø
32Ø       FOR K = 1 TO N
33Ø          Y(J,1) = Y(J,1) + A(J,K)*X(K,1)
34Ø       NEXT K
35Ø    NEXT J
36Ø    PRINT : PRINT
37Ø    PRINT "ITERATION #";I
38Ø    FOR J = 1 TO N
39Ø       PRINT Y(J,1);
4ØØ    NEXT J
41Ø    K = 1
42Ø    FOR J = 2 TO N
43Ø       IF ABS(Y(K,1)) >= ABS(Y(J,1)) THEN 45Ø
44Ø       K = J
45Ø    NEXT J
46Ø    R = Y(K,1)
47Ø    FOR J = 1 TO N
48Ø       Y(J,1) = (1/ABS(R))*Y(J,1)
49Ø       X(J,1) = Y(J,1)
5ØØ    NEXT J
51Ø    PRINT: PRINT: PRINT "THE ADJUSTED VECTOR IS:"
52Ø    FOR J = 1 TO N
53Ø       PRINT X(J,1)
54Ø    NEXT J
55Ø REM ***********************************************************************
56Ø REM *    IF YOU WISH TO BE PROMPTED BETWEEN EACH ITERATION, ZAP LINE 61Ø
```

```
590 REM **********************************************************************
610    IF I < 10 THEN 640
620    PRINT : INPUT "ANOTHER ITERATION (Y OR N)"; D$
630    IF D$ = "N" THEN 670
640 NEXT I
650 DATA 6, 4,  4, -7, -2, -1, 7, 4, 3
660 DATA 1, 1, -2
670 END
```

Convert a Linearly Independent Set of n-Tuples into an Orthonormal Set Using the Gram-Schmidt Orthonormalization Process

```
100 REM **********************************************************************
110 REM *    GRAM-SCHMIDT ORTHONORMALIZATION PROCESS
120 REM *    SOURCE: LINEAR ALGEBRA WITH APPLICATIONS, 3RD EDITION
130 REM *              BY AGNEW & KNAPP, BROOKS/COLE, 1988
140 REM **********************************************************************
150 DIM U(20,20),A(20,20),V(20,20),F(20,20),G(20,20),T(20,20) : CLS
160 PRINT "THIS PROGRAM WILL DETERMINE IF A"
170 PRINT "GIVEN SET OF VECTORS IS LINEARLY"
180 PRINT "INDEPENDENT, AND IF SO, WILL CONVERT"
190 PRINT "THEM TO AN ORTHONORMAL SET." : PRINT
200 PRINT "FIRST, WE'LL ENTER THE VECTORS."
210 PRINT : PRINT
220 PRINT "DO YOU WISH TO READ THE ENTRIES OF"
230 PRINT "THE GIVEN VECTORS FROM DATA LINES"
240 PRINT "(BEGINNING AT LINE 1720) OR FROM"
250 PRINT "THE KEYBOARD?"
260 PRINT : PRINT
270 PRINT "ENTER YOUR CHOICE:"
280 PRINT "    DATA LINES  (1) "
290 PRINT "KEYBOARD INPUT  (2) ";Z
300 IF Z<>1 AND Z<>2 THEN 270
310 CLS : PRINT : INPUT "HOW MANY VECTORS ARE GIVEN ";M
320 PRINT : INPUT "         OF WHAT DIMENSION ";N: PRINT
330 IF Z = 1 THEN 440
340 REM **********************************************************************
350 REM *    DATA ENTRY VIA KEYBOARD
360 REM **********************************************************************
370 FOR J = 1 TO M
380    FOR K = 1 TO N
390       PRINT "VECTOR # ";J;" ENTRY # ";K;" : "; : INPUT U(J,K)
400       A(J,K) = U(J,K)
410    NEXT K
420    PRINT
430 NEXT J
440 IF M < 2 THEN 1780
450 IF M > N THEN  PRINT "..VECTORS CAN'T BE LINEARLY INDEPENDENT": GOTO 1780
460 PRINT : PRINT : PRINT "CHECKING FOR LINEAR INDEPENDENCE..."
470 REM **********************************************************************
480 REM *    READ VECTORS AND CHECK LINEAR INDEPENDENCE (A LA GAUSS)
490 REM **********************************************************************
500 IF Z = 2 THEN 560
```

```
510 FOR J = 1 TO M
520    FOR K = 1 TO N
530       READ U(J,K) : A(J,K) = U(J,K)
540    NEXT K
550 NEXT J
560 Z = 0
570 FOR R = 1 TO N
580    GOSUB 670
590    IF S = 0 THEN 640
600    GOSUB 740
610    GOSUB 790
620    GOSUB 850
630    Z = Z + 1
640 NEXT R
650 IF Z = M THEN 930
660 IF Z <> M THEN 970
670 FOR J = Z + 1 TO M
680    IF A(J,R) = 0 THEN 710
690    S = J
700    RETURN
710 NEXT J
720 S = 0
730 RETURN
740 IF Z + 1 = S THEN RETURN
750 FOR K = 1 TO N + 1
760    T = A(S,K) : A(S,K) = A(Z + 1,K) : A(Z + 1,K) = T
770 NEXT K
780 RETURN
790 T = A(Z + 1,R)
800 IF T = 1 THEN RETURN
810 FOR K = 1 TO N + 1
820    A(Z + 1,K) = A(Z + 1,K) / T
830 NEXT K
840 RETURN
850 FOR J = Z + 2 TO M
860    T = A(J,R)
870    IF T = 0 THEN 910
880    FOR K = 1 TO N + 1
890       A(J,K) = A(J,K) - A(Z + 1,K) * T
900    NEXT K
910 NEXT J
920 RETURN
930 PRINT : PRINT "VECTORS ARE LINEARLY"
940 PRINT "INDEPENDENT...PROCEEDING WITH"
950 PRINT "GRAM-SCHMIDT ORTHONORMALIZATION PROCESS"
960 GOTO 1020 PRINT:
970 PRINT : PRINT TAB( 10);"VECTORS ARE **NOT**"
980 PRINT : PRINT  TAB( 8);"LINEARLY INDEPENDENT...": GOTO 1780
1000 REM ***********************************************************************
1005 REM *   END OF LINEAR INDEPENDENCE CHECK
1010 REM ***********************************************************************
1020 PRINT : PRINT
1030 REM ***********************************************************************
1040 REM *   SET V(1) = U(1)
```

```
1050 REM ************************************************************************************
1060 FOR K = 1 TO N:V(1,K) = U(1,K): NEXT K
1070 J = 1
1080 GOSUB 1630
1090  FOR J = 2 TO M
1100     FOR K = 1 TO N
1110        G(J - 1,K) = V(J - 1,K) * V(J - 1,K) + G(J - 1,K - 1)
1120     NEXT K
1130     FOR I = 1 TO J - 1
1140        FOR K = 1 TO N
1150           T(I,K) = V(I,K) * U(J,K) + T(I,K - 1)
1160        NEXT K
1170     NEXT I
1180     REM ****************************************************************************
1190     REM *   FORM J-TH VECTOR
1200     REM ****************************************************************************
1210    FOR I = 1 TO N
1220       FOR K = 1 TO J - 1
1230          F(J,I) = ( - T(K,N) / G(K,N)) * V(K,I) + F(J,I)
1240       NEXT K
1250       V(J,I) = F(J,I) + U(J,I)
1260    NEXT I
1270 GOSUB 1630
1280 NEXT J
1290 REM ************************************************************************************
1300 REM *    PRINT ANSWER ROUTINE
1310 REM ************************************************************************************
1320 CLS
1330 PRINT : PRINT "THE ORTHOGONAL VECTORS ARE:"
1340 FOR J = 1 TO M
1350    PRINT : PRINT "V(";J;") = (";
1360    FOR K = 1 TO N - 1
1370       PRINT V(J,K);", ";
1380    NEXT K
1390    PRINT V(J,N);")"
1400 NEXT J
1410 PRINT : PRINT
1420 REM ************************************************************************************
1430 REM *    ASK FOR AN ORTHOGONALITY CHECK OF VECTORS
1440 REM ************************************************************************************
1450 PRINT "DO YOU WISH AN"
1460 INPUT "ORTHOGONALITY CHECK (Y/N) ";X$
1470 IF X$ = "N" THEN 1780
1480 PRINT
1490 FOR I = 1 TO M
1500    FOR J = 1 TO I
1510       FOR K = 1 TO N
1520          G(J,K) = V(J,K) * V(I,K) + G(J,K - 1)
1530       NEXT K
1540       PRINT "V(";J;")*V(";I;") = ";G(J,N)
1550       G(J,0) = 0
1560    NEXT J
1570    PRINT
```

```
158Ø NEXT I
159Ø GOTO 178Ø
16ØØ REM ***********************************************************************
161Ø REM *   UNITIZE COMPUTED VECTORS SUBROUTINE
162Ø REM ***********************************************************************
163Ø G(J,Ø) = Ø
164Ø FOR K = 1 TO N
165Ø    G(J,K) = V(J,K) * V(J,K) + G(J,K - 1)
166Ø NEXT K
167Ø FOR K = 1 TO N
168Ø    V(J,K) = V(J,K) / SQR (G(J,N))
169Ø NEXT K
17ØØ RETURN
171Ø REM ***********************************************************************
172Ø REM *   DATA HERE
173Ø REM ***********************************************************************
174Ø DATA Ø,  Ø, -1,  Ø
175Ø DATA 1,  Ø,  Ø,  Ø
176Ø DATA Ø,  Ø,  Ø, -1
177Ø DATA Ø, -1,  Ø,  Ø
178Ø END
```

Index

NOTATION INDEX

■ means end of example

□ means end of theorem

* beside a problem means that this problem contains especially useful information